KU-093-408

ALDOUS HUXLEY

*

R O T U N D A

By Aldous Hulxey

NOVELS

Brave New World
Point Counter Point
Those Barren Leaves
Antic Hay
Crome Yellow

SHORT STORIES

Brief Candles
Two or Three Graces
Little Mexican
Mortal Coils
Limbo

ESSAYS AND BELLES LETTRES

Music at Night
Vulgarity in Literature
Do What You Will
Proper Studies
Jesting Pilate
Along the Road
On the Margin

POETRY

The Cicadas
Leda

DRAMA

The World of Light
The Discovery, adapted from
Frances Sheridan

Chatto & Windus

ROTUNDA

A SELECTION FROM
THE WORKS OF

ALDOUS HUXLEY

CHATTO & WINDUS
97 & 99 ST. MARTIN'S LANE
LONDON

PRINTED IN GREAT BRITAIN
BY BUTLER & TANNER LTD.
FROME & LONDON

*

FIRST PUBLISHED
1932

CONTENTS

FICTION

POEMS

DRAMA

ESSAYS AND TRAVEL

THOSE BARREN LEAVES

PART I

An Evening at Mrs. Aldwinkle's

Chapter I

The little town of Vezza stands at the confluence of two torrents that come down in two deep valleys from the Apuan mountains. Turbulently—for they still remember their mountain source—the united streams run through the town; silence in Vezza is the continuous sound of running waters. Then, gradually, the little river changes its character; the valley broadens out, soon the hills are left behind and the waters, grown placid as a Dutch canal, glide slowly through the meadows of the coastal plain and mingle with the tideless Mediterranean.

Dominating Vezza itself, a bold promontory of hill juts out like a wedge between the two valleys. Near the top of the hill and set in the midst of ilex trees and tall cypresses that rise up blackly out of the misty olives, stands a huge house. A solemn and regular façade, twenty windows wide, looks down over the terraced cypresses and the olive trees on to the town. Behind and above this façade one sees irregular masses of buildings climbing up the slopes beyond. And the whole is dominated by a tall slender tower that blossoms out at the top, after the manner of Italian towers, into overhanging machicolations. It is the summer palace of the Cybo Malaspina, one-time Princes of Massa and Carrara, Dukes of Vezza, and marquesses, counts and barons of various other villages in the immediate neighbourhood.

The road is steep that leads up from Vezza to the palace of the Cybo Malaspina, perched on the hill above the town.

The Italian sun can shine most powerfully, even in September, and olive trees give but little shade. The young man with the peaked cap and the leather wallet slung over his shoulder pushed his bicycle slowly and wearily up the hill. Every now and then he halted, wiped his face and sighed. It was on an evil day, he was thinking, on a black, black day for the poor postmen of Vezza that the insane old Englishwoman with the impossible name bought this palace; and a blacker day still when she had elected to come and live in it. In the old days the place had been quite empty. A couple of peasant families had lived in the out-houses; that was all. Not more than one letter a month between them, and as for telegrams—why, there had never been a telegram for the palace in all the memory of man. But those happy days were now over, and what with letters, what with packets of newspapers and parcels, what with expresses and telegrams, there was never a day and scarcely an hour in the day when some one from the office wasn't toiling up to this accursed house.

True, the young man went on thinking, one got a good tip for bringing a telegram or an express. But being a young man of sense, he preferred leisure, if a choice had to be made, to money. The expense of energy was not to be compensated for by the three francs he would receive at the end of the climb. Money brings no satisfaction if one has to work for it; for if one works for it one has no time to spend it.

The ideal, he reflected, as he replaced his cap and once more started climbing, the ideal would be to win a big prize in the lottery. A really immense prize.

He took out of his pocket a little slip of paper which had been given him only this morning by a beggar in exchange for a couple of soldi. It was printed with rhymed prophecies of good fortune—and what good fortune! The beggar had been very generous. He would marry the woman of his heart, have two children, become one of the most prosperous merchants of his city, and live till eighty-three. To these oracles he gave small faith. Only the last verse seemed to him—though he would have found it difficult to explain why—worthy of serious attention. The last verse embodied a piece of specific good advice.

Intanto se vuoi vincere
Un bel ternone al Lotto,
Giuoca il sette e il sedici,
Uniti al cinquantotto.

He read through the verse several times until he had got it by heart; then folded up the paper and put it away again. Seven, sixteen and fifty-eight—there certainly was something very attractive about those numbers.

Giuoca il sette e il sedici
Uniti al cinquantotto.

He had a very good mind to do as the oracle commanded. It was a charm, a spell to bind fate: one couldn't fail to win with those three numbers. He thought of what he would do when he had won. He had just decided on the make of car he would buy—one of the new 14-40 horse-power Lancias would be more elegant, he thought, than a Fiat and less expensive (for he retained his good sense and his habits of economy even in the midst of overflowing wealth) than an Isotta Fraschini or a Nazzaro—when he found himself at the foot of the steps leading up to the palace door. He leaned his bicycle against the wall and, sighing profoundly, rang the bell. This time the butler only gave him two francs instead of three. Such is life, he thought, as he coasted down through the forest of silver olive trees towards the valley.

The telegram was addressed to Mrs. Aldwinkle; but in the absence of the lady of the house, who had driven down with all her other guests to the Marina di Vezza for a day's bathing, the butler brought the telegram to Miss Thriplow.

Miss Thriplow was sitting in a dark little Gothic room in the most ancient part of the palace, composing the fourteenth chapter of her new novel on a Corona typewriter. She was wearing a printed cotton frock—huge blue checks ruled, tartan-fashion, on a white ground—very high in the waist, very full and long in the skirt; a frock that was at once old-fashioned and tremendously contemporary, schoolgirlish and advanced, demure and more than Chelsea-ishly emancipated. The face that she turned towards the butler as he came in was very smooth and round and pale, so smooth and round that one would never have credited her with all the thirty years of her age. The features were small and regular, the eyes dark brown; and their arched brows looked as though they had been painted on to the porcelain mask by an oriental brush. Her hair was nearly black and she wore it drawn sleekly back from her forehead and twined in a large knot at the base of her neck. Her uncovered ears were quite white and very small. It was an inexpressive face, the face of a doll, but of an exceedingly intelligent doll.

She took the telegram and opened it.

'It's from Mr. Calamy,' she explained to the butler. 'He says he's coming by the three-twenty and will walk up. I suppose you had better have his room got ready for him.'

The butler retired; but instead of going on with her work, Miss Thriplow leaned back in her chair and pensively lighted a cigarette.

Miss Thriplow came down at four o'clock, after her

siesta, dressed, not in the blue and white frock of the morning, but in her best afternoon frock—the black silk one, with the white piping round the flounces. Her pearls, against this dark background, looked particularly brilliant. There were pearls too in her pale small ears; her hands were heavily ringed. After all that she had heard of Calamy from her hostess she had thought it necessary to make these preparations, and she was glad that his unexpected arrival was to leave her alone with him at their first introduction. Alone, it would be easier for her to make the right, the favourable first impression which is always so important.

From what Mrs. Aldwinkle had said about him Miss Thriplow flattered herself that she knew just the sort of man he was. Rich, handsome, and what an amorist! Mrs. Aldwinkle had dwelt, of course, very lengthily and admiringly on that last quality. The smartest hostesses pursued him; he was popular in the best and most brilliant sets. But not a mere social butterfly, Mrs. Aldwinkle had insisted. On the contrary, intelligent, fundamentally serious, interested in the arts and so on. Moreover, he had left London at the height of his success and gone travelling round the world to improve his mind. Yes, Calamy was thoroughly serious. Miss Thriplow had taken all this with a grain of salt; she knew Mrs. Aldwinkle's weakness for being acquainted with great men and her habit, when the admittedly Great were lacking, of promoting her common acquaintances to the rank of greatness. Deducting the usual seventy-five per cent. rebate from Mrs. Aldwinkle's encomiums, she pictured to herself a Calamy who was one of Nature's Guardsmen, touched, as Guardsmen sometimes are, with that awed and simple reverence for the mysteries of art, which makes these aristocratic autodidacts frequent the drawing-rooms where highbrows are to be found, makes them ask poets out to expensive meals, makes them buy cubist drawings, makes them even try, in secret, to write verses and paint themselves. Yes, yes, Miss Thriplow thought, she perfectly knew the type. That was why she had made these preparations—put on that masterpiece of a fashionable black dress, those pearls, those rings; that was why she had donned, at the same time, the dashing manner of one of those brilliant, equivocal-looking, high-born young women at whose expense, according to Mrs. Aldwinkle, he had scored his greatest amorous triumphs. For Miss Thriplow didn't want to owe any of her success with this young man—and she liked to be successful with everybody—to the fact that she was a female novelist of good repute. She wanted, since he was one of Nature's Guardsmen with a fortuitous weakness for artists, to present herself to him as one of Nature's Guardswomen with a talent for writing equally fortuitous and unessential. She wanted to show him that, after all, she was quite up to all this social business, even though she *had* been poor once, and a governess at that (and, knowing her, Miss Thriplow was sure that Mrs. Aldwinkle couldn't have failed to tell him that). She would meet him on level terms, as Guardswoman to Guardsman. Afterwards, when he had liked her for her Guardish qualities, they could get down to art and he could begin to admire her as a stylist as well as a brilliant young woman of his own sort.

Her first sight of him confirmed her in her belief that she had been right to put on all her jewellery and her dashing manner. For the butler ushered into the room positively the young man who, on the covers of illustrated magazines, presses his red lips to those of the young woman of his choice. No, that was a little unfair. He was not quite so intolerably handsome and silly as that. He was just one of those awfully nice, well-brought-up, uneducated young creatures who are such a relief, sometimes, after too much highbrow society. Brown, blue-eyed, soldierly and tall. Frightfully upper class and having all the glorious self-confidence that comes of having been born rich and in a secure and privileged position; a little insolent, perhaps, in his consciousness of good looks, in his memory of amorous successes. But lazily insolent; the roasted quails fell into his mouth; it was unnecessary to make an effort. His eyelids drooped in a sleepy arrogance. She knew all about him, at sight; oh, she knew everything.

He stood in front of her, looking down into her face, smiling and with eyebrows questioningly raised, entirely unembarrassed. Miss Thriplow stared back at him quite as jauntily. She too could be insolent when she wanted to.

'You're Mr. Calamy,' she informed him at last.

He inclined his head.

'My name is Mary Thriplow. Everybody else is out. I shall do my best to entertain you.'

He bowed again, and took her extended hand. 'I've heard a great deal about you from Lilian Aldwinkle,' he said.

That she'd been a governess? Miss Thriplow wondered.

'And from lots of other people,' he went on. 'Not to mention your books.'

'Ah; but don't let's talk of those,' she waved them airily away. 'They're irrelevant, one's old books—irrelevant because they're written by some one who has ceased to exist. Let the dead bury their dead. The only book that counts is the one one's writing at the moment. And by the time that it's published and other people have begun to read it, that too has become irrelevant. So that there never is a book of one's own that it's interesting to talk about.' Miss Thriplow spoke languidly, with a little drawl, smiling as she spoke and looking at Calamy with half-closed eyes. 'Let's talk of something more interesting,' she concluded.

'The weather,' he suggested.

'Why not?'

'Well, it's a subject,' said Calamy, 'about which, as a matter of fact, I can speak at the moment with interest—I might almost say with warmth.' He pulled out a coloured silk handkerchief and wiped his face. 'Such an inferno as those dusty roads in the plain I never walked through before. Sometimes, I confess, in this Italian glare I pine for the glooms of London, the parasol of smoke, the haze that takes the edge off a building at a hundred yards and hangs mosquito netting half-way down every vista.'

'I remember meeting a Sicilian poet,' said Miss Thriplow, who had invented this successor of Theocritus on the spur of the moment, 'who said just the same. Only he preferred Manchester. *Bellissima* Manchester!' She turned up her eyes and brought her hands together with a clap. 'He was a specimen in that glorious menagerie one meets at Lady Trunion's.' That was a good name to drop casually like that. Lady Trunion's was one of the salons where Nature's Guardsmen and Guardswomen encountered the funnies and the fuzzy-wuzzies—in a word, the artists. By using the word 'menagerie,' Miss Thriplow put herself, with Calamy, on the Guardsmen's side of the bars.

But the effect of the talismanic name on Calamy was not what she had expected. 'And does that frightful woman still continue to function?' he said. 'You must remember I've been away for a year; I'm not up to date.'

Miss Thriplow hastily readjusted the expression of her face, the tone of her voice. Smiling with a knowing contempt, she said: 'But she's nothing to Lady Giblet, is she? For real horrors you must go to her. Why, the house is positively a *mauvais lieu.*' She moved her jewelled hand from side to side with the gesture of a connoisseur in horror.

Calamy did not entirely agree. 'Vulgarer, perhaps, at the Giblet's; but not worse,' he said—and in a tone of voice, with an expression on his face that showed Miss Thriplow that he meant what he said and didn't at the bottom of his soul secretly adore these social delights. 'After having been away, as I have, for a year or so, to come back to civilization and find the same old people doing the same idiotic things—it's astonishing. One expects everything to be quite different. I don't know why; perhaps because one's rather different oneself. But everything is exactly the same. The Giblet, the Trunion and even, let's be frank, our hostess—though I'm honestly very fond of poor dear Lilian. There's not the slightest change. Oh, it's more than astonishing—it's positively terrifying.'

It was at this point in the conversation that Miss Thriplow became aware that she had made a huge mistake, that she was sailing altogether on the wrong tack. Another moment and she would have consummated a hideous error in social judgment, have irreparably made what she called, in her jovial undergraduatish moments, a 'floater.' Miss Thriplow was very sensitive about her floaters. Memories of floaters had a way of sticking deep in her spirit, making wounds that never thoroughly healed. Cicatrized, the old scars still hurt from time to time. Suddenly, for no reason, in the middle of the night, or even in the middle of the jolliest party, she would remember an ancient floater—just like that, *à propos de bottes*—would remember and be overcome by a feeling of self-reproach and retrospective shame. And there was no remedy, no spiritual prophylaxis. One might do one's best to invent triumphantly right and tactful alternatives to the floater—imagine oneself, for example, whispering to sister Fanny the mollifying instead of the bitter, wounding phrase; might walk in fancy with the airiest dignity out of Bardolph's studio into the dirty little street, past the house with the canary hanging in the window (an exquisite touch the canary), away, away—when in fact (oh Lord, what a fool one had been, and how miserable, afterwards!), in actual fact one had stayed. One could do one's best; but one could never really persuade oneself that the floater hadn't happened. Imagination might struggle to annihilate the odious memory; but it never had power to win a decisive victory.

And now, if she wasn't careful, she'd have another floater rankling and suppurating in her memory. 'How could I have been so stupid?' she thought, 'how could I?' For it was obvious now that the dashing manner, the fashionable disguise were entirely inappropriate to the occasion. Calamy, it was clear, didn't appreciate that sort of thing at all; he might have once, but he didn't now. If she went on like this she'd have him putting her down as merely frivolous, worldly, a snob; and it would need time and enormous efforts to obliterate the disastrous first impression.

Surreptitiously Miss Thriplow slipped the opal ring from off the little finger of her right hand, held it for a moment, clenched out of sight in her left; then, when Calamy wasn't looking, pushed it down into the crevice between the padded seat and the back of her chintz-covered arm-chair.

'Terrifying!' she echoed. 'Yes, that's exactly the word. Those things *are* terrifying. The size of the footmen!' She held up one hand above her head. 'The diameter of the strawberries!' She brought both hands (still far too glittering, she regretfully noticed, with their freight of rings) to within a foot of one another in front of her. 'The inanity of the lion hunters! The roaring of the lions!' It was unnecessary to do anything with her hands now; she dropped them back into her lap and took the opportunity to rid herself of the scarab and the brilliants. And like the conjuror who makes patter to divert attention from the workings of his trick, she leaned forward and began to talk very rapidly and earnestly. 'And seriously,' she went on, putting seriousness into her voice and smoothing the laughter out of her face, so that it was wonderfully round, earnest and ingenuous, 'what rot the lions do roar! I suppose it's awfully innocent of me; but I always imagined that celebrated people must be more interesting than other people. They're not!' She let herself fall back, rather dramatically, into her chair. In the process, one hand seemed to have got accidentally stuck behind her back. She disengaged it, but not before the scarab and the brilliants had been slipped into the cache. There was nothing left now but the emerald; that could stay. It was very chaste and austere. But she would never be able to take off her pearls without his noticing. Never—even though men are so inconceivably unobservant. Rings were easy enough to get rid of; but a necklace. . . . And they weren't even real pearls.

Calamy, meanwhile, was laughing. 'I remember making the same discovery myself,' he said. 'It's rather painful at first. One feels as though one has been somehow swindled and done in. You remember what Beethoven said: "that he seldom found in the playing of the most distinguished virtuosi that excellence which he supposed he had a right to expect." One has a right to expect celebrated people to live up to their reputations; they *ought* to be interesting.'

Miss Thriplow leaned forward again, nodding her assent with a child-like eagerness. 'I know lots of obscure little people,' she said, 'who are much more interesting and much more genuine, one somehow feels, than the celebrated ones. It's genuineness that counts, isn't it?'

Calamy agreed.

'I think it's difficult to be genuine,' Miss Thriplow went on, 'if one's a celebrity or a public figure, or anything of that sort.' She became very confidential indeed. 'I get quite frightened when I see my name in the papers and photographers want to take pictures of me and people ask me out to dinner. I'm afraid of losing my obscurity. Genuineness only thrives in the dark. Like celery.' How little and obscure she was! How poor and honest, so to speak. Those roaring lions at Lady Trunion's, those boring lion huntresses . . . they had no hope of passing through the needle's eye.

'I'm delighted to hear you saying all this,' said Calamy. 'If only all writers felt as you do!'

Miss Thriplow shook her head, modestly declining the implied compliment. 'I'm like Jehovah,' she said; 'I just am that I am. That's all. Why should I make believe that I'm somebody else? Though I confess,' she added, with a greatly daring candour, 'that I was intimidated by your reputation into pretending that I was more *mondaine* than I really am. I imagined you as being so tremendously worldly and smart. It's a great relief to find you're not.'

'Smart?' repeated Calamy, making a grimace.

'You sounded so dazzlingly social from Mrs. Aldwinkle's accounts.' And as she spoke the words she felt herself becoming correspondingly obscurer and littler.

Calamy laughed. 'Perhaps I was that sort of imbecile once,' he said. 'But now—well, I hope all that's over now.'

'I pictured you,' Miss Thriplow went on, straining, in spite of her obscurity, to be brilliant, 'I pictured you as one of those people in the *Sketch*—"walking in the Park with a friend," you know; a friend who would turn out at the least to be a duchess or a distinguished novelist. Can you wonder that I was nervous?' She dropped back into the depths of her chair. Poor little thing! But the pearls, though not marine, were still rather an embarrassment.

Chapter II

Mrs. Aldwinkle, when she returned, found them on the upper terrace, looking at the view. It was almost the hour of sunset. The town of Vezza at their feet was already eclipsed by the shadow of the great bluff which projected, on the further side of the westernmost of the two valleys, into the plain. But, beyond, the plain was still bright. It lay, stretched out beneath them like a map of itself—the roads marked in white, the pinewoods dark green, the streams as threads of silver, ploughland and meadowland in chequers of emerald and brown, the railway a dark brown line ruled along it. And beyond its furthest fringes of pine-woods and sand, darkly, opaquely blue, the sea. Towards this wide picture, framed between the projecting hills, of which the eastern was still rosily flushed with the light, the western profoundly dark, a great flight of steps descended, past a lower terrace, down, between columnar cypresses, to a grand sculptured gateway half-way down the hill.

They stood there in silence, leaning their elbows on the balustrade. Ever since she had jettisoned the Guardswoman they had got on, Miss Thriplow thought, most awfully well. She could see that he liked her combination of moral ingenuousness and mental sophistication, of cleverness and genuineness. Why she had ever thought of pretending she was anything but simple and natural she couldn't now imagine. After all, that was what she really was—or at least what she had determined that she ought to be.

From the entrance court on the west flank of the palace came the hoot of a motor horn and the sound of voices.

'There they are,' said Miss Thriplow.

'I rather wish they weren't,' he said, and sighing he straightened himself up and turned round, with his back to the view, towards the house. 'It's like heaving a great stone into a calm pool—all this noise, I mean.'

Mentally cataloguing herself among the tranquil charms of evening, Miss Thriplow took the remark to be complimentary to herself. 'What smashings of crystal one has to put up with,' she said. 'Every other moment, if one's at all sensitive.'

Through the huge echoing saloons of the palace the sound of an approaching voice could be heard. 'Calamy,' it called, 'Calamy!' mounting through the syllables of the name from a low to a much higher note, not, however, through any intervals known to music, but in a succession of uncertain and quite unrelated tones. 'Calamy!' It was as vague and tuneless as the call of an articulate wind. There were hurrying footsteps, a rustling of draperies. In the huge pompous doorway at the head of the steps leading down from the house to the terrace appeared the figure of Mrs. Aldwinkle.

'There you are!' she called in a rapture. Calamy walked to meet her.

Mrs. Aldwinkle was one of those large, handsome, old-masterish women who look as though they had been built up from sections of two different people—such broad shoulders they have, so Junonian a form; and growing from between the shoulders such a slender neck, such a small, compact and childish head. They look their best between twenty-eight and, shall we say, five-and-thirty, when the body is in its perfect maturity and the neck, the little head, the unravaged features seem still to belong to a young girl. Their beauty is made the more striking, the more attractive by the curious incongruousness of its components.

'At thirty-three,' Mr. Cardan used to say of her, 'Lilian Aldwinkle appealed to all the instinctive bigamist in one. She was eighteen in the attics and widow Dido on the floors below. One had the impression of being with two women at the same time. It was most stimulating.'

He spoke, alas, in the past tense; for Mrs. Aldwinkle was no longer thirty-three, nor had been these twelve, these fifteen years or more. The Junonian form—that was still stately and as yet not too massive. And from behind, it is true, the head still looked like a child's head set on those broad shoulders. But the face, which had once been so much the younger member of the partnership, had outstripped the body in the race through time and was old and worn beyond its years. The eyes were the youngest feature. Large, blue and rather prominent, they stared very glitteringly and intently out of the face. But the setting of them was pouchy and crow's-footed. There were a couple of horizontal wrinkles across the broad forehead. Two deep folds ran down from the corner of the nose, past the mouth, where they were partially interrupted by another system of folds that moved with the movements of the lips, to the lower edge of the jaw, forming a sharp line of demarcation between the sagging cheeks and the strong, prominent chin. The mouth was wide, with lips of rather vague contour, whose indefiniteness was enhanced by Mrs. Aldwinkle's very careless reddening of them. For Mrs. Aldwinkle was an impressionist; it was the effect at a distance, the grand theatrical flourish that interested her. She had no patience, even at the dressing-table, for niggling pre-Raphaelite detail.

She stood there for a moment at the top of the steps,

an imposing and majestic figure. Her long and ample dress of pale green linen hung down in stiff fluted folds about her. The green veil tied round her wide straw hat floated airily over her shoulders. She carried a large reticule over one arm and from her waist there dangled at the end of little chains a whole treasury of gold and silver objects.

'There you are!' she smiled at the approaching Calamy, smiled what had once been a smile of piercing sweetness, of alluring enchantment. Its interest now, alas, was chiefly historical. With a gesture at once theatrically exaggerated and inexpressive, Mrs. Aldwinkle suddenly stretched out both her hands in welcome and ran down the steps to meet him. Mrs. Aldwinkle's movements were as inharmonious and uncertain as her voice. She moved awkwardly and stiffly. The majesty of her repose was dissipated.

'Dear Calamy,' she cried, and embraced him. 'I must kiss you,' she said. 'It's such ages since I saw you.' Then turning with a look of suspicion to Miss Thriplow:

'How long has he been here?' she asked.

'Since before tea,' said Miss Thriplow.

'Before tea?' Mrs. Aldwinkle echoed shrilly, as though outraged. 'But why didn't you let me know in time when you were coming?' she went on, turning to Calamy. The thought that he had arrived when she was not there, and that he had, moreover, spent all this time talking with Mary Thriplow, annoyed her. Mrs. Aldwinkle was perpetually haunted by the fear that she was missing something. For a number of years now the universe had always seemed to be conspiring to keep her away from the places where the exciting things were happening and the wonderful words being said. She had been loth enough, this morning, to leave Miss Thriplow behind at the palace; Mrs. Aldwinkle didn't want her guests to lead independent existences out of her sight. But if she had known, if she had had the slightest suspicion, that Calamy was going to arrive while she was away, that he would spend hours *en tête à tête* with Mary Thriplow—why then she would never have gone down to the sea at all. She'd have stayed at home, however tempting the prospect of a bathe.

'You seem to have made yourself extremely smart for the occasion,' Mrs. Aldwinkle went on, looking at Miss Thriplow's pearls and her black silk with the white piping round the flounces.

Miss Thriplow looked at the view and pretended not to have heard what her hostess had said. She had no wish to engage in a conversation on this particular subject.

'Well now,' said Mrs. Aldwinkle to her new guest, 'I must show you the view and the house and all that.'

'Miss Thriplow's already very kindly been doing that,' said Calamy.

At this piece of information Mrs. Aldwinkle looked extremely annoyed. 'But she can't have shown you everything,' she said, 'because she doesn't know what there is to show. And besides, Mary knows nothing about the history of the place, or the Cybo Malaspinas, or the artists who worked on the palace, or . . .' she waved her hand with a gesture indicating that, in fine, Mary Thriplow knew nothing whatever and was completely incapable of showing any one round the house and its gardens.

'In any case,' said Calamy, doing his best to say the right thing, 'I've seen enough already to make me think the place perfectly lovely.'

But Mrs. Aldwinkle was not content with this spontaneous and untutored admiration. She was sure that he had not really seen the beauty of the view, that he had not understood it, not known how to analyse it into its component charms. She began to expound the prospect.

'The cypresses make such a wonderful contrast with the olives,' she explained, prodding the landscape with the tip of her parasol, as though she were giving a lantern lecture with coloured slides.

She understood it all, of course; *she* was entirely qualified to appreciate it in every detail. For the view was now her property. It was therefore the finest in the world; but at the same time, she alone had the right to let you know the fact.

We are all apt to value unduly those things which happen to belong to us. Provincial picture galleries are always stuffed with Raphaels and Giorgiones. The most brilliant metropolis in Christendom, according to its inhabitants, is Dublin. My gramophone and my Ford car are better than yours. And how pathetically boring are those poor but cultured tourists who show us their collection of picture postcards with as much pride as if they had been the original paintings themselves.

With the palace Mrs. Aldwinkle had purchased vast domains unmentioned in the contract. She had bought, to begin with, the Cybo Malaspina and their history. This family, whose only claim to fame is to have produced, a little before its extinction, that Prince of Massa Carrara to whom the Old Woman in 'Candide'—when she was young and a Pope's ravishing daughter—was once engaged to be married, had now become for Mrs. Aldwinkle as splendid as the Gonzaga, the Este, the Medici, or the Visconti. Even the dull Dukes of Modena, the tenants of the palace (except during the brief Napoleonic interlude) between the extinction of the Cybo Malaspina and the foundation of the Kingdom of Italy, even the Dukes of Modena had so far profited by their connection with the place that for Mrs. Aldwinkle they were now patrons of letters and fathers of their people. And Napoleon's sister, Elisa Bacciochi, who had, while Princess of Lucca, passed more than one hot summer on these heights, had come to be credited by the present owner with an unbounded enthusiasm for the arts and, what in Mrs. Aldwinkle's eyes was almost more splendid, an unbounded enthusiasm for love. In Elisa Buonaparte-Bacciochi Mrs. Aldwinkle had acquired a sister soul, whom she alone understood.

It was the same with the landscape. It was hers down to the remote horizon, and nobody but she could really give it its due. And then, how she appreciated the Italians! Ever since she had bought a house in Italy, she had become the one foreigner who knew them intimately. The whole peninsula and everything it contained were her property and her secret. She had bought its arts, its music, its melodious language, its literature, its wine and cooking, the beauty of its women and the virility of its Fascists. She had acquired Italian passion: *cuore*, *amore* and *dolore* were hers. Nor had she forgotten to buy the climate—the finest in Europe—the fauna—and how proud she was when she read in her morning paper that a wolf had devoured a Pistoiese sportsman within fifteen miles of home!—the flora—especially the red anemones and the wild tulips—the volcanoes—still so wonderfully active—the earthquakes. . . .

'And now,' said Mrs. Aldwinkle, when she had polished off the view, 'now we must look at the house.'

She turned her back on the view. 'This part of the palace,' she said, continuing her lecture, 'dates from about 1630.' She pointed upwards with her parasol; the coloured slides were now architectural. 'A very fine specimen of early baroque. What remains of the old castle, with the tower, constitutes the eastern wing of the present house. . . .'

Miss Thriplow, who had heard all this before, listened

none the less with the rapt expression of interest that one sees on the faces of children at Royal Institution lectures; partly to atone in Mrs. Aldwinkle's eyes for the offence of having been at home when Calamy arrived, and partly to impress Calamy himself with her capacity for being frankly, totally and uncritically absorbed in the little affairs of the moment.

'Now I'll show you the inside of the palace,' said Mrs. Aldwinkle, mounting the steps that led from the terrace to the house; her treasures jingled at the end of their chains. Obediently Miss Thriplow and Calamy followed in her wake.

'Most of the paintings,' proclaimed Mrs. Aldwinkle, 'are by Pasquale da Montecatini. A great painter—dreadfully underrated.' She shook her head.

Miss Thriplow was somewhat embarrassed when, at this remark, her companion turned to her and made a hardly perceptible grimace. Whether to smile confidentially and ironically back, whether to ignore the grimace and preserve the Royal Institution expression—that was the question. In the end she decided to ignore the tacit confidence.

On the threshold of the great saloon they were met by a young girl dressed in a frock of pale pink linen, with a very young round face (otherwise ingenuous than Miss Thriplow's) looking out of a rectangular window cut in a short smooth bell of copper-coloured hair. A pair of wide-open pale blue eyes looked out from beneath the straight metallic fringe. Her nose was small and delicately snubby. A short upper lip made her look at once pathetic and merry, like a child. It was Mrs. Aldwinkle's niece, Irene.

She shook hands with Calamy.

'I suppose,' he said, 'that I ought to tell you that you've grown up tremendously since I saw you last. But the truth is that I don't think you have at all.'

'I can't help my appearance,' she answered. 'But inside . . .' Inside Irene was older than the rocks on which she sat. It was not for nothing that she had passed the five most impressionable years of her life under her Aunt Lilian's guardianship.

Mrs. Aldwinkle impatiently cut short the conversation. 'I want you to look at this ceiling,' she said to Calamy. Like hens drinking they stared up at the rape of Europa. Mrs. Aldwinkle lowered her gaze. 'And the rustic work with the group of marine deities.' In a pair of large niches, lined with shell-work and sponge-stone, two fishy groups furiously writhed. 'So delightfully *seicento*,' said Mrs. Aldwinkle.

Irene, meanwhile, feeling herself excused by long familiarity from paying much attention to the marine deities, had noticed that the loose cretonne covers of the armchairs were crumpled. Being naturally tidy—and since she had lived with Aunt Lilian she had had to be tidy for two—she tiptoed across the room to smooth them out. Bending down to the nearest of the chairs, she took hold of the loose cover near the front of the seat and gave it a smart pull down, so as to loosen it completely before she tucked it tidily in again. The stuff came forward like a suddenly bellying sail and with it there was shot out—from nowhere, as though Irene had been doing a conjuring trick—a glittering shower of jewels. They rattled on the floor, they rolled over the tiles. The noise disturbed Miss Thriplow in her rapt and child-like contemplation of the sponge-stone niches. She turned round just in time to see a scarab ring racing towards her, with the limp of an eccentric hoop, across the tiles. Arrived within a few feet of her it lost speed, it staggered, it fell on its side. Miss Thriplow picked it up.

'Oh, it's only my rings,' she said airily, as though it

were the most natural thing in the world for her rings to come jumping out of the chair when Irene straightened out the cover. 'That's all,' she added reassuringly to Irene, who was standing, as though petrified by surprise, looking down at the scattered jewels.

Mrs. Aldwinkle was fortunately absorbed in telling Calamy about Pasquale da Montecatini.

Chapter III

DINNER was served in the Saloon of the Ancestors. In Mrs. Aldwinkle's enthusiastic imagination what marvellous symposia had been held within those walls—centuries even before they were built—what intellectual feasts! Aquinas, here, had confided to an early Malaspina his secret doubt on the predicability of rollations, had twitted the robber marquess, over a goblet of wine, with the feebleness of his synderesis. Dante had insisted on the advantages of having a Platonic mistress whom one never met and who could, when necessary, be identified with Theology. Peter of Picardy, meanwhile, on his way to Rome had recited from his rhymed version of *Physiologus* the lines on the Hyaena, a beast which, besides being an hermaphrodite, carries in its eye a stone which, held by a man in his mouth, permits him to see the future; it symbolizes moreover avarice and lasciviousness. Learned Boccaccio had discoursed on the genealogy of the gods. Pico della Mirandola, over the boar's head, quoted the kabbala in support of the doctrine of the Trinity. Michelangelo had expounded his plans for the façade of San Lorenzo in Florence. Galileo had speculated why it is only up to thirty-two feet that Nature abhors a vacuum. Marini had astonished with his conceits. Luca Giordano, for a wager, had painted, between the roast and the dessert, a full-sized picture of

Hannibal crossing the Alps. . . . And then, what brilliant ladies heightened the lustre of these feasts ! Lovely, perennially young, accomplished as the protagonists of Castiglione's *Courtier*, amorous in the extreme—they inspired the men of genius to yet higher flights, they capped their hardiest sallies with a word of feminine grace.

It had been Mrs. Aldwinkle's ambition, ever since she bought the palace, to revive these ancient glories. She saw herself, unofficially a princess, surrounded by a court of poets, philosophers and artists. Beautiful women should swim through the great saloons and the gardens, glowing with love for the men of genius. And periodically—for the apartment of the dwarfs, which the Cybo Malaspina, in imitation of the Gonzaga, had included in their palace, demanded appropriate inhabitants to furnish it—periodically they should bring forth, painlessly, children to the men of genius—all curly-headed, fully toothed and two years old on the day of birth, and all infant prodigies. Rows of little Mozarts. In a word, the palace of Vezza should re-become what it had never been except in Mrs. Aldwinkle's fancy.

What it had been in fact one could only guess by looking at the faces of the Ancestors who gave the banqueting-hall its name.

From circular niches set high in the walls of the huge square room the lords of Massa Carrara looked out, bust after bust, across the intervening centuries. Right round the room they went, beginning on the left of the fireplace and ending, with the penultimate Cybo Malaspina, who arranged the room, on the right. And as marquess succeeded marquess and prince, prince, an expression of ever profounder imbecility made itself apparent on the faces of the Ancestors. The vulture's nose, the formidable jaw of the first robber marquess transformed themselves by gradual degrees into the vague proboscides of ant-eaters, into criminally prognathous deformities. The foreheads grew lower with every generation, the marble eyes stared ever blanklier and the look of conscious pride became more and more strongly marked on every countenance. It was the boast of the Cybo Malaspina that they had never married beneath them and that their heirs had always been legitimate. One had only to look at the faces of the last three Princes to feel sure that the boast was amply justified. Were these the Muses' friends?

'You can imagine the splendour of the scene,' said Mrs. Aldwinkle rapturously as she entered the Saloon of the Ancestors on Calamy's arm. 'The innumerable candles, the silks, the jewels. And all the crowd manœuvring in the most stately manner according to the rules of etiquette.' The last representative, albeit adoptive, of these gorgeous beings, Mrs. Aldwinkle lifted her head still higher and with a still more swelling port sailed across the huge room towards the little table where, in shrunken splendour, the successors of Cybo Malaspina were to dine. The train of her coral-coloured velvet dress rustled after her.

'It must have been very fine,' Calamy agreed. 'Certainly, from the point of view of picturesqueness, we've lost by the passing of etiquette. One wonders how much further informality will go. Mr. Gladstone, in his old age, paid a visit to Oxford and was horrified to observe the new fashions in undergraduates' dress. In his young days every young man who respected himself had at least one pair of trousers in which he never sat down for fear of making them bag at the knees, while the outfit in which he normally walked about the streets was never worth less than seventy or eighty pounds. And yet, in the time of Mr. Gladstone's visit, the undergraduates still wore stiff collars and bowler hats. What would he have said if he could have seen them now? And what shall we say fifty years hence?'

The company disposed itself round the table. Calamy, as the new arrival, occupied the place of honour on Mrs. Aldwinkle's right.

'You've broached a very interesting subject,' said Mr. Cardan, who sat opposite him on their hostess's left. 'Very interesting,' he repeated, as he unfolded his napkin. Mr. Cardan was a middle-sized, thickly built man. The upper hem of his trousers followed an ample geodesic; his shoulders were very broad, his neck short and powerful. The red face looked tough and knobbly like the head of a cudgel. It was an enigmatic and equivocal face, whose normal expression was at once gross and sensitively refined, serious and sly. The mouth was small and its thin lips fitted tightly together, as though they were the moving parts of a very well made piece of furniture. The line that marked the meeting of the lips was almost straight, but at one end its horizontal gravity was deflected a trifle downwards, so that Mr. Cardan seemed to be for ever in process of suppressing a wry smile that was for ever importunately troubling his demureness. The hair was smooth, silvery and saintly. The nose was short and straight, like a lion's—but a lion's that had become, with time and good living, rather bottled. Looking out from the midst of a webwork of fine wrinkles, the eyes were small, but bright and very blue. As the result, perhaps, of an illness—or perhaps it was merely under the weight of five-and-sixty years—one white eyebrow had settled down permanently lower than the other. From the right side of his face Mr. Cardan looked at you mysteriously and confidentially through the gap in a kind of chronic wink. But from the left the glance was supercilious and aristocratic, as though the western socket had been stretched by an invisible monocle a size or so too large for it. An expression of benevolence mingled with malice shone in his glance while he was talking; and when he laughed, every polished red facet of his cudgel's face twinkled with mirth, as though suddenly illumined from within. Mr. Cardan was neither a poet nor a philosopher; nor of a remarkably brilliant family; but Mrs. Aldwinkle, who had known him intimately for many years, justified his inclusion among her courtiers on the ground that he was one of the obscure Great: potentially anything he chose to be, but actually, through indolence, unknown.

Mr. Cardan took a couple of spoonfuls of soup before proceeding. 'A very interesting subject,' he repeated yet again. He had a melodious voice, ripe, round, fruity and powdered, as it were, with a bloom of huskiness—the faint hoarseness of those who have drunk well, eaten well and copiously made love. 'Formality, external pomp, etiquette—their practical disappearance from modern life is really a most extraordinary thing, when you come to think of it. Formality and pomp were one of the essential features of ancient government. Tyranny tempered by transformation scenes—that was the formula of all governments in the seventeenth century, particularly in Italy. Provided you treated your people to a procession or some similarly spectacular function once a month or thereabouts, you could do whatever you pleased. It was the papal method *par excellence*. But it was imitated by every grand seigneur, down to the most piddling little count in the peninsula. Look how all the architecture of the period is conditioned by the need for display. The architect was there to make backgrounds for the incessant amateur theatricals of his employers. Huge vistas of communicating saloons to march down, avenues for processions, vast flights of steps to do the Grand Monarch descent from the skies. No comfort—since comfort is only private—but an immense amount of splendour to impress the spectator from outside. Napoleon was the last ruler to practise it systematically and scientifically on the grand scale. Those reviews, those triumphal entries and exits, those coronations and weddings and christenings, all those carefully prepared stage effects—why, they were half his secret. And now these pomps are no more. Are our rulers so stupid and so regardless of the lessons of history that they neglect these aids to government? Or can it be that tastes have changed, that the public no longer demands these shows and is no longer impressed by them? I put the question to our political friends.' Mr. Cardan leaned forward, and looking past Miss Thriplow, who sat on his left, smiled at the young man who sat beyond her and at the older man occupying the corresponding place on the opposite side of the table, next to Irene Aldwinkle.

The young man, who looked even younger than he really was—and at best it was only two or three months since Lord Hovenden had attained his majority—smiled amiably at Mr. Cardan and shook his head, then turned hopefully to the person who sat opposite him. 'Ask me anover,' he said. Lord Hovenden still found it difficult to pronounce a th. 'What do you say, Mr. Falx?' An expression of respectful attention appeared on his boyish, freckled face as he waited for Mr. Falx's answer. Whatever the answer might be, it was obvious that Lord Hovenden would regard it as oracular. He admired, he revered Mr. Falx.

Mr. Falx, indeed, invited admiration and respect. With his white beard, his long and curly white hair, his large dark liquid eyes, his smooth broad forehead and aquiline nose, he had the air of a minor prophet. Nor were appearances deceptive. In another age, in other surroundings, Mr. Falx would in all probability have been a minor prophet: a denouncer, a mouthpiece of the Lord, a caller to salvation, a threatener of wrath to come. Having been born in the middle of the nineteenth century and having passed the years of his early manhood in the profession which, between three and seven, every male child desires to embrace—that of the engine driver—he had become not exactly a prophet, but a Labour leader.

Lord Hovenden, whose claim to figure in Mrs. Aldwinkle's court was the fact that she had known him since he was a baby, that he was descended from Simon de Montfort, and that he was immensely rich, had added a further merit: he had become an ardent Guild Socialist. An earnest young schoolmaster had first apprised him of the fact—hitherto but very imperfectly realized by Lord Hovenden—that there are a great many poor people whose lives are extremely disagreeable and arduous and who, if justice were done, would be better off than they are at present. His generous impulses were stirred. Youthfully, he desired to precipitate an immediate millennium. Perhaps, too, a certain egotistical ambition to distinguish himself above his fellows had something to do with his enthusiasm. Among persons born in privileged positions and in the midst of wealth, snobbery often takes a form rather different from that which it commonly assumes. Not always, indeed; for there are plenty of rich and titled persons who regard wealth and title with the same abject respect as is shown by those whose acquaintance with the nobility and the plutocracy is only in fiction and the pages of the weekly papers. But others, whose ambition it is to climb out of the familiar surroundings into, at any rate intellectually, higher spheres, become infected with a passionate snobbery in regard to the artistic or political world. This snobbery—the snobbery of blood towards brain—had mingled without his being conscious of it with Lord Hovenden's purely humanitarian ardour, and had given it added strength. Lord Hovenden's pleasure at being introduced to Mr. Falx had been enormous, and the thought that he alone, of all his friends and relations, enjoyed the privilege of Mr. Falx's acquaintance, that he alone was free of the exciting political world in which Mr. Falx lived, had made him more than ever enthusiastic in the cause of justice. There had been occasions, however—and they had become more frequent of late—when Lord Hovenden had found that the demands made on him by a strenuous social life left him very little time for Mr. Falx or Guild Socialism. For one who danced as long and often as he did it was difficult to pay much attention to anything else. In lulls between the merrymaking he remembered with shame that he had not done his duty by his principles. It was to make up for arrears in enthusiasm that he had cut short his grouse shooting to accompany Mr. Falx to an International Labour Conference in Rome. The conference was to be held towards the end of September; but Lord Hovenden had sacrificed a month's more shooting than was necessary by suggesting that, before the conference, Mr. Falx and he should go to stay for a few weeks with Mrs. Aldwinkle. 'Come when you like and bring whom you like.' Those were the words of Lilian's invitation. He telegraphed to Mrs. Aldwinkle to say that Mr. Falx needed a holiday and that he proposed to bring him; Mrs. Aldwinkle replied that she would be delighted to have him. There they were.

Mr. Falx paused for a moment before answering Mr. Cardan's question. He turned his bright dark eyes round the table, as though collecting everybody's attention; then spoke in the penetrating musical voice that had stirred so many audiences to enthusiasm. 'Twentieth-century rulers,' he said, 'respect the educated democracy too much to try to bamboozle it and keep it falsely contented by mere shows. Democracies demand reason.'

'Oh, come,' protested Mr. Cardan. 'What about Mr. Bryan's agitation against Evolution?'

'Moreover,' Mr. Falx went on, ignoring the point,

'we in the twentieth century have outgrown that sort of thing.'

'Perhaps we have,' said Mr. Cardan. 'Though I can't imagine how we should have. Opinions change, of course, but the love of a show isn't an opinion. It's founded on something deeper, something which has no business to change.' Mr. Cardan shook his head. 'It reminds me,' he went on after a little pause, 'of another, similarly deep-rooted change that I can never account for: the change in our susceptibility to flattery. It's impossible to read any ancient moralist without finding copious warnings against flatterers. "A flattering mouth worketh ruin"—it's in the Bible. And the reward of the flatterer is also specified there. "He that speaketh flattery to his friends, even the eyes of his children shall fail"—though one would have thought that the vicariousness of the threatened punishment rendered it a little less formidable. But at any rate, in ancient days the great and the prosperous seem to have been fairly at the mercy of flatterers. And they laid it on so thick, they did their job, from all accounts, so extremely coarsely! Can it be that the educated plutocracy of those days was really taken in by that sort of thing? It wouldn't be now. The flattery would have to be a great deal more subtle nowadays to produce the same effect. Moreover, I never find in the works of the modern moralists any warnings against flatterers. There's been some sort of change; though how it has come about, I really don't quite know.'

'Perhaps there has been a moral progress,' suggested Mr. Falx.

Lord Hovenden turned his eyes from Mr. Falx's face, on which, while he was speaking, they had been reverently fixed, and smiled at Mr. Cardan with an air of inquiring triumph that seemed to ask whether he had any answer to make to that.

'Perhaps,' repeated Mr. Cardan, rather dubiously.

Calamy suggested another reason. 'It's surely due,' he said, 'to the change in the position of the great and the prosperous. In the past they regarded themselves and were regarded by others as being what they were by divine right. Consequently, the grossest flattery seemed to them only their due. But now the right to be a prince or a millionaire seems a little less divine than it did. Flattery which once seemed only an expression of proper respect now sounds excessive; and what in the past was felt to be almost sincere is now regarded as ironical.'

'I think you may be right,' said Mr. Cardan. 'One result, at any rate, of this slump in flattery has been a great alteration in the technique of the parasite.'

'Has the technique of the parasite ever altered?' asked Mr. Falx. Lord Hovenden passed on his question to Mr. Cardan in an interrogating smile. 'Hasn't he always been the same—living on the labours of society without contributing to the common stock?'

'We are speaking of different sorts of parasites,' Mr. Cardan explained, twinkling genially at the minor prophet. 'Your parasites are the idle rich; mine are the idle poor who live on the idle rich. Big fleas have little fleas; I was referring to the tapeworms of tapeworms. A most interesting class, I assure you; and one that has never really had its due from the natural historians of humanity. True, there's Lucian's great work on the art of being a parasite, and a very fine work too; but a little out of date, particularly where flattery is concerned. Better than Lucian is Diderot. But the *Neveu de Rameau* deals with only a single type of parasite, and that not the most successful or the most worthy of imitation. Mr. Skimpole in *Bleak House* isn't bad. But he lacks subtlety; he's not a perfect model for the budding tapeworm. The fact is that no writer, so far as I'm aware, has really gone into the question of parasites. I feel their remissness,' Mr. Cardan added, twinkling first at Mrs. Aldwinkle, then round the table at her guests, 'almost as a personal affront. Professing as I do—or perhaps trying to profess would be a more accurate description—the parasitical mystery, I regard this conspiracy of silence as most insulting.'

'How absurd you are,' said Mrs. Aldwinkle. The complacent references to his own moral defects and weaknesses were frequent in Mr. Cardan's conversation. To disarm criticism by himself forestalling it, to shock and embarrass those susceptible of embarrassment, to air his own freedom from the common prejudices by lightly owning to defects which others would desire to conceal—it was to achieve these ends that Mr. Cardan so cheerfully gave himself away. 'Absurd!' Mrs. Aldwinkle repeated.

Mr. Cardan shook his head. 'Not at all absurd,' he said. 'I'm only telling the truth. For alas, it is true that I've never really been a successful parasite. I could have been a pretty effective flatterer; but unfortunately I happen to live in an age when flattery doesn't work. I might have made a tolerably good buffoon, if I were a little stupider and a little more high-spirited. But even if I could have been a buffoon, I should certainly have thought twice before taking up that branch of parasitism. It's dangerous being a court fool, it's most precarious. You may please for a time; but in the end you either bore or offend your patrons. Diderot's *Neveu de Rameau* is the greatest literary specimen of the type; you know what a wretched sort of life he led. No, your permanently successful parasite, at any rate in modern times, belongs to an entirely different type—a type, alas, to which by no possible ingenuity could I make myself conform.'

'I should hope not,' said Mrs. Aldwinkle, standing up for Mr. Cardan's Better Self.

Mr. Cardan bowed his acknowledgments and continued. 'All the really successful parasites I have come across recently belong to the same species,' he said. 'They're quiet, they're gentle, they're rather pathetic. They appeal to the protective maternal instincts. They generally have some charming talent—never appreciated by the gross world, but recognized by the patron, vastly to his credit of course; (that flattery's most delicate). They never offend, like the buffoon; they don't obtrude themselves, but gaze with dog-like eyes; they can render themselves, when their presence would be tiresome, practically non-existent. The protection of them satisfies the love of dominion and the altruistic parental instinct that prompts us to befriend the weak. You could write at length about all this,' went on Mr. Cardan, turning to Miss Thriplow. 'You could make a big deep book out of it. I should have done it myself, if I had been an author; and but for the grace of God, I might have been. I give you the suggestion.'

In words of one syllable Miss Thriplow thanked him. She had been very mousey all through dinner. After all the risks she had run this afternoon, the floaters she had stood on the brink of, she thought it best to sit quiet and look as simple and genuine as possible. A few slight alterations in her toilet before dinner had made all the difference. She had begun by taking off the pearl necklace and even, in spite of the chastity of its design, the emerald ring. That's better, she had said to herself as she looked at the obscure little person in the simple black frock—without a jewel, and the hands so white and frail, the face so pale and smooth—who stood opposite her in the looking-glass. 'How frankly and innocently she looks at you with those big brown eyes!' She could imagine Calamy saying that to Mr. Cardan; but what Mr. Cardan would answer she couldn't quite guess; he was such a cynic. Opening a drawer, she had pulled out a black silk shawl—not the Venetian one with the long fringes, but the much less romantic bourgeois, English shawl that had belonged to her mother. She draped it over her shoulders and with her two hands drew it together across her bosom. In the pier glass she seemed almost a nun; or better still, she thought, a little girl in a convent school—one of a hundred black-uniformed couples, with lace-frilled pantalettes coming down over their ankles, walking in a long, long crocodile, graded from five foot eight at the head to four foot nothing at the tail. But if she looped the thing up, hood fashion, over her head, she'd be still more obscure, still poorer and honester—she'd be a factory girl, click-clicking along on her clogs to the cotton mill. But perhaps that would be carrying things a little too far. After all, she wasn't a Lancashire lass. Awfully cultured, but not spoilt; clever, but simple and genuine. That was what she was. In the end she had come down to dinner with the black shawl drawn very tightly round her shouders. Very small and mousey. The head girl in the convent school had all the accomplishments; but, for the present, wouldn't speak unless she were spoken to. Modestly, then, demurely, she thanked him.

'Meanwhile,' Mr. Cardan continued, 'the sad fact remains that I have never succeeded in persuading anybody to become completely responsible for me. True, I've eaten quintals of other people's food, drunk hectolitres of their liquor'—he raised his glass and looking over the top of it at his hostess, emptied it to her health—'for which I'm exceedingly grateful. But I've never contrived to live permanently at their expense. Nor have they, for their part, shown the slightest sign of wanting to take me for ever to themselves. Mine's not the right sort of character, alas. I'm not pathetic. I've never struck the ladies as being particularly in need of maternal ministrations. Indeed, if I ever had any success with them—I trust I may say so without fatuity—it was due to my strength rather than to my feebleness. At sixty-six, however . . .' He shook his head sadly. 'And yet one doesn't, by compensation, become any the more pathetic.'

Mr. Falx, whose moral ideas were simple and orthodox, shook his head; he didn't like this sort of thing. Mr. Cardan, moreover, puzzled him. 'Well,' he pronounced, 'all that I can say is this: when we've been in power for a little there won't be any parasites of Mr. Cardan's kind for the simple reason that there won't be any parasites of any kind. They'll all be doing their bit.'

'Luckily,' said Mr. Cardan, helping himself again to the mixed fry, 'I shall be dead by that time. I couldn't face the world after Mr. Falx's friends have dosed it with Keating's and vermifuge. Ah, all you young people,' he went on, turning to Miss Thriplow, 'what a fearful mistake you made, being born when you were!'

'I wouldn't change,' said Miss Thriplow.

'Nor would I,' Calamy agreed.

'Nor I,' Mrs. Aldwinkle echoed, ardently associating herself with the party of youth. She felt as young as they did. Younger indeed; for having been young when the world was younger, she had the thoughts and the feelings of a generation that had grown up placidly in sheltered surroundings—or perhaps had not grown up at all. The circumstances which had so violently and unnaturally matured her juniors had left her, stiffened as she already was by time into a definite mould, unchanged. Spiritually, they were older than she.

'I don't see that it would be possible to live in a more exciting age,' said Calamy. 'The sense that everything's perfectly provisional and temporary—everything, from social institutions to what we've hitherto regarded as the most sacred scientific truths—the feeling that nothing, from the Treaty of Versailles to the rationally explicable universe, is really safe, the intimate conviction that anything may happen, anything may be discovered—another war, the artificial creation of life, the proof of continued existence after death—why, it's all infinitely exhilarating.'

'And the possibility that everything may be destroyed?' questioned Mr. Cardan.

'That's exhilarating too,' Calamy answered, smiling.

Mr. Cardan shook his head. 'It may be rather tame of me,' he said, 'but I confess, I prefer a more quiet life. I persist that you made a mistake in so timing your entry into the world that the period of your youth coincided with the war and your early maturity with this horribly insecure and unprosperous peace. How incomparably better I managed my existence! I made my entry in the late fifties—almost a twin to *The Origin of Species*. . . . I was brought up in the simple faith of nineteenth-century materialism; a faith untroubled by doubts and as yet unsophisticated by that disquieting scientific modernism which is now turning the staunchest mathematical physicists into mystics. We were all wonderfully optimistic then; believed in progress and the ultimate explicability of everything in terms of physics and chemistry, believed in Mr. Gladstone and our own moral and intellectual superiority over every other age. And no wonder. For we were growing richer and richer every day. The lower classes, whom it was still permissible to call by that delightful name, were still respectful, and the prospect of revolution was still exceedingly remote. True, we were at the same time becoming faintly but uncomfortably aware that these lower classes led a rather disagreeable life, and that perhaps the economic laws were not quite so unalterable by human agency as Mr. Buckle had so comfortingly supposed. And when our dividends came rolling in—I still had dividends at that time,' said Mr. Cardan parenthetically and sighed—'came rolling in as regular as the solstices, we did, it is true, feel almost a twinge of social conscience. But we triumphantly allayed those twinges by subscribing to Settlements in the slums, or building, with a little of our redundant cash, a quite superfluous number of white-tiled lavatories for our workers. Those lavatories were to us what papal indulgences were to the less enlightened contemporaries of Chaucer. With the bill for those lavatories in our waistcoat pocket we could draw our next quarter's dividends with a conscience perfectly serene. It justified us, too, even in our little frolics. And what frolics we had! Discreetly, of course. For in those days we couldn't do things quite as openly as you do now. But it was very good fun, all the same. I seem to remember a quite phenomenal number of bachelor dinner parties at which ravishing young creatures used to come popping out of giant pies and dance *pas seuls* among the crockery on the table.' Mr. Cardan slowly shook his head and was silent in an ecstasy of recollection.

'It sounds quite idyl-lic,' said Miss Thriplow, drawlingly. She had a way of lovingly lingering over any particularly rare or juicy word that might find its way into her sentences.

'It was,' Mr. Cardan affirmed. 'And the more so, I think, because it was so entirely against the rules of those good old days, and because so much discretion did have to be used. It may be merely that I'm old and that my wits have thickened with my arteries; but it does seem to me that love isn't quite so exciting now as it used to be in my youth. When skirts touch the ground, the toe of a protruding shoe is an allurement. And there were skirts, in those days, draping everything. There was no frankness, no seen reality; only imagination. We were powder magazines of repression and the smallest hint was a spark. Nowadays, when young women go about in kilts and are as bare-backed as wild horses, there's no excitement. The cards are all on the table, nothing's left to fancy. All's above-board and consequently boring. Hypocrisy, besides being the tribute vice pays to virtue, is also one of the artifices by which vice renders itself more interesting. And between ourselves,' said Mr. Cardan, taking the whole table into his confidence, 'it can't do without those artifices. There's a most interesting passage on this subject in Balzac's *Cousine Bette.* You remember the story?'

'Such a wonderful . . . !' exclaimed Mrs. Aldwinkle, with that large and indistinct enthusiasm evoked in her by every masterpiece of art.

'It's where Baron Hulot falls under the spell of Madame Marneffe: the old beau of the empire and the young woman brought up on the Romantic Revival and early Victorian virtues. Let me see if I can remember it.' Mr. Cardan thoughtfully frowned, was silent for a moment, then proceeded in an almost flawless French. '"Cet homme de l'empire, habitué au genre empire, devait ignorer absolument les façons de l'amour moderne, les nouveaux scrupules, les différentes conversations inventées depuis 1830, et où la 'pauvre faible femme' finit par se faire considérer comme la victime des désirs de son amant, comme une sœur de charité qui panse des blessures, comme un ange qui se dévoue. Ce nouvel art d'aimer consomme énormément de paroles évangéliques à l'œuvre du diable. La passion est un martyre. On aspire à l'idéal, à l'infini de part et d'autre; l'on veut devenir meilleur par l'amour. Toutes ces belles phrases sont un prétexte à mettre encore plus d'ardeur dans la pratique, plus de rage dans les chutes (Mr. Cardan rolled out these words with a particular sonority) que par le passé. Cette hypocrisie, le caractère de notre temps a gangrené la galanterie." How sharp that is,' said Mr. Cardan, 'how wide and how deep! Only I can't agree with the sentiment expressed in the last sentence. For if, as he says, hypocrisy puts more ardour into the practice of love and more "rage in the chutes," then it cannot be said to have gangrened gallantry. It has improved it, revivified it, made it interesting. Nineteenth-century hypocrisy was a concomitant of nineteenth-century literary romanticism: an inevitable reaction, like that, against the excessive classicism of the eighteenth century. Classicism in literature is intolerable because there are too many restrictive rules; it is intolerable in love because there are too few. They have this in common, despite their apparent unlikeness, that they are both matter-of-fact and unemotional. It is only by inventing rules about it which can be broken, it is only by investing it with an almost supernatural importance, that love can be made interesting. Angels, philosophers and demons must haunt the alcove; otherwise it is no place for intelligent men and women. No such personages were to be found there in classical times; still less in the neo-classic. The whole process was as straightforward, prosaic, quotidian, and *terre à terre* as it could be. It must really have become very little more interesting than eating dinner—not that I disparage that, mind you, particularly nowadays; but in my youth'—Mr. Cardan sighed—'I set less stock in those days by good food. Still, even now, I have to admit, there's not much excitement, not much poetry in eating. It is, I suppose, only in countries where powerful taboos about food prevail that the satisfaction of hunger takes on a romantic aspect. I can imagine that a strictly-brought-up Jew in the time of Samuel might sometimes have been seized by almost irresistible temptations to eat a lobster or some similar animal that divides the hoof but does not chew the cud. I can imagine him pretending to his wife that he was going to the synagogue; but in reality he slinks surreptitiously away down a sinister alley to gorge himself illicitly in some house of ill fame on pork and lobster mayonnaise. Quite a drama there. I give you the notion, gratis, as the subject for a story.'

'I'm most grateful,' said Miss Thriplow.

'And then, remember, the next morning, after the most portentous dreams all the night through, he'll wake up tremendously strict, a Pharisee of the Pharisees, and he'll send a subscription to the society for the Protection of Public Morals and another to the Anti-Lobster League. And he'll write to the papers saying how disgraceful it is that young novelists should be allowed to publish books containing revolting descriptions of ham being eaten in mixed company, of orgies in oyster shops, with other culinary obscenities too horrible to be mentioned. He'll do all that, won't he, Miss Mary?'

'Most certainly. And you forgot to say,' added Miss Thriplow, forgetting that she was the head girl in the convent school, 'that he'll insist more strictly than ever on his daughters being brought up in perfect ignorance of the very existence of sausages.'

'Quite right,' said Mr. Cardan. 'All of which was merely meant to show how exciting even eating might become if religion were brought into it, if dinner were made a mystery and the imagination thoroughly stirred every time the gong sounded. Conversely, how tedious love becomes when it is taken as matter-of-factly as eating dinner. It was essential for the men and women of 1830, if they didn't want to die of pure boredom, to invent the *pauvre faible femme*, the martyr, the angel, the sister of charity, to talk like the Bible while they were consummating the devil's work. The sort of love that their predecessors of the eighteenth century and the empire had made was too prosaic a business. They turned to hypocrisy in mere self-preservation. But the present generation, tired of playing at Madame Marneffe, has reverted to the empire notions of Baron Hulot. . . . Emancipation is excellent, no doubt, in its way. But in the end it defeats its own object. People ask for freedom; but what they finally get turns out to be boredom. To those for whom love has become as obvious an affair as eating dinner, for whom there are no blushful mysteries, no reticences, no fancy-fostering concealments, but only plain speaking and the facts of nature—how flat and stale the whole business must become! It needs crinolines to excite the imagination and dragonish duennas to inflame desire to passion. Too much light conversation about the Oedipus complex and anal erotism is taking the edge off love. In a few years, I don't mind prophesying, you young people will be whispering to one another sublime things about angels, sisters of charity and the infinite. You'll be sheathed in Jaeger and pining behind bars. And love, in consequence, will seem incomparably more romantic, more alluring than it does in these days of emancipation.' Mr. Cardan spat out the pips of his last grape, pushed the fruit plate away from him, leaned back in his chair and looked about him triumphantly.

'How little you understand women,' said Mrs. Aldwinkle, shaking her head. 'Doesn't he, Mary?'

'Some women, at any rate,' Miss Thriplow agreed. 'You seem to forget, Mr. Cardan, that Diana is quite as real a type as Venus.'

'Exactly,' said Mrs. Aldwinkle. 'You couldn't have put it more succinctly.' Eighteen years ago, she and Mr. Cardan had been lovers. Elzevir, the pianist, had succeeded him—a short reign—to be followed by Lord Trunion—or was it Dr. Lecoing?—or both? At the moment Mrs. Aldwinkle had forgotten these facts. And when she did remember, it was not quite in the way that other people—Mr. Cardan, for example—remembered them. It was all wonderfully romantic, now; and she had been Diana all the time.

'But I entirely agree with you,' said Mr. Cardan. 'I

unequivocally admit the existence of Artemis. I could even prove it for you empirically.'

'That's very good of you,' said Mrs. Aldwinkle, trying to be sarcastic.

'The only figure on Olympus whom I have always regarded as being purely mythical,' Mr. Cardan went on, 'as having no foundation in the facts of life, is Athena. A goddess of wisdom—a *goddess* !' he repeated with emphasis. 'Isn't that a little too thick ?'

Majestically Mrs. Aldwinkle rose from the table. 'Let us go out into the garden,' she said.

Chapter IV

MRS. ALDWINKLE had even bought the stars.

'How bright they are !' she exclaimed, as she stepped out at the head of her little troop of guests on to the terrace. 'And how they twinkle ! How they palpitate ! As though they were alive. They're never like this in England, are they, Calamy ?'

Calamy agreed. Agreeing, he had found, was a labour-saving device—positively a necessity in this Ideal Home. He always tried to agree with Mrs. Aldwinkle.

'And how clearly one sees the Great Bear !' Mrs. Aldwinkle went on, speaking almost perpendicularly upwards into the height of heaven. The Bear and Orion were the only constellations she could recognize. 'Such a strange and beautiful shape, isn't it ?' It might almost have been designed by the architect of the Malaspina palace.

'Very strange,' said Calamy.

Mrs. Aldwinkle dropped her eyes from the zenith, turned and smiled at him, penetratingly, forgetting that in the profound and moonless darkness her charm would be entirely wasted.

Miss Thriplow's voice spoke softly, with a kind of childish drawl through the darkness. 'They might be Italian tenors,' she said, 'tremoloing away like that so passionately in the sky. No wonder, with those stars overhead, no wonder life tends to become a bit operatic in this country at times.'

Mrs. Aldwinkle was indignant. 'How can you blaspheme like that against the stars?' she said. Then, remembering that she had also bought Italian music, not to mention the habits and customs of the whole Italian people, she went on: 'Besides, it's such a cheap joke about the tenors. After all, this is the only country where *bel canto* is still . . .' She waved her hand. 'And you remember how much Wagner admired what's-his-name. . . .'

'Bellini,' prompted the little niece as self-effacingly as possible. She had heard her aunt speak of Wagner's admiration before.

'Bellini,' repeated Mrs. Aldwinkle. 'Besides, life isn't operatic in Italy. It's genuinely passionate.'

Miss Thriplow was, for a moment, rather at a loss for an answer. She had a faculty for making these little jokes; but at the same time she was so very much afraid that people might regard her as merely clever and unfeeling, a hard and glittering young woman. Half a dozen smart repartees were possible, of course; but then she mustn't forget that she was fundamentally so simple, so Wordsworthian, such a violet by a mossy stone—particularly this evening, in her shawl.

However much we should like to do so, however highly, in private, we think of our abilities, we generally feel that it is bad form to boast of our intelligence. But in regard to our qualities of heart we feel no such shame; we talk freely of our kindness, bordering on weakness, of our generosity carried almost to the point of folly (tempering our boasting a little by making out that our qualities are so excessive as to be defects). Miss Thriplow, however, was one of those rare people so obviously and admittedly clever that there could be no objection to her mentioning the fact as often as she liked; people would have called it only justifiable self-esteem. But Miss Thriplow, perversely, did not want to be praised or to praise herself for her intelligence. She was chiefly anxious to make the world appreciative of her heart. When, as on this occasion, she followed her natural bent towards smartness too far, or when, carried away by the desire to make herself agreeable in flashing company, she found herself saying something whose brilliance was not in harmony with the possession of simple and entirely natural emotions, she would recollect herself and hastily try to correct the misapprehension she had created among her hearers. Now, therefore, at the end of a moment's lightning meditation, she managed to think of a remark which admirably combined, she flattered herself, the most genuine feeling for Nature with an elegantly recondite allusion—this last for the benefit particularly of Mr. Cardan, who as a scholarly gentleman of the old school was a great appreciator and admirer of learning.

'Yes, Bellini,' she said rapturously, picking up the reference from the middle of Mrs. Aldwinkle's last sentence. 'What a wonderful gift of melody! *Casta diva*—do you remember that?' And in a thin voice she sang the first long phrase. 'What a lovely line the melody traces out! Like the line of those hills against the sky.' She pointed.

On the further side of the valley to westward of the promontory of hill on which the palace stood, projected a longer and higher headland. From the terrace one looked up at its huge impending mass. . . . It was at this that Miss Thriplow now pointed. With her forefinger she followed the scalloped and undulating outline of its silhouette.

'Even Nature, in Italy, is like a work of art,' she added.

Mrs. Aldwinkle was mollified. 'That's very true,' she said; and stepping out, she began the evening's promenading along the terrace. The train of her velvet robe rustled after her over the dusty flagstones. Mrs. Aldwinkle didn't mind in the least if it got dirty. It was the general effect that mattered; stains, dust, clinging twigs and millepedes—those were mere details. She treated her clothes, in consequence, with a fine aristocratic carelessness. The little troop followed her.

There was no moon; only stars in a dark blue firmament. Black and flat against the sky, the Herculeses and the bowed Atlases, the kilted Dianas and the Venuses who concealed their charms with a two-handed gesture of alluring modesty, stood, like as many petrified dancers, on the piers of the balustrade. The stars looked between them. Below, in the blackness of the plain, burned constellations of yellow lights. Unremittingly, the croaking of frogs came up, thin, remote, but very clear, from invisible waters.

'Nights like this,' said Mrs. Aldwinkle, halting and addressing herself with intensity to Calamy, 'make one understand the passion of the South.' She had an alarming habit, when she spoke to any one at all intimately or seriously, of approaching her face very close to that of her interlocutor, opening her eyes to their fullest extent and staring for a moment with the fixed penetrating stare of an oculist examining his patient.

Like trucks at the tail of a suddenly braked locomotive, Mrs. Aldwinkle's guests came joltingly to a stop when she stopped.

Calamy nodded. 'Quite,' he said, 'quite.' Even in this faint starlight, he noticed, Mrs. Aldwinkle's eyes glittered alarmingly as she approached her face to his.

'In this horrible bourgeois age'—Mrs. Aldwinkle's

vocabulary (like Mr. Falx's, though for different reasons) contained no word of bitterer disparagement than 'bourgeois'—'it's only Southern people who still understand or even, I believe, feel passion.' Mrs. Aldwinkle believed in passion, passionately.

From behind the glowing red end of his cigar Mr. Cardan began to speak. In the darkness his voice sounded more than ever ripe and fruity. 'You're quite right,' he assured Mrs. Aldwinkle, 'quite right. It's the climate, of course. The warmth has a double effect on the inhabitants, direct and indirect. The direct effect needs no explaining; warmth calls to warmth. It's obvious. But the indirect is fully as important. In a hot country one doesn't care to work too hard. One works enough to keep oneself alive (and it's tolerably easy to keep alive under these stars), and one cultivates long leisures. Now it's sufficiently obvious that practically the only thing that anybody who is not a philosopher can do in his leisure is to make love. No serious-minded, hard-working man has the time, the spare energy or the inclination to abandon himself to passion. Passion can only flourish among the well-fed unemployed. Consequently, except among women and men of the leisured class, passion in all its luxuriant intricacy hardly exists in the hard-working North. It is only among those whose desires and whose native idleness are fostered by the cherishing Southern heat that it has flourished and continues to flourish, as you rightly point out, my dear Lilian, even in this burgess age.'

Mr. Cardan had hardly begun to speak before Mrs. Aldwinkle indignantly moved on again. He outraged all her feelings.

Mr. Cardan talking all the way, they passed the silhouettes of modest Venus, of Diana and her attendant dog, of Hercules leaning on his club and Atlas bending under the weight of his globe, of Bacchus lifting to heaven the stump of a broken arm whose hand had once held the wine cup. Arrived at the end of the terrace, they turned and walked back again past the same row of symbols.

'It's easy to talk like that,' said Mrs. Aldwinkle, when he had finished. 'But it doesn't make any difference to the grandeur of passion, to its purity and beauty and . . .' She faded out breathlessly.

'Wasn't it Bossuet,' asked Irene timidly, but with determination, for she felt that she owed it to Aunt Lilian to intervene; and besides, Aunt Lilian liked her to take part in the conversation, 'wasn't it Bossuet who said that there was something of the Infinite in passion?'

'Splendid, Irene,' Mr. Cardan cried encouragingly.

Irene blushed in the concealing darkness. 'But I think Bossuet's quite right,' she declared. She could become a lioness, in spite of her blushes, when it was a question of supporting Aunt Lilian. 'I think he's absolutely right,' she confirmed, after a moment of recollection, out of her own experience. She herself had felt most infinitely, more than once—for Irene had run through a surprising number of passions in her time. 'I can't think,' her Aunt Lilian used to say to her, when Irene came in the evenings to brush her hair before she went to bed, 'I can't think how it is that you're not wildly in love with Peter—or Jacques—or Mario.' (The name might change as Mrs. Aldwinkle and her niece moved in their seasonal wanderings, backwards and forwards across the map of Europe; but, after all, what's in a name?) 'If I were your age I should be quite bowled over by him.' And thinking more seriously now of Peter, or Jacques, or Mario, Irene would discover that Aunt Lilian was quite right; the young man was indeed a very remarkable young man. And for the remainder of their stay at the Continental, the Bristol, the Savoia, she would be in love—passionately. What she had felt on these occasions was decidedly infinite.

Bossuet, there was no doubt of it, knew what he was talking about.

'Well, if *you* think he's right, Irene,' said Mr. Cardan, 'why then, there's nothing for me to do but retire from the argument. I bow before superior authority.' He took the cigar out of his mouth and bowed.

Irene felt herself blushing once more. 'Now you're making fun of me,' she said.

Mrs. Aldwinkle put her arm protectively round the young girl's shoulders. 'I won't let you tease her, Cardan,' she said. 'She's the only one of you all who has a real feeling for what is noble and fine and grand.' She drew Irene closer to her, pressed her in a sidelong and peripatetic embrace. Happily, devotedly, Irene abandoned herself. Aunt Lilian was wonderful!

'Oh, I know,' said Mr. Cardan apologetically, 'that I'm nothing but an old capripede.'

Meanwhile Lord Hovenden, humming loudly and walking a little apart from the rest of the company, was making it clear, he hoped, to every one that he was occupied with his own thoughts and had not heard anything that had been said for the last five minutes. What had been said disturbed him none the less. How did Irene know so much about passion, he wondered? Had there been, could there still be . . . other people? Painfully and persistently the question asked itself. With the idea of dissociating himself still more completely from all that had been said, he addressed himself to Mr. Falx.

'Tell me, Mr. Falx,' he said in a pensive voice, as though he had been thinking about the subject for some time before he spoke, 'what do you think of the Fascist Trades Unions?'

Mr. Falx told him.

Passion, Calamy was thinking, passion. . . . One could have enough of it, good Lord! He sighed. If one could say: Never again, and be sure of meaning what one said, it would be a great comfort. Still, he reflected, there was something rather perversely attractive about this Thriplow woman.

Miss Thriplow meanwhile would have liked to say something showing that she too believed in passion—but in a passion of a rather different brand from Mrs. Aldwinkle's; in a natural, spontaneous and almost childish kind of passion, not the hot-house growth that flourishes in drawing-rooms. Cardan was right in not thinking very seriously of that. But he could hardly be expected to know much about the simple and dewy loves that she had in mind. Nor Mrs. Aldwinkle, for that matter. She herself understood them perfectly. On second thoughts, however, Miss Thriplow decided that they were too tenuous and delicate—these gossamer passions of hers—to be talked of here, in the midst of unsympathetic listeners.

Casually, as she passed, she plucked a leaf from one of the overhanging trees. Absent-mindedly she crushed it between her fingers. From the bruised leaf a fragrance mounted to her nostrils. She lifted her hand towards her face, she sniffed, once, again. And suddenly she was back in the barber's shop at Weltringham, waiting there while her cousin Jim had his hair cut. Mr. Chigwell, the barber, had just finished with the revolving brush. The shaft of the machine was still turning, the elastic driving band went round and round over the wheel, writhing from side to side as it went round, like a dying snake suspended, dangerously, above Jim's cropped head.

'A little brilliantine, Mr. Thriplow? Hair's rather dry, you know, rather dry, I'm afraid. Or the usual bay rum?'

'Bay rum,' said Jim in the gruffest, most grown-up voice he could get out of his chest.

And Mr. Chigwell would pick up a vaporizer and squirt

Jim's hair with clouds made out of a clear brown liquid. And the air in the shop was filled with a fragrance which was the fragrance of this leaf, this leaf from Apollo's tree, that she held in her hand. It all happened years ago and Jim was dead. They had loved one another childishly, with that profound and delicate passion of which she could not speak—not here, not now.

The others went on talking. Miss Thriplow sniffed at her crushed bay leaf and thought of her girlhood, of the cousin who had died. Darling, darling Jim, she said to herself; darling Jim! Again and again. How much she had loved him, how terribly unhappy she had been when he died. And she still suffered; still, after all these years. Miss Thriplow sighed. She was proud of being able to suffer so much; she encouraged her suffering. This sudden recollection of Jim, when he was a little boy, in the barber's shop, this vivid remembrance conjured up by the smell of a crushed leaf, was a sign of her exquisite sensibility. Mingled with her grief there was a certain sense of satisfaction. After all, this had happened quite by itself of its own accord, and spontaneously. She had always told people that she was sensitive, had a deep and quivering heart. This was a proof. Nobody knew how much she suffered, underneath. How could people guess what lay behind her gaiety? 'The more sensitive one is,' she used to tell herself, 'the more timid and spiritually chaste, the more necessary it is for one to wear a mask.' Her laughter, her little railleries were the mask that hid from the outside world what was in her soul; they were her armour against a probing and wounding curiosity. How could they guess, for example, what Jim had meant to her, what he still meant—after all these years? How could they imagine that there was a little holy of holies in her heart where she still held communion with him? Darling Jim, she said to herself, darling, darling Jim. The tears came into her eyes. With a finger that still smelt of crushed bay leaves she brushed them away.

It suddenly occurred to her that this would make a splendid short story. There would be a young man and a young girl walking like this under the stars—the huge Italian stars, tremoloing away like tenors (she would remember to bring that into the description) overhead in the velvet sky. Their conversation edges nearer and nearer to the theme of love. He's rather a timid young man. (His name, Miss Thriplow decided, would be Belamy.) One of those charming young men who adore at long range, feel that the girl's too good for them, daren't hope that she might stoop from her divinity, and all that. He's afraid of saying definitely that he loves her for fear of being ignominiously rejected. She, of course, likes him most awfully and her name is Edna. Such a delicate, sensitive creature; his gentleness and diffidence are the qualities in him that particularly charm her.

The conversation gets nearer and nearer to love; the stars palpitate more and more ecstatically. Edna picks a leaf from the fragrant laurel as she passes. 'What must be so wonderful about love,' the young man is just saying (it's a set speech and he's been screwing up his courage to get it out for the last half-hour), 'about real love, I mean, is the complete understanding, the fusion of spirits, the ceasing to be oneself and the becoming some one else, the . . .' But sniffing at the crushed leaf, she suddenly cries out, uncontrollably (impulsiveness is one of Edna's charms), 'Why, it's the barber's shop at Weltringham! Funny little Mr. Chigwell with the squint! And the rubber band still going round and round over the wheel, wriggling like a snake.' But the poor young man, poor Belamy, is most dreadfully upset. If that's the way she's going to respond when he talks about love, he may as well be silent.

There's a long pause; then he begins talking about Karl

Marx. And of course she somehow can't explain—it's a psychological impossibility—that the barber's shop at Weltringham is a symbol of her childhood and that the smell of the crushed laurel leaf brought back her dead brother—in the story it would be a brother—to her. She simply can't explain that her apparently heartless interruption was prompted by a sudden anguish of recollection. She longs to, but somehow she can't bring herself to begin. It's too difficult and too elusive to be talked about, and when one's heart is so sensitive, how can one uncover it, how can one probe the wound? And besides, he ought somehow to have guessed, he ought to have loved her enough to understand; she has her pride too. Every second she delays, the explanation becomes more impossible. In a flat, miserable voice he goes on talking about Karl Marx. And suddenly, unrestrainedly, she begins sobbing and laughing at the same time.

Chapter V

THE black silhouette that on the terrace had so perfunctorily symbolized Mr. Cardan transformed itself as he entered the lamp-lit saloon into the complete and genial man. His red face twinkled in the light; he was smiling.

'I know Lilian,' he was saying. 'She'll sit out there under the stars, feeling romantic and getting colder and colder, for hours. There's nothing to be done, I assure you. To-morrow she'll have rheumatism. We can only resign ourselves and try to bear her sufferings in patience.' He sat down in an arm-chair in front of the enormous empty hearth. 'That's better,' he said, sighing. Calamy and Miss Thriplow followed his example.

'But don't you think I'd better bring her a shawl?' suggested Miss Thriplow after a pause.

'She'd only be annoyed,' Mr. Cardan answered. 'If Lilian has said that it's warm enough to sit out of doors, then it *is* warm enough. We've already proved ourselves fools by wanting to go indoors; if we brought her a shawl, we should become something worse than fools: we should be rude and impertinent, we should be giving her the lie. "My dear Lilian," we'd be as good as saying, "it isn't warm. And when you say that it is, you're talking nonsense. So we have brought you your shawl." No, no, Miss Mary. You must surely see yourself that it wouldn't do.'

Miss Thriplow nodded. 'How diplomatic!' she said. 'You're obviously right. We're all children compared to you, Mr. Cardan. Only so high,' she added irrelevantly—but it was all in the childish part—reaching down her hand to within a foot or two of the floor. Childishly she smiled at him.

'Only *so*,' said Mr. Cardan ironically; and lifting his right hand to the level of his eyes, he measured between his thumb and forefinger a space of perhaps half an inch. With his winking eye he peeped at her through the gap. 'I've seen children,' he went on, 'compared to whom Miss Mary Thriplow would be . . .' He threw up his hands and let them fall with a clap on to his thighs, leaving the sentence to conclude itself in the pregnant silence.

Miss Thriplow resented this denial of her child-like simplicity. Of such is the Kingdom of Heaven. But circumstances did not permit her to insist on the fact too categorically in Mr. Cardan's presence. The history of their friendship was a little unfortunate. At their first meeting, Mr. Cardan, summing her up at a glance (wrongly, Miss Thriplow insisted), had taken her into a kind of cynical and diabolic confidence, treating her as though she were a wholly 'modern' and unprejudiced young woman, one of those young women who not only *do* what they like (which is nothing; for the demurest and the most 'old-fashioned' can and do act), but who also airily and openly talk of their diversions. Inspired by her desire to please, and carried away by her facility for adapting herself to her spiritual environment, Miss Thriplow had gaily entered into the part assigned to her. How brilliant she had been, how charmingly and wickedly daring! until finally, twinkling benevolently all the time, Mr. Cardan had led the conversation along such strange and such outrageous paths that Miss Thriplow began to fear that she had put herself in a false position. Goodness only knew what mightn't, with such a man, happen next. By imperceptible degrees Miss Thriplow transformed herself from a salamander, sporting gaily among the flames, into a primrose by the river's brim. Henceforward, whenever she talked to Mr. Cardan, the serious young female novelist—so cultured and intelligent, but so unspoiled—put in an appearance. For his part, with that tact which distinguished him in all his social negotiations, Mr. Cardan accepted the female novelist without showing the least astonishment at the change. At most, he permitted himself from time to time to look at her through his winking eye and smile significantly. Miss Thriplow on these occasions pretended not to notice. In the circumstances, it was the best thing she could do.

'People always seem to imagine,' said Miss Thriplow with a martyr's sigh, 'that being educated means being sophisticated. And what's more, they never seem to be able to give one credit for having a good heart as well as a good head.'

And she had *such* a good heart. Any one can be clever, she used to say. But what matters is being kind and good, and having nice feelings. She felt more than ever pleased about that bay-leaf incident. That was having nice feelings.

'They always seem entirely to misunderstand what one writes,' Miss Thriplow went on. 'They like my books because they're smart and unexpected and rather paradoxical and cynical and elegantly brutal. They don't see how serious it all is. They don't see the tragedy and the tenderness underneath. You see,' she explained, 'I'm trying to do something new—a chemical compound of all the categories. Lightness and tragedy and loveliness and wit and fantasy and realism and irony and sentiment all combined. People seem to find it merely amusing, that's all.' She threw out her hands despairingly.

'It's only to be expected,' said Mr. Cardan comfortingly. 'Any one who has anything to say can't fail to be misunderstood. The public only understands the things with which it is perfectly familiar. Something new makes it lose its orientation. And then think of the misunderstandings between even intelligent people, people who know one another personally. Have you ever corresponded with a distant lover?' Miss Thriplow slightly nodded; she was familiar, professionally, with every painful experience. 'Then you must know how easy it is for your correspondent to take the expression of one of your passing moods—forgotten long before the arrival of the letter at its destination—as your permanent spiritual condition. Haven't you been shocked to receive, by the returning post, a letter rejoicing with you in your gaiety, when in fact, at the moment you are plunged in gloom; or astonished, when you come whistling down to breakfast, to find beside your plate sixteen pages of sympathy and consolation? And have you ever had the misfortune to be loved by somebody you do not love? Then you know very well how expressions of affection which must have been written with tears in the eyes and from the depth of the heart seem to you not merely silly and irritating, but in the worst possible bad taste. Positively vulgar, like those deplorable letters that are read in the divorce courts. And yet these are precisely the expressions that you habitually use when writing to the person you yourself are in love with. In the same way, the reader of a book who happens to be out of tune with the author's prevailing mood will be bored to death by the things that were written with the greatest enthusiasm. Or else, like the far-away correspondent, he may seize on something which for you was not essential, to make of it the core and kernel of the whole book. And then, you admitted it yourself, you make it very hard for your readers. You write sentimental tragedies in terms of satire and they see only the satire. Isn't it to be expected?'

'There's something in that, of course,' said Miss Thriplow. But not everything, she added to herself.

'And then you must remember,' Mr. Cardan went on, 'that most readers don't really read. When you reflect that the pages which cost a week of unremitting and agonizing labour to write are casually read through—or, more likely, skipped through—in a few minutes, you cannot be surprised if little misunderstandings between author and reader should happen from time to time. We all read too much nowadays to be able to read properly. We read with the eyes alone, not with the imagination; we don't take the trouble to reconvert the printed word into a living image. And we do this, I may say, in sheer self-defence. For though we read an enormous number of words, nine hundred and ninety out of every thousand of them are not worth reading properly, are not even susceptible of being read except superficially, with the eye alone. Our perfunctory reading of nonsense habituates us to be careless and remiss with all our reading, even of good books. You may take endless pains with your writing, my dear Miss Mary; but out of every hundred of your readers, how many, do you suppose, ever take the pains to read what you write—and when I say read,' Mr. Cardan added, 'I mean really *read*—how many, I repeat?'

'Who knows ?' said Miss Thriplow. But even if they did read properly, she was thinking, would they really unearth that Heart ? That was the vital question.

'It's this mania for keeping up to date,' said Mr. Cardan, 'that has killed the art of reading. Most of the people I know read three or four daily newspapers, look at half a dozen weeklies between Saturday and Monday, and a dozen reviews at the end of every month. And the rest of the time, as the Bible with justifiable vigour would put it, the rest of the time they are whoring after new fiction, new plays and verses and biographies. They've no time to do anything but skim along uncomprehendingly. If you must complicate the matter by writing tragedy in terms of farce you can only expect confusion. Books have their destinies like men. And their fates, as made by generations of readers, are very different from the destinies foreseen for them by their authors. *Gulliver's Travels*, with a minimum of expurgation, has become a children's book ; a new illustrated edition is produced every Christmas. That's what comes of saying profound things about humanity in terms of a fairy story. The publications of the Purity League figure invariably under the heading "Curious" in the booksellers' catalogues. The theological and, to Milton himself, the fundamental and essential part of *Paradise Lost* is now so ludicrous that we ignore it altogether. When somebody speaks of Milton, what do we call to mind ? A great religious poet ? No. Milton means for us a collection of isolated passages, full of bright light, colour and thunderous harmony, hanging like musical stars in the lap of nothing. Sometimes the adult masterpieces of one generation become the reading of schoolboys in the next. Does any one over sixteen now read the poems of Sir Walter Scott ? or his novels, for that matter ? How many books of piety and morality survive only for their fine writing ! and how our interest in the merely aesthetic qualities of these books would have scandalized their authors! No, at the end of the account it is the readers who make the book what it ultimately is. The writer proposes, the readers dispose. It's inevitable, Miss Mary. You must reconcile yourself to fate.'

'I suppose I must,' said Miss Thriplow.

Calamy broke silence for the first time since they had entered the room. 'But I don't know why you complain of being misunderstood,' he said, smiling. 'I should have thought that it was much more disagreeable to be understood. One can get annoyed with imbeciles for failing to understand what seems obvious to oneself; one's vanity may be hurt by their interpretation of you—they make you out to be as vulgar as themselves. Or you may feel that you have failed as an artist, in so far as you haven't managed to make yourself transparently plain. But what are all these compared to the horrors of being understood—completely understood? You've given yourself away, you're known, you're at the mercy of the creatures into whose keeping you have committed your soul—why, the thought's terrifying. If I were you,' he went on, 'I'd congratulate myself. You have a public which likes your books, but for the wrong reasons. And meanwhile you're safe, you're out of their reach, you possess yourself intact.'

'Perhaps you're right,' said Miss Thriplow. Mr. Cardan understood her, she reflected, or at least understood part of her—an unreal, superficial part, it was true; but still, she had to admit, a part. And it certainly wasn't agreeable.

Chapter VI

To be torn between divided allegiances is the painful fate of almost every human being. Pull devil, pull baker; pull flesh, pull spirit; pull love, pull duty; pull reason and pull hallowed prejudice. The conflict, in its various forms, is the theme of every drama. For though we have learnt to feel disgust at the spectacle of a bull-fight, an execution or a gladiatorial show, we still look on with pleasure at the contortions of those who suffer spiritual anguish. At some distant future date, when society is organized in a rational manner so that every individual occupies the position and does the work for which his capacities really fit him, when education has ceased to instil into the minds of the young fantastic prejudices instead of truths, when the endocrine glands have been taught to function in perfect harmony and diseases have been suppressed, all our literature of conflict and unhappiness will seem strangely incomprehensible; and our taste for the spectacle of mental torture will be regarded as an obscene perversion of which decent men should feel ashamed. Joy will take the place of suffering as the principal theme of art; in the process, it may be, art will cease to exist. A happy people, we now say, has no history; and we might add that happy individuals have no literature. The novelist dismisses in a paragraph his hero's twenty years of happiness; over a week of misery and spiritual debate he will linger through twenty chapters. When there is no more misery, he will have nothing to write about. Perhaps it will be all for the best.

The conflict which had raged during the last few months within Irene's spirit, though not so serious as some of the inward battles that have distracted strong men in their search for the salvation of integrity, was still for her a painful one. Put baldly in its most concrete form, the question at issue was this: should she paint pictures and write? or should she make her own underclothing?

But for Aunt Lilian the conflict would never have become serious; indeed, it would never, in all probability, have begun at all. For if it had not been for Aunt Lilian, the Natural

Woman in Irene would have remained undisputed mistress of the field, and she would have passed her days in a placid contentment over the lacy intricacies of her undergarments. Aunt Lilian, however, was on the side of the Unnatural Woman; it was she who had practically called the writer and the painter of pictures into existence, had invented Irene's higher talents and ranged them against the homelier.

Mrs. Aldwinkle's enthusiasm for the arts was such that she wanted every one to practise one or other of them. It was her own greatest regret that she herself had no aptitude for any of them. Nature had endowed her with no power of self-expression; even in ordinary conversation she found it difficult to give utterance to what she wanted to say. Her letters were made up of the fragments of sentences; it was as though her thoughts had been blown to ungrammatical pieces by a bomb and scattered themselves on the page. A curious clumsiness of hand united with her native impatience to prevent her from drawing correctly or even doing plain sewing. And though she listened to music with an expression of rapture, she had an ear that could not distinguish a major from a minor third. 'I'm one of those unfortunate people,' she used to say, 'who have an artistic temperament without an artist's powers.' She had to content herself with cultivating her own temperament and developing other people's capacities. She never met a young person of either sex without encouraging him or her to become a painter, a novelist, a poet or a musician. It was she who had persuaded Irene that her little dexterity with camel's-hair brushes was a talent and that she ought on the strength of her amusing letters to write lyrics. 'How can you spend your time so stupidly and frivolously?' she used to ask, whenever she found Irene busy at her underlinen. And Irene, who adored her Aunt Lilian with the dog-like devotion that is only possible when one is eighteen, and rather young for one's age at that, put her sewing away and devoted all her energy to portraying in water-colours and describing in rhyme the landscape and the flowers of the garden. But the underclothing remained, none the less, a permanent temptation. She found herself wondering whether her chain-stitch wasn't better than her painting, her button-holing superior to her verse. She asked herself whether nightdresses weren't more useful than water-colours. More useful—and besides she was so awfully particular about what she wore next her skin; and she adored pretty things. So did Aunt Lilian, who used to laugh at her when she wore ugly, dowdy ones. At the same time Aunt Lilian didn't give her much of an allowance. For thirty shillings Irene could make a garment that it would have cost her five or six guineas to buy in a shop. . . .

Underclothing became for Irene the flesh, became illicit love and rebellious reason; poetry and water-colour painting, invested by her adoration of Aunt Lilian with a quality of sacredness, became spirit, duty and religion. The struggle between her inclination and what Aunt Lilian considered good was prolonged and distressing.

On nights like this, however, the Natural Woman faded completely out. Under the stars, in the solemn darkness, how could one think of underclothing? And Aunt Lilian was being so affectionate. Still, it certainly *was* rather cool.

'Art's the great thing,' Mrs. Aldwinkle was saying earnestly, 'the thing that really makes life worth living and justifies one's existence.' When Mr. Cardan was away she let herself go more confidently on her favourite themes.

And Irene, sitting at her feet, leaning against her knee, couldn't help agreeing. Mrs. Aldwinkle stroked the girl's soft hair, or with combing fingers disordered its sleek surface. Irene shut her eyes; happily, drowsily, she listened. Mrs.

Aldwinkle's talk came to her in gusts—here a phrase, there a phrase.

'Disinterested,' she was saying, 'disinterested . . .' Mrs. Aldwinkle had a way, when she wanted to insist on an idea, of repeating the same word several times. 'Disinterested . . .' It saved her the trouble of looking for phrases which she could never find, of making explanations which always turned out, at the best, rather incoherent. 'Joy in the work for its own sake. . . . Flaubert spent days over a single sentence. . . . Wonderful. . . .'

'Wonderful!' Irene echoed.

A little breeze stirred among the bay trees. Their stiff leaves rattled dryly together, like scales of metal. Irene shivered a little; it was downright cold.

'It's the only really creative . . .' Mrs. Aldwinkle couldn't think of the word 'activity' and had to content herself with making a gesture with her free hand. 'Through art man comes nearest to being a god . . . a god. . . .'

The night wind rattled more loudly among the bay leaves. Irene crossed her arms over her chest, hugging herself to keep warm. Unfortunately, this boa of flesh and blood was itself sensitive. Her frock was sleeveless. The warmth of her bare arms drifted off along the wind; the temperature of the surrounding atmosphere rose by a hundred-billionth of a degree.

'It's the highest life,' said Mrs. Aldwinkle. 'It's the only life.'

Tenderly she rumpled Irene's hair. And at this very moment, Mr. Falx was meditating, at this very moment, on tram-cars in the Argentine, among Peruvian guano-beds, in humming power-stations at the foot of African waterfalls, in Australian refrigerators packed with slaughtered mutton, in the heat and darkness of Yorkshire coal-mines, in tea-plantations on the slopes of the Himalaya, in Japanese banks, at the mouth of Mexican oil-wells, in steamers walloping along across the China Sea—at this very moment, men and women of every race and colour were doing their bit to supply Mrs. Aldwinkle with her income. On the two hundred and seventy thousand pounds of Mrs. Aldwinkle's capital the sun never set. People worked; Mrs. Aldwinkle led the higher life. She for art only, they—albeit unconscious of the privilege—for art in her.

Young Lord Hovenden sighed. If only it were he whose fingers were playing in the smooth thick tresses of Irene's hair! It seemed an awful waste that she should be so fond of her Aunt Lilian. Somehow, the more he liked Irene the less he liked Aunt Lilian.

'Haven't you sometimes longed to be an artist yourself, Hovenden?' Mrs. Aldwinkle suddenly asked. She leaned forward, her eyes glittering with the reflected light of two or three hundred million remote suns. She was going to suggest that he might try his hand at poetical rhapsodies about political injustice and the condition of the lower classes. Something half-way between Shelley and Walt Whitman.

'Me!' said Hovenden in astonishment. Then he laughed aloud: Ha, ha, ha! It was a jarring note.

Mrs. Aldwinkle drew back, pained. 'I don't know why you should think the idea so impossibly comic,' she said.

'Perhaps he has other work to do,' said Mr. Falx out of the darkness. 'More important work.' And at the sound of that thrilling, deep, prophetical voice Lord Hovenden felt that, indeed, he had.

'More important?' queried Mrs. Aldwinkle. 'But can anything be more important? When one thinks of Flaubert . . .' One thought of Flaubert—working through all a fifty-four hour week at a relative clause. But Mrs. Aldwinkle was too enthusiastic to be able to say what followed when one had thought of Flaubert.

'Think of coal-miners for a change,' said Mr. Falx in answer. 'That's what I suggest.'

'Yes,' Lord Hovenden agreed, gravely nodding. A lot of his money came from coal. He felt particularly responsible for miners when he had time to think of them.

'Think,' said Mr. Falx in his deep voice; and he relapsed into a silence more eloquently prophetical than any speech.

For a long time nobody spoke. The wind came draughtily and in ever chillier gusts. Irene clasped her arms still tightlier over her breast; she shivered, she yawned with cold. Mrs. Aldwinkle felt the shaking of the young body that leaned against her knees. She herself was cold too; but after what she had said to Cardan and the others it was impossible for her to go indoors yet awhile. She felt, in consequence, annoyed with Irene for shivering. 'Do stop,' she said crossly. 'It's only a stupid habit. Like a little dog that shivers even in front of the fire.'

'All ve same,' said Lord Hovenden, coming to Irene's defence, 'it is getting raver cold.'

'Well, if you find it so,' retorted Mrs. Aldwinkle, with overwhelming sarcasm, 'you'd better go in and ask them to light a fire.'

It was nearly midnight before Mrs. Aldwinkle finally gave the word to go indoors.

Chapter VII

To say good-night definitely and for the last time was a thing which Mrs. Aldwinkle found most horribly difficult. With those two fatal words she pronounced sentence of death on yet another day (on yet another, and the days were so few now, so agonizingly brief); she pronounced it also, temporarily at least, on herself. For, the formula once finally uttered, there was nothing for her to do but creep away out of the light and bury herself in the black unconsciousness of sleep. Six hours, eight hours would be stolen from her and never given back. And what marvellous things might not be happening while she was lying dead between the sheets! Extraordinary happinesses might present themselves and, finding her asleep and deaf to their calling, pass on. Or some one, perhaps, would be saying the one supremely important, revealing, apocalyptic thing that she had been waiting all her life to hear. 'There!' she could imagine somebody winding up, 'that's the secret of the Universe. What a pity poor Lilian should have gone to bed. She would have loved to hear it.' Good-night—it was like parting with a shy lover who had not yet ventured to declare himself. A minute more and he would speak, would reveal himself the unique soul-mate. Good-night, and he would remain for ever merely diffident little Mr. Jones. Must she part with this day too, before it was transfigured?

Good-night. Every evening she put off the saying of it as long as she possibly could. It was generally half-past one or two before she could bring herself to leave the drawing-room. And even then the words were not finally spoken. For on the threshold of her bed-chamber she would halt, desperately renewing the conversation with whichever of her guests had happened to light her upstairs. Who knew? Perhaps in these last five minutes, in the intimacy, in the nocturnal silence, the important thing really would be said. The five minutes often lengthened themselves out to forty, and still Mrs. Aldwinkle stood there, desperately putting off and putting off the moment when she would have to pronounce the sentence of death.

When there was nobody else to talk to, she had to be content with the company of Irene, who always, when she herself had undressed, came back in her dressing-gown to help Mrs. Aldwinkle—since it would have been unfair to keep a maid up to such late hours—make ready for the night. Not that little Irene was particularly likely to utter the significant word or think the one apocalyptic thought. Though of course one never knew: out of the mouths of babes and sucklings . . . And in any case, talking with Irene, who was a dear child and so devoted, was better than definitely condemning oneself to bed.

To-night, it was one o'clock before Mrs. Aldwinkle made a move towards the door. Miss Thriplow and Mr. Falx, protesting that they too were sleepy, accompanied her. And like an attendant shadow, Irene silently rose when her aunt rose and silently walked after her. Half-way across the room Mrs. Aldwinkle halted and turned round. Formidable she was, a tragedy queen in coral-red velvet. Her little white muslin mirage halted too. Less patient, Mr. Falx and Miss Thriplow moved on towards the door.

'You must all come to bed soon, you know,' she said, addressing herself to the three men who remained at the further end of the room in a tone at once imperious and cajoling. 'I simply won't allow you, Cardan, to keep those poor young men out of their beds to all hours of the night. Poor Calamy has been travelling all day. And Hovenden needs all the sleep, at his age, that he can get.' Mrs. Aldwinkle took it hardly that any of her guests should be awake and talking while she was lying dead in the tomb of sleep. '*Poor* Calamy!' she pathetically exclaimed, as though it were a case of cruelty to animals. She felt herself filled, all at once, with an enormous and maternal solicitude for this young man.

'Yes, poor Calamy!' Mr. Cardan repeated, twinkling. 'Out of pure sympathy I was suggesting that we should drink a pint or two of red wine before going to bed. There's nothing like it for making one sleep.'

Mrs. Aldwinkle turned her bright blue eyes on Calamy,

smiled her sweetest and most piercing smile. 'Do come,' she said. 'Do.' She extended her hand in a clumsy and inexpressive gesture. 'And you, Hovenden,' she added, almost despairingly.

Hovenden looked uncomfortably from Mr. Cardan to Calamy, hoping that one or other of them would answer for him.

'We shan't be long,' said Calamy. 'The time to drink a glass of wine, that's all. I'm not a bit tired, you know. And Cardan's suggestion of Chianti is very tempting.'

'Ah well,' said Mrs. Aldwinkle, 'if you prefer a glass of wine . . .' She turned away with a sad indignation and rustled off towards the door, sweeping the tiled floor with the train of her velvet dress. Mr. Falx and Miss Thriplow, who had been lingering impatiently near the door, drew back in order that she might make her exit in full majesty. With a face that looked very gravely out of the little window in her bell of copper hair, Irene followed. The door closed behind them.

Calamy turned to Mr. Cardan. 'If I prefer a glass of wine?' he repeated on a note of interrogation. 'But prefer it to what? She made it sound as if I had had to make a momentous and eternal choice between her and a pint of Chianti—and had chosen the Chianti. It passes my understanding.'

'Ah, but then you don't know Lilian as well as I do,' said Mr. Cardan. 'And now, let's go and hunt out that flask and some glasses in the dining-room.'

Half-way up the stairs—they were a grand and solemn flight sloping gradually upwards under a slanting tunnel of barrel vaulting—Mrs. Aldwinkle paused. 'I always think of them,' she said ecstatically, 'going up, coming down. Such a spectacle!'

'Who?' asked Mr. Falx.

'Those grand old people.'

'Oh, the tyrants.'

Mrs. Aldwinkle smiled pityingly. 'And the poets, the scholars, the philosophers, the painters, the musicians, the beautiful women. You forget those, Mr. Falx.' She raised her hand, as though summoning their spirits from the abyss. Psychical eyes might have seen a jewelled prince with a nose like an ant-eater's slowly descending between obsequious human hedges. Behind him a company of buffoons and little hunch-backed dwarfs, stepping cautiously, sidelong, from stair to stair. . . .

'I forget nothing,' said Mr. Falx. 'But I think tyrants are too high a price to pay.'

Mrs. Aldwinkle sighed and resumed her climbing. 'What a queer fellow Calamy is, don't you think?' she said, addressing herself to Miss Thriplow. Mrs. Aldwinkle, who liked discussing other people's characters and who prided herself on her perspicacity and her psychological intuition, found almost everybody 'queer,' even, when she thought it worth while discussing her, little Irene. She liked to think that every one she knew was tremendously complicated; had strange and improbable motives for his simplest actions, was moved by huge, dark passions; cultivated secret vices; in a word, was larger than life and a good deal more interesting. 'What did you think of him, Mary?'

'Very intelligent,' thought Miss Thriplow.

'Oh, of course, of course,' Mrs. Aldwinkle agreed almost impatiently; that wasn't anything much to talk about. 'But one hears odd stories of his amorous tastes, you know.' The party halted at the door of Mrs. Aldwinkle's room. 'Perhaps that was one of the reasons,' she went on mysteriously, 'why he went travelling all that time—right away from civilization. . . .' On such a theme a conversation might surely be almost indefinitely protracted; the moment for uttering the final, fatal good-night had not yet come.

Downstairs in the great saloon the three men were sitting over their red wine. Mr. Cardan had already twice refilled his glass. Calamy was within sight of the bottom of his first tumbler; young Lord Hovenden's was still more than half full. He was not a very accomplished drinker and was afraid of being sick if he swallowed too much of this young and generous brew.

'Bored, you're just bored. That's all it is,' Mr. Cardan was saying. He looked at Calamy over the top of his glass and took another sip, as though to his health. 'You haven't met any one of late who took your fancy; that's all. Unless, of course, it's a case of catarrh in the bile ducts.'

'It's neither,' said Calamy, smiling.

'Or perhaps it's the first great climacteric. You don't happen to be thirty-five, I suppose? Five times seven—a most formidable age. Though not quite so serious as sixty-three. That's the grand climacteric.' Mr. Cardan shook his head. 'Thank the Lord, I got past it without dying, or joining the Church of Rome, or getting married. Thank the Lord; but you?'

'I'm thirty-three,' said Calamy.

'A most harmless time of life. Then it's just boredom. You'll meet some little ravishment and all the zest will return.'

Young Lord Hovenden laughed in a very ventriloquial, man-of-the-worldly fashion.

Calamy shook his head. 'But I don't really want it to return,' he said. 'I don't want to succumb to any more little ravishments. It's too stupid; it's too childish. I used to think that there was something rather admirable and enviable about being an *homme à bonnes fortunes*. Don Juan has an honoured place in literature; it's thought only natural that a Casanova should complacently boast of his successes. I accepted the current view, and when I was lucky in love —and I've always been only too deplorably fortunate—I used to think the more highly of myself.'

'We have all thought the same,' said Mr. Cardan. 'The weakness is a pardonable one.'

Lord Hovenden nodded and took a sip of wine to show that he entirely agreed with the last speaker.

'Pardonable, no doubt,' said Calamy. 'But when one comes to think it over, not very reasonable. For, after all, there's nothing really to be very proud of, there's nothing very much to boast about. Consider first of all the other heroes who have had the same sort of successes—more notable, very probably, and more numerous than one's own. Consider them. What do you see? Rows of insolent grooms and pugilists; leather-faced ruffians and disgusting old satyrs; louts with curly hair and no brains, and cunning little pimps like weasels; soft-palmed young epicenes and hairy gladiators—a vast army composed of the most odious specimens of humanity. Is one to be proud of belonging to their numbers?'

'Why not?' asked Mr. Cardan. 'One should always thank God for whatever native talents one possesses. If your talent happens to lie in the direction of higher mathematics, praise God; and if in the direction of seduction, praise God just the same. And thanking God, when one comes to examine the process a little closely, is very much the same as boasting or being proud. I see no harm in boasting a little of one's Casanovesque capacities. You young men are always so damned intolerant. You won't allow any one to go to heaven, or hell, or nowhere, whichever the case may be, by any road except the one you happen to approve of. . . . You should take a leaf out of the Indians' book. The Indians calculate that there are eighty-four thousand different types of human beings, each with its own way of getting through life. They probably underestimate.'

Calamy laughed. 'I only speak for my type,' he said.

'And Hovenden and I for ours,' said Mr. Cardan. 'Don't we, Hovenden?'

'Oh yes. Yes, of course,' Lord Hovenden answered; and for some reason he blushed.

'Proceed,' said Mr. Cardan, refilling his glass.

'Well then,' Calamy went on, 'belonging to the species I do belong to, I can't take much satisfaction in these successes. The more so when I consider their nature. For either you're in love with the woman or you aren't; either you're carried away by your inflamed imagination (for, after all, the person you're really violently in love with is always your own invention and the wildest of fancies) or by your senses and your intellectual curiosity. If you aren't in love, it's a mere experiment in applied physiology, with a few psychological investigations thrown in to make it a little more interesting. But if you are, it means that you become enslaved, involved, dependent on another human being in a way that's positively disgraceful, and the more disgraceful the more there is in you to be enslaved and involved.'

'It wasn't Browning's opinion,' said Mr. Cardan.

> 'The woman yonder, there's no use in life
> But just to obtain her.'

'Browning was a fool,' said Calamy.

But Lord Hovenden was silently of opinion that Browning was quite right. He thought of Irene's face, looking out of the little window in the copper bell.

'Browning belonged to another species,' Mr. Cardan corrected.

'A foolish species, I insist,' said Calamy.

'Well, to tell the truth,' Mr. Cardan admitted, closing his

winking eye a little further, 'I secretly agree with you about that. I'm not really as entirely tolerant as I should like to be.'

Calamy was frowning pensively over his own affairs, and without discussing the greater or less degree of Mr. Cardan's tolerance he went on. 'The question is, at the end of it all: what's the way out? what's to be done about it? For it's obvious, as you say, that the little ravishments will turn up again. And appetite grows with fasting. And philosophy, which knows very well how to deal with past and future temptations, always seems to break down before the present, the immediate ones.'

'Happily,' said Mr. Cardan. 'For, when all is said, is there a better indoor sport? Be frank with me; *is* there?'

'Possibly not,' said Calamy, while young Lord Hovenden smiled at Mr. Cardan's last remark, but unenthusiastically, in a rather painful indecision between amusement and horror. 'But the point is, aren't there better occupations for a man of sense than indoor sports, even the best of indoor sports?'

'No,' said Mr. Cardan, with decision.

'For you, perhaps, there mayn't be. But it seems to me,' Calamy went on, 'that I'm beginning to have had enough of sports, whether indoor or out-of-door. I'd like to find some more serious occupation.'

'But that's easier said than done.' Mr. Cardan shook his head. 'For members of our species it's precious hard to find any occupation that seems entirely serious. Eh?'

Calamy laughed, rather mournfully. 'That's true,' he said. 'But at the same time the sports begin to seem rather an outrage on one's human dignity. Rather immoral, I would say, if the word weren't so absurd.'

'Not at all absurd, I assure you, when used as you use it.' Mr. Cardan twinkled more and more genially over the top of his glass. 'As long as you don't talk about moral laws and all that sort of thing there's no absurdity. For, its obvious, there are no moral laws. There are social customs on the one hand, and there are individuals with their individual feelings and moral reactions on the other. What's immoral in one man may not matter in another. Almost nothing, for example, is immoral for me. Positively, you know, I can do anything and yet remain respectable in my own eyes, and in the eyes of others not merely wonderfully decent, but even noble.

> Ah, what avail the loaded dice?
> Ah, what the tubs of wine?
> What every weakness, every vice?
> Tom Carden, all were thine.

I won't bore you with the rest of this epitaph which I composed for myself some little time ago. Suffice to say that I point out in the two subsequent stanzas that these things availed absolutely nothing and that, *malgré tout*, I remained the honest, sober, pure and high-minded man that every one always instinctively recognizes me to be.' Mr. Cardan emptied his glass and reached out once more for the fiasco.

'You're fortunate,' said Calamy. 'It's not all of us whose personalities have such a natural odour of sanctity that they can disinfect our septic actions and render them morally harmless. When I do something stupid or dirty I can't help feeling that it is stupid or dirty. My soul lacks virtues to make it wise or clean. And I can't dissociate myself from what I do. I wish I could. One does such a devilish number of stupid things. Things one doesn't want to do. If only one could be a hedonist and only do what was pleasant! But to be a hedonist one must be wholly rational; there's no such thing as a genuine hedonist, there never has been. Instead of doing what one wants to do or what would give one pleasure, one drifts through existence doing exactly the opposite, most of the time—doing what one has no desire to do, following insane promptings that lead one, fully conscious, into every sort of discomfort, misery, boredom and remorse. Sometimes,' Calamy went on, sighing, 'I positively regret the time I spent in the army during the war. Then, at any rate, there was no question of doing what one liked; there was no liberty, no choice. One did what one was told and that was all. Now I'm free; I have every opportunity for doing exactly what I like—and I consistently do what I don't like.'

'But do you know exactly what you do like?' asked Mr. Cardan.

Calamy shrugged his shoulders. 'Not exactly,' he said. 'I suppose I should say reading, and satisfying my curiosity about things, and thinking. But about what, I don't feel perfectly certain. I don't like running after women, I don't like wasting my time in futile social intercourse, or in the pursuit of what is technically known as pleasure. And yet for some reason and quite against my will I find myself passing the greater part of my time immersed in precisely these occupations. It's an obscure kind of insanity.'

Young Lord Hovenden, who knew that he liked dancing and desired Irene Aldwinkle more than anything in the world, found all this a little incomprehensible. 'I can't see what vere is to prevent a man from doing what he wants to do. Except,' he qualified, remembering the teaching of Mr. Falx, 'economic necessity.'

'And himself,' added Mr. Cardan.

'And what's the most depressing of all,' Calamy went on, without paying attention to the interruption, 'is the feeling that one will go on like this for ever, in the teeth of every effort to stop. I sometimes wish I weren't externally free. For then at any rate I should have something to curse at, for getting in my way, other than my own self. Yes, positively, I sometimes wish I were a navvy.'

'You wouldn't if you had ever been one,' said Lord Hovenden, gravely and with a knowing air of speaking from personal experience.

Calamy laughed. 'You're perfectly right,' he said, and drained his glass. 'Shouldn't we think of going to bed?'

Chapter VIII

To Irene fell the privilege every evening of brushing her aunt's hair. For her these midnight moments were the most precious in the day. True, it was sometimes an agony for her to keep awake and the suppression of yawns was always painful; three years of incessant practice had not yet accustomed her to her Aunt Lilian's late hours. Aunt Lilian used to twit her sometimes on her childish longing for sleep; at other times she used to insist, very solicitously, that Irene should rest after lunch and go to bed at ten. The teasing made Irene feel ashamed of her babyishness; the solicitude made her protest that she wasn't a baby, that she was never tired and could easily do with five or six hours' sleep a night. The important thing, she had found, was not to be seen yawning by Aunt Lilian and always to look fresh and lively. If Aunt Lilian noticed nothing there was neither teasing nor solicitude.

But in any case, every inconvenience was paid for a thousand times by the delights of these confidential conversations in front of the dressing-table mirror. While the young girl brushed and brushed away at the long tresses of pale golden-brown hair, Mrs. Aldwinkle, her eyes shut, and with an expression of beatitude on her face—for she took a cat's pleasure in the brushing—would talk, spasmodically, in broken sentences, of the events of the day, of her guests, of the people they had met; or of her own past, of plans for the future—hers or Irene's—of love. On all these subjects Mrs. Aldwinkle spoke intimately, confidentially, without reserve. Feeling that she was being treated by her Aunt Lilian as entirely grown-up and almost as an equal, Irene was proud and grateful. Without deliberately setting out to complete the subjugation of her niece, Mrs. Aldwinkle had discovered, in those midnight conversations, the most perfect means for achieving this end. If she talked like this to Irene, it was merely because she felt the need of talking intimately to some one, and because there was nobody else to talk to. Incidentally, however, she had contrived in the process to make the girl her slave. Made her Aunt Lilian's confidante, invested, so to speak, with a title of honour, Irene felt a gratitude which strengthened her original childish attachment to her aunt.

Meanwhile, she had learned to talk with an airy familiarity of many things concerning which young girls are supposed to be ignorant, and of which, indeed, she herself knew, except intellectually and at second hand, nothing. She had learned to be knowing and worldly wise, in the void, so to speak, and with no personal knowledge of the world. Gravely, ingenuously, she would say things that could only be uttered out of the depths of the profoundest innocence, amplifying and making embarrassingly explicit in public things that Mrs. Aldwinkle had only fragmentarily hinted at in the confidential small hours. She regarded herself as immensely mature.

To-night Mrs. Aldwinkle was in a rather gloomy, complaining mood.

'I'm getting old,' she said, sighing, and opening her eyes for a moment to look at her image in the glass that confronted her. The image did not deny the statement. 'And yet I always feel so young.'

'That's what really matters,' Irene declared. 'And besides, it's nonsense; you're not old; you don't look old.' In Irene's eyes, moreover, she really didn't look old.

'People don't like one any more when one gets old,' Mrs. Aldwinkle continued. 'Friends are terribly faithless. They fall away.' She sighed. 'When I think of all the friends . . .' She left the sentence unfinished.

All her life long Mrs. Aldwinkle had had a peculiar genius for breaking with her friends and lovers. Mr. Cardan was almost the sole survivor from an earlier generation of friends. From all the rest she had parted, and she had parted with a light heart. It had seemed easy to her, when she was younger, to make new friends in place of the old. Potential friends, she thought, were to be found everywhere, every day. But now she was beginning to doubt whether the supply was, after all, so inexhaustible as she had once supposed. People of her own age, she found, were already set fast in the little social worlds they had made for themselves. And people of the younger generation seemed to find it hard to believe that she felt, in her heart, just as young as they did. They mostly treated her with the rather distant politeness which one accords to a stranger and an elder person.

'I think people are horrid,' said Irene, giving a particularly violent sweep with the hair-brush to emphasize her indignation.

'You won't be faithless?' asked Mrs. Aldwinkle.

Irene bent over and, for all answer, kissed her on the forehead. Mrs. Aldwinkle opened her glittering blue eyes and looked up at her, smiling, as she did so, that siren smile that, for Irene, was still as fascinating as it had ever been.

'If only everybody were like my little Irene!' Mrs. Aldwinkle let her head fall forward and once more closed her eyes. There was a silence. 'What are you sighing about in that heart-breaking way?' she suddenly asked.

Irene's blush ran tingling up into her temples and disappeared under the copper-coloured fringe. 'Oh, nothing,' she said, with an off-handedness that expressed the depth of her guilty embarrassment. That deep intake of breath, that brief and passionate expiry were not the components of a sigh. She had been yawning with her mouth shut.

But Mrs. Aldwinkle, with her bias towards the romantic, did not suspect the truth. 'Nothing, indeed !' she echoed incredulously. 'Why, it was the noise of the wind blowing through the cracks of a broken heart. I never heard such a sigh.' She looked at the reflection of Irene's face in the mirror. 'And you're blushing like a peony. What is it ?'

'But it's nothing, I tell you,' Irene declared, speaking almost in a tone of irritation. She was annoyed with herself for having yawned so ineptly and blushed so pointlessly, rather than with her aunt. She immersed herself more than ever deeply in her brushing, hoping and praying that Mrs. Aldwinkle would drop the subject.

But Mrs. Aldwinkle was implacable in her tactlessness. 'I never heard anything that sounded so love-sick,' she said, smiling archly into the looking-glass. Mrs. Aldwinkle's humorous sallies had a way of falling ponderously, like bludgeon strokes, on the objects of her raillery. One never knew, when she was being sprightly, whether to feel sorrier for the victim or for Mrs. Aldwinkle herself. For though the victim might get hard knocks, the spectacle of Mrs. Aldwinkle laboriously exerting herself to deliver them was sadly ludicrous ; one wished, for her sake, for the sake of the whole human race, that she would desist. But she never did. Mrs. Aldwinkle always carried all her jokes to the foreseen end, and generally far further than was foreseeable by any one less ponderously minded than herself. 'It was like a whale sighing !' she went on with a frightful playfulness. 'It must be a grand passion of the largest size. Who is it ? Who is it ?' She raised her eyebrows, she smiled with what seemed to her, as she studied it in the glass, a most wickedly sly but charming smile—like a smile in a comedy by Congreve, it occurred to her.

'But, Aunt Lilian,' protested Irene, almost in despair, almost in tears, 'it was nothing, I tell you.' At moments like this she could almost find it in her to hate Aunt Lilian. 'As a matter of fact, I was only . . .' She was going to blurt it out courageously; she was just going to tell Aunt Lilian—at the risk of a teasing or an almost equally unwelcome solicitude: either were better than this—that she had been merely yawning. But Mrs. Aldwinkle, still relentlessly pursuing her fun, interrupted her.

'But I guess who it is,' she said, wagging a forefinger at the glass. 'I guess. I'm not such a blind stupid old auntie as you think. You imagine I haven't noticed. Silly child! Did she think I didn't see that he was very assiduous and that she rather liked it? Did she think her stupid old auntie was blind?'

Irene blushed again; the tears came into her eyes. 'But who are you talking about?' she said in a voice that she had to make a great effort to keep from breaking and trembling out of control.

'What an innocent!' mocked Mrs. Aldwinkle, still very Congreve. And at this point—earlier than was usual with her on these occasions—she had mercy and consented to put poor Irene out of her agony. 'Why, Hovenden,' she said. 'Who else should it be?'

'Hovenden?' Irene repeated with genuine surprise.

'Injured innocence!' Mrs. Aldwinkle momentarily renewed her trampling fun. 'But it's sufficiently obvious,' she went on in a more natural voice. 'The poor boy follows you like a dog.'

'Me?' Irene had been too much preoccupied in following her Aunt Lilian to notice that she in her turn was being followed.

'Now don't pretend,' said Mrs. Aldwinkle. 'It's so stupid pretending. Much better to be frank and straightforward. Admit, now, that you like him.'

Irene admitted. 'Yes, of course I like him. But not . . . not in any special way. I'd really not thought of him like that.'

A shade contemptuously, benevolently amused, Mrs. Aldwinkle smiled. She forgot her depression, forgot her causes of personal complaint against the universal order of things. Absorbed in the uniquely interesting subject, in the sole and proper study of mankind, she was once more happy. Love—it was the only thing. Even Art, compared with it, hardly existed. Mrs. Aldwinkle was almost as much interested in other people's love as in her own. She wanted every one to love, constantly and complicatedly. She liked to bring people together, to foster tender feelings, to watch the development of passion, to assist—when it happened; and Mrs. Aldwinkle was always rather disappointed when it did not—at the tragic catastrophe. And then, when the first love, growing old, had lingeringly or violently died, there was the new love to think of, to arrange, to foster, to watch; and then the third, the fourth. . . . One must always follow the spontaneous motions of the heart; it is the divine within us that stirs in the heart. And one must worship Eros so reverently that one can never be content with anything but the most poignant, most passionate manifestations of his power. To be content with a love that has turned in the course of time to mere affection, kindliness and quiet comprehension is almost to blaspheme against the name of Eros. Your true lover, thought Mrs. Aldwinkle, leaves the old, paralytic love and turns whole-heartedly to the young passion.

'What a goose you are!' said Mrs. Aldwinkle. 'I sometimes wonder,' she went on, 'whether you're capable of being in love at all, you're so uncomprehending, so cold.'

Irene protested with all the energy of which she was capable. One could not have lived as long as she had in Mrs. Aldwinkle's company without regarding the imputation of coldness, of insensitiveness to passion, as the most damning of all possible impeachments. It was better to be accused of being a murderess—particularly if it were a case of *crime passionnel.* 'I don't know how you say that,' she said indignantly. 'I'm always in love.' Had there not been Peter, and Jacques, and Mario?

'You may think you have,' said Mrs. Aldwinkle contemptuously, forgetting that it was she herself who had persuaded Irene that she was in love. 'But it was more imagination than the real thing. Some women are born like that.' She shook her head. 'And they die like that.' One might have inferred from Mrs. Aldwinkle's words and the tone of her voice that Irene was a superannuated spinster of forty, proved conclusively, after twenty years of accumulated evidence, to be incapable of anything remotely resembling an amorous passion.

Irene made no answer, but went on brushing her aunt's hair. Mrs. Aldwinkle's aspersions were particularly wounding to her. She wished that she could do something startling to prove their baselessness. Something spectacular.

'And I've always thought Hovenden an extremely nice boy,' Mrs. Aldwinkle continued, with the air of pursuing an argument. She talked on. Irene listened and went on brushing.

Chapter IX

In the silence and solitude of her room, Miss Thriplow sat up for a long time, pen in hand, in front of an open note-book. 'Darling Jim,' she wrote, 'darling Jim. To-day you came back to me so suddenly and unexpectedly that I could almost have cried aloud in front of all those people. Was it an accident that I picked that stiff leaf from Apollo's tree and crushed it to fragrance between my fingers? Or were you there? was it you who secretly whispered to the unconscious part of me, telling me to pick that leaf? I wonder; oh, I wonder and wonder. Sometimes I believe that there are no accidents, that we do nothing by chance. To-night I felt sure of it.

'But I wonder what made you want to remind me of Mr. Chigwell's little shop at Weltringham. Why did you want to make me see you sitting in the barber's chair, so stiff and grown-up, with the wheel of the mechanical brush still turning overhead and Mr. Chigwell saying, "Hair's very dry, Mr. Thriplow"? And the rubber driving band used always to remind me . . .' Miss Thriplow recorded the simile of the wounded snake which had first occurred to her this evening. There was no particular reason why she should have antedated the conceit and attributed its invention to her childhood. It was just a question of literary tact; it seemed more interesting if one said that it had been made up when one was a child; that was all. 'I ask myself whether there is any particular significance in this reminder. Or perhaps it's just that you find me neglectful and unremembering—poor darling, darling Jim—and take whatever opportunity offers of reminding me that you existed, that you still exist. Forgive me, Jim. Everybody forgets. We should all be kind and good and unselfish if we always remembered—remembered that other people are just as much alive and individual and complicated as we are, remembered that everybody can be just as easily hurt, that everybody needs love just as much, that the only visible reason why we exist in the world is to love and be loved. But that's no excuse for me. It's no excuse for any one to say that other people are just as bad. I ought to remember more. I oughtn't to let my mind be choked with weeds. It's not only the memory of you that the weeds choke; it's everything that's best and most delicate and finest. Perhaps you reminded me of Mr. Chigwell and the bay rum in order to remind me at the same time to love more, and admire more, and sympathize more, and be more aware. Darling Jim.'

She put down her pen, and looking out through the open window at the starry sky she tried to think of him, tried to think of death. But it was difficult to think of death. It was difficult, she found, to keep the mind uninterruptedly on the idea of extinction, of non-life instead of life, of nothingness. In books one reads about sages meditating. She herself had often tried to meditate. But somehow it never seemed to come to much. All sorts of little irrelevant thoughts kept coming into her head. There was no focusing death, no keeping it steadily under the mind's eye. In the end she found herself reading through what she had written, putting in a stop here and there, correcting slips in the style, where it seemed to be too formal, too made-up, insufficiently spontaneous and unsuitable to the secret diary.

At the end of the last paragraph she added another 'darling Jim,' and she repeated the words to herself, aloud, again and again. The exercise produced its usual effect; she felt the tears coming into her eyes.

The Quakers pray as the spirit moves them; but to let oneself be moved by the spirit is an arduous business. Kindlier and more worldly churches, with a feeling for human weakness, provide their worshippers with rituals, litanies, beads and prayer wheels.

'Darling Jim, darling Jim.' Miss Thriplow had found the form of words for her worship. 'Darling Jim.' The tears did her good; she felt better, kinder, softer. And then, suddenly, she seemed to be listening to herself from outside. 'Darling Jim.' But did she really care at all? Wasn't it all a comedy, all a pretence? He had died so long ago; he had nothing to do with her now. Why should she care or remember? And all this systematic thinking about him, this writing of things in a secret diary devoted to his memory —wasn't all that merely for the sake of keeping her emotions in training? Wasn't she deliberately scratching her heart to make it bleed, and then writing stories with the red fluid?

Miss Thriplow put away the thoughts as soon as they occurred to her: put them aside indignantly. They were monstrous thoughts, lying thoughts.

She picked up her pen again and wrote, very quickly, as though she were writing an exorcizing spell and the sooner it had been put on paper the sooner the evil thoughts would vanish.

'Do you remember, Jim, that time we went out in the canoe together and nearly got drowned? . . .'

PART II

FRAGMENTS *from the* AUTOBIOGRAPHY *of* FRANCIS CHELIFER

Chapter I

OLD gentlemen in clubs were not more luxuriously cradled than I along the warm Tyrrhenian. Arms outstretched like a live cross, I floated face upwards on that blue and tepid sea. The sun beat down on me, turning the drops on my face and chest to salt. My head was pillowed in the unruffled water; my limbs and body dimpled the surface of a pellucid mattress thirty feet thick and cherishingly resilient through all its thickness, down to the sandy bed on which it was spread. One might lie paralysed here for a life-time and never get a bedsore.

The sky above me was filmy with the noonday heat. The mountains, when I turned towards the land to look for them, had almost vanished behind a veil of gauze. But the Grand Hotel, on the other hand, though not perhaps quite so grand as it appeared in its illustrated prospectus—for there the front door was forty feet high and four tall acrobats standing on one another's shoulders could not have reached to the sills of the ground-floor windows—the Grand Hotel made no attempt to conceal itself; the white villas glared out unashamedly from their groves of pines; and in front of them, along the tawny beach, I could see the bathing huts, the striped umbrellas, the digging children, the bathers splashing and wallowing in the hot shallows—half-naked men like statues of copper, girls in bright tunics, little boiled shrimps instead of little boys, and sleek ponderous walruses with red heads, who were the matrons in their rubber caps and their wet black bathing garments. Here and there over the surface of the sea moved what the natives called *patini*—catamarans made of a pair of boxed-in pontoons joined together near the ends and with a high seat for the rower in the middle. Slowly, trailing behind them as they went loud wafts of Italian gallantry, giggles and song, they crawled across the flat blueness. Sometimes, at the head of its white wake, its noise and its stink, a motor-boat would pass, and suddenly my transparent mattress would rock beneath me, as the waves of its passage lifted me and let me drop and lifted me up again, more and ever more languidly, till all was once more smooth.

So much for that. The description, as I see now that I come to re-read it, is not inelegant. For though I may not have played a hand of Bridge since I was eight and have never learned Mah Jong, I can claim at least to have studied the rules of style. I have learned the art of writing well, which is the art of saying nothing elaborately. I have acquired all the literary accomplishments. But then, if I may say so without fatuity, I also have a talent. 'Nothing profits more than self-esteem founded on just and right.' I have Milton on my side to justify me in my assertion. When I write well, it is not merely another way of writing badly about nothing. In this respect my effusions differ a little from those of my cultured colleagues. I occasionally have something to say, and I find that the elegant but florid saying of it is as easy to me as walking. Not, of course, that I attach the slightest importance to that. I might have as much to say as La Rochefoucauld and as much facility for saying it as Shelley. But what of that? It would be great art, you say. No doubt; but what of *that*? It's a queer prejudice, this one of ours in favour of art. Religion, patriotism, the moral order, humanitarianism, social reform—we have all of us, I imagine, dropped all those overboard long ago. But we still cling pathetically to art. Quite unreasonably; for the thing has far less reason for existence than most of the objects of worship we have got rid of, is utterly senseless, indeed, without their support and justification. Art for art's sake—halma for halma's sake. It is time to smash the last and silliest of the idols. My friends, I adjure you, put away the ultimate and sweetest of the inebriants and wake up at last completely sober—among the dustbins at the bottom of the area steps.

This little digression will suffice, I hope, to show that I labour, while writing, under no illusions. I do not suppose that anything I do has the slightest importance, and if I take so much pains in imparting beauty and elegance to these autobiographical fragments, it is chiefly from force of habit. I have practised the art of literature so long that it comes natural to me to take the pains I have always taken. You may ask why I write at all, if I regard the process as being without importance? It is a pertinent question. Why do you do this inconsistent thing? I can only plead weakness in justification. On principle I disapprove of writing; on principle I desire to live brutishly like any other ordinary human being. The flesh is willing, but the spirit is weak. I confess I grow bored. I pine for amusements other than those legitimate distractions offered by the cinema and the Palais de Danse. I struggle, I try to resist the temptation; but in the end I succumb. I read a page of Wittgenstein, I play a little Bach; I write a poem, a few aphorisms, a fable, a fragment of autobiography. I write with care, earnestly, with passion even, just as if there were some point in what I were doing, just as if it were important for the world to know my thoughts, just as if I had a soul to save by giving expression to them. But I am well aware, of course, that all these delightful hypotheses are inadmissible. In reality I write as I do merely to kill time and amuse a mind that is still, in spite of all my efforts, a prey to intellectual self-indulgence. I look forward to a placid middle age when, having finally overcome the old Adam in me, finally quenched all the extravagant spiritual cravings, I shall be able to settle down in tranquillity to that life of the flesh, that natural human existence which still, I fear, seems to me so forbidding, so austerely monotonous, so tedious. I have not yet attained to that blessed state. Hence these divagations into art; let me beg forgiveness for them. And above all, let me implore you once more not to imagine that I attach the slightest importance to them. My vanity would be hurt if I thought you did.

Poor Mrs. Aldwinkle, for example—there was some one who could never believe that I was not an art-for-arter. 'But Chelifer,' she used to say to me in her aimed, intent, breathless way, 'how *can* you blaspheme like that against your own talent?' And I would put on my most Egyptian air—I have always been accused of looking like an Egyptian sculpture—my most Sphingine smile, and say: 'But I am a democrat; how can I allow my talent to blaspheme against my humanity?'—or something enigmatic of that kind. Poor Mrs. Aldwinkle! But I run on too fast. I have begun to talk of Mrs. Aldwinkle and you do not know who Mrs. Aldwinkle is. Nor did I, for that matter, as I reclined that morning along the soft resilient water—I knew no more, then, than her name; who does not? Mrs. Aldwinkle the salonnière, the hostess, the giver of literary parties and agapes of lions—is she not classical? a household word? a familiar quotation? Of course. But in the flesh, till that moment, I had never seen her. Not through any lack of exertions on her part. For only a few months before, a telegram had arrived for me at my publisher's: 'PRINCE PAPADIAMANTOPOULOS JUST ARRIVED MOST ANXIOUS TO KNOW BEST LITERARY ARTISTIC INTELLECTUAL SOCIETY IN LONDON COULD YOU DINE MEET HIM THURSDAY EIGHT FIFTEEN 112 BERKELEY SQUARE LILIAN ALDWINKLE.' In this telegraphic form, and couched in those terms, the invitation had certainly seemed alluring. But a little judicious inquiry showed me that the prospect was not really quite so attractive as it appeared. For Prince Papadiamantopoulos turned out, in spite of his wonderfully promising title and name, to be a perfectly serious intellectual like the rest of us. More serious indeed; for I discovered, to my horror, that he was a first-class geologist and could understand the differential calculus. Among the other guests were to be at least three decent writers and one painter. And Mrs. Aldwinkle herself was rumoured to be quite well educated and not entirely a fool. I filled up the reply-paid form and took it to the nearest post office. 'MUCH REGRET NEVER DINE OUT EXCEPT IN LENT FRANCIS CHELIFER.' During Lent I confidently expected to receive another invitation. I was relieved, however, and a little disappointed, to hear no more from Mrs. Aldwinkle. I should have liked her to make, in vain, a further effort to lure me from my allegiance to Lady Giblet.

Ah, those evenings at Lady Giblet's—I never miss a single one if I can help it. The vulgarity, ignorance and stupidity of the hostess, the incredible second-rateness of her mangy lions—these are surely unique. And then those camp-followers of the arts, those delicious Bohemians who regard their ability to appreciate the paintings of the cubists and the music of Stravinsky as a sufficient justification for helping themselves freely to one another's wives—nowhere can you see such brilliant specimens of the type as at Lady Giblet's. And the conversations one hears within those marble halls—nowhere, surely, are pretensions separated from justifying facts by a vaster gulf. Nowhere can you hear the ignorant, the illogical, the incapable of thought talking so glibly about things of which they have not the slightest understanding. And then you should hear them boasting parenthetically, as they express an imbecile's incoherent opinion, of their own clear-headedness, their modern outlook, their ruthless scientific intelligence. Surely you can find nothing so perfect in its kind as at Lady Giblet's—I at least know of nothing more complete. At Mrs. Aldwinkle's one might very likely hear a serious conversation; never by any chance in the salon of *my* choice.

But that morning in the blue Tyrrhenian was the last of my life to be passed beyond the pale of Mrs. Aldwinkle's acquaintanceship; it was also as nearly as possible the first of my future life. Fate seemed that morning to be in doubt whether to extinguish me completely or merely to make me acquainted with Mrs. Aldwinkle. Fortunately, as I like to think, it chose the latter alternative. But I anticipate.

I first saw Mrs. Aldwinkle on this particular morning without knowing who she was. From where I was lying on my mattress of blue brine I noticed a heavily laden *patino* bearing slowly down upon me from the shore. Perched high on the rower's bench a tall young man was toiling languidly at the oars. His back against the bench, his hairy legs stretched out along the prow of one of the pontoons, sat a thick-set oldish man with a red face and short white hair. The bow of the other pontoon accommodated two women. The elder and larger of them sat in front, trailing her legs in the water; she was dressed in a kilted bathing costume of flame-coloured silk and her hair was tied up in a pink bandana handkerchief. Immediately behind her there squatted, her knees drawn up to her chin, a very youthful slender little creature in a black maillot. In one of her hands she held a green parasol with which she kept off the sunlight from her elder companion. Within the cylinder of greenish shadow the pink and flame-coloured lady, whom I afterwards learnt to be Mrs. Aldwinkle herself, looked like a Chinese lantern lighted in a conservatory; and when an accidental movement of the young girl's umbrella allowed the sunlight for a moment to touch her face, one could imagine that the miracle of the raising of Lazarus was being performed before one's eyes—for the green and corpse-like hue suddenly left the features, the colours of health, a little inflamed by the reflections from the bathing dress, seemed to rush back. The dead lived. But only for an instant; for the solicitous care of the young girl soon reversed the miracle. The sunshade swung back into position, the penumbra of the greenhouse enveloped the glowing lamp and the living face once more became ghastly, as though it belonged to some one who had lain for three days in the tomb.

At the stern, seen clearly only when the ponderous boat was already beginning to pass me, sat another young woman with a pale face and large dark eyes. A tendril of almost black hair escaped from under her bathing cap and fell, like a curling whisker, down her cheek. A handsome young man with a brown face and brown muscular arms and legs sprawled along the stern of the other pontoon, smoking a cigarette.

The voices that faintly came to me from the approaching boat sounded, somehow, more familiar than those I had heard from other *patini*. I became aware, all at once, that they were speaking English.

'The clouds,' I heard the old red-faced gentleman saying (he had just turned round, in obedience to a gesture from the Chinese lantern in the conservatory, to look at the piled-up masses of vapour that hung like another fantastic range above the real mountains), 'the clouds you so much admire are only made possible by the earth's excrementitious dust hanging in the air. There are thousands of particles to every cubic centimetre. The water vapour condenses round them in droplets sufficiently large to be visible. Hence the clouds—marvellous and celestial shapes, but with a core of dust. What a symbol of human idealism !' The melodious voice grew louder and louder as the young man dipped and dipped his oars. 'Earthly particles transfigured into heavenly forms. The heavenly forms are not self-existent, not absolute. Dust writes these vast characters across the sky.'

Preserve me, I thought. Did I come to Marina di Vezza to listen to this sort of thing?

In a voice loud but indistinct, and strangely unmusical, the Chinese lantern lady began to quote Shelley, incorrectly. '"From peak to peak in a bridge-like . . ."' she began, and relapsed into silence, clawing the air in search of the synonym for shape which ought to rhyme with peak. '"Over a something sea." I think *The Cloud* is almost the loveliest of all. It's wonderful to think that Shelley sailed in this sea. And that he was burnt only a little way off, down there.' She pointed down the coast to where, behind the haze, the interminable sea-front of Viareggio stretched away mile after mile. Faintly now one might discern the ghost of its nearest outskirts. But at evening it would emerge; clear and sharp in the sloping light, as though they had been cut from gems, Palace and Grande Bretagne, Europe (*già* Aquila Nera) and Savoia would twinkle there, majestic toys, among the innumerable lesser inns and boarding-houses, reduced at this distance to an exquisite loveliness and so pathetically small and delicate that one could almost have wept over them. At this very moment, on the other side of the curtain of haze, a hundred thousand bathers were thronging the empty beaches where Shelley's body had been committed to the fire. The pinewoods in which, riding out from Pisa, he hunted lovely thoughts through the silence and the fragrant shadows teemed now with life. Unnumbered country copulatives roamed at this moment through those glades. . . . And so forth. Style pours out of my fountain pen. In every drachm of blue-black ink a thousand *mots justes* are implicit like the future characteristics of a man in a piece of chromosome. I apologize.

Youth, then, at the prow and pleasure at the helm—and the flesh was so glossy under the noonday sun, the colours so blazingly bright, that I was really reminded of Etty's little ravishment—the laden boat passed slowly within a few yards of me. Stretched like a live cross on my mattress of brine I looked at them languidly through half-closed eyes. They looked at me; a blank incuriosity was on their faces—for a glimpse only, then they averted their eyes as though I had been one of those exhausted frogs one sees, after the breeding season, floating belly upwards on the surface of a pond. And yet I was what is technically known as an immortal soul. It struck me that it would have been more reasonable if they had stopped their boat and hailed me across the water. 'Good morning, stranger. How goes your soul? And what shall we do to be saved?' But on the other hand, our habit of regarding strangers as being nothing more to us than exhausted frogs probably saves a good deal of trouble.

'From cape to cape,' emended the red-faced gentleman, as they receded from me.

And very diffidently, in a soft shy voice, the solicitous young creature suggested that the something sea was a torrent sea.

'Whatever vat may be,' said the young rower, whose exertions under the broiling sun entitled him to take the professionally nautical, commonsense view about the matter.

'But it's obvious what it is,' said the Chinese lantern lady, rather contemptuously. The young man at the stern threw away his cigarette and started meditatively whistling the tune of '*Deh, vieni alla finestra*' from *Don Giovanni*.

There was a silence; the boat receded, stroke after

stroke. The last words I heard were uttered, drawlingly and in a rather childish voice, by the young woman in the stern. 'I wish I could get brown more quickly,' she said, lifting one foot out of the water and looking at the white bare leg. 'One might have been living in a cellar. Such a dreadfully unwholesome look of blanched asparagus. Or even mushrooms,' she added pensively.

The Chinese lantern lady said something, then the red-faced man. But the conversation had ceased to be articulately audible. Soon I could hear no more; they had gone, leaving behind them, however, the name of Shelley. It was here, along these waters, that he had sailed his flimsy boat. In one hand he held his Sophocles, with the other the tiller. His eyes looked now at the small Greek letters, now to the horizon, or landwards towards the mountains and clouds. 'Port your helm, Shelley,' Captain Williams would shout. And the helm went hard over to starboard; the ship staggered, almost capsized. Then, one day, flash! the black opaque sky split right across; crash and rumble! the thunder exploded overhead and with the noise of boulders being trundled over the surface of the metal clouds, the echoes rolled about the heavens and among the mountains —'from peak to peak,' it occurred to me, adopting the Chinese lantern lady's emendation, 'from peak to peak with a gong-like squeak.' (What an infamy!) And then, with a hiss and a roar, the whirl-blast was upon them. It was all over.

Even without the Chinese lantern lady's hint I should probably have started thinking of Shelley. For to live on this coast, between the sea and the mountains, among alternate flawless calms and shattering sudden storms, is like living inside one of Shelley's poems. One walks through a transparent and phantasmagorical beauty. But for the hundred thousand bathers, the jazz band in the Grand

Hotel, the unbroken front which civilization, in the form of boarding-houses, presents for miles at a time to the alien and empty sea, but for all these, one might seriously lose one's sense of reality and imagine that fancy had managed to transform itself into fact. In Shelley's days, when the coast was all but uninhabited, a man might have had some excuse for forgetting the real nature of things. Living here in an actual world practically indistinguishable from one of imagination, a man might almost be justified for indulging his fancy to the extravagant lengths to which Shelley permitted his to go.

But a man of the present generation, brought up in typical contemporary surroundings, has no justifications of this sort. A modern poet cannot permit himself the mental luxuries in which his predecessors so freely wallowed. Lying there on the water, I repeated to myself some verses, inspired by reflections like these, which I had written some few months before.

The Holy Ghost comes sliding down
On Ilford, Golders Green and Penge.
His hosts infect him as they rot;
The victims take their just revenge.

For if of old the sons of squires
And livery stable keepers turned
To flowers and hope, to Greece and God,
We in our later age have learned

That we are native where we walk
Through the dim streets of Camden Town.
But hopeful still through twice-breathed air
The Holy Ghost comes shining down.

I wrote these lines, I remember, one dark afternoon in my office in Gog's Court, Fetter Lane. It is in the same office, on an almost perfectly similar afternoon, that I am writing now. The reflector outside my window reflects a faint and muddy light that has to be supplemented by electricity from within. An inveterate smell of printer's ink haunts the air. From the basement comes up the thudding and clanking of presses; they are turning out the weekly two hundred thousand copies of the 'Woman's Fiction Budget.' We are at the heart, here, of our human universe. Come, then, let us frankly admit that we are citizens of this mean city, make the worst of it resolutely and not try to escape.

To escape, whether in space or in time, you must run a great deal further now than there was any need to do a hundred years ago when Shelley boated on the Tyrrhenian and conjured up millennial visions. You must go further in space, because there are more people, more and faster vehicles. The Grand Hotel, the hundred thousand bathers, the jazz bands have introduced themselves into that Shelleian poem which is the landscape of Versilia. And the millennium which seemed in the days of Godwin not so very remote has receded further and further from us, as each Reform Bill, each victory over entrenched capitalism dashed yet another illusion to the ground. To escape, in 1924, one must go to Tibet, one must look forward to at least the year 3000; and who knows? they are probably listening-in in the Dalai Lama's palace; and it is probable that the millennial state of a thousand years hence will be millennial only because it has contrived to make slavery, for the first time, really scientific and efficient.

An escape in space, even if one contrives successfully to make one, is no real escape at all. A man may live in Tibet or among the Andes; but he cannot therefore deny that London and Paris actually exist, he cannot forget that there are such places as New York and Berlin. For the majority of contemporary human beings, London and Manchester are the rule; you may have fled to the eternal spring of Arequipa, but you are not living in what is, for the mass of human consciousness, reality.

An escape in time is no more satisfactory. You live in the radiant future, live for the future. You console yourself for the spectacle of things as they are by the thought of what they will be. And you work, perhaps, to make them be what you think they ought to be. I know all about it, I assure you. I have done it all myself—lived in a state of permanent intoxication at the thought of what was to come, working happily for a gorgeous ideal of happiness. But a little reflection suffices to show how absurd these forward lookings, these labours for the sake of what is to be, really are. For, to begin with, we have no reason to suppose that there is going to be a future at all, at any rate for human beings. In the second place we do not know whether the ideal of happiness towards which we are striving may not turn out either to be totally unrealizable or, if realizable, utterly repellent to humanity. Do people want to be happy? If there were a real prospect of achieving a permanent and unvarying happiness, wouldn't they shrink in horror from the boring consummation? And finally, the contemplation of the future, the busy working for it, does not prevent the present from existing. It merely partially blinds us to the present.

The same objections apply with equal force to the escapes which do not launch out into space or time, but into Platonic eternity, into the ideal. An escape into mere fancy does not prevent facts from going on; it is a disregarding of the facts.

Finally there are those people, more courageous than the escapers, who actually plunge into the real contemporary life around them, and are consoled by finding in the midst of its squalor, its repulsiveness and stupidity, evidences of a widespread kindliness, of charity, pity and the like. True, these qualities exist and the spectacle of them is decidedly cheering; in spite of civilization, men have not fallen below the brutes. Parents, even in human society, are devoted to their offspring; even in human society the weak and the afflicted are sometimes assisted. It would be surprising, considering the origins and affinities of man, if this were not the case. Have you ever read an obituary notice of which the subject did not possess, under his rough exterior and formidable manner, a heart of gold? And the obituarists, however cloying their literary productions, are perfectly right. We all have hearts of gold, though we are sometimes, it is true, too much preoccupied with our own affairs to remember the fact. The really cruel, the fundamentally evil man is as rare as the man of genius or the total idiot. I have never met a man with a really bad heart. And the fact is not surprising; for a man with a really bad heart is a man with certain instincts developed to an abnormal degree and certain others more or less completely atrophied. I have never met a man like Mozart for that matter.

Charles Dickens, it is true, managed to feel elated and chronically tearful over the existence of virtues among the squalor. 'He shows,' as one of his American admirers so fruitily puts it, 'that life in its rudest forms may wear a tragic grandeur; that amidst follies and excesses the moral feelings do not wholly die, and that the haunts of the blackest crime are sometimes lighted up by the presence of the noblest souls.' And very nice too. But is there any great reason to feel elated by the emergence of virtues in human society? We are not specially elated by the fact that men have livers and pancreases. Virtues are as natural to man as his digestive organs; any sober biologist, taking into consideration his gregarious instincts, would naturally expect to find them.

This being the case, there is nothing in these virtues *à la* Dickens to 'write home about'—as we used to say at a time when we were remarkably rich in such virtues. There is no reason to be particularly proud of qualities which we inherit from our animal forefathers and share with our household pets. The gratifying thing would be if we could find in contemporary society evidences of peculiarly human virtues—the conscious rational virtues that ought to belong by definition to a being calling himself Homo Sapiens. Open-mindedness, for example, absence of irrational prejudice, complete tolerance and a steady, reasonable pursuit of social goods. But these, alas, are precisely what we fail to discover. For to what, after all, are all this squalor, this confusion and ugliness due but to the lack of the human virtues? The fact is that—except for an occasional sport of Nature, born now here, now there, and always out of time—we sapient men have practically no human virtues at all. Spend a week in any great town, and the fact is obvious. So complete is this lack of truly human qualities that we are reduced, if we condescend to look at reality at all, to act like Charles Dickens and congratulate the race on its merely animal virtues. The jolly, optimistic fellows who assure us that humanity is all right, because mothers love their children, poor folk pity and help one another, and soldiers die for a flag, are comforting us on the grounds that we resemble the whales, the elephants and the bees. But when we ask them to adduce evidence of human sapience, to give us a few specimens of conscious and reasonable well-doing, they rebuke us for our intellectual coldness and our general 'inhumanity' —which means our refusal to be content with the standards of the animals. However grateful we may feel for the existence in civilized society of these homely jungle virtues, we cannot justifiably set them off against the horrors and squalors of civilized life. The horrors and squalors arise from men's lack of reason—from their failure to be completely and sapiently human. The jungle virtues are merely the obverse of this animalism, whose Heads is instinctive kindliness and whose Tails is stupidity and instinctive cruelty.

So much for the last consolation of philosophy. We are left with reality. My office in Gog's Court is situated, I repeat, at the very heart of it, the palpitating heart.

Chapter II

GOG'S COURT, the navel of reality ! Repeating those verses of mine in the silence, I intimately felt the truth of it.

> For if of old the sons of squires
> And livery stable keepers turned
> To flowers and hope, to Greece and God,
> We in our later age have learned
> That we are native where we walk.

My voice boomed out oracularly across the flat sea. Nothing so richly increases the significance of a statement as to hear it uttered by one's own voice, in solitude. 'Resolved, so help me God, never to touch another drop !' Those solemn words, breathed out in a mist of whiskey—how often, in dark nights, on icy mornings, how often have they been uttered ! And the portentous imprecation seems to engage the whole universe to do battle on behalf of the Better Self against its besetting vice. Thrilling and awful moment ! Merely for the sake of living through it again, for the sake of once more breaking the empty silence with the reverberating Stygian oath, it is well worth neglecting the good resolution. I say nothing of the pleasures of inebriation.

My own brief recital served to confirm for me the truth of my speculations. For not only was I uttering the substance of my thoughts aloud; I was voicing it in terms of a formula that had an element, I flatter myself, of magic about it. What is the secret of these verbal felicities? How does it come about that a commonplace thought embodied by a poet in some abracadabrical form seems bottomlessly profound, while a positively false and stupid notion may be made by its expression to seem true? Frankly, I don't know. And what is more, I have never found any one who could give an answer to the riddle. What is it that makes the two words 'defunctive music' as moving as the dead march out of the *Eroica* and the close of *Coriolan*? Why should it be somehow more profoundly comic to 'call Tullia's ape a marmosite' than to write a whole play of Congreve? And the line, 'Thoughts that do often lie too deep for tears'—why should it in effect lie where it does? Mystery. This game of art strangely resembles conjuring. The quickness of the tongue deceives the brain. It has happened, after all, often enough. Old Shakespeare, for example. How many critical brains have been deceived by the quickness of *his* tongue! Because he can say 'Shoughs, water-rugs and demi-wolves,' and 'defunctive music,' and 'the expense of spirit in a waste of shame' and all the rest of it, we credit him with philosophy, a moral purpose and the most penetrating psychology. Whereas his thoughts are incredibly confused, his only purpose is to entertain and he has created only three characters. One, Cleopatra, is an excellent copy from the life, like a character out of a good realistic novel, say one of Tolstoy's. The other two—Macbeth and Falstaff—are fabulous imaginary figures, consistent with themselves but not real in the sense that Cleopatra is real. My poor friend Calamy would call them more real, would say that they belong to the realm of Absolute Art. And so forth. I cannot go into poor Calamy's opinions, at any rate in this context; later on, perhaps. For me, in any case, Macbeth and Falstaff are perfectly genuine and complete mythological characters, like Jupiter or Gargantua, Medea or Mr. Winkle. They are the only two well-invented mythological monsters in the whole of Shakespeare's collection; just as Cleopatra is the only well-copied reality. His boundless capacity for abracadabra has deceived innumerable people into imagining that all the other characters are as good.

But the Bard, heaven help me, is not my theme. Let me return to my recitation on the face of the waters. As I have said, my conviction 'that we are native where we walk' was decidedly strengthened by the sound of my own voice pronouncing the elegant formula in which the notion was embalmed. Repeating the words, I thought of Gog's Court, of my little room with the reflector at the window, of the light that burns in winter even at noon, of the smell of printer's ink and the noise of the presses. I was back there, out of this irrelevant poem of a sunshiny landscape, back in the palpitating heart of things. On the table before me lay a sheaf of long galleys; it was Wednesday; I should have been correcting proofs, but I was idle that afternoon! On the blank six inches at the bottom of a galley I had been writing those lines: 'For if of old the sons of squires . . .' Pensively, a halma player contemplating his next move, I hung over them. What were the possible improvements? There was a knock at the door. I drew a sheet of blotting paper across the bottom of the galley—'Come in'—and went on with my interrupted reading of the print. '. . . Since Himalayas were made to breed true to colour, no event has aroused greater enthusiasm in the fancier's world than the fixation of the new Flemish-Angora type. Mr. Spargle's achievement is indeed an epoch-making one. . . .' I restored the n of nepoch to its widowed a, and looked up. Mr. Bosk, the sub-editor, was standing over me.

'Proof of the leader, sir,' he said, bowing with that exquisitely contemptuous politeness which characterized all his dealings with me, and handed me another galley.

'Thank you, Mr. Bosk,' I said.

But Mr. Bosk did not retire. Standing there in his favourite and habitual attitude, the attitude assumed by our ancestors (of whom, indeed, old Mr. Bosk was one) in front of the half-draped marble column of the photographer's studio, he looked at me, faintly smiling through his thin white beard. The third button of his waistcoat was undone and his right hand, like a half-posted letter, was inserted in the orifice. He rested his weight on a rigid right leg. The other leg was slightly bent, and the heel of one touching the toe of the other, his left foot made with his right a perfect right angle. I could see that I was in for a reproof.

'What is it, Mr. Bosk?' I asked.

Among the sparse hairs Mr. Bosk's smile became piercingly sweet. He put his head archly on one side. His voice when he spoke was mellifluous. On these occasions when I was to be dressed down and put in my place his courtesy degenerated into a kind of affected girlish coquetry. 'If you don't mind my saying so, Mr. Chelifer,' he said mincingly, 'I think you'll find that *rabear* in Spanish does not mean "to wag the tail" as you say in your leader on the derivation of the word "rabbit," so much as "to wag the hind quarters."'

'Wag the hind quarters, Mr. Bosk?' I said. 'But that sounds to me a very difficult feat.'

'Not in Spain, apparently,' said Mr. Bosk, almost giggling.

'But this is England, Mr. Bosk.'

'Nevertheless, my authority is no less than Skeat himself.' And triumphantly, with the air of one who, at a critical moment of the game, produces a fifth ace, Mr. Bosk brought forward his left hand, which he had been keeping mysteriously behind his back. It held a dictionary; a strip of paper marked the page. Mr. Bosk laid it, opened, on the table before me; with a thick nail he pointed "". . . or possibly," I read aloud, "from Spanish *rabear*, to wag the hind quarters." Right as usual, Mr. Bosk. I'll alter it in the proof.'

'Thank you, sir,' said Mr. Bosk with a mock humility. Inwardly he was exulting in his triumph. He picked up his dictionary, repeated his contemptuously courteous bow and walked with a gliding noiseless motion towards the door. On the threshold he paused. 'I remember that the question arose once before, sir,' he said; his voice was poisonously honeyed. 'In Mr. Parfitt's time,' and he slipped out, closing the door quietly behind him.

It was a Parthian shot. The name of Mr. Parfitt was meant to wound me to the quick, to bring the blush of shame to my cheek. For had not Mr. Parfitt been the perfect, complete and infallible editor? Whereas I . . . Mr. Bosk left it to my own conscience to decide what I was.

And indeed I was well aware of my short-comings. 'The Rabbit Fanciers' Gazette,' with which, as every schoolboy knows, is incorporated 'The Mouse Breeders' Record,' could hardly have had a more unsuitable editor than I. To this day, I confess, I hardly know the right end of a rabbit from the wrong. Mr. Bosk was a survivor from the grand old days of Mr. Parfitt, the founder and for thirty years the editor of the Gazette.

'Mr. Parfitt, sir,' he used to tell me every now and then,

'was a *real* fancier.' His successor, by implication, was not.

It was at the end of the war. I was looking for a job—a job at the heart of reality. The illusory nature of the position had made me decline my old college's offer of a fellowship. I wanted something—how shall I put it?—more palpitating. And then in *The Times* I found what I had been looking for. 'Wanted Editor of proved literary ability for livestock trade paper. Apply Box 92.' I applied, was interviewed, and conquered. The directors couldn't finally resist my testimonial from the Bishop of Bosham. 'A life-long acquaintance with Mr. Chelifer and his family permits me confidently to assert that he is a young man of great ability and high moral purpose. (signed) Hartley Bosh.' I was appointed for a probationary period of six months.

Old Mr. Parfitt, the retiring editor, stayed on a few days at the office to initiate me into the secrets of the work. He was a benevolent old gentleman, short, thick and with a very large head. His square face was made to seem even broader than it was by the grey whiskers which ran down his cheeks to merge imperceptibly into the ends of his moustache. He knew more about mice and rabbits than any man in the country; but what he prided himself on was his literary gift. He explained to me the principles on which he wrote his weekly leaders.

'In the fable,' he told me, smiling already in anticipation of the end of this joke which he had been elaborating and polishing since 1892, 'in the fable it is the mountain which, after a long and, if I may say so, geological labour, gives birth to the mouse. My principle, on the contrary, has always been, wherever possible, to make my mice parturate mountains.' He paused expectantly. When I had laughed, he went on. 'It's astonishing what reflections on life and art and politics and philosophy and what not you can get out of a mouse or a rabbit. Quite astonishing!'

The most notable of Mr. Parfitt's mountain thoughts still hangs, under glass and in an Oxford frame, on the wall above the editorial desk. It was printed in the Rabbit Fancier for August 8, 1914.

'It is not the readers of the Rabbit Fanciers' Gazette,' Mr. Parfitt had written on that cardinal date, 'who have made this war. No Mouse Breeder, I emphatically proclaim, has desired it. No! Absorbed in their harmless and indeed beneficent occupations, they have had neither the wish nor the leisure to disturb the world's peace. If all men whole-heartedly devoted themselves to avocations like ours, there would be no war. The world would be filled with the innocent creators and fosterers of life, not, as at present, with its tigerish destroyers. Had Kaiser William the Second been a breeder of rabbits or mice, we should not find ourselves to-day in a world whose very existence is threatened by the unimaginable horrors of modern warfare.'

Noble words! Mr. Parfitt's righteous indignation was strengthened by his fears for the future of his paper. The war, he gloomily foreboded, would mean the end of rabbit breeding. But he was wrong. Mice, it is true, went rather out of fashion between 1914 and 1918. But in the lean years of rationing, rabbits took on a new importance. In 1917 there were ten fanciers of Flemish Giants to every one there had been before the war. Subscriptions rose, advertisements were multiplied.

'Rabbits,' Mr. Parfitt assured me, 'did a great deal to help us win the war.'

And conversely, the war did so much to help rabbits that Mr. Parfitt was able to retire in 1919 with a modest but adequate fortune. It was then that I took over control. And in spite of Mr. Bosk's contempt for my ignorance and incompetence, I must in justice congratulate myself on the way in which I piloted the concern through the evil times which followed. Peace found the English people at once less prosperous and less hungry than they had been during the war. The time had passed when it was necessary for them to breed rabbits; and they could not afford the luxury of breeding them for pleasure. Subscriptions declined, advertisements fell off. I averted an impending catastrophe by adding to the paper a new section dealing with goats. Biologically, no doubt, as I pointed out to the directors in my communication on the subject, this mingling of ruminants with rodents was decidedly unsound. But commercially, I felt sure, the innovation would be justified. It was. The goats brought half a dozen pages of advertisements in their train and several hundred new subscribers. Mr. Bosk was furious at my success; but the directors thought very highly of my capacities.

They did not, it is true, always approve of my leading articles. 'Couldn't you try to make them a little more popular,' suggested the managing director, 'a little more practical too, Mr. Chelifer? For instance,' and clearing his throat, he unfolded the typewritten sheet of complaints which he had had prepared and had brought with him to the board meeting, 'for instance, what's the practical value of this stuff about the use of the word "cony" as a term of endearment in the Elizabethan dramatists? And this article on the derivation of "rabbit"'—he looked at his paper again and coughed. 'Who wants to know that there's a Walloon word "robett"? Or that our word may have something to do with the Spanish *rabear*, to wag the hind quarters? And who, by the way,' he added, looking up at me over his pince-nez with an air—prematurely put on—of triumph, 'who ever heard of an animal wagging its hind quarters?' 'Nevertheless,' I said, apologetically, but firmly, as befits a man who knows that he is right, 'my authority is no less than Skeat himself.'

The managing director, who had hoped to score a point, went on, defeated, to the next count in the indictment. 'And then, Mr. Chelifer,' he said, 'we don't very much like, my fellow directors and I, we don't much like what you say in your article on "Rabbit Fancying and its Lesson to Humanity." It may be true that breeders have succeeded in producing domesticated rabbits that are four times the weight of wild rabbits and possess only half the quantity of brains—it may be true. Indeed, it is true. And a very remarkable achievement it is, Mr. Chelifer, very remarkable indeed. But that is no reason for upholding, as you do, Mr. Chelifer, that the ideal working man, at whose production the eugenist should aim, is a man eight times as strong as the present-day workman, with only a sixteenth of his mental capacity. Not that my fellow directors and I entirely disagree with what you say, Mr. Chelifer; far from it. All right-thinking men must agree that the modern workman is too well educated. But we have to remember, Mr. Chelifer, that many of our readers actually belong to that class.'

'Quite.' I acquiesced in the reproof.

'And finally, Mr. Chelifer, there is your article on the "Symbology of the Goat." We feel that the facts you have there collected, however interesting to the anthropologist and the student of folk-lore, are hardly of a kind to be set before a mixed public like ours.'

The other directors murmured their assent. There was a prolonged silence.

Chapter III

I REMEMBER an advertisement—for some sort of cough drops I think it was—which used to figure very largely in my boyhood on the back covers of the illustrated weeklies. Over the legend, 'A Pine Forest in every Home,' appeared a picture of three or four magnificent Norway spruces growing out of the drawing-room carpet, while the lady of the house, her children and guests took tea, with a remarkable air of unconcern and as though it was quite natural to have a sequoia sprouting out of the hearth-rug, under their sanitary and aromatic shade. A Pine Forest in every Home. . . . But I have thought of something even better. A Luna Park in every Office. A British Empire Exhibition Fun Fair in every Bank. An Earl's Court in every Factory. True, I cannot claim to bring every attraction of the Fun Fair into your place of labour —only the switchback, the water-shoot and the mountain railway. Merry-go-round, wiggle-woggle, flip-flap and the like are beyond the power of my magic to conjure up. Horizontal motion and a rotary giddiness I cannot claim to reproduce ; my speciality is headlong descents, breathlessness and that delicious sickening feeling that your entrails have been left behind on an upper storey. Those who chafe at the tameness and sameness of office life, who pine for a little excitement to diversify the quotidian routine, should experiment with this little recipe of mine and bring the water-shoot into the counting-house. It is quite simple. All you have got to do is to pause for a moment in your work and ask yourself: Why am I doing this? What is it all for? Did I come into the world, supplied with a soul which may very likely be immortal, for the sole purpose of sitting every day at this desk? Ask yourself these questions thoughtfully, seriously. Reflect even for a moment on their significance—and I can guarantee that, firmly seated though you may be in your hard or your padded chair, you will feel all at once that the void has opened beneath you, that you are sliding headlong, fast and faster, into nothingness.

For those who cannot dispense with formularies and fixed prayers, I recommend this little catechism, to be read through in office hours whenever time hangs a little heavy.

Q. Why am I working here?

A. In order that Jewish stockbrokers may exchange their Rovers for Armstrong-Siddeleys, buy the latest jazz records and spend the week-end at Brighton.

Q. Why do I go on working here?

A. In the hope that I too may some day be able to spend the week-end at Brighton.

Q. What is progress?

A. Progress is stockbrokers, more stockbrokers and still more stockbrokers.

Q. What is the aim of social reformers?

A. The aim of social reformers is to create a state in which every individual enjoys the greatest possible amount of freedom and leisure.

Q. What will the citizens of this reformed state do with their freedom and leisure?

A. They will do, presumably, what the stockbrokers do with these things to-day, *e.g.* spend the week-end at Brighton, ride rapidly in motor vehicles and go to the theatre.

Q. On what condition can I live a life of contentment?

A. On the condition that you do not think.

Q. What is the function of newspapers, cinemas, radios, motor-bikes, jazz bands, etc?

A. The function of these things is the prevention of thought and the killing of time. They are the most powerful instruments of human happiness.

Q. What did Buddha consider the most deadly of the deadly sins?

A. Unawareness, stupidity.

Q. And what will happen if I make myself aware, if I actually begin to think?

A. Your swivel chair will turn into a trolley on the mountain railway, the office floor will gracefully slide away from beneath you and you will find yourself launched into the abyss.

Down, down, down! The sensation, though sickening, is really delightful. Most people, I know, find it a little too much for them and consequently cease to think, in which case the trolley reconverts itself into the swivel chair, the floor closes up and the hours at the desk seem once more to be hours passed in a perfectly reasonable manner; or else, more rarely, flee in panic horror from the office to bury their heads like ostriches in religion or what not. For a strong-minded and intelligent person both courses are inadmissible; the first because it is stupid and the second because it is cowardly. No self-respecting man can either accept unreflectingly or, having reflected upon it, irresponsibly run away from the reality of human life. The proper course, I flatter myself, is that which I have adopted. Having sought out the heart of reality—Gog's Court, to be explicit—I have taken up my position there; and though fully aware of the nature of the reality by which I am surrounded, though deliberately keeping myself reminded of the complete imbecility of what I am doing, I yet remain heroically at my post. My whole time is passed on the switchback; all my life is one unceasing slide through nothing.

All my life, I insist; for it is not merely into Gog's Court that I magically introduce the fun of the fair. I so arrange my private life that I am sliding even out of office hours. My heart, to borrow the poetess's words, is like a singing bird whose nest is permanently in a water-shoot. Miss Carruthers's boarding-house in Chelsea is, I assure you, as suitable a place to slither in as any east of Temple Bar. I have lived there now for four years. I am a pillar of the establishment and every evening, when I sit down to dinner with my fellow guests, I feel as though I were taking my place in a specially capacious family trolley on the switchback railway. All aboard ! and away we go. With gathering momentum the trolley plunges down into vacancy.

Let me describe an evening on the Domestic water-shoot. At the head of the table sits Miss Carruthers herself; thirty-seven, plump though unmarried, with a face broadening towards the base and very flabby about the cheeks and chin—bull-doggy, in a word; and the snub nose, staring at you out of its upward-tilted nostrils, the small brown eyes do not belie the comparison. And what activity ! never walks, but runs about her establishment like a demoniac, never speaks but shrilly shouts, carves the roast beef with scientific fury, laughs like a giant woodpecker. She belongs to a distinguished family which would never, in its days of glory, have dreamed of allowing one of its daughters to become what Miss Carruthers calls, applying to herself the most humiliating of titles and laughing as she does so, to emphasize the picturesque contrast between what she is by birth and what circumstance has reduced her to becoming, ' a common lodging-house keeper.' She is a firm believer in her class, and to her more distinguished guests deplores the necessity under which she labours to admit into her establishment persons not really, really . . . She is careful not to mix people of different sorts together. Her most genteel guests sit the closest to her at table; it is implied that, in the neighbourhood of

Miss Carruthers, they will feel at home. For years I have had the honour of sitting at her left hand; for if less prosperous than Mrs. Cloudesley Shove, the broker's widow (who sits in glory on the right), I have at least attended in my youth an ancient seat of learning.

The gong reverberates; punctually I hurry down to the dining-room. With fury and precision, like a conductor immersed in a Wagner overture, Miss Carruthers is carving the beef.

'Evening, Mr. Chelifer,' she loudly calls, without interrupting her labours. 'What news have you brought back with you from the city to-day?'

Affably I smile, professionally I rub the hands. 'Well, I don't know that I can think of any.'

'Evening, Mrs. Fox. Evening, Mr. Fox.' The two old people take their places near the further end of the table. They are not quite, quite . . . 'Evening, Miss Monad.' Miss Monad does responsible secretarial work and sits next to the Fox's. 'Evening, Mr. Quinn. Evening, Miss Webber. Evening, Mrs. Crotch.' But the tone in which she responds to Mr. Dutt's courteous greeting is much less affable. Mr. Dutt is an Indian—a black man, Miss Carruthers calls him. Her 'Evening, Mr. Dutt' shows that she knows her place and hopes that the man of the inferior race knows his. The servant comes in with a steaming dish of greens. *Crambe ripetita*—inspiring perfume! Mentally I burst into song.

These like remorse inveterate memories,
Being of cabbage, are prophetic too
Of future feasts, when Mrs. Cloudesley Shove
Will still recall lamented Cloudesley.
Still

Among the moonlit cedars Philomel
Calls back to mind, again, again,

The ancient pain, the everlasting pain;
And still inveterately the haunted air
Remembers and foretells that roses were
Red and to-morrow will again be red,
But, 'Cloudesley, Cloudesley!' Philomel in vain
Sobs on the night; for Cloudesley Shove is dead. . . .

And in the flesh, as though irresistibly summoned by my incantation, Mrs. Cloudesley Shove blackens the doorway with her widowhood.

'Not a very naice day,' said Mrs. Cloudesley, as she sits down.

'Not at all,' Miss Carruthers heartily agrees. And then, without turning from the beef, without abating for an instant the celerity of her carving, 'Fluffy!' she shouts through the increasing din, 'don't giggle like that.'

Politely Mr. Chelifer half raises himself from his chair as Miss Fluffy comes tumbling, on the tail end of her giggle, into the chair next to his. Always the perfect gent.

'I wasn't giggling, Miss Carruthers,' Fluffy protests. Her smile reveals above the roots of her teeth a line of almost bloodless gums.

'Quite true,' says young Mr. Brimstone, following her less tumultuously from the door and establishing himself in the seat opposite, next to Mrs. Cloudesley. 'She wasn't giggling. She was merely cachinnating.'

Everybody laughs uproariously, even Miss Carruthers, though she does not cease to carve. Mr. Brimstone remains perfectly grave. Behind his rimless pince-nez there is hardly so much as a twinkle. As for Miss Fluffy, she fairly collapses.

'What a horrible man!' she screams through her laughter, as soon as she has breath enough to be articulate. And picking up her bread, she makes as though she were going to throw it across the table in Mr. Brimstone's face.

Mr. Brimstone holds up a finger. 'Now you be careful,' he admonishes. 'If you don't behave, you'll be put in the corner and sent to bed without your supper.'

There is a renewal of laughter.

Miss Carruthers intervenes. 'Now don't tease her, Mr. Brimstone.'

'Tease?' says Mr. Brimstone, in the tone of one who has been misjudged. 'But I was only applying moral suasion, Miss Carruthers.'

Inimitable Brimstone! He is the life and soul of Miss Carruthers's establishment. So serious, so clever, such an alert young city man—but withal so exquisitely waggish, so gallant! To see him with Fluffy—it's as good as a play.

'There!' says Miss Carruthers, putting down her carving tools with a clatter. Loudly, energetically, she addresses herself to her duties as a hostess. 'I went to Buszard's this afternoon,' she proclaims, not without pride. We old county families have always bought our chocolate at the best shops. 'But it isn't what it used to be.' She shakes her head; the high old feudal times are past. 'It isn't the same. Not since the A B C took it over.'

'Do you see,' asks Mr. Brimstone, becoming once more his serious self, 'that the new Lyons Corner House in Piccadilly Circus will be able to serve fourteen million meals a year?' Mr. Brimstone is always a mine of interesting statistics.

'No, really?' Mrs. Cloudesley is astonished.

But old Mr. Fox, who happens to have read the same evening paper as Mr. Brimstone, takes almost the whole credit of Mr. Brimstone's erudition to himself by adding, before the other has time to say it: 'Yes, and that's just twice as many meals as any American restaurant can serve.'

'Good old England!' cried Miss Carruthers patriotically. 'These Yanks haven't got us beaten in everything yet.'

'So naice, I always think, these Corner Houses,' says Mrs. Cloudesley. 'And the music they play is really quite classical, you know, sometimes.'

'Quite,' says Mr. Chelifer, savouring voluptuously the pleasure of dropping steeply from the edge of the convivial board into interstellar space.

'And so sumptuously decorated,' Mrs. Cloudesley continues.

But Mr. Brimstone knowingly lets her know that the marble on the walls is less than a quarter of an inch thick.

And the conversation proceeds. 'The Huns,' says Miss Carruthers, 'are only shamming dead.' Mr. Fox is in favour of a business government. Mr. Brimstone would like to see a few strikers shot, to encourage the rest; Miss Carruthers agrees. From below the salt Miss Monad puts in a word for the working classes, but her remark is treated with the contempt it deserves. Mrs. Cloudesley finds Charlie Chaplin so vulgar, but likes Mary Pickford. Miss Fluffy thinks that the Prince of Wales ought to marry a nice simple English girl. Mr. Brimstone says something rather cutting about Mrs. Asquith and Lady Diana Manners. Mrs. Cloudesley, who has a profound knowledge of the Royal Family, mentions the Princess Alice. Contrapuntally to this, Miss Webber and Mr. Quinn have been discussing the latest plays and Mr. Chelifer has engaged Miss Fluffy in a conversation which soon occupies the attention of all the persons sitting at the upper end of the table —a conversation about flappers. Mrs. Cloudesley, Miss Carruthers and Mr. Brimstone agree that the modern girl is too laxly brought up. Miss Fluffy adheres in piercing tones to the opposite opinion. Mr. Brimstone makes some splendid jokes at the expense of co-education, and all concur in deploring cranks of every variety. Miss Carruthers, who has a short way with dissenters, would like to see them tarred and feathered—all except pacifists, who, like strikers, could do with a little shooting. Lymphatic Mrs. Cloudesley, with sudden and surprising ferocity, wants to treat the Irish in the same way. (Lamented Cloudesley had connections with Belfast.) But at this moment a deplorable incident occurs. Mr. Dutt, the Indian, who ought never, from his lower sphere, even to have listened to the conversation going on in the higher, leans forward and speaking loudly across the intervening gulf ardently espouses the Irish cause. His eloquence rolls up the table between two hedges of horrified silence. For a moment nothing can be heard but ardent nationalistic sentiments and the polite regurgitation of prune stones. In the presence of this shocking and unfamiliar phenomenon nobody knows exactly what to do. But Miss Carruthers rises, after the first moment, to the occasion.

'Ah, but then, Mr. Dutt,' she says, interrupting his tirade about oppressed nationalities, 'you must remember that Mrs. Cloudesley Shove is English. *You* can hardly expect to understand what *she* feels. Can you?'

We all feel inclined to clap. Without waiting to hear Mr. Dutt's reply, and leaving three prunes uneaten on her plate, Miss Carruthers gets up and sweeps with dignity towards the door. Loudly, in the corridor, she comments on the insolence of black men. And what ingratitude, too!

'After I had made a special exception in his case to my rule against taking coloured people!'

We all sympathize. In the drawing-room the conversation proceeds. Headlong the trolley plunges.

A home away from home—that was how Miss Carruthers described her establishment in the prospectus. It was the awayness of it that first attracted me to the place. The vast awayness from what I had called home up till the time I first stayed there—that was what made me decide to settle for good at Miss Carruthers's. From the house where I I was born Miss Carruthers's seemed about as remote as any place one could conveniently find.

'I remember, I remember . . .' It is a pointless and futile occupation, difficult none the less not to indulge in. I remember. Our house at Oxford was dark, spiky and tall. Ruskin himself, it was said, had planned it. The front windows looked out on to the Banbury Road. On rainy days, when I was a child, I used to spend whole mornings staring down into the thoroughfare. Every twenty minutes a tram-car drawn by two old horses, trotting in their sleep, passed with an undulating motion more slowly than a man could walk. The little garden at the back once seemed enormous and romantic, the rocking-horse in the nursery a beast like an elephant. The house is sold now and I am glad of it. They are dangerous, these things and places inhabited by memory. It is as though, by a process of metempsychosis, the soul of dead events goes out and lodges itself in a house, a flower, a landscape, in a group of trees seen from the train against the sky-line, an old snapshot, a broken pen-knife, a book, a perfume. In these memory-charged places, among these things haunted by the ghosts of dead days, one is tempted to brood too lovingly over the past, to live it again, more elaborately, more consciously, more beautifully and harmoniously, almost as though it were an imagined life in the future. Surrounded by these ghosts one can neglect the present in which one bodily lives. I am glad the place is sold; it was dangerous. *Evviva* Miss Carruthers!

Nevertheless my thoughts, as I lay on the water that morning, reverted from the Home Away to the other home from which it was so distant. I recalled the last visit I had paid to the old house, a month or two since, just before my mother finally decided herself to move out. Mounting the steps that led up to the ogival porch I had felt like an excavator on the threshold of a tomb. I tugged at the wrought-iron bell pull; joints creaked, wires wheezily rattled, and far off, as though accidentally, by an afterthought, tinkled the cracked bell. In a moment the door would open, I should walk in, and there, there in the unrifled chamber the royal mummy would be lying—my own.

Nothing within those Gothic walls ever changed. Imperceptibly the furniture grew older; the wall-papers and the upholstery recalled with their non-committal russets and sage-greens the refinements of another epoch. And my mother herself, pale and grey-haired, draped in the dateless dove-grey dresses she had always worn, my mother was still the same. Her smile was the same dim gentle smile; her voice still softly modulated, like a studied and cultured music, from key to key. Her hair was hardly greyer—for it had whitened early and I was a late-born child—than I always remember it to have been. Her face was hardly more deeply wrinkled. She walked erect, seemed still as active as ever, she had grown no thinner and no stouter.

And she was still surrounded by those troops of derelict dogs, so dreadfully profuse, poor beasts! in their smelly gratitude. There were still the same moth-eaten cats picked up starving at a street corner to be harboured in luxury—albeit on a diet that was, on principle, strictly vegetarian—in the best rooms of the house. Poor children still came for buns and tea and traditional games in the garden—so traditional, very often, that nobody but my mother had ever heard of them; still came, when the season happened to be winter, for gloves and woolly stockings and traditional games indoors. And the writing-table in the drawing-room was piled high, as it had always been piled, with printed appeals for some deserving charity. And still in her beautiful calligraphy my mother addressed the envelopes that were to contain them, slowly, one after another—and each a little work of art, like a page from a mediaeval missal, and each destined, without reprieve, to the waste-paper basket.

All was just as it had always been. Ah, but not quite, all the same! For though the summer term was in full swing and the afternoon bright, the little garden behind the house was deserted and unmelodious. Where were the morris dancers, where the mixolydian strains? And remembering that music, those dances, those distant afternoons, I could have wept.

In one corner of the lawn my mother used to sit at the little harmonium; I sat beside her to turn the pages of the music. In the opposite corner were grouped the dancers. My mother looked up over the top of the instrument; melodiously she inquired:

'Which dance shall we have next, Mr. Toft? "Trenchmore"? Or "Omnium Gatherum"? Or "John come kiss me now"? Or what do you say to "Up tails all"? Or "Rub her down with straw"? Or "An old man's a bed full of bones"? Such an *embarras de richesse*, isn't there?'

And Mr. Toft would break away from his little company of dancers and come across the lawn wiping his face—for 'Hoite-cum-Toite' a moment before had been a most furious affair. It was a grey face with vague indeterminate features and a bright almost clerical smile in the middle of it. When he spoke it was in a very rich voice.

'Suppose we try "Fading," Mrs. Chelifer,' he suggested. '"Fading is a fine dance"—you remember the immortal words of the Citizen's Wife in the *Knight of the Burning Pestle*? Ha ha!' And he gave utterance to a little laugh, applausive of his own wit. For to Mr. Toft every literary allusion was a joke, and the obscurer the allusion the more exquisite the waggery. It was rarely, alas, that he found any one to share his merriment. My mother was one of the few people who always made a point of smiling whenever Mr. Toft laughed at himself. She smiled even when she could not track the allusion to its source. Sometimes she even went so far as to laugh. But my mother had no facility for laughter; by nature she was a grave and gentle smiler.

And so 'Fading' it would be. My mother touched the keys and the gay, sad mixolydian air came snoring out of the harmonium like a strangely dissipated hymn tune. 'One, two, three . . .' called Mr. Toft richly. And then in unison all five—the don, the two undergraduates, the two young ladies from North Oxford—would beat the ground with their feet, would prance and stamp till the garters of little bells round the gentlemen's grey flannel trousers (it went without saying, for some reason, that the ladies should not wear them) jingled like the bells of a runaway hansom-cab horse. One, two, three. . . . The Citizen's Wife (ha ha!) was right. Fading is a fine dance indeed. Everybody dances Fading. Poor Mr. Toft had faded out of Oxford, had danced completely out of life, like Lycidas (tee-hee!) before his prime. Influenza had faded him. And of the undergraduates who had danced here, first and last, with Mr. Toft—how many of them had danced Fading under the German barrage? Young Flint, the one who used always to address his tutor as 'Mr. Toft—oh, I mean Clarence' (for Mr. Toft was one of those genial boyish dons who insisted on being called by their Christian names), young Flint was dead for certain. And Ramsden too, I had a notion that Ramsden too was dead.

And then there were the young women from North Oxford. What, for example, of Miss Dewball's cheeks? How had those cabbage roses weathered the passage of the years? But for Miss Higlett, of course, there could be no more fading, no further desiccation. She was already a harebell baked in sand. Unwithering Higlett, blowsy Dewball. . . .

And I myself, I too had faded. The Francis Chelifer who, standing by the dissipated harmonium, had turned the pages of his mother's music, was as wholly extinct as Mr. Toft. Within this Gothic tomb reposed his mummy. My week-end visits were archaeological expeditions.

'Now that poor Mr. Toft's dead,' I asked as we walked, my mother and I, that afternoon, up and down the little garden behind the house, 'isn't there any one else here who's keen on morris dancing?' Or were those folky days, I wondered, for ever past?

My mother shook her head. 'The enthusiasm for it is gone,' she said sadly. 'This generation of undergraduates doesn't seem to take much interest in that kind of thing. I don't really know,' she added, 'what it *is* interested in.'

What indeed, I reflected. In my young days it had been Social Service and Fabianism; it had been long hearty walks in the country at four and a half miles an hour, with draughts of Five X beer at the end of them, and Rabelaisian song and conversations with yokels in incredibly picturesque little wayside inns; it had been reading parties in the Lakes and climbing in the Jura; it had been singing in the Bach Choir and even—though somehow I had never been able quite to rise to that—even morris dancing with Mr. Toft. . . . But Fading is a fine dance, and all these occupations seemed now a little queer. Still, I caught myself envying the being who had lived within my skin and joined in these activities.

'Poor Toft!' I meditated. 'Do you remember the way he had of calling great men by little pet names of his own? Just to show that he was on terms of familiarity with them, I suppose. Shakespeare was always Shake-bake, which was short, in its turn, for Shake-Bacon. And Oven, *tout court*, was Beethoven.'

'And always J. S. B. for Bach,' my mother continued, smiling elegiacally.

'Yes, and Pee Em for Philipp Emanuel Bach. And Madame Dudevant for George Sand, or, alternatively, I remember, "The Queen's Monthly Nurse"—because Dickens thought she looked like that the only time he saw her.' I recalled the long-drawn and delighted laughter which used to follow that allusion.

'You were never much of a dancer, dear boy.' My mother sadly shook her head over the past.

'Ah, but at any rate,' I answered, 'at any rate I was a Fabian. And I went for hearty long walks in the country. I drank my pint of Five X at the Red Lion.'

'I wish you could have gone without the beer,' said my mother. That I had not chosen to be a total abstainer had always a little distressed her. Moreover, I had a taste for beefsteaks.

'It was my substitute for morris dancing, if you follow me.'

But I don't think she did follow me. We took two or three turns up and down the lawn in silence.

'How is your paper doing?' she asked at last.

I told her with a great show of enthusiasm about the cross between Angoras and Himalayans which we had just announced.

'I often wish,' she said after a pause, 'that you had

accepted the college's offer. It would have been so good to have you here, filling the place your dear father occupied.'

She looked at me sadly. I smiled back at her as though from across a gulf. The child, I thought, grows up to forget that he is of the same flesh with his parents; but they do not forget. I wished, for her sake, that I were only five years old.

Chapter IV

At five years old, among other things, I used to write poems which my mother thoroughly and whole-heartedly enjoyed. There was one about larks which she still preserves, along with the locks of my pale childish hair, the faded photographs, the precocious drawings of railway trains and all the other relics of the period.

Oh lark, how you do fly
Right up into the sky.
How loud he sings
And quickly wags his wings.
The sun does shine,
The weather is fine.
Father says, Hark,
Do you hear the lark?

My mother likes that poem better, I believe, than anything I have written since. And I dare say that my father, if he had lived, would have shared her opinion. But then he was an ardent Wordsworthian. He knew most of the *Prelude* by heart. Sometimes, unexpectedly breaking that profound and god-like silence with which he always enveloped himself, he would quote a line or two. The effect was always portentous; it was as though an oracle had spoken.

I remember with particular vividness one occasion when

Wordsworth broke my father's prodigious silence. It was one Easter time, when I was about twelve. We had gone to North Wales for the holidays; my father liked walking among hills and even amused himself occasionally with a little mild rock climbing. Easter was early that year, the season backward and inclement; there was snow on all the hills. On Easter Sunday my father, who considered a walk among the mountains as the equivalent of church-going, suggested that we should climb to the top of Snowdon. We started early; it was cold; white misty clouds shut off the distant prospects. Silently we trudged upwards through the snow. Like the page of King Wenceslas I followed in my father's footsteps, treading in the holes he had kicked in the snow. Every now and then he would look round to see how I was getting on. Icy dewdrops hung in his brown beard. Gravely he smiled down on me as I came panting up, planting my small feet in his large tracks. He was a huge man, tall and broad-shouldered, with a face that might have been the curly-bearded original of one of those Greek busts of middle-aged statesmen or philosophers. Standing beside him, I always felt particularly small and insignificant. When I had come up with him, he would pat me affectionately on the shoulder with his large heavy hand, then turning his face towards the heights he addressed himself once more to the climb. Not a word was spoken.

As the sun mounted higher, the clouds dispersed. Through the rifted mist we saw the sky. Great beams of yellow light went stalking across the slopes of snow. By the time we reached the summit the sky was completely clear; the landscape opened out beneath us. The sun was shining brightly, but without heat; the sky was pale blue, remote and icy. Every northern slope of the glittering hills was shadowed with transparent blues or purples. Far down, to the westward, was the scalloped and indented coast, and seeming in its remoteness utterly calm, the grey sea stretched upwards and away towards the horizon. We stood there for a long time in silence, gazing at the astonishing landscape. Sometimes, I remember, I stole an anxious look at my father. What was he thinking about? I wondered. Huge and formidable he stood there, leaning on his ice-axe, turning his dark bright eyes slowly and meditatively this way and that. He spoke no word. I did not dare to break the silence. In the end he straightened himself up. He raised his ice-axe and with an emphatic gesture dug the pointed ferrule into the snow. 'Bloody fine!' he said slowly in his deep, cavernous voice. He said no more. In silence we retraced our steps towards the Pen-y-pass Hotel.

But my father had not, as I supposed, spoken his last word. When we were about half-way down I was startled and a little alarmed to hear him suddenly begin to speak. 'For I have learned,' he began abruptly (and he seemed to be speaking less for my benefit than to himself), 'to look on nature, not as in the hour of thoughtless youth; but hearing oftentimes the still sad music of humanity, not harsh, nor grating, but of ample power to chasten and subdue. And I have felt a presence that disturbs me with the joy of elevated thoughts; a sense sublime of something far more deeply interfused, whose dwelling is the light of setting suns and the round ocean and the living air, and the blue sky, and in the minds of men.' I listened to him with a kind of terror. The strange words (I had no idea at that time whence they came) reverberated mysteriously in my mind. It seemed an oracle, a divine revelation. My father ceased speaking as abruptly as he had begun. The words hung, as it were, isolated in the midst of his portentous silence. We walked on. My father spoke no more till on the threshold of the inn, sniffing the frozen air, he remarked with a profound satisfaction: 'Onions!' And then, after a second sniff: 'Fried.'

'A sense of something far more deeply interfused.' Ever since that day those words, pronounced in my father's cavernous voice, have rumbled through my mind. It took me a long time to discover that they were as meaningless as so many hiccoughs. Such is the nefarious influence of early training.

My father, however, who never contrived to rid himself of the prejudices instilled into him in childhood, went on believing in his Wordsworthian formulas till the end. Yes, he too, I am afraid, would have preferred the precocious larks to my maturer lucubrations. And yet, how competently I have learned to write! In mere justice to myself I must insist on it. Not, of course, that it matters in the least. The larks might be my masterpiece; it would not matter a pin. Still, I insist. I insist. . . .

Chapter V

'QUITE the little poet'—how bitterly poor Keats resented the remark! Perhaps because he secretly knew that it was just. For Keats, after all, was that strange, unhappy chimaera—a little artist and a large man. Between the writer of the Odes and the writer of the letters there is all the gulf that separates a halma player from a hero.

Personally, I do not go in for heroic letters. I only modestly lay claim to being a competent second-class halma player—but a good deal more competent, I insist (though of course it doesn't matter), than when I wrote about the larks. 'Quite the little poet'—always and, alas, incorrigibly I am that.

Let me offer you a specimen of my matured competence. I select it at random, as the reviewers say, from my long-projected and never-to-be-concluded series of poems on the first six Caesars. My father, I flatter myself, would have liked the title. That, at any rate, is thoroughly Wordsworthian; it is in the great tradition of that immortal 'Needle Case in the form of a Harp.' 'Caligula crossing the bridge of boats between Baiae and Puteoli. By Peter Paul Rubens (b. 1577: d. 1640).' The poem itself, however, is not very reminiscent of the Lake District.

Prow after prow the floating ships
Bridge the blue gulph; the road is laid.
And Caesar on a piebald horse
Prances with all his cavalcade.

Drunk with their own quick blood they go.
The waves flash as with seeing eyes;
The tumbling cliffs mimic their speed,
And they have filled the vacant skies

With waltzing Gods and Virtues, set
Aeolus roaring with their shout,
Made Vesta's temple on the headland
Spin like a twinkling roundabout.

The twined caduceus in his hand,
And having golden wings for spurs,
Young Caesar dressed as God looks on
And cheers his jolly mariners;

Cheers as they heave from off the bridge
The trippers from the seaside town;
Laughs as they bang the bobbing heads
And shove them bubbling down to drown.

There sweeps a spiral whirl of gesture
From the allegoric sky:
Beauty, like conscious lightning, runs
Through Jove's ribbed trunk and Juno's thigh,

Slides down the flank of Mars and takes
From Virtue's rump a dizzier twist,
Licks round a cloud and whirling stoops
Earthwards to Caesar's lifted fist.

A burgess tumbles from the bridge
Headlong, and hurrying Beauty slips
From Caesar through the plunging legs
To the blue sea between the ships.

Reading it through, I flatter myself that this is very nearly up to international halma form. A little more, and I shall be playing in critical test-matches against Monsieur Cocteau and Miss Amy Lowell. Enormous honour! I shrink from beneath its impendence.

But ah! those Caesars. They have haunted me for years. I have had such schemes for putting half the universe into two or three dozen poems about those monsters. All the sins, to begin with, and complementarily all the virtues . . . . Art, science, history, religion—they too were to have found their place. And God knows what besides. But they never came to much, these Caesars. The notion, I soon came to see, was too large and pretentious ever to be realized. I began (deep calls to deep) with Nero, the artist. 'Nero and Sporus walking in the gardens of the Golden House.'

Dark stirrings in the perfumed air
Touch your cheeks, lift your hair.
With softer fingers I caress,
Sporus, all your loveliness.
Round as a fruit, tree-tangled shines
The moon; and fire-flies in the vines,
Like stars in a delirious sky,
Gleam and go out. Unceasingly
The fountains fall, the nightingales
Sing. But time flows and love avails
Nothing. The Christians smoulder red;
Their brave blue-hearted flames are dead;

And you, sweet Sporus, you and I,
We too must die, we too must die.

But the soliloquy which followed was couched in a more philosophic key. I set forth in it all the reasons for halma's existence—reasons which, at the time when I composed the piece, I almost believed in still. One lives and learns. Meanwhile, here it is.

The Christians by whose muddy light
Dimly, dimly I divine
Your eyes and see your pallid beauty
Like a pale night-primrose shine,

Colourless in the dark, revere
A God who slowly died that they
Might suffer the less, who bore the pain
Of all time in a single day,
The pain of all men in a single
Wounded body and sad heart.

The yellow marble, smooth as water,
Builds me a Golden House; and there
The marble Gods sleep in their strength
And the white Parian girls are fair.

Roses and waxen oleanders,
Green grape bunches and the flushed peach—
All beautiful things I taste, touch, see,
Knowing, loving, becoming each.

The ship went down, my mother swam:
I wedded and myself was wed:
Old Claudius died of emperor-bane:
Old Seneca too slowly bled.

The wild beast and the victim both,
The ravisher and the wincing bride,
King of the world and a slave's slave,
Terror-haunted, deified—

All these, sweet Sporus, I, an artist,
Am and, an artist, needs must be.
Is the tune Lydian? I have loved you.
And you have heard my symphony

Of wailing voices and clashed brass,
With long shrill flutings that suspend
Pain o'er a muttering gulph of terrors,
And piercing blasts of joy that end,

Gods, in what discord!—could I have
So hymned the Furies, were the bane
Still sap within the hemlock stalk,
The red swords virgin bright again?

Or take a child's love that is all
Worship, all tenderness and trust,
A dawn-web, dewy and fragile—take
And with the violence of lust

Tear and defile it. You shall hear
The breaking dumbness and the thin
Harsh crying that is the very music
Of shame and the remorse of sin.

Christ died; the artist lives for all;
Loves, and his naked marbles stand
Pure as a column on the sky,
Whose lips, whose breasts, whose thighs demand

Not our humiliation, not
The shuddering of an after-shame;
And of his agonies men know
Only the beauty born of them.

Christ died, but living Nero turns
Your mute remorse to song; he gives
To idiot Fate eyes like a lover's,
And while his music plays, God lives.

Romantic and noble sentiments! I protest, they do me credit.

And then there are the fragments about Tiberius; Tiberius, need I add, the representative in my symbolic scheme of love. Here is one. 'In the gardens at Capri.' (All my scenes are laid in gardens, I notice, at night, under the moon. Perhaps the fact is significant. Who knows?)

> Hour after hour the stars
> Move, and the moon towards remoter night
> Averts her cheek.
> Blind now, these gardens yet remember
> That there were crimson petals glossy with light,
> And their remembrance is this scent of roses.
> Hour after hour the stars march slowly on,
> And year by year mysteriously the flowers
> Unfold the same bright pattern towards the sky.
>
> Incurious under the streaming stars,
> Breathing this new yet immemorial perfume
> Unmoved, I lie along the tumbled bed;
> And the two women who are my bedfellows,
> Whose breath is sour with wine and their soft bodies
> Still hot and rank, sleep drunkenly at my side.

Commendable, I should now think, this fixture of the attention upon the relevant, the human reality in the centre of the pointless landscape. It was just at the time I wrote this fragment that I was learning the difficult art of this exclusive concentration on the relevant. They were painful lessons. War had prepared me to receive them; Love was the lecturer.

Her name was Barbara Waters. I saw her first when I was about fourteen. She was a month or two older than I. It was at one of those enormous water picnics on the Cherwell that were organized from time to time during the summer vacation by certain fiery and energetic spirits among the dons' wives. We would start out at seven, half a dozen punt-loads of us, from the most northerly of the Oxford boat-houses and make our way up-stream for an hour or so until night had fairly set in. Then, disembarking in some solitary meadow, we would spread cloths, unpack hampers, eat hilariously. And there were so many midges that even the schoolboys were allowed to smoke cigarettes to keep them off—even the schoolgirls. And how knowingly and with what a relish we, the boys, puffed away, blowing the smoke through our noses, opening our mouths like frogs to make rings! But the girls always managed to make their cigarettes come to pieces, got the tobacco into their mouths and, making faces, had to pick the bitter-tasting threads of it from between their lips. In the end, after much giggling, they always threw their cigarettes away, not half smoked; the boys laughed, contemptuously and patronizingly. And finally we packed ourselves into the punts again and floated home, singing; our voices across the water sounded praeternaturally sweet. A yellow moon as large as a pumpkin shone overhead; there were gleamings on the crests of the ripples and in the troughs of the tiny waves, left in the wake of the punts, shadows of almost absolute blackness. The leaves of the willow trees shone like metal. A white mist lay along the meadows. Corncrakes incessantly ran their thumbs along the teeth of combs. A faint weedy smell came up from the river; the aroma of tobacco cut violently across it in pungent gusts; sometimes the sweet animal smell of cows insinuated itself into the watery atmosphere, and looking between the willows, we would see a company of the large and gentle beasts kneeling in the grass, their heads and backs projecting like the crests of mountains above the mist, still hard at work, though the laborious day was long since over, chewing and chewing away at a green breakfast that had merged into luncheon, at the tea that had become in due course a long-drawn-out vegetarian dinner. Munchily, squelchily, they moved their indefatigable jaws. The sound came faintly to us through the silence. Then a small clear voice would begin singing 'Drink to me only with thine eyes' or 'Greensleeves.'

Sometimes, for the fun of the thing, though it was quite unnecessary, and if the weather happened to be really warm, positively disagreeable, we would light a fire, so that we might have the pleasure of eating our cold chicken and salmon mayonnaise with potatoes baked—or generally either half baked or burnt—in their jackets among the glowing cinders. It was by the light of one of these fires that I first saw Barbara. The punt in which I came had started some little time after the others; we had had to wait for a late arrival. By the time we reached the appointed supping place the others had disembarked and made all ready for the meal. The younger members of the party had collected materials for a fire, which they were just lighting as we approached. A group of figures, pale and colourless in the moonlight, were standing or sitting round the white cloth. In the black shadow of a huge elm tree a few yards further off moved featureless silhouettes. Suddenly a small flame spurted from a match and was shielded between a pair of hands that were transformed at once into hands of transparent coral. The silhouettes began to live a fragmentary life. The fire-bearing hands moved round the pyre; two or three new little flames were born. Then, to the sound of a great hurrah, the bonfire flared up. In the heart of the black shadow of the elm tree a new small universe, far vivider than the ghostly world of moonlight beyond, was suddenly created. By the light of the bright flames I saw half a dozen familiar faces belonging to the boys and girls I knew. But I hardly noticed them; I heeded only one face, a face I did not know. The leaping flame revealed it apocalyptically. Flushed, bright and with an air of being almost supernaturally alive in the quivering, changing light of the flames, it detached itself with an incredible clarity and precision from against a background of darkness which the fire had made to seem yet darker. It was the face of a young girl. She had dark hair with ruddy golden lights in it. The nose was faintly aquiline. The openings of the eyes were narrow, long and rather slanting, and the dark eyes looked out through them as though through mysterious loopholes, brilliant, between the fringed eyelids, with an intense and secret and unutterable happiness.

The mouth seemed to share in the same exquisite secret. Not full, but delicately shaped, the unparted lips were curved into a smile that seemed to express a delight more piercing than any laughter, any outburst of joy could give utterance to. The corners of the mouth were drawn upwards so that the line of the meeting of the lips was parallel with her tilted eyes. And this slanting close-lipped smile seemed as though suspended on two little folds that wrinkled the cheeks at the corners of the mouth. The face, which was rather broad across the cheek-bones, tapered away to a pointed chin, small and firm. Her neck was round and slender; her arms, which were bare in her muslin dress, very thin.

The punt moved slowly against the current. I gazed and gazed at the face revealed by the flickering light of the fire. It seemed to me that I had never seen anything so beautiful and wonderful. What was the secret of that inexpressible joy? What nameless happiness dwelt behind those dark-fringed eyes, that silent, unemphatic, close-lipped smile? Breathlessly I gazed. I felt the tears coming into my eyes—she was so beautiful. And I was almost awed, I felt something that was almost fear, as though I had suddenly come into the presence of more than a mere mortal being, into the presence of life itself. The flame leapt up. Over the silent, secret-smiling face the tawny reflections came and went, as though wild blood were fluttering deliriously beneath the skin. The others were shouting, laughing, waving their arms. She remained perfectly still, close-lipped and narrow-eyed, smiling. Yes, life itself was standing there.

The punt bumped against the bank. 'Catch hold,' somebody shouted, 'catch hold, Francis.'

Reluctantly I did as I was told; I felt as though something precious were being killed within me.

In the years that followed I saw her once or twice. She was an orphan, I learned, and had relations in Oxford with whom she came occasionally to stay. When I tried to speak to her, I always found myself too shy to do more than stammer or say something trivial or stupid. Serenely, looking at me steadily between her eyelids, she answered. I remember not so much what she said as the tone in which she spoke—cool, calm, assured, as befitted the embodiment of life itself.

'Do you play tennis?' I would ask in desperation—and I could have wept at my own stupidity and lack of courage. Why are you so beautiful? What do you think about behind your secret eyes? Why are you so inexplicably happy? Those were the questions I wanted to ask her.

'Yes, I love tennis,' she gravely answered.

Once, I remember, I managed to advance so far along the road of coherent and intelligent conversation as to ask her what books she liked best. She looked at me unwaveringly while I spoke. It was I who reddened and turned away. She had an unfair advantage over me—the advantage of being able to look out from between her narrowed eyelids as though from an ambush. I was in the open and utterly without protection.

'I don't read much,' she said at last, when I had finished. 'I don't really very much like reading.'

My attempt to approach, to make contact, was baffled. At the same time I felt that I ought to have known that she wouldn't like reading. After all, what need was there for her to read? When one is life itself, one has no use for mere books. Years later she admitted that she had always made an exception for the novels of Gene Stratton-Porter. When I was seventeen she went to live with another set of relations in South Africa.

Time passed. I thought of her constantly. All that I read of love in the poets arranged itself significantly round the memory of that lovely and secretly smiling face. My friends would boast about their little adventures. I smiled unenviously, knowing not merely in theory but by actual experience that that sort of thing was not love. Once, when I was a freshman at the university, I myself, at the end of a tipsy evening in a night club, lapsed from the purity in which I had lived up till then. Afterwards, I was horribly ashamed. And I felt that I had made myself unworthy of love. In consequence—the link of cause and effect seems to me now somewhat difficult to discover, but at the time, I know, I found my action logical enough—in consequence I overworked myself, won two university prizes, became an ardent revolutionary and devoted many hours of my leisure to 'social service' in the college Mission. I was not a good social servant, got on only indifferently well with fierce young adolescents from the slums and thoroughly disliked every moment I spent in the Mission.

But it was precisely for that reason that I stuck to the job. Once or twice, even, I consented to join in the morris dancing in my mother's garden. I was making myself worthy—for what? I hardly know. The possibility of marriage seemed almost infinitely remote; and somehow I hardly desired it. I was fitting myself to go on loving and loving, and incidentally to do great things.

Then came the war. From France I wrote her a letter, in which I told her all the things I had lacked the power to say in her presence. I sent the letter to the only address I knew—she had left it years before—not expecting, not even hoping very much, that she would receive it. I wrote it for my own satisfaction, in order to make explicit all that I felt. I had no doubt that I should soon be dead. It was a letter addressed not so much to a woman as to God, a letter of explanation and apology posted to the universe.

In the winter of 1916 I was wounded. At the end of my spell in hospital I was reported unfit for further active service and appointed to a post in the contracts department of the Air Board. I was put in charge of chemicals, celluloid, rubber tubing, castor oil, linen and balloon fabrics. I spent my time haggling with German Jews over the price of chemicals and celluloid, with Greek brokers over the castor oil, with Ulstermen over the linen. Spectacled Japanese came to visit me with samples of crêpe de Chine which they tried to persuade me—and they offered choice cigars—would be both better and cheaper than cotton for the manufacture of balloons. Of every one of the letters I dictated first eleven, then seventeen, and finally, when the department had flowered to the height of its prosperity, twenty-two copies were made, to be noted and filed by the various sub-sections of the ministry concerned. The Hotel Cecil was filled with clerks. In basements two stories down beneath the surface of the ground, in attics above the level of the surrounding chimney-pots, hundreds of young women tapped away at typewriters. In a subterranean ball-room, that looked like the setting for Belshazzar's feast, a thousand cheap lunches were daily consumed. In the hotel's best bedrooms overlooking the Thames sat the professional civil servants of long standing with letters after their names, the big business men who were helping to win the war, the staff officers. A fleet of very large motor cars waited for them in the courtyard. Sometimes, when I entered the office of a morning, I used to imagine myself a visitor from Mars. . . .

One morning—it was after I had been at the Air Board for several months—I found myself faced with a problem which could only be solved after consultation with an expert in the Naval Department. The naval people lived in the range of buildings on the opposite side of the courtyard from that in which our offices were housed. It was only after ten minutes of labyrinthine wanderings that I at last managed to find the man I was looking for. He was a genial fellow, I remember; asked me how I liked Bolo House (which was the nickname among the knowing of our precious Air Board office), gave me an East Indian cheroot and even offered whiskey and soda. After that we settled down to a technical chat about non-inflammable celluloid. I left him at last, much enlightened.

'So long,' he called after me. 'And if ever you want to know any mortal thing about acetone or any other kind of bloody dope, come to me and I'll tell you.'

'Thanks,' I said. 'And if by any chance you should happen to want to know about Apollonius Rhodius, shall we say, or Chaucer, or the history of the three-pronged fork . . .'

He roared very heartily. 'I'll come to you,' he concluded.

Still laughing, I shut the door behind me and stepped out into the corridor. A young woman was hurrying past with a thick bundle of papers in her hand, humming softly as she went. Startled by my sudden emergence, she turned and looked at me. As though with fear, my heart gave a sudden thump, then seemed to stop for a moment altogether, seemed to drop down within me.

'Barbara!'

At the sound of the name she halted and looked at me with that steady unwavering gaze between the narrowed eyelids that I knew so well. A little frown appeared on her forehead; puzzled, she pursed her lips. Then all at once her face brightened, she laughed; the light in the dark eyes joyously quivered and danced.

'Why, it's Francis Chelifer,' she exclaimed. 'I didn't know you for the first minute. You've changed.'

'You haven't,' I said. 'You're just the same.'

She said nothing, but smiled, close-lipped, and from between her lashes looked at me as though from an ambush. In her young maturity she was more beautiful than ever. Whether I was glad or sorry to see her again, I hardly know. But I do know that I was moved, profoundly; I was shaken and troubled out of whatever equanimity I possessed. That memory of a kind of symbolic loveliness for which and by which I had been living all these years was now reincarnated and stood before me, no longer a symbol, but an individual; it was enough to make one feel afraid.

'I thought you were in South Africa,' I went on. 'Which is almost the same as saying I thought you didn't exist.'

'I came home a year ago.'

'And you've been working here ever since?'

Barbara nodded.

'And you're working in Bolo House too?' she asked.

'For the last six months.'

'Well I never! And to think we never met before! But how small the world is—how absurdly small.'

We met for luncheon.

'Did you get my letter?' I summoned up courage to ask her over the coffee.

Barbara nodded. 'It was months and months on its way,' she said; and I did not know whether she made the remark deliberately, in order to stave off for a moment the inevitable discussion of the letter, or if she made it quite spontaneously and without afterthought, because she found it interesting that the letter should have been so long on its way. 'It went to South Africa and back again,' she explained.

'Did you read it?'

'Of course.'

'Did you understand what I meant?' As I asked the question I wished that I had kept silence. I was afraid of what the answer might be.

She nodded and said nothing, looking at me mysteriously, as though she had a secret and profound comprehension of everything.

'It was something almost inexpressible,' I said. Her look encouraged me to go on. 'Something so deep and so vast that there were no words to describe it. You understood? You really understood?'

Barbara was silent for some time. Then with a little sigh she said: 'Men are always silly about me. I don't know why.'

I looked at her. Could she really have uttered those words? She was still smiling as life itself might smile. And at that moment I had a horrible premonition of what I was going to suffer. Nevertheless I asked how soon I might see her again. To-night? Could she dine with me to-night? Barbara shook her head; this evening she was engaged. What about lunch to-morrow? 'I must think.' And she frowned, she pursed her lips. No, she remembered in the end, to-morrow was no good. Her first moment of liberty was at dinner-time two days later.

I returned to my work that afternoon feeling particularly Martian. Eight thick files relating to the Imperial Cellulose Company lay on my desk. My secretary showed me the experts' report on proprietary brands of castor oil, which had just come in. A rubber tubing man was particularly anxious to see me. And did I still want her to get a trunk call through to Belfast about that linen business? Pensively I listened to what she was saying. What was it all for?

'Are men often silly about you, Miss Masson?' it suddenly occurred to me to ask. I looked up at my secretary, who was waiting for me to answer her questions and tell her what to do.

Miss Masson became surprisingly red and laughed in an embarrassed, unnatural way. 'Why, no,' she said. 'I suppose I'm an ugly duckling.' And she added: 'It's rather a relief. But what makes you ask?'

She had reddish hair, bobbed and curly, a very white skin and brown eyes. About twenty-three, I supposed; and she wasn't an ugly duckling at all. I had never talked to her except about business, and seldom looked at her closely, contenting myself with being merely aware that she was there—a secretary, most efficient.

'What makes you ask?' A strange expression that was like a look of terror came into Miss Masson's eyes.

'Oh, I don't know. Curiosity. Perhaps you'll see if you can get me through to Belfast some time in the afternoon. And tell the rubber tubing man that I can't possibly see him.'

Miss Masson's manner changed. She smiled at me efficiently, secretarially. Her eyes became quite impassive. 'You can't possibly see him,' she repeated. She had a habit of repeating what other people had just said, even reproducing like an echo opinions or jokes uttered an instant before as though they were her own. She turned away and walked towards the door. I was left alone with the secret history of the Imperial Cellulose Company, the experts' report on proprietary brands of castor oil, and my own thoughts.

Two days later Barbara and I were dining very expensively at a restaurant where the diners were able very successfully to forget that the submarine campaign was in full swing and that food was being rationed.

'I think the decorations are so pretty,' she said, looking round her. 'And the music.' (Mrs. Cloudesley Shove thought the same of the Corner Houses.)

While she looked round at the architecture, I looked at her. She was wearing a rose-coloured evening dress, cut low and without sleeves. The skin of her neck and shoulders was very white. There was a bright rose in the opening of her corsage. Her arms without being bony were still very slender, like the arms of a little girl; her whole figure was slim and adolescent.

'Why do you stare at me like that?' she asked, when the fascination of the architecture was exhausted. She had heightened the colour of her cheeks and faintly smiling lips. Between the darkened eyelids her eyes looked brighter than usual.

'I was wondering why you were so happy. Secretly happy, inside, all by yourself. What's the secret? That's what I was wondering.'

'Why shouldn't I be happy?' she asked. 'But, as a matter of fact,' she added an instant later, 'I'm not happy.

How can one be happy when thousands of people are being killed every minute and millions more are suffering?' She tried to look grave, as though she were in church. But the secret joy glittered irrepressibly through the slanting narrow openings of her eyes. Within its ambush her soul kept incessant holiday.

I could not help laughing. 'Luckily,' I said, 'our sympathy for suffering is rarely strong enough to prevent us from eating dinner. Do you prefer lobster or salmon?'

'Lobster,' said Barbara. 'But how stupidly cynical you are! You don't believe what I say. But I do assure you, there's not a moment when I don't remember all those killed and wounded. And poor people too: the way they live—in the slums. One can't be happy. Not really.' She shook her head.

I saw that if I pursued this subject of conversation, thus forcing her to continue her pretence of being in church, I should ruin her evening and make her thoroughly dislike me. The waiter with the wine list made a timely diversion. I skimmed the pages. 'What do you say to a quart of champagne cup?' I suggested.

'That would be delicious,' she said, and was silent, looking at me meanwhile with a questioning, undecided face that did not know how to adjust itself—whether to continued gravity or to a more natural cheerfulness.

I put an end to her indecision by pointing to a diner at a neighbouring table and whispering: 'Have you ever seen anything so like a tapir?'

She burst into a peal of delighted laughter; not so much because what I had said was particularly funny, but because it was such a tremendous relief to be allowed to laugh again with a good conscience.

'Or wouldn't you have said an ant-eater?' she suggested, looking in the direction I had indicated and then leaning across the table to speak the words softly and intimately into my ear. Her face approached, dazzlingly beautiful. I could have cried aloud. The secret happiness in her eyes was youth, was health, was uncontrollable life. The close lips smiled with a joyful sense of power. A rosy perfume surrounded her. The red rose between her breasts was brilliant against the white skin. I was aware suddenly that under the glossy silk of her dress was a young body, naked. Was it for this discovery that I had been preparing myself all these years?

After dinner we went to a music hall, and when the show was over to a night club where we danced. She told me that she went dancing almost every night. I did not ask with whom. She looked appraisingly at all the women who came in, asked me if I didn't think this one very pretty, that most awfully attractive; and when, on the contrary, I found them rather repulsive, she was annoyed with me for being insufficiently appreciative of her sex. She pointed out a red-haired woman at another table and asked me if I liked women with red hair. When I said that I preferred Buckle's *History of Civilization*, she laughed as though I had said something quite absurdly paradoxical. It was better when she kept silence; and fortunately she had a great capacity for silence, could use it even as a defensive weapon, as when, to questions that at all embarrassed or nonplussed her, she simply returned no answer, however often they were repeated, smiling all the time mysteriously and as though from out of another universe.

We had been at the night club about an hour, when a stoutish and flabby young man, very black-haired, very dark-skinned, with a large fleshy nose and a nostril curved in an opulent oriental volute, came sauntering in with a lordly air of possession. He wore a silver monocle in his left eye, and among the irrepressible black stubbles of his chin the grains of poudre de riz glittered like little snow-flakes. Catching sight of Barbara he smiled, lavishly, came up to our table and spoke to her. Barbara seemed very glad to see him.

'Such a clever man,' she explained, when he had moved away to another table with the red-haired lady to whom I preferred the *History of Civilization*. 'He's a Syrian. You ought to get to know him. He writes poetry too, you know.'

I was unhappy the whole evening; but at the same time I wished it would never end. I should have liked to go on for ever sitting in that stuffy cellar, where the jazz band sounded so loud that it seemed to be playing inside one's head. I would have breathed the stale air and wearily danced for ever, I would even have listened for ever to Barbara's conversation—for ever, so that I might have been allowed to be near her, to look at her, to speculate, until she next spoke, on the profound and lovely mysteries behind her eyes, on the ineffable sources of that secret joy which kept her faintly and yet how intently and how rapturously smiling.

The weeks passed. I saw her almost every day. And every day I loved her more violently and painfully, with a love that less and less resembled the religious passion of my boyhood. But it was the persistent memory of that passion which made my present desire so parching and tormenting, that filled me with a thirst that no possible possession could assuage. No possible possession, since whatever I might possess, as I realized more and more clearly each time I saw her, would be utterly different from what I had desired all these years to possess. I had desired all beauty, all that exists of goodness and truth, symbolized and incarnate in one face. And now the face drew near, the lips touched mine; and what I had got was simply a young woman with a 'temperament,' as the euphemists who deplore the word admiringly and lovingly qualify the lascivious thing. And yet, against all reason, in spite of all the evidence, I could not help believing that she was somehow and secretly what I had imagined her. My love for her as a symbol strengthened my desire for her as an individual woman.

All this, were it to happen to me now, would seem perfectly natural and normal. If I were to make love to a young woman, I should know precisely what I was making love to. But that, in those days, was something I still had to learn. In Barbara's company I was learning it with a vengeance. I was learning that it is possible to be profoundly and slavishly in love with some one for whom one has no esteem, whom one does not like, whom one regards as a bad character and who, finally, not only makes one unhappy but bores one. And why not, I might now ask, why not? That things should be like this is probably the most natural thing in the world. But in those days I imagined that love ought always to be mixed up with affection and admiration, with worship and an intellectual rapture, as unflagging as that which one experiences during the playing of a symphony. Sometimes, no doubt, love does get involved with some or all of these things; sometimes these things exist by themselves, apart from love. But one must be prepared to swallow one's love completely neat and unadulterated. It is a fiery, crude and somewhat poisonous draught.

Every hour I spent with Barbara brought fresh evidence of her inability to play the ideal part my imagination had all these years been assigning to her. She was selfish, thirsty for pleasures of the most vulgar sort, liked to bask in an atmosphere of erotic admiration, amused herself by collecting adorers and treating them badly, was stupid and a liar—in other words, was one of the normal types of healthy young womanhood. I should have been less disturbed by these discoveries if only her face had been different. Unfortunately, however, the healthy young woman who now revealed herself had the same features as that symbolic child on the memory of whose face I had brooded through all an ardent adolescence. And the contrast between what she was and what—with that dazzling and mysteriously lovely face—she ought to have been, what in my imagination she indeed had been, was a perpetual source of surprise and pain. And at the same time the nature of my passion for her had changed—changed inevitably and profoundly, the moment she ceased to be a symbol and became an individual. Now, I desired her; before, I had loved her for God's sake and almost as though she were herself divine. And contrasting this new love with the love I had felt before, I was ashamed, I fancied myself unworthy, base, an animal. And I tried to persuade myself that if she seemed different it was because I felt differently and less nobly towards her. And sometimes, when we sat silent through long summer twilights under the trees in the Park, or at my Chelsea rooms, looking out on to the river, I could persuade myself for a precarious moment that Barbara was what she had been in my imagination and that I felt towards her now what I had felt towards the memory of her. In the end, however, Barbara would break the magic silence and with it the illusion.

'It's such a pity,' she would say pensively, 'that July hasn't got an r in it. Otherwise we might have had supper in an oyster bar.'

Or else, remembering that I was a literary man, she would look at the gaudy remains of the sunset and sigh. 'I wish *I* were a poet,' she would say.

And I was back again among the facts, and Barbara was once more a tangible young woman who bored me, but whom I desired—with what a definite and localized longing !—to kiss, to hold fast and caress.

It was a longing which, for some time, I rigorously suppressed. I fought against it as against an evil thing, too horribly unlike my previous love, too outrageously incompatible with my conception of Barbara's higher nature. I had not yet learned to reconcile myself to the fact that Barbara's higher nature was an invention of my own, a figment of my proper imagination.

One very hot evening in July I drove her to the door of the house in Regent Square, Bloomsbury, in which she occupied a little flat under the roof. We had been dancing and it was late; a hunch-backed moon had climbed a third of the way up the sky and was shining down into the square over the shoulder of the church that stands on its eastern side. I paid off the cabman and we were left alone on the pavement. I had been bored and irritated the whole evening; but at the thought that I should have to bid her good-night and walk off by myself I was filled with such an anguish that the tears came into my eyes. I stood there in silent irresolution, looking into her face. It was calmly and mysteriously smiling as though to itself and for some secret reason; her eyes were very bright. She too was silent, not restlessly, not irresolutely as I was silent, but easily, with a kind of majesty. She could live in silence, when she so desired, like a being in its proper element.

'Well,' I brought myself to say at last, 'I must go.'

'Why not come in for a final cup of tea?' she suggested.

Actuated by that spirit of perversity which makes us do what we do not want to do, what we know will make us suffer as much as it is possible in the given circumstance to suffer, I shook my head. 'No,' I said. 'I must get back.'

I had never longed for anything more passionately than I longed to accept Barbara's invitation.

She repeated it. 'Do come in,' she said. 'It won't take a minute to make tea on the gas ring.'

Again I shook my head, in too much anguish, this time, to be able to speak. My trembling voice, I was afraid, would have betrayed me. Instinctively I knew that if I went into the house with her we should become lovers. My old determination to resist what had seemed the baser desires strengthened my resolution not to go in.

'Well, if you won't,' she shrugged her shoulders, 'then good-night.' Her voice had a note of annoyance in it.

I shook her hand and walked dumbly away. When I had gone ten yards my resolution abjectly broke down. I turned. Barbara was still standing on the doorstep, trying to fit the latchkey into the lock.

'Barbara,' I called in a voice that sounded horribly unnatural in my own ears. I hurried back. She turned to look at me. 'Do you mind if I change my mind and accept your invitation after all? I find I really am rather thirsty.' What a humiliation, I thought.

She laughed. 'What a goose you are, Francis.' And she added in a bantering tone: 'If you weren't such a silly old dear I'd tell you to go to the nearest horse-trough and drink there.'

'I'm sorry,' I said. Standing once more close to her, breathing once again her rosy perfume, I felt as I had felt when, a child, I had run down from my terrifying night nursery to find my mother sitting in the dining-room—reassured, relieved of a hideous burden, incredibly happy, but at the same time profoundly miserable in the consciousness that what I was doing was against all the rules, was a sin, the enormity of which I could judge from the very mournful tenderness of my mother's eyes and the severe, portentous silence out of which, as though from a thundercloud, my huge and bearded father looked at me like an outraged god. I was happy, being with Barbara; I was utterly miserable because I was not with her, so to speak, in the right way: I was not I; she, for all that the features were the same, was no longer herself. I was happy at the thought that I should soon be kissing her; miserable because that was not how I wanted to love my imaginary Barbara; miserable too, when I secretly admitted to myself the existence of the real Barbara, because I felt it an indignity to be the slave of such a mistress.

'Of course, if you want me to go,' I said, reacting feebly again towards revolt, 'I'll go.' And desperately trying to be facetious, 'I'm not sure that it wouldn't be best if I drowned myself in that horse-trough,' I added.

'As you like,' she said lightly. The door was open now; she walked into the darkness. I followed her, closing the door behind me carefully. We groped our way up steep dark stairs. She unlocked another door, turned a switch. The sudden light was dazzling.

'All's well that ends well,' she said, smiling at me, and she slipped the cloak from off her bare shoulders.

On the contrary, I thought, it was the tragedy of errors. I stepped towards her, I stretched out my hands and gripped her by her two thin arms a little below the shoulder. I bent down and kissed her averted cheek; she turned her face towards me, and it was her mouth.

> There is no future, there is no more past,
> No roots nor fruits, but momentary flowers.
> Lie still, only lie still and night will last,
> Silent and dark, not for a space of hours,
> But everlastingly. Let me forget

All but your perfume, every night but this,
The shame, the fruitless weeping, the regret.
Only lie still: this faint and quiet bliss
Shall flower upon the brink of sleep and spread,
Till there is nothing else but you and I
Clasped in a timeless silence. But like one
Who, doomed to die, at morning will be dead,
I know, though night seem dateless, that the sky
Must brighten soon before to-morrow's sun.

It was then that I learned to live only in the moment—to ignore causes, motives, antecedents, to refuse responsibility for what should follow. It was then that I learned, since the future was always bound to be a painful repetition of what had happened before, never to look forward for comfort or justification, but to live now and here in the heart of human reality, in the very centre of the hot dark hive. But there is a spontaneous thoughtlessness which no thoughtful pains can imitate. Being what I am, I shall never rival with those little boys who throw their baby sisters over the cliff for the sake of seeing the delightful splash; never put a pistol to my head and for the mere fun of the thing pull the trigger; never, looking down from the gallery at Covent Garden at the thronged Wagnerites or Saint-Saënsians in the stalls below, lightly toss down that little hand-grenade (however piercingly amusing the jest might be), which I still preserve, charged with its pound of high explosive, in my hat-box, ready for all emergencies. Such gorgeous carelessness of all but the immediate sensation I can only remotely imitate. But I do my best, and I did it always conscientiously with Barbara. Still, the nights always did come to an end. And even during them, lapped in the temperament, I could never, even for an instant, be quite unaware of who she was, who I was and had been and would be to-morrow. The recollection of these things deprived every rapture of its passionate integrity and beneath the surface of every calm and silent trance spread out a profound uneasiness. Kissing her I wished that I were not kissing her, holding her in my arms I wished that it were somebody else I was holding. And sometimes in the dark quiet silences I thought that it would be better if I were dead.

Did she love me? At any rate she often said so, even in writing. I have all her letters still—a score of scribbled notes sent up by messenger from one wing of the Hotel Cecil to the other and a few longer letters written when she was on her holiday or week-ending somewhere apart from me. Here, I spread out the sheets. It is a competent, well-educated writing; the pen rarely leaves the paper, running on from letter to letter, from word to word. A rapid writing, flowing, clear and legible. Only here and there, generally towards the ends of her brief notes, is the clarity troubled; there are scrawled words made up of formless letters. I pore over them in an attempt to interpret their meaning. 'I adore you, my beloved . . . kiss you a thousand times . . . long for it to be night . . . love you madly.' These are the fragmentary meanings I contrive to disengage from the scribbles. We write such things illegibly for the same reason as we clothe our bodies. Modesty does not permit us to walk naked, and the expression of our most intimate thoughts, our most urgent desires and secret memories, must not—even when we have so far done violence to ourselves as to commit the words to paper—be too easily read and understood. Pepys, when he recorded the most scabrous details of his loves, is not content with writing in cipher; he breaks into bad French as well. And I remember, now that I mention Pepys, having done the same sort of thing in my own letters to Barbara; winding up with a 'Bellissima, ti voglio un bene enorme,' or a 'Je t'embrasse un peu partout.'

But did she love me? In a kind of way I think she did. I gratified her vanity. Her successes so far had mostly been with genial young soldiers. She had counted few literary men among her slaves. And being infected with the queer snobbery of those who regard an artist, or any one calling himself by that name, as somehow superior to other beings—she was more impressed by a Café Royal loafer than by an efficient officer, and considered that it was a more arduous and finer thing to be able to paint, or even appreciate, a cubist picture or play a piece by Bartok on the piano than to run a business or plead in a court of law—being therefore deeply convinced of my mysterious importance and significance—she was flattered to have me abjectly gambolling around her. There is a German engraving of the sixteenth century, made at the time of the reaction against scholasticism, which represents a naked Teutonic beauty riding on the back of a bald and bearded man, whom she directs with a bridle and urges on with a switch. The old man is labelled Aristotle. After two thousand years of slavery to the infallible sage it was a good revenge. To Barbara, no doubt, I appeared as a kind of minor Aristotle. But what made the comparison somewhat less flattering to me was the fact that she was equally gratified by the attentions of another literary man, the swarthy Syrian with the blue jowl and the silver monocle. Even more gratified, I think; for he wrote poems which were frequently published in the monthly magazines (mine, alas, were not) and, what was more, he never lost an opportunity of telling people that he was a poet; he was for ever discussing the inconveniences and compensating advantages of possessing an artistic temperament. That, for a time at any rate, she preferred me to the Syrian was due to the fact that I was quite unattached and far more hopelessly in love with Barbara than he. The red-haired and, to me, inferior substitute for Buckle's *History* engrossed the greater part of his heart at this time. Moreover, he was a calm and experienced lover who did not lose his head about trifles. From me Barbara got passion of a kind she could not have hoped for from the Syrian—a passion which, in spite of my reluctance, in spite of my efforts to resist it, reduced me to a state of abjection at her feet. It is pleasant to be worshipped, to command and inflict pain; Barbara enjoyed these things as much as any one.

It was the Syrian who in the end displaced me. I had noticed in October that friends from South Africa, with whom it was necessary for Barbara to lunch and dine, kept arriving in ever increasing quantities. And when it wasn't friends from South Africa it was Aunt Phoebe, who had become suddenly importunate. Or old Mr. Goble, the one who had known her grandfather so well.

When I asked her to describe these festivities, she either said: 'Oh, it was dreadfully dull. We talked about the family,' or merely smiled, shrugged her shoulders and retired into her impregnable silence.

'Why do you lie to me?' I asked.

She preserved her silence and her secret smile.

There were evenings when I insisted that she should throw over the friends from South Africa and dine with me. Reluctantly she would consent; but she took her revenge on these occasions by talking about all the jolly men she had known.

One evening, when, in spite of all my entreaties, my threats and commands, she had gone to dine with Aunt Phoebe in Golders Green and stay the night, I kept watch in Regent Square. It was a damp, cold night. From nine o'clock till past midnight I remained at my post, marching up and down opposite the house where she lived. As I walked I ran the point of my stick with a rattling noise along the railings which surrounded the gardens in the middle of the square; that rattling accompanied my thoughts. From the dank black trees overhead an occasional heavy drop would fall. I must have walked twelve miles that evening.

In those three hours I thought of many things. I thought of the suddenly leaping bonfire and the young face shining in the darkness. I thought of my boyish love, and then how I had seen that face again and the different love it had inspired in the man. I thought of kisses, caresses, whispers in the darkness. I thought of the Syrian with his black eyebrows and his silver monocle, his buttery dark skin damply shining through the face-powder, and the powder snowy white among the black stubbles of his jowl. She was probably with him at this moment. Monna Vanna, Monna Bice—'Love's not so pure and abstract as they use to say, who have no mistress but their Muse.' Reality gives imagination the lie direct. Barbara is the truth, I thought, and that she likes the man with the silver monocle is the truth, and that I have slept with her is the truth, and that he has too is quite probably the truth.

And it is the truth that men are cruel and stupid and that they suffer themselves to be driven even to destruction by shepherds as stupid as themselves. I thought of my passion for universal justice, of my desire that all men should be free, leisured, educated, of my imaginations of a future earth peopled by human beings who should live according to reason. But of what use is leisure, when leisure is occupied with listening-in and going to football matches? freedom, when men voluntarily enslave themselves to politicians like those who now rule the world? education, when the literate read the evening papers and the fiction magazines? And the future, the radiant future—supposing that it should differ from the past in anything but the spread of material comfort and spiritual uniformity, suppose it conceivably were to be in some way superior, what has that to do with me? Nothing whatever. Nothing, nothing, nothing.

I was interrupted in my meditations by a policeman who came up to me, politely touched his helmet and asked me what I was doing. 'I seen you walking up and down here for the last hour,' he said. I gave him half a crown and told him I was waiting for a lady. The policeman laughed discreetly. I laughed too. Indeed, the joke was a marvellously good one. When he was gone, I went on with my walking.

And this war, I thought. Was there the slightest prospect that any good would come of it? The war to end war! The argument was forcible enough this time; it was backed up with a kick in the breech, the most terrific kick ever administered. But would it convince humanity more effectively than any other argument had ever done?

Still, men are courageous, I thought, are patient, kind, self-sacrificing. But they are all the contradictory things, as well—and both, good and bad, because they can't help it. Forgive them, for they know not what they do. Everything arises from a great primeval animal stupidity. That is the deepest of all realities—stupidity, the being unaware.

And the aware, the not stupid—they are the odd exceptions, they are irrelevant to the great reality, they are lies like the ideal of love, like dreams of the future, like belief in justice. To live among their works is to live in a world of bright falsehoods, apart from the real world; it is to escape. Escape is cowardly; to be comforted by what is untrue or what is irrelevant to the world in which we live is stupid.

And my own talents, such as they are, are irrelevant. So is the art to whose service I devote them, a lying consolation. A Martian would find the writing of phrases containing words of similar sound at fixed recurrent intervals as queer as buying castor oil for the lubrification of machines of destruction. I remembered the lines I had written for Barbara—the cheerful comic-amorous lines——at the time of the last epidemic of air raids. The octosyllables jingled in my head.

> But when the next full moon invites
> New bugaboos and fly-by-nights,
> Let us seek out some deep alcove,
> Some immemorial haunt of love.
> There we'll retire with cakes and wine
> And dare the imbecile to shine. . . .

I was just repeating them to myself, when a taxi turned into the quiet square, rolled slowly along the curb and came to a halt in front of the house where Barbara lived. By the dim light of a muffled street lamp I saw two people stepping out of it, a man and a woman. The masculine silhouette moved forward and, bending over his hand, began to count money by the light of the little lamp at the recording clock-face. In the narrow beam I saw the glitter of a monocle. Money clinked, the taxi drove away. The two figures mounted the steps; the door opened before them, they passed into the house.

I walked away, repeating to myself every injurious and abusive word that can be applied to a woman. I felt, if anything, rather relieved. It pleased me to think that all was over, all was now definitely and for ever done with.

''Night, sir.'

It was the friendly policeman; I thought I heard an almost imperceptible note of amusement in his voice.

For the next four days I made no sign of life. Every day I hoped that she would write or telephone to ask what had become of me. She did nothing of the kind. My sense of relief had turned into a feeling of misery. On the fifth day, as I was going out to lunch, I met her in the courtyard. She made no reference to the unprecedented length of my silence. I said none of the bitter things that I had planned to say in the event of just such an accidental meeting as this. Instead, I asked her, I implored her even, to come to lunch. Barbara declined the invitation; she had a South African engagement.

'Come to dinner, then,' I abjectly begged. Humiliation, I felt, could go no further. I would give anything to be received back into grace.

Barbara shook her head. 'I wish I could,' she said. 'But that tiresome old Mr. Goble . . .'

Chapter VI

SUCH, then, were the phantoms that my recitation called up to dance on the surface of the Tyrrhenian. Salutarily they reminded me that I was only on my holiday, that the landscape in the midst of which I was now floating was hardly better than an illusion and that life was only real and earnest during the eleven months of each year which I spent between Gog's Court and Miss Carruthers's. I was a democratic Englishman and a Londoner at that, living in an age when the *Daily Mail* sells two million copies every morning; I had no right to so much sunlight, so tepid and clear a sea, such spiky mountains, such clouds, such blue expanses of sky; I had no right to Shelley; and if I were a true democrat, then I ought not even to think. But again I must plead my congenital weakness.

Couched on the water, I was dreaming of the ideal democratic state where no irrelevant Holy Ghost-possessed exception should trouble the flat serenity of the rule—the rule of Cloudesley and Carruthers, Fluffy and the alert, inimitable Brimstone—when all at once I became aware that a sailing-boat was coming up behind me, was right on top of me, in fact. The white sail towered over me; with a little sizzling ripple at the prow, with a clop clop of tiny waves against its flanks, the brown varnished boat bore quickly down on me. It is a horrible thing to be afraid, to be shaken by that sudden spasm of fear which cannot be controlled because it comes so quickly that the controlling forces of the mind are taken unaware. Every cell in the body, it seems, feels terror; from a man one is humiliated for a moment into a congeries of shrinking amoebae. One descends the scale of being; one drops down the evolutionary gamut to become for a second no more than a startled and terrified beast. One moment I had been dozing on my translucent mattress, like a philosopher; the next I was inarticulately shouting, frantically moving my limbs to escape from the approaching and now inevitable peril.

'Hi!' I was yelling, and then something caught me a fearful crack on the side of the head and pushed me down into the water. I was conscious of swallowing a vast quantity of brine, of breathing water into my lungs and violently choking. Then for a time I knew nothing; the blow must momentarily have stunned me. I became more or less conscious again, to find myself just coming to the surface, my face half in, half out of water. I was coughing and gasping—coughing to get rid of the water that was in my lungs, gasping for air. Both processes, I now perceive, achieved exactly the contrary of what they were intended to achieve. For I coughed up all the stationary air that was in my lungs and, my mouth being under water, I drew in fresh gulps of brine. Meanwhile my blood, loaded with carbonic acid gas, kept rushing to my lungs in the hope of exchanging the deadly stuff for oxygen. In vain; there was no oxygen to exchange it for.

I felt an extraordinary pain in the back of my neck—not excruciating, but dull; dull and far-reaching and profound, and at the same time strangely disgusting—a sickening, revolting sort of pain. The nerves controlling my respiratory system were giving up in despair; that disgusting pain in my neck was their gesture of farewell, their last spasm of agony. Slowly I ceased to be conscious; I faded gradually out of life like the Cheshire Cat in *Alice in Wonderland.* The last thing that was left of me, that continued to hang in my consciousness when everything else had vanished, was the pain.

In the circumstances, I know, it would have been the classical thing if all my past life had unwound itself in a flash before the mind's eye. Whiz—an uninteresting drama in thirty-two reels ought duly to have run its course and I should have remembered everything, from the taste of the baby food in my bottle to the taste of yesterday's marsala at the Grand Hotel, from my first caning to my last kiss. In point of fact, however, none of the correct things happened. The last thoughts I remember thinking as I went down were about the Rabbit Fanciers' Gazette and my mother. In a final access of that conscientiousness which has haunted and handicapped me all my life long, I reflected that I ought to have another leading article ready by next Friday. And it struck me very forcibly that my mother would be most seriously inconvenienced when she arrived in a few days' time to find that I was no longer in a position to accompany her on her journey to Rome.

When I next came to my senses I was lying face downwards on the beach with somebody sitting astride of my back, as though we were playing horses, using Professor Schaefer's method of producing artificial respiration. 'Uno, due, tre, quattro '—and at every ' quattro ' the man on my back threw his weight forward on to his hands, which were resting, one on either side of the spine, on my lower ribs. The contents of my lungs were violently expelled. Then my rescuer straightened himself up again, the pressure was relaxed and my lungs replenished themselves with air. ' Uno, due, tre, quattro '—the process began again.

' He's breathing! He's all right. He's opening his eyes!'

Carefully, as though I were a crate of very valuable china, they turned me right way up. I was aware of the strong sunshine, of a throbbing headache centred somewhere above the left temple, of a crowd of people standing round. With deliberation and consciously I breathed the air; loud voices shouted instructions. Two people began to rub the soles of my feet. A third ran up with a child's bucket full of sun-scorched sand and poured it on the pit of my stomach. This happy thought immediately had an immense success. All the curious and sympathetic spectators who had been standing round my corpse, looking on while Professor Schaefer was being applied to me and wishing that they could do something to help, now discovered that there was actually something helpful that they could do. They could help to restore my circulation by sprinkling hot sand on me. In a moment I had a dozen sympathizers busy around me, skimming the cream off the hot tideless beach in little buckets, with spades or in the palms of their scooping hands, to pour it over me. In a few seconds I was almost buried under a mound of burning grey sand. On the faces of all my good Samaritans I noticed an expression of child-like earnestness. They rushed backwards and forwards with their little buckets as though there were nothing more serious in life than building sand castles on the stomachs of drowned men. And the children themselves joined in. Horrified at first by the spectacle of my limp and livid corpse, they had clung to paternal hands, shrunk away behind protecting skirts, looking on while Professor Schaefer was being practised on me, with a reluctant and disgusted curiosity. But when I had come alive again, when they saw their elders burying me with sand and understood that it was really only a tremendously good game, then how violent was their reaction ! Shrilly laughing, whooping with excitement and delight, they rushed on me with their little implements. It was only with difficulty that they could be prevented from throwing handfuls of sand in my face, from pouring it into my ears, from making me eat it. And one small boy, ambitious to do something that nobody else had done, rushed down to the sea, filled his bucket with water and stale foam, ran back and emptied its contents, with what a shout of triumph ! plop, from a height on to my solar plexus.

That was too much for my gravity. I began to laugh. But I did not get very far with my laughter. For after the first outburst of it, when I wanted to take breath for the next, I found that I had forgotten how to breathe, and it was only after a long choking struggle that I managed to reacquire the art. The children were frightened ; this was no part of the delightful game. The grown-ups stopped being helpful and allowed themselves to be driven away from my corpse by the competent authorities. An umbrella was planted in the sand behind me. Within its rosy shadow I was left in peace to make secure my precarious footing on existence. For a long time I lay with my eyes shut. An immensely long way off, it seemed, somebody was still rubbing my feet. Periodically, somebody else pushed a spoon with brandy and milk in it into my mouth. I felt very tired, but wonderfully comfortable. And it seemed to me at that moment that there could be nothing more exquisitely pleasurable than merely breathing.

After a while, I felt sufficiently strong and sufficiently safe in my strength to open my eyes again and look about me. How novel, how wonderfully charming everything seemed! The first thing I saw was a half-naked young giant crouching obsequiously at my feet, rubbing my bloodless soles and ankles. Under his shining copper skin there was a sliding of muscles. His face was like a Roman's, his hair jet black and curly. When he noticed that I had opened my eyes and was looking at him he smiled, and his teeth were brilliantly white, his brown eyes flashed from a setting of shiny bluish enamel.

A voice asked me in Italian how I was feeling. I looked round. A stout man with a large red, rubbery face and a black moustache was sitting beside me. In one hand he held a teacup, in the other a spoon. He was dressed in white duck. The sweat was pouring off his face; he looked as though he had been buttered. From all round his very bright black eyes little wrinkles spread out like rays from a gloria. He proffered the spoon. I swallowed. The backs of his large brown hands were covered with fine hairs.

'I am the doctor,' he explained, and smiled.

I nodded and smiled back. It seemed to me that I had never seen such a lovely doctor before.

And then, when I looked up, there was the blue sky, beautifully scalloped by the edge of the pink umbrella. And lowering my eyes I saw people standing round looking at me—all smiling. Between them I caught glimpses of the blue sea.

'Belli sono,' I said to the doctor, and shut my eyes again.

And many men so beautiful. . . . In the blood-red darkness behind my eyelids I listened to their voices. Slowly, voluptuously, I breathed the salty air. The young giant went on rubbing my feet. With an effort I lifted one of my hands and laid it on my chest. Lightly, like a blind man feeling for the sense of a page of Braille, I ran my fingers over the smooth skin. I felt the ribs and the little depressions between them. And all at once, under my finger tips, I was aware of a hardly perceptible throbbing—pulse, pulse, pulse—it was that I had been searching for. The blind fingers creeping across the page had spelled out a strange word. I did not try to interpret it. It was enough to be glad that the word was there. For a long time I lay quite still, feeling my beating heart.

'Si sente meglio?' asked the doctor.

I opened my eyes. 'Mi sento felice.' He smiled at me. The rays round the twin bright glories of his eyes emphasized themselves. It was as though the holy symbol had somehow suddenly become more holy.

'It is good not to be dead,' he said.

'It is very good.'

And I looked once more at the sky and the pink umbrella overhead. I looked at the young giant, so strong and yet so docile at my feet. I turned my eyes to right and left. The circle of curious spectators had dissolved. Out of danger, I had ceased to be an object of sympathy or curiosity. The holiday-makers were going about their business as usual. I watched them, happily.

A young couple in bathing dresses walked slowly past me towards the sea. Their faces, their necks and shoulders, their bare arms and legs were burned to a soft transparent brown. They walked slowly, holding hands, walked with such a grace, such an easy majesty that I felt like weeping. They were very young, they were tall, slender and strong. They were beautiful as a couple of young thoroughbred horses; gracefully, idly, majestically they seemed to be walking in a world that was beyond good and evil. It did not matter what they might do or say; they were justified by the mere fact that they existed. They paused, looked at me for a moment, one with brown eyes, one with grey, flashed at me with their white teeth, asked how I was, and when I told them that I was better, smiled again and passed on.

A little girl dressed in a primrose-coloured garment that was paler in tone than her dark face and limbs came running up, halted two or three yards away and began to look at me earnestly. Her eyes were very large and fringed by absurdly long black lashes. Above them there expanded an immense domed forehead that would have done credit to a philosopher. Her snub nose was so small that you hardly noticed it was there at all. Black and frizzy, her hair stood out, in a state of permanent explosion, round her head. For a long time she stared at me. I stared back.

'What do you want?' I asked at last.

And suddenly, at the sound of my voice, the child was overwhelmed by shyness. She covered her face with her forearm as though she were warding off a blow. Then, after a second or two, she peeped out at me cautiously from under her elbow. Her face had become quite red. I called again. It was once too often. She turned and ran away, ran back to her family, who were sitting, twenty yards down the beach, in the precarious and shifting oasis of shadow cast by a large striped umbrella. I saw her hurl herself into the arms of a large placid mother in white muslin. Then, having successfully abolished my existence by burying her face in the comfortable bosom, she slid down again from her mother's knee and went on playing with her little sister, serenely, as though the untoward incident had never occurred.

Mournfully, from somewhere in the distance, came the long, suspended cry of the vendor of doughnuts. 'Bomboloni.' Two young American marchesas in purple bathing gowns went past, talking together on one note, in indefatigable even voices. '. . . and he has such a lovely mentality,' I heard one of them saying. 'But what I like,' said the other, who seemed to have acquired more completely the Latin habit of mind, 'what I like is his teeth.' A middle-aged man, with the large stomach that comes of too much *pasta*, and a very thin little boy of twelve now entered my field of vision, all wet and shiny from the sea. The hot sand burned their feet and they went hopping across the scorching beach with an agility which it was good to see. But the soles of mad Concetta's feet were made of hornier stuff. Barefooted, she walked down every morning from the mountains, carrying her basket of fruit over one arm and holding in the other hand a long staff. She hawked her wares along the beach, she went the round of the villas until her basket was empty. Then she walked back again, across the plain and up into the hills. Turning from the fat man and the little thin boy I saw her standing before me. She was dressed in a stained and tattered old dress. Her grey hair escaped in wisps from under a wide straw hat. Her old face was eager, thin and sharp; the wrinkled skin was like brown parchment stretched over the bones. Leaning on her staff, she looked at me for a little in silence.

'So you're the drowned foreigner,' she said at last.

'If he were drowned, how could he be alive?' asked the doctor. The young giant found this exquisitely witty; he laughed profoundly, out of the depths of his huge chest. 'Go away now, Concetta,' the doctor went on. 'He must be kept quiet. We can't have you treating him to one of your discourses.'

Concetta paid no attention to him. She was used to this sort of thing.

'The mercy of God,' she began, shaking her head, 'where should we be without it? You are young, signorino. You still have time to do much. God has preserved you. I am old. But I lean on the cross.' And straightening herself up, she lifted her staff. A cross-piece of wood had been nailed near the top of it. Affectionately she kissed it. 'I love the cross,' she said. 'The cross is beautiful, the cross is . . .' But she was interrupted by a young nurserymaid who came running up to ask for half a kilo of the best grapes. Theology could not be allowed to interfere with business. Concetta took out her little steelyard, put a bunch of grapes in the pan and moved the weight back and forth along the bar in search of equilibrium. The nurserymaid stood by. She had a round face, red cheeks, dimples, black hair and eyes like black buttons. She was as plump as a fruit. The young giant looked up at her in frank admiration. She rolled the buttons towards him—for an instant, then utterly ignored him, and humming nonchalantly to herself as though she were alone on a desert island and wanted to keep her spirits up, she gazed pensively away at the picturesque beauties of nature.

'Six hundred grammes,' said Concetta.

The nurserymaid paid for them, and still humming, still on her desert island, she walked off, taking very small steps, undulating rotundly, like a moon among wind-driven clouds. The young giant stopped rubbing my feet and stared after her. With the moon's beauty and the moon's soft pace the nurserymaid tottered along, undulating unsteadily on her high heels across the sand.

Rabear, I thought: old Skeat was perfectly right to translate the word as he did.

'Bella grassa,' said the doctor, voicing what were obviously the young giant's sentiments. Mine too; for after all, she was alive, obeyed the laws of her nature, walked in the sun, ate grapes and *rabear'd.* I shut my eyes again. Pulse, pulse, pulse; the heart beat steadily under my fingers. I felt like Adam, newly created and weak like a butterfly fresh from its chrysalis—the red clay still too wet and limp to allow of my standing upright. But soon, when it had dried to firmness, I should arise and scamper joyously about this span new world, and be myself a young giant, a graceful and majestic thoroughbred, a child, a wondering Bedlamite.

There are some people who contrive to pass their lives in a state of permanent convalescence. They behave at every moment as though they had been miraculously preserved from death the moment before; they live exhilaratedly for the mere sake of living and can be intoxicated with happiness just because they happen not to be dead. For those not born convalescent it may be that the secret of happiness consists in being half-drowned regularly three times a day before meals. I recommend it as a more drastic alternative to my 'water-shoot-in-every-office' remedy for ennui.

'You're alone here?' asked the doctor.

I nodded.

'No relations?'

'Not at present.'

'No friends of any kind?'

I shook my head.

'H'm,' he said.

He had a wart growing on one side of his nose where it joined the cheek. I found myself studying it intently; it was a most interesting wart, whitish, but a little flushed on its upper surface. It looked like a small unripe cherry. 'Do you like cherries?' I asked.

The doctor seemed rather surprised. 'Yes,' he said, after a moment's silence and with great deliberation, as though he had been carefully weighing the matter in his mind.

'So do I.' And I burst out laughing. This time, however, my breathing triumphantly stood the strain. 'So do I. But not unripe ones,' I added, gasping with mirth. It seemed to me that nothing funnier had ever been said.

And then Mrs. Aldwinkle stepped definitely into my life. For, looking round, still heaving with the after-swell of my storm of laughter, I suddenly saw the Chinese lantern lady of the *patino* standing before me. Her flame-coloured costume, a little less radiant now that it was wet, still shone among the aquarium shadows of her green parasol, and her face looked as though it were she who had been drowned, not I.

'They tell me that you're an Englishman,' she said in the same ill-controlled, unmusical voice I had heard, not long since, misquoting Shelley.

Still tipsy, still light-headed with convalescence, I laughingly admitted it.

'I hear you were nearly drowned.'

'Quite right,' I said, still laughing; it was such a marvellous joke.

'I'm most sorry to hear . . .' She had a way of leaving her sentences unfinished. The words would tail off into a dim inarticulate blur of sound.

'Don't mention it,' I begged her. 'It isn't at all disagreeable, you know. Afterwards, at any rate . . .' I stared at her affectionately and with my convalescent's boundless curiosity. She stared back at me. Her eyes, I thought, must have the same bulge as those little red lenses one screws to the rear forks of bicycles; they collected all the light diffused around them and reflected it again with a concentrated glitter.

'I came to ask whether I could be of any assistance,' said the Chinese lantern lady.

'Most kind.'

'You're alone here?'

'Quite, for the present.'

'Then perhaps you might care to come and stay a night or two at my house, until you're entirely . . .' She mumbled, made a gesture that implied the missing word and went on. 'I have a house over there.' She waved her hand in the direction of the mountainous section of the Shelleian landscape.

Gleefully, in my tipsy mood, I accepted her invitation.

'Too delightful,' I said. Everything, this morning, was too delightful. I should have accepted with genuine, unmixed pleasure an invitation to stay with Miss Carruthers or Mr. Brimstone.

'And your name?' she asked. 'I don't know that yet.'

'Chelifer.'

'Chelifer? Not Francis Chelifer?'

'Francis Chelifer,' I affirmed.

'Francis Chelifer!' Positively, her soul was in my name. 'But how *won*derful! I've wanted to meet you for years.'

For the first time since I had risen intoxicated from the dead I had an awful premonition of to-morrow's sobriety. I remembered for the first time that round the corner, only just round the corner, lay the real world.

'And what's your name?' I asked apprehensively.

'Lilian Aldwinkle,' said the Chinese lantern lady; and she shaped her lips into a smile that was positively piercing in its sweetness. The blue lamps that were her eyes glittered with such a focused intensity that even the colour-blind chauffeurs who see green omnibuses rolling down Piccadilly and in the Green Park blood-coloured grass and vermilion trees would have known them for the danger signals they were.

An hour later I was reclining on cushions in Mrs. Aldwinkle's Rolls-Royce. There was no escape.

Chapter VII

No escape. . . . But I was still tipsy enough not seriously to desire escape. My premonition of sobriety had been no more than a momentary flash. It came and it passed again, almost immediately, as I became once more absorbed in what seemed to me the endless and lovely comedy that was being acted all around me. It was enough for me that I existed and that things were happening to me. I was carried by two or three young giants to the hotel, I was dressed, my clothes were packed for me. In the entrance hall, while I was waiting for Mrs. Aldwinkle to come and fetch me, I made some essays at walking; the feebleness of my legs was a source to me of delighted laughter.

Dressed in pale yellow tussore with a large straw hat on her head, Mrs. Aldwinkle finally appeared. Her guests, she explained, had gone home in another machine; I should be able to lie flat, or very nearly, in her empty car. And in case I felt bad—she shook a silver brandy flask at me. Escape? I did not so much as think of it, I was enchanted.

Luxuriously I reclined among the cushions. Mrs. Aldwinkle tapped the forward-looking window. The chauffeur languidly moved his hand and the machine rolled forward, nosing its way through the crowd of admiring car-fanciers which, in Italy, collects as though by magic round every stationary automobile. And Mrs. Aldwinkle's was a particularly attractive specimen. Young men called to their friends: '*Venite. È una Ro-Ro.*' And in awed voices little boys whispered to one another: '*Una Ro-Ro.*' The crowd reluctantly dispersed before our advance; we glided away from before the Grand Hotel, turned into the main street, crossed the piazza, in the centre of which, stranded high and dry by the receding sea, stood the little pink fort which had been built by the Princes of Massa Carrara to keep watch on a Mediterranean made dangerous by Barbary pirates, and rolled out of the village by the road leading across the plain towards the mountains.

Shuffling along in a slowly moving cloud of dust, a train of white oxen advanced, shambling and zig-zagging along the road to meet us. Eight yoke of them there were, a long procession, with half a dozen drivers shouting and tugging at the leading ropes and cracking their whips. They were dragging a low truck, clamped to which was a huge monolith of flawless white marble. Uneasily, as we crawled past them, the animals shook their heads, turning this way and that, as though desperately seeking some way of escape. Their long curving horns clashed together; their soft white dewlaps shook; and into their blank brown eyes there came a look of fear, an entreaty that we should take pity on their invincible stupidity and remember that they simply could not, however hard they tried, get used to motor-cars.

Mrs. Aldwinkle pointed at the monolith. 'Imagine what Michelangelo could have made out of that,' she said. Then, noticing that her pointing hand still grasped the silver flask, she became very solicitous. 'You're sure you wouldn't like a sip of this?' she asked, leaning forward. The twin blue danger signals glittered in my face. Her garments exhaled a scent in which there was ambergris. Her breath smelt of heliotrope cachous. But even now I did not take fright; I made no effort to escape. Guided by their invincible stupidity, the white oxen had behaved more sensibly than I.

We rolled on. The hills came nearer. The far-away peaks of bare limestone were hidden by the glowing mass of the tilled and wooded foot-hills. Happily I looked at those huge hilly forms. 'How beautiful!' I said. Mrs. Aldwinkle seemed to take my words as a personal compliment. 'I'm so glad you think so. So awfully . . .' she replied in the tone of an author to whom you have just said that you enjoyed his last book so much.

We drew nearer; the hills towered up, they opposed themselves like a huge wall. But the barrier parted before us; we passed through the gates of a valley that wound up into the mountain. Our road now ran parallel with the bed of a torrent. In the flanks of the hill to our right a marble quarry made a huge bare scar, hundreds of feet long. The crest of the hill was fringed with a growth of umbrella pines.

The straight slender tree trunks jetted up thirty feet without a branch; their wide-spreading flattened domes of foliage formed a thin continuous silhouette, between which and the dark mass of the hill one could see a band of sky, thinly barred by the bare stems. It was as though, to emphasize the outlines of his hills, an artist had drawn a fine and supple brush stroke parallel with the edge of the silhouette and a little apart from it.

We rolled on. The high road narrowed into the squalid street of a little town. The car crept along, hooting as it went.

'Vezza,' Mrs. Aldwinkle explained. 'Michelangelo used to come here for his marbles.'

'Indeed?' I was charmed to hear it.

Over the windows of a large shop filled with white crosses, broken columns and statues, I read the legend: 'Anglo-American Tombstone Company.' We emerged from the narrow street on to an embankment running along the edge of a river. From the opposite bank the ground rose steeply.

'There,' said Mrs. Aldwinkle on a note of triumph as we crossed the bridge, 'that's my house.' She pointed up. From the hill-top a long façade stared down through twenty windows; a tall tower pricked the sky. 'The palace was built in 1630,' she began. I even enjoyed the history lesson.

We had crossed the bridge, we were climbing by a steep and winding road through what was almost a forest of olive trees. The abrupt grassy slope had been built up into innumerable little terraces on which the trees were planted. Here and there, in the grey luminous shadow beneath the trees, little flocks of sheep were grazing. The barefooted children who attended them came running to the side of the road to watch us passing.

'I like to think of these old princely courts,' Mrs. Aldwinkle was saying. 'Like abbeys of . . . abbeys of . . .'

She shook her brandy flask impatiently. 'You know . . . in Thingumy.'

'Abbeys of Thelema,' I suggested.

'That's it,' said Mrs. Aldwinkle. 'Sort of retiring-places where people were free to live intelligently. That's what I want to make this house. I'm so delighted to have met you like this. You're exactly the sort of person I want.' She leaned forward, smiling and glittering. But even at the prospect of entering the Abbey of Thelema I did not blench.

At this moment the car passed through a huge gateway. I caught a glimpse of a great flight of steps, set between cypresses, mounting up past a series of terraced landings to a carved doorway in the centre of the long façade. The road turned, the car swung round and the vista was closed. By an ilex avenue that wound round the flank of the hill we climbed more gradually towards the house, which we approached from the side. The road landed us finally in a large square court opposite a shorter reproduction of the great façade. At the head of a double flight of steps curving horse-shoe fashion from the landing at its threshold, a tall pompous doorway surmounted by a coat of arms cavernously invited. The car drew up.

And about time too, as I notice on re-reading what I have written. Few things are more profoundly boring and unprofitable than literary descriptions. For the writer, it is true, there is a certain amusement to be derived from the hunt for apt expressive words. Carried away by the excitement of the chase he dashes on, regardless of the poor readers who follow toilsomely through his stiff and clayey pages like the runners at the tail of a hunt, seeing nothing of the fun. All writers are also readers—though perhaps I should make exceptions in favour of a few of my colleagues who make a speciality of native wood-notes—and must therefore know how dreary description is. But that does not prevent them from inflicting upon others all that they themselves have suffered. Indeed I sometimes think that some authors must write as they do purely out of a desire for revenge.

Mrs. Aldwinkle's other guests had arrived and were waiting for us. I was introduced and found them all equally charming. The little niece rushed to Mrs. Aldwinkle's assistance; the young man who had rowed the *patino* rushed in his turn to the little niece's and insisted on carrying all the things of which she had relieved her aunt. The old man with the red face, who had talked about the clouds, looked on benevolently at this little scene. But another elderly gentleman with a white beard, whom I had not seen before, seemed to view it with a certain disapproval. The young lady who had talked about the whiteness of her legs and who turned out to be my distinguished colleague, Miss Mary Thriplow, was now dressed in a little green frock with a white turned-down collar, white cuffs and buttons, which made her look like a schoolgirl in a comic opera by Offenbach. The brown young man stood near her.

I got out of the car, refused all proffered assistance and contrived, a little wamblingly, it is true, to mount the steps.

'You must be very careful for a little,' said Mrs. Aldwinkle with a maternal solicitude. 'These,' she added, waving her hand in the direction of a vista of empty saloons, the entrance to which we were just then passing, 'these are the apartments of the Princesses.'

We walked right through the house into a great quadrangle surrounded on three sides by buildings and on the fourth, towards the rising hill, by an arcade. On a pedestal in the centre of the court stood a more than life-sized marble statue, representing, my hostess informed me, the penultimate Prince of Massa Carrara, wearing a very curly full-bottomed wig, Roman kilts, buskins, and one of those handsome classical breastplates which have the head of a Gorgon embossed in the middle of the chest and a little dimple to indicate the position of the navel in the middle of the round and polished belly. With the expression of one who is about to reveal a delightful secret and who can hardly wait until the moment of revelation comes to give vent to his pleasure, Mrs. Aldwinkle, smiling as it were below the surface of her face, led me to the foot of the statue. 'Look!' she said. It was one of those pretty peep-shows on which, for the sake of five minutes' amusement and titillation of the eye, Grand Monarchs used to spend the value of a rich province. From the central arch of the arcade a flight of marble steps climbed up to where, set against a semi-circle of cypresses, at the crest of the hill, a little round temple played gracefully at paganism, just as the buskined and corseleted statue in the court below played heroically at Plutarch.

'And now look here!' said Mrs. Aldwinkle; and taking me round to the other side of the statue, she led me towards a great door in the centre of the long range of buildings opposite the arcade. It was open; a vaulted corridor, like a tunnel, led clean through the house. Through it I could see the blue sky and the remote horizon of the sea. We walked along it; from the further threshold I found myself looking down the flight of steps which I had seen from below, at the entrance gate. It was a stage scene, but made of solid marble and with growing trees.

'What do you think of that?' asked Mrs. Aldwinkle.

'Magnificent,' I answered, with an enthusiasm that was beginning to be tempered by a growing physical weariness.

'Such a view,' said Mrs. Aldwinkle, poking at it with the tip of her sunshade. 'The contrast between the cypresses and the olive trees . . .'

'But the view's still lovelier from the temple,' said the little niece, who was evidently very anxious to make me realize the full pricelessness of her Aunt Lilian's possessions.

Mrs. Aldwinkle turned on her. 'How utterly thoughtless you are!' she said severely. 'Do try to remember that poor Mr. Chelifer is still suffering from the effects of his accident. And you expect him to go climbing up to the temple!'

The little niece blushed and drooped beneath the reproach. We sat down.

'How are you feeling now?' asked Mrs. Aldwinkle, remembering once more to be solicitous. . . . 'Too appalling to think,' she added, 'how nearly . . . And I've always so enormously admired your work.'

'So have I,' declared my colleague in the green frock. 'Most awfully. Still, I confess, I find some of your things a little, how shall I say, a little alembicated. I like my poetry to be rather straightforwarder.'

'A very sophisticated desire,' said the red-faced gentleman. 'Really simple, primitive people like their poetry to be as complicated, conventional, artificial and remote from the language of everyday affairs as possible. We reproach the eighteenth century with its artificiality. But the fact is that *Beowulf* is couched in a diction fifty times more complicated and unnatural than that of the *Essay on Man*. And when you compare the Icelandic Sagas with Dr. Johnson, you find that it's the Doctor who lisps and prattles. Only the most complicated people, living in the midst of the most artificial surroundings, desire their poetry to be simple and straightforward.'

I shut my eyes and allowed the waves of conversation to roll over me. And what a classy conversation! Prince Papadiamantopoulos could hardly have kept the ball rolling on a higher level. Fatigue was sobering me.

Fatigue, the body's weariness—some industrious little scientific emmet ought to catalogue and measure all its various effects. All—for it isn't enough to show that when wage-slaves have worked too long they tend to fall into the machines and get pulped. The fact is interesting, no doubt; but there are other facts of no less significance. There is the fact, for example, that slight fatigue increases our capacity for sentiment. Those compromising love letters are always written in the small hours; it is at night, not when we are fresh and reposed, that we talk about ideal love and indulge our griefs. Under the influence of slight fatigue we feel more ready than at other times to discuss the problems of the universe, to make confidences, to dogmatize about the nature of God and to draw up plans for the future. We are also inclined to be more languidly voluptuous. When, however, the fatigue is increased beyond a certain point, we cease entirely to be sentimental, voluptuous, metaphysical or confiding. We cease to be aware of anything but the decrepitude of our being. We take no further interest in other people or the outside world—no further interest unless they will not leave us in peace, when we come to hate them with a deep but ineffectual loathing, mingled with disgust.

With me, fatigue had almost suddenly passed the critical point. My convalescent's delight in the world evaporated. My fellow beings no longer seemed to me beautiful, strange and amiable. Mrs. Aldwinkle's attempts to bring me into the conversation exasperated me; when I looked at her, I thought her a monster. I realized, too late (which made the realization the more vexatious), what I had let myself in for when I accepted Mrs. Aldwinkle's invitation. Fantastic surroundings, art, classy chats about the cosmos, the intelligentsia, love. . . . It was too much, even on a holiday.

I shut my eyes. Sometimes, when Mrs. Aldwinkle interpellated me, I said yes or no, without much regard to the sense of her remark. Discussion raged around me. From the alembication of my poetry they had gone on to art in general. Crikey, I said to myself, crikey. . . . I did my best to close the ears of my mind; and for some little time I did, indeed, contrive to understand nothing of what was said. I thought of Miss Carruthers, of Fluffy and Mr. Brimstone, of Gog's Court and Mr. Bosk.

Mrs. Aldwinkle's voice, raised by irritation to a peculiar loudness, made itself audible to my muffled mind. 'How often have I told you, Cardan,' it said, 'that you understand nothing of modern art?'

'At least a thousand times,' Mr. Cardan replied cheerfully. 'But bless your heart,' he added (and I opened my eyes in time to see his benevolent smile), 'I never mind at all.'

The smile was evidently too much for Mrs. Aldwinkle's patience. With the gesture of a queen who implies that the audience is at an end she rose from her seat. 'Just time,' she said, looking at her watch, 'there's just time. I really must give Mr. Chelifer some idea of the inside of the palace before lunch. You'd like to come?' She smiled at me like a siren.

Too polite to remind her of her recent outburst against the little niece, I declared myself delighted by the idea. Wamblingly I followed her into the house. Behind me I heard the young rower exclaiming on a note of mingled astonishment and indignation: 'But a moment ago she was saying that Mr. Chelifer was too ill to . . .'

'Ah, but that was different,' said the voice of the red-faced man.

'Why was it different?'

'Because, my young friend, the other fellow is in all cases the rule; but *I* am invariably the exception. Shall we follow?'

Mrs. Aldwinkle made me look at painted ceilings till I almost fell down from giddiness. She dragged me through room after baroque room; then drove me up dark stairs into the Middle Ages. By the time we were back in the *trecento* I was so much exhausted that I could hardly stand. My knees trembled, I felt sick.

'This is the old armoury,' said Mrs. Aldwinkle with mounting enthusiasm. 'And there are the stairs leading up to the tower.' She pointed to a low archway, through which, in a dusty twilight, the bottom of a steep stair could be seen corkscrewing up to unknown heights. 'There are two hundred and thirty-two steps,' she added.

At this moment the gong for luncheon rumbled remotely from the other end of the huge empty house.

'Thank God!' said the red-faced man devoutly.

But our hostess, it was evident, had no feeling for punctuality. 'What a bore!' she exclaimed. 'But never mind. We can make time. I wanted just to run up the tower before lunch. There's such a wonderful bird's-eye . . .' She looked inquiringly round. 'What do you think, all of you? Shouldn't we just dash up? It won't take a minute.' She repeated the siren smile. 'Do let's. Do!' And without waiting for the result of her plebiscite she walked rapidly towards the stairs.

I followed her. But before I had taken five steps, the floor, the walls of the room seemed to fade into the distance. There was a roaring in my ears. It grew suddenly dark. I felt myself falling. For the second time since breakfast I lost consciousness.

When I came to, I was lying on the floor, with my head on Mrs. Aldwinkle's knees; and she was dabbing my forehead with a wet sponge. The first objects of which I was aware were her bright blue eyes hanging over me, very close, very bright and alarming. 'Poor fellow,' she was saying, 'poor fellow.' Then, looking up, she shouted angrily to the owners of the various legs and skirts which I distinguished mistily to right and left of me: 'Stand back, you must stand back! Do you want to suffocate the poor fellow?'

PART III

The Loves of the Parallels

Chapter I

Do all he could, Lord Hovenden had somehow found it impossible, these last few days, to get Irene for a moment to himself. The change had come about almost suddenly, just after that fellow Chelifer had made his appearance. Before he came, there had been a time—beginning, strangely enough, almost as suddenly as it had ended—a time of blissful happiness. Whenever during those days an opportunity for a *tête-à-tête* presented itself Irene had been always at hand and, what was more, always delighted to seize the opportunity. They had been for long walks together, they had swum together far out into the sea, sat together in the gardens, sometimes talking, sometimes silent; but very happy, whether they spoke or not. He had talked to her about motoring and dancing and shooting, and occasionally, feeling rather shamefaced and embarrassed by the disquieting gravity of the subject, about the working classes. And Irene had listened with pleasure to everything he said and had talked too. They found that they had many tastes in common. It had been an enchantment while it lasted. And then, all at once, with the coming of that creature Chelifer, it all came to an end. Irene was never on the spot when opportunities offered, she never suggested spontaneously, as once or twice, during the heavenly time, she had actually done, that they should go for a walk together. She had no time to talk to him; her thoughts, it seemed, were elsewhere, as with grave and preoccupied face she hurried mysteriously about the palace and the gardens. With an extreme anguish of spirit Lord Hovenden observed that it was always in the direction of Chelifer that Irene seemed to be hurrying. Did he slip out unobtrusively into the garden after lunch, Irene was sure, a moment later, to slip out after him. When he proposed a stroll with Calamy or Mr. Cardan, Irene always asked, shyly but with the pallid resolution of one who by an effort of will overcomes a natural weakness for the sake of some all-important cause, to be allowed to join the party. And if ever Chelifer and Miss Thriplow happened to find themselves for a moment together, Irene was always certain to come gliding silently after them.

For all this Lord Hovenden could find only one explanation. She was in love with the man. True, she never made any effort to talk to him when she was in his company; she seemed even rather intimidated by his polished silences, his pointedly insincere formulas of courtesy and compliment. And for his part Chelifer, as far as his rival could see, behaved with a perfect correctitude. Too correctly, indeed, in Hovenden's opinion. He couldn't tolerate the fellow's sarcastic politeness; the man ought to be more human with little Irene. Lord Hovenden would have liked to wring his neck; wring it for two mutually exclusive offences—luring the girl on and being too damned stand-offish. And she looked so wretched. Looking out of its square window in the thick bright bell of copper hair, the little face, so childish in the largeness and limpidity of the eyes, in the shortness of the upper lip, had been, these last days, the face of a pathetic, not a merry child. Lord Hovenden could only suppose that she was pining with love for that creature—though what the devil she contrived to see in him he, for one, couldn't imagine. And it was so obvious, too, that old Lilian was also quite gone on the fellow and making a fool of herself about him. Did she want to compete with her Aunt Lilian? There'd be the devil and all to pay if Mrs. Aldwinkle discovered that Irene was trying to cut her out.

The more he thought of the wretched business, the wretcheder it seemed. Lord Hovenden was thoroughly miserable.

So too was Irene. But not for the reasons Lord Hovenden supposed. It was true that she had spent most of her days since Chelifer's arrival in following the new guest like an unhappy shadow. But it had not been on her own account, not at her own desire. Chelifer did indeed intimidate her; so far Lord Hovenden had guessed aright. He had been hopelessly at fault in imagining that Irene adored the man in spite of her fear of him. If she followed him about, it was because Mrs. Aldwinkle had asked her to. And if she looked unhappy, it was because Aunt Lilian was unhappy—and a little, too, because the task which Aunt Lilian had set her was a disagreeable one; disagreeable not only in itself, but because it prevented her from continuing those pleasant talks with Hovenden. Ever since that evening when Aunt Lilian twitted her on her coldness and her blindness, Irene had made a point of seeing Hovenden as much as she could. She wanted to prove that Aunt Lilian had been wrong. She wasn't cold, she wasn't blind; she could see as clearly as any one when people liked her, and she could be as warmly appreciative. And really, after the episodes with Jacques, Mario and Peter, it wasn't fair of Aunt Lilian to tease her like that. It simply wasn't. Moved by an indignant desire to confute Aunt Lilian as quickly as possible, she had positively made advances to Hovenden; he was so shy that, if she hadn't, it would have been months before she could have offered her aunt anything like convincing rebuttal of her imputation. She had talked with him, gone for walks with him, quite prepared to feel at any moment the infinitude of passion. But the affair passed off, somehow, very differently from the others. She began to feel something indeed, but something quite unlike that which she had felt for Peter and Jacques. For them it had been a fizzy, exciting, restless feeling, intimately connected with large hotels, jazz bands, coloured lights and Aunt Lilian's indefatigable desire to get everything out of life, her haunting fear that she was missing something, even in the heart of the fun. 'Enjoy yourself, let yourself go,' Aunt Lilian was always telling her. And 'How handsome he is! what a lovely fellow!' she would say as one of the young men passed. Irene had done her best to take Aunt Lilian's advice. And it had seemed to her, sometimes, when she was dancing and the lights, the music, the moving crowd had blended together into a single throbbing whole, it had seemed to her that she had indeed climbed to the peak of happiness. And the young man, the Peter or Jacques whom Aunt Lilian had hypnotized her into thinking a marvel among young men, was regarded as the source of this bliss. Between the dances, under the palm trees in the garden, she had even suffered herself to be kissed; and the experience had been rather momentous. But when the time came for them to move on, Irene departed without regret. The fizzy feeling had gone flat. But with Hovenden it was different. She just liked him quietly, more and more. He was so nice and simple and eager and young. So young—she liked that particularly. Irene felt that he was really younger, in spite of his age, than she. The other ones had all been older, more knowing and accomplished; all rather bold and insolent. But Hovenden wasn't in the least like that. One felt very secure with him, Irene thought. And there was somehow no question of love when one was with him—at any rate the question wasn't at all pressing or urgent. Aunt Lilian used to ask her every evening how they were getting on and if it were getting exciting. And Irene never quite knew what to answer. She found very soon that she didn't want to talk about Hovenden; he was so different from the others, and their friendship had nothing infinite about it. It was just a sensible friendship. She dreaded Aunt Lilian's questions; and she found herself almost disliking Aunt Lilian when, in that dreadful bantering way of hers, she ruthlessly insisted on putting them. In some ways, indeed, the coming of Chelifer had been a relief; for Aunt Lilian became at once so profoundly absorbed in her own emotions that she had no time or inclination to think of any one else's. Yes, that had been a great relief. But on the other hand, the work of supervision and espionage to which Aunt Lilian had set her made it all but impossible for Irene ever to talk to Hovenden. She might as well not be there, Irene sadly reflected. Still, poor Aunt Lilian was so dreadfully unhappy. One must do all one could for her. Poor Aunt Lilian!

'I want to know what he thinks of me,' Aunt Lilian had said to her in the secret hours of the night. 'What does he say about me to other people?' Irene answered that she had never heard him say anything about her. 'Then you must listen, you must keep your ears open.'

But however much she listened, Irene never had anything to report. Chelifer never mentioned Aunt Lilian. For Mrs. Aldwinkle that was almost worse than if he had spoken badly of her. To be ignored was terrible. 'Perhaps he likes Mary,' she had suggested. 'I thought I saw him looking at her to-day in a strange, intent sort of way.' And Irene had been ordered to watch them. But for all she could discover, Mrs. Aldwinkle's jealousies were utterly unfounded. Between Chelifer and Mary Thriplow there passed no word or look that the most suspicious imagination could interpret in terms of amorous intimacy. 'He's queer, he's an extraordinary creature.' That was the refrain of Mrs. Aldwinkle's talk about him. 'He seems to care for nothing. So cold, such a fixed, frigid mask. And yet one has only to look at him—his eyes, his mouth—to see that underneath . . .' And Mrs. Aldwinkle would shake her head and sigh. And her speculations about him would go rambling on and on, round and round, treading the same ground again and again, arriving nowhere. Poor Aunt Lilian! She was dreadfully unhappy.

In her own mind Mrs. Aldwinkle had begun by saving Chelifer's life. She saw herself standing there on the beach between sea and sky, and with the mountains in the middle distance, looking like one of those wonderfully romantic figures who, in the paintings of Augustus John, stand poised in a meditative and passionate ecstasy against a cosmic background. She *saw* herself—a John down even to her flame-coloured tunic and her emerald-green parasol. And at her feet, like Shelley, like Leander washed up on the sands of Abydos, lay the young poet, pale, naked and dead. And she had bent over him, had called him back to life, had raised him up and, figuratively speaking, had carried him off in maternal arms to a haven of peace where he should gather new strength and, for his poetry, new inspiration.

Such were the facts as they appeared to Mrs. Aldwinkle, after passing through the dense refractive medium of her imagination. Given these facts, given the resultant situation, given her character, it was almost necessary and inevitable that Mrs. Aldwinkle should feel romantically towards her latest guest. The mere fact that he was a new arrival, hitherto unknown, and a poet at that, would have been enough in any circumstances to make Mrs. Aldwinkle take a lively interest in the young man. But seeing that she had saved him from a watery grave and was now engaged in supplying him with inspiration, she felt something more than interest. She would have been disobeying the laws of her being if she had not fallen in love with him. Moreover, he made it easier for her by being so darkly and poetically handsome. And then he was queer—queer to the point of mysteriousness. His very coldness attracted while it filled her with despair.

'He can't really be so utterly indifferent to everything and everybody as he makes out,' she kept insisting to Irene.

The desire to break down his barriers, enter into his intimacy and master his secret quickened her love.

From the moment of her discovery of him, in those romantic circumstances which her imagination had made so much more romantic, Mrs. Aldwinkle had tried to take possession of Chelifer; she had tried to make him as much her property as the view, or Italian art. He became at once the best living poet; but it followed as a corollary that she was his only interpreter. In haste she had telegraphed to London for copies of all his books.

'When I think,' she would say, leaning forward embarrassingly close and staring into his face with those bright dangerous eyes of hers, 'when I think how nearly you were drowned. Like Shelley . . .' She shuddered. 'It's too appalling.'

And Chelifer would bend his full Egyptian lips into a smile and answer: 'They'd have been inconsolable on the staff of the Rabbit Fancier,' or something of the sort. Oh, queer, queer, queer!

'He slides away from one,' Mrs. Aldwinkle complained to her young confidante of the small hours.

She might try to take his barriers by storm, might try to creep subtly into his confidence from the flank, so to speak; but Chelifer was never to be caught napping. He evaded her. There was no taking possession of him. It was for nothing, so far as Mrs. Aldwinkle was concerned, that he was the best living poet and she his prophetess.

He evaded her—evaded her not merely mentally and spiritually, but even in the flesh. For after a day or two in the Cybo Malaspina palace he developed an almost magical faculty for disappearing. One moment he'd be there, walking about in the garden or sitting in one of the saloons;

something would distract Mrs. Aldwinkle's attention, and the next moment, when she turned back towards the place where he had been, he was gone, he was utterly vanished. Mrs. Aldwinkle would search; there was no trace of him to be found. But at the next meal he'd walk in, punctual as ever; he would ask his hostess politely if she had had an agreeable morning or afternoon, whichever the case might be, and when she asked him where he had been, would answer vaguely that he'd gone for a little walk, or that he'd been writing letters.

After one of these disappearances Irene, who had been set by her aunt to hunt for him, finally ran him to earth on the top of the tower. She had climbed the two hundred and thirty-two steps for the sake of the commanding view of the whole garden and hillside to be obtained from the summit. If he was anywhere above ground, she ought to see him from the tower. But when at last, panting, she emerged on to the little square platform from which the ancient marquesses had dropped small rocks and molten lead on their enemies in the court below, she got a fright that nearly made her fall backwards down the steps. For as she came up through the trap-door into the sunlight, she suddenly became aware of what seemed, to eyes that looked up from the level of the floor, a gigantic figure advancing, toweringly, towards her.

Irene uttered a little scream; her heart jumped violently and seemed to stop beating.

'Allow me,' said a very polite voice. The giant bent down and took her by the hand. It was Chelifer. 'So you've climbed up for a bird's-eye view of the picturesque beauties of nature?' he went on, when he had helped her up through the hatch way. 'I'm very partial to bird's-eye views myself.'

'You gave me such a start,' was all that Irene could say. Her face was quite pale.

'I'm exceedingly sorry,' said Chelifer. There was a long and, for Irene, embarrassing silence.

After a minute she went down again.

'Did you find him?' asked Mrs. Aldwinkle, when her niece emerged a little while later on to the terrace.

Irene shook her head. Somehow she lacked the courage to tell Aunt Lilian the story of her adventure. It would make her too unhappy to think that Chelifer was prepared to climb two hundred and thirty-two steps for the sake of getting out of her way.

Mrs. Aldwinkle tried to guard against his habit of vanishing by never, so far as it was practicable, letting him out of her sight. She arranged that he should always sit next to her at table. She took him for walks and drives in the motor car, she made him sit with her in the garden. It was with difficulty and only by the employment of stratagems that Chelifer managed to procure a moment of liberty and solitude. For the first few days of his stay Chelifer found that 'I must go and write' was a good excuse to get away. Mrs. Aldwinkle professed such admiration for him in his poetical capacity that she could not decently refuse to let him go. But she soon found a way of controlling such liberty as he could get in this way by insisting that he should write under the ilex trees, or in one of the mouldering sponge-stone grottoes hollowed in the walls of the lower terrace. Vainly Chelifer protested that he loathed writing or reading out of doors.

'These lovely surroundings,' Mrs. Aldwinkle insisted, 'will inspire you.'

'But the only surroundings that really inspire me,' said Chelifer, 'are the lower middle class quarters of London, north of the Harrow Road, for example.'

'How can you say such things?' said Mrs. Aldwinkle.

'But I assure you,' he protested, 'it's quite true.'

None the less, he had to go and write under the ilexes or in the grotto. Mrs. Aldwinkle, at a moderate distance, kept him well in sight. Every ten minutes or so she would come tip-toeing into his retreat, smiling, as she imagined, like a sibyl, her finger on her lips, to lay beside his permanently virgin sheet of paper a bunch of late-flowering roses, a dahlia, some Michaelmas daisies or a few pink berries from the spindle tree. Courteously, in some charming and frankly insincere formula, Chelifer would thank her for the gift, and with a final smile, less sibylline, but sweeter, tenderer, Mrs. Aldwinkle would tip-toe away again, like Egeria bidding farewell to King Numa, leaving her inspiration to do its work. It didn't seem to do its work very well, however. For whenever she asked him how much he had written, he regularly answered 'Nothing,' smiling at her meanwhile that courteous and Sphingine smile which Mrs. Aldwinkle always found so baffling, so pre-eminently 'queer.'

Often Mrs. Aldwinkle would try to lead the conversation upwards on to those high spiritual planes from which the most satisfactory and romantic approach to love is to be made. Two souls that have acclimatized themselves to the thin air of religion, art, ethics or metaphysics have no difficulty in breathing the similar atmosphere of ideal love, whose territory lies contiguous to those of the other inhabitants of high mental altitudes. Mrs. Aldwinkle liked to approach love from the heights. One landed, so to speak, by aeroplane on the snowy summit of Popocatepetl, to descend by easy stages into the tropical *tierra caliente* in the plains below. But with Chelifer it was impossible to gain a footing on any height at all. When, for example, Mrs. Aldwinkle started rapturously on art and the delights of being an artist, Chelifer would modestly admit to being a tolerable second-rate halma player.

'But how can you speak like that?' cried Mrs. Aldwinkle. 'How can you blaspheme so against art and your own talent? What's your talent for?'

'For editing the Rabbit Fanciers' Gazette, it appears,' Chelifer answered, courteously smiling.

Sometimes she started on the theme of love itself; but with no greater success. Chelifer just politely agreed with everything she said, and when she pressed him for a definite opinion of his own replied, 'I don't know.'

'But you must know,' Mrs. Aldwinkle insisted, 'you must have some opinion. You have had experience.'

Chelifer shook his head. 'Alas,' he deplored, 'never.'

It was hopeless.

'What am I to do?' asked Mrs. Aldwinkle despairingly in the small hours.

Wise in the experience of eighteen years, Irene suggested that the best thing to do would be to think no more about him—in that way.

Mrs. Aldwinkle only sighed and shook her head. She had started loving because she believed in love, because she wanted to love and because a romantic opportunity had presented itself. She had rescued a Poet from death. How could she help loving him? The circumstances, the person were her invention; she had fallen in love, deliberately almost, with the figments of her own imagination. But there was no deliberately falling out again. The romantic yearnings had aroused those profounder instincts of which they were but the polite and literary emanation. The man was young, was beautiful—these were facts, not imaginings. These deep desires once started by the conscious mind from their sleep, once made aware of their quarry, how could they be held back? 'He is a poet. For the love of poetry, for the love of passion and because I saved him from death, I love him. If that had been all, it might have been possible for Mrs. Aldwinkle to take Irene's advice. But from the obscure caves of her being another voice was speaking. He is young, he is beautiful. The days are so few and short. I am growing old. My body is thirsty.' How could she cease to think of him?

'And suppose he did come to love me a little,' Mrs. Aldwinkle went on, taking a perverse delight in tormenting herself in every possible way, 'suppose he should come to love me just a little for what I am and think and do—should come to love me because, to begin with, I love him and admire his work, and because I understand what an artist feels and can sympathize with him—suppose all that, wouldn't he be repelled at the same time by the fact that I'm old?' She peered into the mirror. 'My face looks terribly old,' she said.

'No, no,' protested Irene encouragingly.

'He'd be disgusted,' Mrs. Aldwinkle went on. 'It would be enough to drive him away even if he were attracted in some other way.' She sighed profoundly. The tears trickled slowly down her sagging cheeks.

'Don't talk like that, Aunt Lilian,' Irene implored her. 'Don't talk like that.' She felt the tears coming into her own eyes. At that moment she would have done anything, given anything to make Aunt Lilian happy. She threw her arms round Mrs. Aldwinkle's neck and kissed her. 'Don't be unhappy,' she whispered. 'Don't think any more about it. What does it matter about that man? What does it matter? You must think only of the people who *do* love you. I love you, Aunt Lilian. So much, so much.'

Mrs. Aldwinkle suffered herself to be a little comforted. She dried her eyes. 'I shall make myself look still uglier,' she said, 'if I go on crying.' There was a silence. Irene went on brushing her aunt's hair; she hoped that Aunt Lilian had turned her thoughts elsewhere.

'At any rate,' said Mrs. Aldwinkle at last, breaking the long silence, 'my body is still young.'

Irene was distressed. Why couldn't Aunt Lilian think of something else? But her distress turned into an uneasy sense of embarrassment and shame as Mrs. Aldwinkle pursued the subject started by her last words into more and more intimate detail. In spite of her five years' training in Aunt Lilian's school, Irene felt profoundly shocked.

Chapter II

'WE two,' said Mr. Cardan one late afternoon some fortnight after Chelifer's arrival, 'we two seem to be rather left out of it.'

'Left out of what?' asked Mr. Falx.

'Out of love,' said Mr. Cardan. He looked down over the balustrade. On the next terrace below, Chelifer and Mrs. Aldwinkle were walking slowly up and down. On the terrace below that strolled the diminished and foreshortened figures of Calamy and Miss Thriplow. 'And the other two,' said Mr. Cardan, as if continuing aloud the enumeration which he and his companion had made in silence, with the eye alone, 'your young pupil and the little niece, have gone for a walk in the hills. Can you ask what we're left out of?'

Mr. Falx nodded. 'To tell you the truth,' he said, 'I don't much like the atmosphere of this house. Mrs. Aldwinkle's an excellent woman, of course, in many respects. But . . .' he hesitated.

'Yes; but . . .' Mr. Cardan nodded. 'I see your point.'

'I shall be rather glad when I have got young Hovenden away from here,' said Mr. Falx.

'If you get him alone I shall be surprised.'

Mr. Falx went on, shaking his head: 'There's a certain

moral laxity, a certain self-indulgence. . . . I confess I don't like this way of life. I may be prejudiced; but I don't like it.'

'Every one has his favourite vice,' said Mr. Cardan. 'You forget, Mr. Falx, that we probably don't like *your* way of life.'

'I protest,' said Mr. Falx hotly. 'Is it possible to compare my way of life with the way of life in this house? Here am I, working incessantly for a noble cause, devoting myself to the public good . . .'

'Still,' said Mr. Cardan, 'they do say that there's nothing more intoxicating than talking to a crowd of people and moving them the way you want them to go; they do say, too, that it's piercingly delicious to listen to applause. And people who have tried both have told me that the joys of power are far preferable, if only because they are a good deal more enduring, to those one can derive from wine or love. No, no, Mr. Falx; if we chose to climb on to our high horses we should be as amply justified in disapproving of your laxity and self-indulgence as you are in disapproving of ours. I always notice that the most grave and awful denunciations of obscenity in literature are to be found precisely in those periodicals whose directors are most notoriously alcoholic. And the preachers and politicians with the greatest vanity, the most inordinate itch for power and notoriety, are always those who denounce most fiercely the corruptions of the age. One of the greatest triumphs of the nineteenth century was to limit the connotation of the word "immoral" in such a way that, for practical purposes, only those were immoral who drank too much or made too copious love. Those who indulged in any or all of the other deadly sins could look down in righteous indignation on the lascivious and the gluttonous. And not only could but can—even now. This exaltation of two out of the seven deadly sins is most unfair. In the name of all lechers and boozers I most solemnly protest against the invidious distinction made to our prejudice. Believe me, Mr. Falx, we are no more reprehensible than the rest of you. Indeed, compared with some of your political friends, I feel I have a right to consider myself almost a saint.'

'Still,' said Mr. Falx, whose face, where it was not covered by his prophetical white beard, had become very red with ill-suppressed indignation, 'you won't persuade me out of my conviction that these are not the most healthy surroundings for a young fellow like Hovenden at the most impressionable period of his life. Be as paradoxical and ingenious as you like: you will not persuade me, I repeat.'

'No need to repeat, I assure you,' said Mr. Cardan, shaking his head. 'Did you think I ever supposed I could persuade you? You don't imagine I'd waste my time trying to persuade a full-grown man with fixed opinions of the truth of something he doesn't already believe? If you were twelve years old, even if you were twenty, I might try. But at your age—no, no.'

'Then why do you argue, if you don't want to persuade?' asked Mr. Falx.

'For the sake of argument,' Mr. Cardan replied, 'and because one must murder the time somehow.

> Come ingannar questi noiosi e lenti
> Giorni di vita cui si lungo tedio
> E fastidio insoffribile accompagna
> Or io t'insegnero.

I could write a better handbook of the art than old Parini.'

'I'm sorry,' said Mr. Falx, 'but I don't know Italian.'

'Nor should I,' said Mr. Cardan, 'if I had your unbounded resources for killing time. Unhappily, I was born without much zeal for the welfare of the working classes.'

'Working classes . . .' Mr. Falx swooped down on the words. Passionately he began to talk. What was that text, thought Mr. Cardan, about the measure with which ye mete? How fearfully applicable it was! For the last ten minutes he'd been boring poor old Mr. Falx. And now Mr. Falx had turned round and was paying him back with his own measure—but, oh Lord, pressed down and, heaven help us! running over. He looked down over the balustrade. On the lower terraces the couples were still parading up and down. He wondered what they were saying; he wished he were down there to listen. Boomingly, Mr. Falx played his prophetic part.

Chapter III

It was a pity that Mr. Cardan could not hear what his hostess was saying. He would have been delighted; she was talking about herself. It was a subject on which he specially loved to hear her. There were few people, he used to say, whose Authorized Version of themselves differed so strikingly from that Revised, formed of them by others. It was not often, however, that she gave him a chance to compare them. With Mr. Cardan she was always a little shy; he had known her so long.

'Sometimes,' Mrs. Aldwinkle was saying, as she walked with Chelifer on the second of the three terraces, 'sometimes I wish I were less sensitive. I feel everything so acutely—every slightest thing. It's like being . . . like being . . .' she fumbled in the air with groping fingers, feeling for the right word, 'like being flayed,' she concluded triumphantly, and looked at her companion.

Chelifer nodded sympathetically.

'I'm so fearfully aware,' Mrs. Aldwinkle went on, 'of other people's thoughts and feelings. They don't have to speak to make me know what they've got in their minds. I know it, I *feel* it just by seeing them.'

Chelifer wondered whether she felt what was going on in his mind. He ventured to doubt it. 'A wonderful gift,' he said.

'But it has its disadvantages,' insisted Mrs. Aldwinkle. 'For example, you can't imagine how much I suffer when people round me are suffering, particularly if I feel myself in any way to blame. When I'm ill, it makes me miserable to think of servants and nurses and people having to sit up without sleep and run up and downstairs, all because of me. I know it's rather stupid; but, do you know, my sympathy for them is so . . . so . . . profound, that it actually prevents me from getting well as quickly as I should. . . .'

'Dreadful,' said Chelifer in his polite, precise voice.

'You've no idea how deeply all suffering affects me.' She looked at him tenderly. 'That day, that *first* day, when you fainted—you can't imagine . . .'

'I'm sorry it should have had such a disagreeable effect on you,' said Chelifer.

'You would have felt the same yourself—in the circumstances,' said Mrs. Aldwinkle, uttering the last words in a significant tone.

Chelifer shook his head modestly. 'I'm afraid,' he answered, 'I'm singularly stoical about other people's sufferings.'

'Why do you always speak against yourself?' asked Mrs. Aldwinkle earnestly. 'Why do you malign your own character? You know you're not what you pretend to be. You pretend to be so much harder and dryer than you really are. Why do you?'

Chelifer smiled. 'Perhaps,' he said, 'it's to re-establish the universal average. So many people, you see, try to make themselves out softer and damper than they are. Don't they?'

Mrs. Aldwinkle ignored his question. 'But you,' she insisted, 'I want to know about you.' She stared into his face. Chelifer smiled and said nothing. 'You won't tell me?' she went on. 'But it doesn't matter. I know already. I have an intuition about people. It's because I'm so sensitive. I *feel* their character. I'm never wrong.'

'You're to be envied,' said Chelifer.

'It's no good thinking you can deceive me,' she went on. 'You can't. I understand you.' Chelifer sighed, inwardly; she had said that before, more than once. 'Shall I tell you what you are really like?'

'Do.'

'Well, to begin with,' she said, 'you're sensitive, just as sensitive as I am. I can see that in your face, in your actions. I can hear it when you speak. You can pretend to be hard and . . . and . . . armour-plated, but I . . .'

Wearily, but with patience, Chelifer listened. Mrs. Aldwinkle's hesitating voice, moving up and down from note to unrelated note, sounded in his ears. The words became blurred and vague. They lost their articulateness and sense. They were no more than the noise of the wind, a sound that accompanied, but did not interrupt his thoughts. Chelifer's thoughts, at the moment, were poetical. He was engaged in putting the finishing touches to a little 'Mythological Incident,' the idea of which had recently occurred to him and to which, during the last two days, he had been giving its definite form. Now it was finished; a little polishing, that was all it needed now.

Through the pale skeleton of woods
Orion walks. The North wind lays
Its cold lips to the twin steel flutes
That are his gun, and plays.

Knee-deep he goes, where penny-wiser
Than all his kind who steal and hoard,
Year after year some sylvan miser
His copper wealth has stored.

The Queen of Love and Beauty lays
In neighbouring beechen aisles her baits—
Bread-crumbs and the golden maize.
Patiently she waits.

And when the unwary pheasant comes
To fill his painted maw with crumbs,
Accurately the sporting Queen
Takes aim. The bird has been.

Secure, Orion walks her way.
The Cyprian loads, presents, makes fire.
He falls. 'Tis Venus all entire
Attached to her recumbent prey.

Chelifer repeated the verses to himself and was not displeased. The second stanza was a little too 'quaint,' perhaps; a little too—how should he put it?—too Walter-Crane's-picture-book. One might omit it altogether, perhaps; or substitute, if one could think of it, something more perfectly in harmony with the silver-age, allusive elegance of the rest. As for the last verse, that was really masterly. It gave Racine his *raison d'être*; if Racine had never existed, it would have been necessary to invent him, merely for the sake of those last lines.

He falls. 'Tis Venus all entire
Attached to her recumbent prey.

Chelifer lingered over them in ecstasy. He became aware, all at once, that Mrs. Aldwinkle was addressing herself to him more directly. From inharmoniously Aeolian, her voice became once more articulate.

'That's what you're like,' she was saying. 'Tell me I'm right. Say I understand you.'

'Perhaps,' said Chelifer, smiling.

Meanwhile, on the terrace below, Calamy and Miss Thriplow strolled at leisure. They were discussing a subject about which Miss Thriplow professed a special competence; it was—to speak in the language of the examination room—her Special Subject. They were discussing Life. 'Life's so wonderful,' Miss Thriplow was saying. 'Always. So rich, so gay. This morning, for instance, I woke up and the first thing I saw was a pigeon sitting on the window sill—a big fat grey pigeon with a captive rainbow pinned to his stomach.' (That phrase, peculiarly charming and felicitous, Miss Thriplow thought, had already been recorded for future reference in her note-books.) 'And then high up on the wall above the washstand there was a little black scorpion standing tail-upwards, looking quite unreal, like something out of the signs of the Zodiac. And then Eugenia came in to call me—think of having one's hot water brought by a maid called Eugenia to begin with!—and spent a quarter of an hour telling me about her fiancé. It seems that he's so dreadfully jealous. So should I be, if I were engaged to a pair of such rolling eyes. But think of all that happening before breakfast, just casually! What extravagance! But Life's so generous, so copious.' She turned a shining face to her companion.

Calamy looked down at her, through half-closed eyes, smiling, with that air of sleepy insolence, of indolent power, characteristic of him, especially in his relations with women. 'Generous!' he repeated. 'Yes, I should think it was. Pigeons before breakfast. And at breakfast it offers you.'

'As if I were a broiled kipper,' said Miss Thriplow, laughing.

But Calamy was not disturbed by her laughter. He continued to look at her between his puckered eyelids with the same steady insolence, the same certainty of power—a certainty so complete that he could afford to make no exertions; placidly, drowsily, he could await the inevitable triumph. He disquieted Miss Thriplow. That was why she liked him.

They strolled on. Fifteen days ago they could never have walked like this, two on a terrace, talking at leisure of Miss Thriplow's Special Subject. Their hostess would have put an end to any such rebellious attempt at independence in the most prompt and ruthless fashion. But since the arrival of Chelifer Mrs. Aldwinkle had been too much preoccupied with the affairs of her own heart to be able to take the slightest interest in the doings, the sayings, the comings and goings of her guests. Her gaoler's vigilance was relaxed. Her guests might talk together, might wander off alone or in couples, might say good-night when they pleased; Mrs. Aldwinkle did not care. So long as they did not interfere with Chelifer, they might do what they liked. *Fay ce que vouldras* had become the rule in Cybo Malaspina's palace.

'I can never understand,' Miss Thriplow went on, meditatively pursuing her Special Subject, 'I can never understand how it is that everybody isn't happy—I mean fundamentally happy, underneath; for of course there's suffering, there's pain, there are a thousand reasons why one can't always be consciously happy, on the top, if you see what I mean. But fundamentally happy, underneath—how can any one help being that? Life's so extraordinary, so rich and beautiful—there's no excuse for not loving it always, even when one's consciously miserable. Don't you think so?' She was fairly carried away by her love of Life. She was young, she was ardent; she saw herself as a child who goes and turns head over heels, out of pure joy, in the perfumed haycocks. One could be as clever as one liked, but if one had that genuine love of Life it didn't matter; one was saved.

'I agree,' said Calamy. 'It's always worth living, even at the worst of times. And if one happens to be in love, it's really intoxicating.'

Miss Thriplow glanced at him. Calamy was walking with bent head, his eyes fixed on the ground. There was a faint smile on his lips; his eyelids were almost closed, as though he were too drowsy to keep them apart. Miss Thriplow felt annoyed. He made a remark like that and then didn't even take the trouble to look at her.

'I don't believe you've ever been in love,' she said.

'I can't remember ever having been out of it,' Calamy answered.

'Which is the same thing as saying that you've never really been in. Not really,' Miss Thriplow repeated. She knew what the real thing was like.

'And you?' asked Calamy.

Mary Thriplow did not answer. They took two or three turns in silence. It was a folly, Calamy was thinking. He wasn't really in love with the woman. It was a waste of time and there were other things far more important to be done, to be thought about. Other things. They loomed up enormously behind the distracting bustle of life, silently on the further side of the noise and chatter. But what were they? What was their form, their name, their meaning? Through the fluttering veil of movement it was impossible to do more than dimly guess; one might as well try to look at the stars through the London smoke. If one could stop the movement, or get away from it, then surely one would be able to see clearly the large and silent things beyond. But there was no stopping the movement and there was, somehow, no escaping from it. To check it was impossible; and the gesture of escape was ludicrous. The only sensible thing to do was to go on in the usual way and ignore the things outside the world of noise. That was what Calamy tried to do. But he was conscious, none the less, that the things were still there. They were still calmly and immutably there, however much he might agitate himself and distractedly pretend to ignore them. Mutely they claimed attention. They had claimed it, of late, with a most irritating persistence. Calamy's response had been to make love to Mary Thriplow. That was something which ought to keep him well occupied. And up to a point it did. Up to a point. The best indoor sport, old Cardan had called it; but one demanded something better. Could he go on like this? Or if not, what should he do? The questions exasperated him. It was because the things were there, outside the tumult, that he had to ask them. They forced themselves on him, those questions. But it was intolerable to be bullied. He refused to let himself be bullied. He'd do what he damned well liked. But then, did he really like philandering with Mary Thriplow? In a way, no doubt, up to a point. But the real answer was no; frankly, no. But yes, yes, he insisted with another part of his mind. He did like it. And even if he didn't, he'd damned well say that he did. And if necessary he'd damned well do what he didn't like—just because he chose to. He'd do what he didn't like; and that was the end of it. He worked himself up into a kind of fury.

'What are you thinking about?' Miss Thriplow suddenly asked.

'You,' he said; and there was a savage exasperation in his voice, as though he passionately resented the fact that he was thinking about Mary Thriplow.

'*Tiens!*' she said on a note of polite curiosity.

'What would you say if I told you I was in love with you?' he asked.

'I should say that I didn't believe you.'

'Do you want me to compel you to believe?'

'I'd be most interested to know, at any rate, how you proposed to set about it.'

Calamy halted, put his hand on Mary Thriplow's shoulder and turned her round towards him. 'By force, if necessary,' he said, looking into her face.

Miss Thriplow returned his stare. He looked insolent still, still arrogantly conscious of power; but all the drowsiness and indolence that had veiled his look were now fallen away, leaving his face bare, as it were, and burning with a formidable and satanic beauty. At the sight of this strange and sudden transformation Miss Thriplow felt at once exhilarated and rather frightened. She had never seen that expression on a man's face before. She had aroused passions, but never a passion so violent, so dangerous as this seemed to be.

'By force?' By the tone of her voice, by the mockery of her smile she tried to exasperate him into yet fiercer passion.

Calamy tightened his grip on her shoulder. Under his hand the bones felt small and fragile. When he spoke, he found that he had been clenching his teeth. 'By force,' he said. 'Like this.' And taking her head between his two hands he bent down and kissed her, angrily, again and again. Why do I do this? he was thinking. This is a folly. There are other things, important things. 'Do you believe me now?' he asked.

Mary Thriplow's face was flushed. 'You're insufferable,' she said. But she was not really angry with him.

Chapter IV

'WHY have you been so funny all vese days?' Lord Hovenden had at last brought himself to put the long-premeditated question.

'Funny?' Irene echoed on another note, trying to make a joke of it, as though she didn't understand what he meant. But of course she did understand, perfectly well.

They were sitting in the thin luminous shadow of the olive trees. The bright sky looked down at them between the sparse twi-coloured leaves. On the parched grass about the roots of the trees the sunlight scattered an innumerable golden mintage. They were sitting at the edge of a little terrace scooped out of the steep slope, their legs dangling, their backs propped against the trunk of a hoary tree.

'You know,' said Hovenden. 'Why did you suddenly avoid me?'

'Did I?'

'You know you did.'

Irene was silent for a moment before she admitted: 'Yes, perhaps I did.'

'But why,' he insisted, 'why?'

'I don't know,' she answered unhappily. She couldn't tell him about Aunt Lilian.

Her tone emboldened Lord Hovenden to become more insistent. 'You don't know?' he repeated sarcastically, as though he were a lawyer carrying out a cross-examination. 'Perhaps you were walking in your sleep all ve time.'

'Don't be stupid,' she said in a weary little voice.

'At any rate, I'm not too stupid to see vat you were running after vat fellow Chelifer.' Lord Hovenden became quite red in the face as he spoke. For the sake of his manly dignity, it was a pity that his th's should sound quite so childish.

Irene said nothing, but sat quite still, her head bent, looking down at the slanting grove of olives. Framed within the square-cut hair, her face was sad.

'If you were so much interested in him, why did you suggest vat we should go for a walk vis afternoon?' he asked.

'Perhaps you fought I was Chelifer.' He was possessed by an urgent desire to say disagreeable and hurting things. And yet he was perfectly aware, all the time, that he was making a fool of himself and being unfair to her. But the desire was irresistible.

'Why do you try to spoil everything?' she asked with an exasperating sadness and patience.

'I don't try to spoil anyfing,' Hovenden answered irritably. 'I merely ask a simple question.'

'You know I don't take the slightest interest in Chelifer,' she said.

'Ven why do you trot after him all day long, like a little dog?'

The boy's stupidity and insistence began to annoy her. 'I don't,' she said angrily. 'And in any case it's no business of yours.'

'Oh, it's no business of mine, is it?' said Hovenden in a provocative voice. 'Fanks for ve information.' And he was pointedly silent.

For a long time neither of them spoke. Some dark brown sheep with bells round their necks came straying between the trees a little way down the slope. With set, sad faces the two young people looked at them. The bells made a tinkling as the creatures moved. The sweet thin noise sounded, for some reason, extremely sad in their ears. Sad, too, was the bright sky between the leaves; profoundly melancholy the redder, richer light of the declining sun, colouring the silver leaves, the grey trunks, the parched thin grass. It was Hovenden who at last broke silence. His anger, his desire to say hurting, disagreeable things had utterly evaporated; there remained only the conviction that he had made a fool of himself and been unfair—only that and the profound aching love which had given his anger, his foolish cruel desire such force. 'You know I don't take the slightest interest in Chelifer.' He hadn't known, but now that she had said so, and in that tone of voice, now he knew. One couldn't doubt; and even if one could, was it worth doubting?

'Look here,' he said at last, in a muffled voice, 'I made a fool of myself, I'm afraid. I've said stupid things. I'm sorry, Irene. Will you forgive me?'

Irene turned towards him the little square window in her hair. Her face looked out of it smiling. She gave him her hand. 'One day I'll tell you,' she said.

They sat there hand in hand for what seemed to them at once a very long time and a timeless instant. They said nothing, but they were very happy. The sun set. A grey half-night came creeping in under the trees. Between the black silhouetted leaves the sky looked exceedingly pale. Irene sighed.

'I think we ought to be getting back,' she said reluctantly.

Hovenden was the first to scramble to his feet. He offered Irene his hand. She took it and raised herself lightly up, coming forward as she rose towards him. They stood for a moment very close together. Lord Hovenden suddenly took her in his arms and kissed her again and again. Irene uttered a cry. She struggled, she pushed him away.

'No, no,' she entreated, averting her face, leaning back, away from his kisses. 'Please.' And when he let her go, she covered her face with her hands and began to cry. 'Why did you spoil it again?' she asked through her tears. Lord Hovenden was overwhelmed with remorse. 'We'd been so happy, such friends.' Irene dabbed her eyes with her handkerchief; but her voice still came sobbingly.

'I'm a brute,' said Hovenden; and he spoke with such a passion of self-condemnation that Irene couldn't help laughing. There was something positively comic about a repentance so sudden and whole-hearted.

'No, you're not a brute,' she said. Her sobs and her laughter were getting curiously mixed up together. 'You're a dear and I like you. So much, so much. But you mustn't do that, I don't know why. It spoils everything. I was a goose to cry. But somehow . . .' She shook her head. 'I like you so much,' she repeated. 'But not like that. Not now. Some day, perhaps. Not now. You won't spoil it again? Promise.'

Lord Hovenden promised devoutly. They walked home through the grey night of the olive orchard.

That evening at dinner the conversation turned on feminism. Under pressure from Mr. Cardan, Mrs. Aldwinkle reluctantly admitted that there *was* a considerable difference between Maud Valerie White and Beethoven and that Angelica Kauffmann compared unfavourably with Giotto. But she protested, on the other hand, that in matters of love women were, definitely, treated unfairly.

'We claim *all* your freedom,' she said dramatically.

Knowing that Aunt Lilian liked her to take part in the conversation, and remembering—for she had a good memory—a phrase that her aunt used at one time to employ frequently, but which had recently faded out of the catalogue of her favourite locutions, Irene gravely brought it out. 'Contraception,' she pronounced, 'has rendered chastity superfluous.'

Mr. Carden leaned back in his chair and roared with laughter.

But across the prophetical face of Mr. Falx there passed a pained expression. He looked anxiously at his pupil, hoping that he had not heard, or at least had not understood what had just been said. He caught Mr. Cardan's winking eye and frowned. Could corruption and moral laxity go further? his glance seemed to inquire. He looked at Irene; that such a youthful, innocent appearance should be wedded to so corrupt a mind appalled him. He felt glad, for Hovenden's sake, that their stay in this bad house was not to last much longer. If it were not for the necessity of behaving politely, he would have left the place at once; like Lot, he would have shaken the dust of it from his feet.

Chapter V

'WHEN the butcher's boy tells you in confidence, and with an eye to a tip, that the grocer's brother has a very fine piece of very old sculpture which he is prepared to part with for a moderate consideration, what do you suppose he means?' Walking slowly up-hill among the olive trees, Mr. Cardan meditatively put the question.

'I suppose he means what he says,' said Miss Thriplow.

'No doubt,' said Mr. Cardan, halting for a moment to wipe his face, which shone, even though the sun came only slantingly through the thin foliage of the olive trees, with an excess of heat. Miss Thriplow in the green uniform of the musical comedy schoolgirl looked wonderfully cool and neat beside her unbuttoned companion. 'But the point is this: what exactly is it that he says? What is a butcher's boy likely to mean when he says that a piece of sculpture is very beautiful and very old?' They resumed their climbing. Below them, through a gap in the trees, they could see the roofs and the slender tower of the Cybo Malaspina palace, and below these again the dolls' village of Vezza, the map-like plain, the sea.

'I should ask him, if you want to know.' Miss Thriplow spoke rather tartly; it was not to talk of butchers' boys that she had accepted Mr. Cardan's invitation to go for a walk with him. She wanted to hear Mr. Cardan's views on life, literature and herself. He knew a thing or two, it seemed to her, about all these subjects. Too many things, and not exactly the right ones at that, about the last. Too many—it was precisely for that reason that Miss Thriplow liked to talk with him. Horrors always exercise a fascination. And now, after the prolonged silence, he was starting on butchers' boys.

'I have asked him,' said Mr. Cardan. 'But do you suppose there's anything intelligible to be got out of him? All I can gather is that the sculpture represents a man—not a whole man, part of a man, and that it's made of marble. Beyond that I can discover nothing.'

'Why do you want to discover?' asked Miss Thriplow.

Mr. Cardan shook his head. 'Alas,' he said, 'for sordid reasons. You remember what the poet wrote?

> I have been in love, in debt and in drink
> This many and many a year;
> And these are three evils too great, one would think,
> For one poor mortal to bear.
> 'Twas love that first drove me to drinking,
> And drinking first drove me to debt,
> And though I have struggled and struggled and strove,
> I cannot get out of them yet.
> There's nothing but money can cure me
> And ease me of all my pain;
> 'Twill pay all my debts and remove all my lets,
> And my mistress who cannot endure me
> Will turn to and love me again,
> Will turn to and love me again.

There's a summary of a lifetime for you. One has no regrets, of course. But still, one does need cash—needs it the more, alas, the older one grows, and has less of it. What other reason, do you think, would send me sweating up this hill to talk with the village grocer about his brother's statuary?'

'You mean that you'd buy it if it were worth anything?'

'At the lowest possible price,' confirmed Mr. Cardan. 'And sell it at the highest. If I had ever adopted a profession,' he continued, 'I think it would have been art dealing. It has the charm of being more dishonest than almost any other form of licensed brigandage in existence. And dishonest, moreover, in a much more amusing way. Financiers, it is true, can swindle on a larger scale; but their swindling is mostly impersonal. You may ruin thousands of trusting investors; but you haven't the pleasure of knowing your victims. Whereas if you're an art dealer, your swindling, though less extensive, is most amusingly personal. You meet your victims face to face and do them down. You take advantage of the ignorance or urgent poverty of the vendor to get the work for nothing. You then exploit the snobbery and the almost equally profound ignorance of the rich buyer to make him take the stuff off your hands at some fantastic price. What huge elation one must feel when one has succeeded in bringing off some splendid *coup*! bought a blackened panel from some decayed gentleman in need of a new suit, cleaned it up and sold it again to a rich snob who thinks that a collection and the reputation of being a patron of the ancient arts will give him a leg up in society—what vast Rabelaisian mirth! No, decidedly if I were not Diogenes and idle, I would be Alexander, critic and dealer. A really gentlemanly profession.'

'Can you never be serious?' asked Miss Thriplow, who would have preferred the conversation to turn on something more nearly related to her own problems.

Mr. Cardan smiled at her. 'Can anybody fail to be serious when it's a question of making money?'

'I give you up,' said Miss Thriplow.

'I'm sorry,' Mr. Cardan protested. 'But perhaps it's all for the best. Meanwhile, what about that butcher's boy? What *does* he mean by a bit of very old sculpture? Is it the head of some rich Etruscan cheese-monger of Lunae that they've dug up? Some long-nosed primitive oriental with a smile of imbecile rapture on his face? Or a fragment of one of his Hellenized posterity, reclining on the lid of his sarcophagus as though along his prandial couch and staring blankly out of a head that might, if Praxiteles had carved it, have been Apollo's, but which the Etruscan mason has fattened into an all too human grossness? Or perhaps it's a Roman bust, so thoroughly real, life-like and up-to-date that, but for the toga, we might almost take it for our old friend Sir William Midrash, the eminent civil servant. Or perhaps—and I should like that better—perhaps it dates from that strange, grey Christian dawn that followed the savage night into which the empire went down. I can imagine some fragment from Modena or Toscanella—some odd, unpredictable figure bent by excess of faith into the most profoundly expressive and symbolic of attitudes: a monster physically, a barbarism, a little mumbo-jumbo, but glowing so passionately with inward life—it may be lovely, it may be malignant—that it is impossible to look at it with indifference or merely as a shape, ugly or beautiful. Yes. I should like the thing to be a piece of Romanesque carving. I'd give the butcher's boy an extra five francs if it were. But if it turned out to be one of those suave Italian Gothic saints elegantly draped and leaning a little sideways, like saplings in the mystical breeze—and it might be, you never can tell—I'd deduct five francs. Not but what it mightn't fetch just as much in the American market. But how they bore me, those accomplished Gothicisms, how they bore me!'

They were at the top of the hill. Emerging from the sloping forest of olive trees, the road now ran along a bare and almost level ridge. Some little way off, where the ground began to rise once more towards further heights, one could see a cluster of houses and a church tower. Mr. Cardan pointed.

'There,' he said, 'we shall find out what the butcher's boy really did mean. But in the meantime it's amusing to go on speculating. For example, suppose it were a chunk of a bas-relief designed by Giotto. Eh? Something so grand, so spiritually and materially beautiful that you could fall down and worship it. But I'd be very well pleased, I assure you, with a bit of a sarcophagus from the earliest renaissance. Some figure marvellously bright, ethereal and pure, like an angel, but an angel, not of the kingdom of heaven; an angel of some splendid and, alas, imaginary kingdom of earth. Ah,' pursued Mr. Cardan, shaking his head, 'that's the kingdom one would like to live in—the kingdom of ancient Greece, purged of every historical Greek that ever existed, and colonized out of the imaginations of modern artists, scholars and philosophers. In such a world one might live positively, so to speak—live with the stream, in the direction of the main current—not negatively, as one has to now, in reaction against the general trend of existence.'

Positive and negative living. Miss Thriplow made a mental note of the notions. It might be an idea to work up in an article. It might even throw light on her own problems. Perhaps what one suffered from was the sense of being negative and in reaction. More positiveness—that was what one needed. The conversation, she thought, seemed to be growing more serious. They walked on for a moment in silence. Mr. Cardan broke it at last.

'Or can it possibly be,' he said, 'that the grocer's brother has lighted on some fragmentary rough-hewing by Michelangelo, begun in a frenzy while he was living among these mountains and abandoned when he left them? Some tormented Slave, struggling to free himself more of his inward than his outward chains; straining with more than human violence, but at the same time pensively, with a passion concentrated upon itself instead of explosively dissipated, as in the baroque, which all too fatally and easily developed out of him? And after all our hopes and speculations, that's what my treasure will probably resolve itself into—a bit of seventeenth-century baroque. I picture the torso of a waltzing angel in the middle of a whirlwind of draperies turning up to heaven the ecstatic eye of the clergyman in a Lyceum melodrama; or perhaps a Bacchus, dancing by a miracle of virtuosity on one marble leg, his mouth open in a tipsy laugh and the fingers of both hands splayed out to their fullest extent, just to show what can be done by a sculptor who knows his business; or the bust of a prince, prodigiously alive and characteristic, wearing a collar of Brussels lace imitated in stone down to the finest thread. The butcher's boy kept on insisting that the thing was very beautiful as well as very old. And it's obvious, now I come to think of it, that he'd really and sincerely like baroque and baroque only, just because it would be so familiar to him, because it would be just like everything he had been brought up to admire. For by some strange and malignant fate the Italians, once arrived at baroque, seem to have got stuck there. They are still up to the eyes in it. Consider their literature, their modern painting and architecture, their music—it's all baroque. It gesticulates rhetorically, it struts across stages, it sobs and bawls in its efforts to show you how passionate it is. In the midst, like a huge great Jesuit church, stands d'Annunzio.'

'I should have thought,' said Miss Thriplow with barbed ingenuousness, 'that you'd have liked that sort of elaboration and virtuosity. It's "amusing"—isn't that the word?'

'True,' answered Mr. Cardan, 'I like being amused. But I demand from my art the added luxury of being moved. And, somehow, one can't feel emotion about anything so furiously and consciously emotional as these baroque things. It's not by making wild and passionate gestures that an artist can awake emotion in the spectator. It isn't done that way. These seventeenth-century Italians tried to express passion by making use of passionate gestures. They only succeeded in producing something that either leaves us cold—though it may, as you say, amuse us—or which actually makes us laugh. Art which is to move its contemplator must itself be still; it is almost an aesthetic law. Passion must never be allowed to dissipate itself in wild splashings and boilings over. It must be shut up, so to speak, and compressed and moulded by the intellect. Concentrated within a calm, untroubled form, its strength will irresistibly move. Styles that protest too much are not fit for serious, tragical use. They are by nature suited to comedy, whose essence is exaggeration. That is why good romantic art is so rare. Romanticism, of which the seventeenth-century baroque style is a queer sub-species, makes violent gestures; it relies on violent contrasts of light and shade, on stage effects; it is ambitious to present you with emotion in the raw and palpitating form. That is to say, the romantic style is in essence a comic style. And, except in the hands of a few colossal geniuses, romantic art is, in point of historical fact, almost always comic. Think of all the hair-raising romances written during the later eighteenth and earlier nineteenth centuries; now that the novelty has worn off them, we perceive them for what they are—the broadest comedies. Even writers of a great and genuine talent were betrayed by the essentially comic nature of the style into being farcical when they meant to be romantically tragical. Balzac, for example, in a hundred serious passages; George Sand in all her earlier novels; Beddoes, when he tries to make his *Death's Jest Book* particularly blood-curdling; Byron in *Cain*; de Musset in *Rolla*. And what prevents Herman Melville's *Moby Dick* from being a really great book is precisely the pseudo-Shakespearean idiom in which what are meant to be the most tragical passages are couched—an idiom to whose essential suitability to comedy the exceptional tragic successes of Shakespeare himself, of Marlowe and a few others has unfortunately blinded all their imitators. Moreover, if the romantic style is essentially fitted to comedy, it is also true, conversely, that the greatest comic works have been written in a romantic style. *Pantagruel* and the *Contes Drolatiques*; the conversation of Falstaff and Wilkins Micawber; Aristophanes' *Frogs*; *Tristram Shandy*. And who will deny that the finest passages in Milton's reverberating prose are precisely those where he is writing satirically and comically? A comic writer is a very large and copious man with a zest for all that is earthy, who unbuttons himself and lets himself freely go, following wherever his indefatigably romping spirit leads him. The unrestrained, exaggerated, wildly gesticulating manner which is the romantic manner exactly fulfils his need.'

Miss Thriplow listened with growing attention. This was serious; moreover, it seemed really to touch her own problems. In her new novel she had done her best to throw off the light satiric vestments in which, in the past, she had clothed her tendernesses; this time, she had decided to give the public her naked heart. Mr. Cardan was making her wonder whether she wasn't exposing it in too palpitating a manner.

'When you come to pictorial art,' Mr. Cardan went on, 'you find that seriousness and romanticism are even less frequently combined than in literature. The greatest triumphs of the nineteenth-century romantic style are to be found precisely among the comedians and the makers of grotesques. Daumier, for example, produced at once the most comic and the most violently romantic pictures ever made. And Doré, when he ceased from trying to paint serious pictures in the romantic style—with what involuntarily ludicrous results I leave you to recall to mind—and applied himself to illustrating *Don Quixote* and the *Contes Drolatiques* in the same romantic terms, Doré produced masterpieces. Indeed, the case of Doré quite clinches my argument. Here was a man who did precisely the same romantic things in both his serious and his comic works, and who succeeded in making what was meant to be sublime ludicrous and what was meant to be ludicrous sublime in its rich, extravagant, romantic grotesqueness.'

They had passed the outlying houses of the village and were walking slowly up its single, steep street.

'That's very true,' said Miss Thriplow pensively. She was wondering whether she oughtn't to tone down a little that description in her new novel of the agonies of the young wife when she discovers that her husband had been unfaithful to her. A dramatic moment, that. The young wife has just had her first baby—with infinite suffering—and now, still very frail, but infinitely happy, lies convalescent. The handsome young husband, whom she adores and who, she supposes, adores her, comes in with the afternoon post. He sits down by her bed, and putting the bunch of letters on the counterpane begins opening his correspondence. She opens hers too. Two boring notes. She tosses them aside. Without looking at the address, she opens another envelope, unfolds the sheet within and reads: 'Doodlums darling, I shall be waiting for you to-morrow evening in our love-nest. . . .' She looks at the envelope; it is addressed to her husband. Her feelings . . . Miss Thriplow wondered; yes, perhaps, in the light of what Mr. Cardan had been saying, the passage was a little too palpitating. Particularly that bit where the baby is brought in to be suckled. Miss Thriplow sighed; she'd read through the chapter critically when she got home.

'Well,' said Mr. Cardan, interrupting the course of her thoughts, 'here we are. It only remains to find out where the grocer lives, and to find out from the grocer where his brother lives, and to find out from the brother what his treasure is and how much he wants for it, and then to find some one to buy it for fifty thousand pounds—and we'll live happily ever after. What?'

He stopped a passing child and put his question. The child pointed up the street. They walked on.

At the door of his little shop sat the grocer, unoccupied at the moment, taking the sun and air and looking on at such stray drops from the flux of life as trickled occasionally along the village street. He was a stout man with a large fleshy face that looked as though it had been squeezed perpendicularly, so broadly it bulged, so close to one another the horizontal lines of eyes, nose and mouth. His cheeks and chin were black with five days' beard—for to-day was Thursday and shaving-time only came round on Saturday evening. Small, sly, black eyes looked out from between pouchy lids. He had thick lips, and his teeth when he smiled were yellow. A long white apron, unexpectedly clean, was tied at neck and waist and fell down over his knees. It was the apron that struck Miss Thriplow's imagination—the apron and the thought that this man wore it, draped round him like an ephod, when he was cutting up ham and sausages, when he was serving out sugar with a little shovel. . . .

'How extraordinarily nice and jolly he looks!' she said enthusiastically, as they approached.

'Does he?' asked Mr. Cardan in some surprise. To his eyes the man looked like a hardly mitigated ruffian.

'So simple and happy and contented!' Miss Thriplow went on. 'One envies them their lives.' She could almost have wept over the little shovel—momentarily the masonic emblem of prelapsarian ingenuousness. 'We make everything so unnecessarily complicated for ourselves, don't we?'

'Do we?' said Mr. Cardan.

'These people have no doubts, or after-thoughts,' pursued Miss Thriplow, 'or—what's worse than after-thoughts—simultaneous-thoughts. They know what they want and what's right; they feel just what they ought to feel by nature—like the heroes in the *Iliad*—and act accordingly. And the result is, I believe, that they're much better than we are, much gooder, we used to say when we were children; the word's more expressive. Yes, much gooder. Now you're laughing at me!'

Mr. Cardan twinkled at her with benevolent irony. 'I assure you I'm not,' he declared.

'But I shouldn't mind if you were,' said Miss Thriplow. 'For after all, in spite of all that you people may say or think, it's the only thing that matters—being good.'

'I entirely agree,' said Mr. Cardan.

'And it's easier if you're like that.' She nodded in the direction of the white apron.

Mr. Cardan nodded, a little dubiously.

'Sometimes,' Miss Thriplow continued, with a gush of confidence that made her words come more rapidly, 'sometimes, when I get on a bus and take my ticket from the conductor, I suddenly feel the tears come into my eyes at the thought of this life, so simple and straightforward, so easy to live well, even if it is a hard one—and perhaps, too, just because it is a hard one. Ours is so difficult.' She shook her head.

By this time they were within a few yards of the shopkeeper, who, seeing that they were proposing to enter his shop, rose from his seat at the door and darted in to take up his stand, professionally, behind the counter.

They followed him into the shop. It was dark within

and filled with a violent smell of goat's milk cheese, pickled tunny, tomato preserve and highly flavoured sausage.

'Whee-ew!' said Miss Thriplow, and pulling out a small handkerchief, she took refuge with the ghost of Parma violets. It was a pity that these simple lives in white aprons had to be passed amid such surroundings.

'Rather deafening, eh?' said Mr. Cardan, twinkling. 'Puzza,' he added, turning to the shopkeeper. 'It stinks.'

The man looked at Miss Thriplow, who stood there, her nose in the oasis of her handkerchief, and smiled indulgently. 'I forestieri sono troppo delicati. Troppo delicati,' he repeated.

'He's quite right,' said Mr. Cardan. 'We are. In the end, I believe, we shall come to sacrifice everything to comfort and cleanliness. Personally, I always have the greatest suspicion of your perfectly hygienic and well-padded Utopias. As for this particular stink,' he sniffed the air, positively with relish, 'I don't really know what you have to object to it. It's wholesome, it's natural, it's tremendously historical. The shops of the Etruscan grocers, you may be sure, smelt just as this does. No, on the whole, I entirely agree with our friend here.'

'Still,' said Miss Thriplow, speaking in a muffled voice through the folds of her handkerchief, 'I shall stick to my violets. However synthetic.'

Having ordered a couple of glasses of wine, one of which he offered to the grocer, Mr. Cardan embarked on a diplomatic conversation about the object of his visit. At the mention of his brother and the sculpture, the grocer's face took on an expression of altogether excessive amiability. He bent his thick lips into smiles; deep folds in the shape ot arcs of circles appeared in his fat cheeks. He kept bowing again and again. Every now and then he joyously laughed, emitting a blast of garlicky breath that smelt so powerfully like acetylene that one was tempted to put a match to his mouth in the hope that he would immediately break out into a bright white flame. He confirmed all that the butcher's boy had said. It was all quite true; he had a brother; and his brother had a piece of marble statuary that was beautiful and old, old, old. Unfortunately, however, his brother had removed from this village and had gone down to live in the plain, near the lake of Massaciuccoli, and the sculpture had gone with him. Mr. Cardan tried to find out from him what the work of art looked like; but he could gather nothing beyond the fact that it was beautiful and old and represented a man.

'It isn't like this, I suppose?' asked Mr. Cardan, bending himself into the attitude of a Romanesque demon and making a demoniac grimace.

The grocer thought not. Two peasant women who had come in for cheese and oil looked on with a mild astonishment. These foreigners . . .

'Or like this?' He propped his elbow on the counter and, half reclining, conjured up, by his attitude and his fixed smile of imbecile ecstasy, visions of Etruscan revelry.

Again the grocer shook his head.

'Or like this?' He rolled his eyes towards heaven, like a baroque saint.

But the grocer seemed doubtful even of this.

Mr. Cardan wiped his forehead. 'If I could make myself look like a Roman bust,' he said to Miss Thriplow, 'or a bas-relief of Giotto, or a renaissance sarcophagus, or an unfinished group by Michelangelo, I would. But it's beyond my powers.' He shook his head. 'For the moment I give it up.'

He took out his pocket-book and asked for the brother's address. The grocer gave directions; Mr. Cardan carefully took them down. Smiling and bowing, the grocer ushered them out into the street, Miss Thriplow vailed her handkerchief and drew a breath of air—redolent, however, even here, of organic chemistry.

'Patience,' said Mr. Cardan, 'tenacity of purpose. One needs them here.'

They walked slowly down the street. They had only gone a few yards when the noise of a violent altercation made them turn round. At the door of the shop the grocer and his two customers were furiously disputing. Voices were raised, the grocer's deep and harsh, the women's shrill; hands moved in violent and menacing gestures, yet gracefully withal, as was natural in the hands of those whose ancestors had taught the old masters of painting all they ever knew of expressive and harmonious movement.

'What is it?' asked Miss Thriplow. 'It looks like the preliminaries of a murder.'

Mr. Cardan smiled and shrugged his shoulders. 'It's nothing,' he said. 'They're just calling him a robber; that's all.' He listened for a moment more to the shouting. 'A little question of short weight, it seems.' He smiled at Miss Thriplow. 'Should we go on?'

They turned away; the sound of the dispute followed them down the street. Miss Thriplow did not know whether to be grateful to Mr. Cardan for saying nothing more about her friend in the white apron. These simple folk . . . the little shovel for the sugar . . . so much better, so much *gooder* than we. . . . In the end she almost wished that he would say something about it. Mr. Cardan's silence seemed more ironic than any words.

Chapter VI

THE sun had set. Against a pale green sky the blue and purple mountains lifted a jagged silhouette. Mr. Cardan found himself alone in the middle of the flat plain at their feet. He was standing on the bank of a broad ditch, brimming with gleaming water, that stretched away in a straight line apparently for miles across the land, to be lost in the vague twilight distance. Here and there a line of tall thin poplars marked the position of other dykes, intersecting the plain in all directions. There was not a house in sight, not a human being, not even a cow or a grazing donkey. Far away on the slopes of the mountains, whose blue and purple were rapidly darkening to a uniform deep indigo, little yellow lights began to appear, singly or in clusters, attesting the presence of a village or a solitary farm. Mr. Cardan looked at them with irritation; very pretty, no doubt, but he had seen it done better on many musical comedy stages. And in any case, what was the good of a light six or seven miles away, on the hills, when he was standing in the middle of the plain, with nobody in sight, night coming on, and these horrible ditches to prevent one from taking the obvious bee-line towards civilization? He had been a fool, he reflected, three or four times over: a fool to refuse Lilian's offer of the car and go on foot (this fetish of exercise! still, he would certainly have to cut down his drinking if he didn't take it); a fool to have started so late in the afternoon; a fool to have accepted Italian estimates of distance; and a fool to have followed directions for finding the way given by people who mixed up left and right and, when you insisted on knowing which they meant, told you that either would bring you where you wanted to go. The path which Mr. Cardan had been following seemed to have come to a sudden end in the waters of this ditch; perhaps it was a suicides' path. The lake of Massaciuccoli should be somewhere on the further side of the ditch; but where? and how to get across? The twilight rapidly deepened. In a few minutes the sun would have gone down its full eighteen degrees below the horizon and it would be wholly dark. Mr. Cardan swore; but that got him no further. In the end he decided that the best thing to do would be to walk slowly and cautiously along this ditch, in the hope that in time one might arrive, at any rate somewhere. Meanwhile, it would be well to fortify oneself with a bite and a sup. He sat down on the grass and opening his jacket, dipped into the capacious poacher's pockets excavated in its lining, producing first a loaf, then a few inches of a long polony, then a bottle of red wine; Mr. Cardan was always prepared against emergencies.

The bread was stale, the sausage rather horsey and spiced with garlic; but Mr. Cardan, who had had no tea, ate with a relish. Still more appreciatively he drank. In a little while he felt a little more cheerful. Such are the little crosses, he reflected philosophically, the little crosses one has to bear when one sets out to earn money. If he got through the evening without falling into a ditch, he'd feel that he had paid lightly for his treasure. The greatest bore was these mosquitoes; he lighted a cigar and tried to fumigate them to a respectful distance. Without much success, however. Perhaps the brutes were malarial, too. There might be a little of the disease still hanging about in these marshes; one never knew. It would be tiresome to end one's days with recurrent fever and an enlarged spleen. It would be tiresome, for that matter, to end one's days anyhow, in one's bed or out, naturally or unnaturally, by the act of God or of the King's enemies. Mr. Cardan's thoughts took on, all at once, a dismal complexion. Old age, sickness, decrepitude; the bath-chair, the doctor, the bright efficient nurse; and the long agony, the struggle for breath, the thickening darkness, the end, and then—how did that merry little song go?

> More work for the undertaker,
> 'Nother little job for the coffin-maker.
> At the local cemetery they are
> Very very busy with a brand new grave.
> He'll keep warm next winter.

Mr. Cardan hummed the tune to himself cheerfully enough. But his tough, knobbly face became so hard, so strangely still, an expression of such bitterness, such a profound melancholy, appeared in his winking and his supercilious eye, that it would have startled and frightened a man to look at him. But there was nobody in that deepening twilight to see him. He sat there alone.

> At the local cemetery they are
> Very very busy with a brand new grave . . .

He went on humming. 'If I were to fall sick,' he was thinking, 'who would look after me? Suppose one were to have a stroke. Hemorrhage on the brain; partial paralysis; mumbling speech; the tongue couldn't utter what the brain thought; one was fed like a baby; clysters; such a bright doctor, rubbing his hands and smelling of disinfectant and eau-de-Cologne; saw nobody but the nurse; no friends; or once a week, perhaps, for an hour, out of charity; "Poor old Cardan, done for, I'm afraid; must send the old chap a fiver—hasn't a penny, you know; get up a subscription; what a bore; astonishing that he can last so long. . . ."'

> He'll keep warm next winter.

The tune ended on a kind of trumpet call, rising from the dominant to the tonic—one dominant, three repeated tonics, drop down again to the dominant and then on the final syllable of 'winter' the last tonic. Finis, and no *de capo*, no second movement.

Mr. Cardan took another swig from his bottle; it was nearly empty now

Perhaps one ought to have married. Kitty, for example. She would be old now and fat; or old and thin, like a skeleton very imperfectly disguised. Still, he had been very much in love with Kitty. Perhaps it would have been a good thing if he had married her. Pooh! with a burst of mocking laughter Mr. Cardan laughed aloud savagely. Marry indeed! She looked very coy, no doubt; but you bet, she was a little tart underneath, and lascivious as you make them. He remembered her with hatred and contempt. Portentous obscenities reverberated through the chambers of his mind.

He thought of arthritis, he thought of gout, of cataract, of deafness. . . . And in any case, how many years were left him? Ten, fifteen, twenty if he were exceptional. And what years, what years!

Mr. Cardan emptied the bottle and replacing the cork threw it into the black water beneath him. The wine had done nothing to improve his mood. He wished to God he were back at the palace, with people round him to talk to. Alone, he was without defence. He tried to think of something lively and amusing; indoor sports, for example. But instead of indoor sports he found himself contemplating visions of disease, decrepitude, death. And it was the same when he tried to think of reasonable, serious things: what is art, for example? and what was the survival value to a species of eyes or wings or protective colouring in their rudimentary state, before they were developed far enough to see, fly or protect? Why should the individuals having the first and still quite useless variation in the direction of something useful have survived more effectively than those who were handicapped by no eccentricity? Absorbing themes. But Mr. Cardan couldn't keep his attention fixed on them. General paralysis of the insane, he reflected, was luckily an ailment for which he had not qualified in the past; luckily! miraculously, even! But stone, but neuritis, but fatty degeneration, but diabetes. . . . Lord, how he wished he had somebody to talk to!

And all at once, as though in immediate answer to his

prayer, he heard the sound of voices approaching through the now complete darkness. 'Thank the Lord!' said Mr. Cardan, and scrambling to his feet he walked in the direction from which the voices came. Two black silhouettes, one tall and masculine, the other, very small, belonging to a woman, loomed up out of the dark. Mr. Cardan removed the cigar from his mouth, took off his hat and bowed in their direction.

'*Nel mezzo del cammin di nostra vita*,' he began,
'*mi ritrovai per una selva oscura,*
che la diritta via era smarrita.'

How lucky that Dante should also have lost his way, six hundred and twenty-four years ago! 'In a word,' Mr. Cardan went on, '*ho perso la mia strada*—though I have my doubts whether that's very idiomatic. *Forse potrebbero darmi qualche indicazione.*' In the presence of the strangers and at the sound of his own voice conversing, all Mr. Cardan's depression had vanished. He was delighted by the fantastic turn he had managed to give the conversation at its inception. Perhaps with a little ingenuity he would be able to find an excuse for treating them to a little Leopardi. It was so amusing to astonish the natives.

The two silhouettes, meanwhile, had halted at a little distance. When Mr. Cardan had finished his macaronic self-introduction, the taller of them answered in a harsh and, for a man's, a shrill voice: 'There's no need to talk Italian. We're English.'

'I'm enchanted to hear it,' Mr. Cardan protested. And he explained at length and in his mother tongue what had happened to him. It occurred to him, at the same time, that this was a very odd place to find a couple of English tourists.

The harsh voice spoke again. 'There's a path to Massarosa through the fields,' it said. 'And there's another, in the opposite direction, that joins the Viareggio road. But they're not very easy to find in the dark, and there are a lot of ditches.'

'One can but perish in the attempt,' said Mr. Cardan gallantly.

This time it was the woman who spoke. 'I think it would be better,' she said, 'if you slept at our house for the night. You'll never find the way. I almost tumbled into the ditch myself just now.' She laughed shrilly and more loudly, Mr. Cardan thought, at greater length, than was necessary.

'But have we room?' asked the man in a tone which showed that he was very reluctant to receive a guest.

'But you know we've got room,' the feminine voice answered in a tone of child-like astonishment. 'It's rough, though.'

'That doesn't matter in the least,' Mr. Cardan assured her. 'I'm most grateful to you for your offer,' he added, making haste to accept the invitation before the man could take it back. He had no desire to go wandering at night among these ditches. Moreover, the prospect of having company, and odd company, he guessed, was alluring. 'Most grateful,' he repeated.

'Well, if you think there's room,' said the man grudgingly.

'Of course there is,' the feminine voice replied, and laughed again. 'Isn't it six spare rooms that we've got? or is it seven? Come with us, Mr. . . . Mr. . . .'

'Cardan.'

'. . . Mr. Cardan. We're going straight home. Such fun,' she added, and repeated her excessive laughter.

Mr. Cardan accompanied them, talking as agreeably as he could all the time. The man listened in a gloomy silence. But his sister—Mr. Cardan had discovered that they were brother and sister and that their name was Elver—laughed heartily at the end of each of Mr. Cardan's sentences, as though everything he said were a glorious joke; laughed extravagantly and then made some remark which showed that she could have had no idea what Mr. Cardan had meant. Mr. Cardan found himself making his conversation more and more elementary, until as they approached their destination it was frankly addressed to a child of ten.

'Here we are at last,' she said, as they emerged from the denser night of a little wood of poplar trees. In front of them rose the large square mass of a house, utterly black but for a single lighted window.

To the door, when they knocked, came an old woman with a candle. By its light Mr. Cardan saw his hosts for the first time. That the man was tall and thin he had seen even without the light; he revealed himself now as a stooping, hollow-chested creature of about forty, with long spidery legs and arms and a narrow yellow face, long-nosed, not too powerfully chinned, and lit by small and furtive grey eyes that looked mostly on the ground and seemed afraid of encountering other eyes. Mr. Cardan fancied there was something faintly clerical about his appearance. The man might be a broken-down clergyman—broken-down and possibly, when one considered the furtive eyes, unfrocked as well. He was dressed in a black suit, well cut and not old, but baggy at the knees and bulgy about the pockets of the coat. The nails of his long bony hands were rather dirty and his dark brown hair was too long above the ears and at the back of his neck.

Miss Elver was nearly a foot shorter than her brother; but she looked as though Nature had originally intended to make her nearly as tall. For her head was too large for her body and her legs too short. One shoulder was higher than the other. In face she somewhat resembled her brother. One saw in it the same long nose, but better shaped, the same weakness of chin; compensated for, however, by an amiable, ever-smiling mouth and large hazel eyes, not at all furtive or mistrustful, but on the contrary exceedingly confiding in their glance, albeit blank and watery in their brightness and not more expressive than the eyes of a young child. Her age, Mr. Cardan surmised, was twenty-eight or thirty. She wore a queer little shapeless dress, like a sack with holes in it for the head and arms to go through, made of some white material with a large design, that looked like an inferior version of the willow pattern, printed on it in bright red. Round her neck she wore two or three sets of gaudy beads. There were bangles on her wrists, and she carried a little reticule made of woven gold chains.

Using gesture to supplement his scanty vocabulary, Mr. Elver gave instructions to the old woman. She left him the candle and went out. Holding the light high, he led the way from the hall into a large room. They sat down on hard uncomfortable chairs round the empty hearth.

'Such an uncomfy house!' said Miss Elver. 'You know I don't like Italy much.'

'Dear, dear,' said Mr. Cardan. 'That's bad. Don't you even like Venice? All the boats and gondolas?' And meeting those blank infantile eyes, he felt that he might almost go on about there being no gee-gees. The cat is on the mat; the pig in the gig is a big pig; the lass on the ass a crass lass. And so on.

'Venice?' said Miss Elver. 'I've not been there.'

'Florence, then. Don't you like Florence?'

'Nor there, either.'

'Rome? Naples?'

Miss Elver shook her head.

'We've only been here,' she said. 'All the time.'

Her brother, who had been sitting, bent forward, his elbows on his knees, his hands clasped in front of him, looking down at the floor, broke silence. 'The fact is,' he said in his harsh high voice, 'my sister has to keep quiet; she's doing a rest cure.'

'Here?' asked Mr. Cardan. 'Doesn't she find it a bit hot? Rather relaxing?'

'Yes, it's awfully hot, isn't it?' said Miss Elver. 'I'm always telling Philip that.'

'I should have thought you'd have been better at the sea, or in the mountains,' said Mr. Cardan.

Mr. Elver shook his head. 'The doctors,' he said mysteriously, and did not go on.

'And the risk of malaria?'

'That's all rot,' said Mr. Elver, with so much violence, such indignation, that Mr. Cardan could only imagine that he was a landed proprietor in these parts and meant to develop his estate as a health resort.

'Oh, of course it's mostly been got rid of,' he said mollifyingly. 'The Maremma isn't what it was.'

Mr. Elver said nothing, but scowled at the floor.

Chapter VII

THE dining-room was also large and bare. Four candles burned on the long narrow table; their golden brightness faded in the remoter corners to faint twilight; the shadows were huge and black. Entering, Mr. Cardan could fancy himself Don Juan walking down to supper in the Commander's vault.

Supper was at once dismal and exceedingly lively. While his sister chattered and laughed unceasingly with her guest, Mr. Elver preserved throughout the meal an unbroken silence. Gloomily he ate his way through the mixed and fragmentary meal which the old woman kept bringing in, relay after unexpected relay, on little dishes from the kitchen. Gloomily too, with the air of a weak man who drinks to give himself courage and the illusion of strength, he drank glass after glass of the strong red wine. He kept his eyes fixed most of the time on the table-cloth in front of his plate; but every now and then he would look up for a second to dart a glance at the other two—for a moment only, then, fearful of being caught in the act and looked at straight in the face, he turned away again.

Mr. Cardan enjoyed his supper. Not that the food was particularly good; it was not. The old woman was one of those inept practitioners of Italian cookery who disguise their shortcomings under floods of tomato sauce, with a pinch of garlic thrown in to make the disguise impenetrable. No, what Mr. Cardan enjoyed was the company. It was a long time since he had sat down with such interesting specimens. One's range, he reflected, is altogether too narrowly limited. One doesn't know enough people; one's acquaintanceship isn't sufficiently diversified. Burglars, for example, millionaires, imbeciles, clergymen, Hottentots, sea captains—one's personal knowledge of these most interesting human species is quite absurdly small. To-night, it seemed to him, he was doing something to widen his range.

'I'm so glad we met you,' Miss Elver was saying. 'In the dark—such a start you gave me too!' She shrieked with laughter. 'We were getting so dull here. Weren't we, Phil?' She appealed to her brother; but Mr. Elver said nothing, did not even look up. 'So dull. I'm awfully glad you were there.'

'Not so glad as I am, I assure you,' said Mr. Cardan gallantly.

Miss Elver looked at him for a moment, coyly and confidentially; then putting up her hand to her face, as though she were screening herself from Mr. Cardan's gaze, she turned away, tittering. Her face became quite red. She peeped at him between her fingers and tittered again.

It occurred to Mr. Cardan that he'd be in for a breach of promise case very soon if he weren't careful. Tactfully he changed the subject; asked her what sort of food she liked best and learned that her favourites were strawberries, cream ice and mixed chocolates.

The dessert had been eaten. Mr. Elver suddenly looked up and said: 'Grace, I think you ought to go to bed.'

Miss Elver's face, from having been bright with laughter, became at once quite overcast. A film of tears floated up into her eyes, making them seem more lustrous; she looked at her brother appealingly. 'Must I go?' she said. 'Just this once!' She tried to coax him. 'This once!'

But Mr. Elver was not to be moved. 'No, no,' he said sternly. 'You must go.'

His sister sighed and made a little whimpering sound. But she got up, all the same, and walked obediently towards the door. She was almost on the threshold, when she halted, turned and ran back to say good-night to Mr. Cardan. 'I'm so glad,' she said, 'that we found you. Such fun. Good-night. But you mustn't look at me like that.' She put up her hand again to her face. 'Oh, not like that.' And still giggling, she ran out of the room.

There was a long silence.

'Have some wine,' said Mr. Elver at last, and pushed the flask in Mr. Cardan's direction.

Mr. Cardan replenished his glass and then, politely, did the same for his host. Wine—it was the only thing that was likely to make this dismal devil talk. With his practised and professional eye, Mr. Cardan thought he could detect in his host's expression certain hardly perceptible symptoms of incipient tipsiness. A spidery creature like that, thought Mr. Cardan contemptuously, couldn't be expected to hold his liquor well; and he had been putting it down pretty steadily all through supper. A little more and, Mr. Cardan was confident, he'd be as clay in the hands of a sober interrogator (and Mr. Cardan could count on being sober for at least three bottles longer than a poor feeble creature like this); he'd talk, he'd talk; the only difficulty would be to get him to stop talking.

'Thanks,' said Mr. Elver, and gloomily gulped down the replenished glass.

That's the style, thought Mr. Cardan; and in his liveliest manner he began to tell the story of the grocer's brother's statue and of his pursuit of it, ending up with an account, already more florid than the previous version, of how he lost himself.

'I console myself superstitiously,' he concluded, 'by the reflection that fate wouldn't have put me to these little troubles and inconveniences if it weren't intending to do something handsome by me in the end. I'm paying in advance; but I trust I'm paying for something round and tidy. All the same, what a curse this hunt for money is!'

Mr. Elver nodded. 'It's the root of all evil,' he said, and emptied his glass. Unobtrusively Mr. Cardan replenished it.

'Quite right,' he confirmed. 'And it's twice cursed, if you'll allow me to play Portia for a moment: it curses him that hath—can you think of a single really rich person of your acquaintance who wouldn't be less avaricious, less tyrannous, self-indulgent and generally porkish if he didn't pay supertax? And it also curses him that hath not, making him do all manner of absurd, humiliating, discreditable things which he'd never think of doing if the hedgerows grew breadfruit and bananas and grapes enough to keep one in free food and liquor.'

'It curses him that hath not the most,' said Mr. Elver with a sudden savage animation. This was a subject, evidently, on which he felt deeply. He looked sharply at

Mr. Cardan for a moment, then turned away to dip his long nose once more in his tumbler.

'Perhaps,' said Mr. Cardan judicially. 'At any rate there are more complaints about this curse than about the other. Those that have not complain about their own fate. Those that have do not, it is only those in contact with them—and since the havers are few these too are few—who complain of the curse of having. In my time I have belonged to both categories. Once I had; and I can see that to my fellow men I must then have been intolerable. Now'—Mr. Cardan drew a deep breath and blew it out between trumpeting lips, to indicate the way in which the money had gone—'now I have not. The curse of insolence and avarice has been removed from me. But what low shifts, what abjections this not-having has, by compensation, reduced me to! Swindling peasants out of their artistic property, for example!'

'Ah, but that's not so bad,' cried Mr. Elver excitedly, 'as what I've had to do. That's nothing at all. You've never been an advertisement canvasser.'

'No,' Mr. Cardan admitted, 'I've never been an advertisement canvasser.'

'Then you can't know what the curse of not-having really is. You can't have an idea. You've no right to talk about the curse.' Mr. Elver's harsh, unsteady voice rose and fell excitedly as he talked. 'No right,' he repeated.

'Perhaps I haven't,' said Mr. Cardan mollifyingly. He took the opportunity to pour out some more wine for his host. Nobody has a right, he reflected, to be more miserable than we are. Each one of us is the most unhappily circumstanced creature in the world. Hence it's enormously to our credit that we bear up and get on as well as we do.

'Look here,' Mr. Elver went on confidentially, and he tried to look Mr. Cardan squarely in the face as he spoke; but the effort was too great and he had to avert his eyes;

'look here, let me tell you.' He leaned forward eagerly and slapped the table in front of where Mr. Cardan was sitting to emphasize what he was saying and to call his guest's attention to it. 'My father was a country parson,' he began, talking rapidly and excitedly. 'We were very poor—horribly. Not that he minded much : he used to read Dante all the time. That annoyed my mother—I don't know why. You know the smell of very plain cooking? Steamed puddings—the very thought of them makes me sick now.' He shuddered. 'There were four of us then. But my brother was killed in the war and my elder sister died of influenza. So now there's only me and the one you saw to-night.' He tapped his forehead. 'She never grew up, but got stuck somehow. A moron.' He laughed compassionlessly. 'Though I don't know why I need tell you that. For it's obvious enough, isn't it?'

Mr. Cardan said nothing. His host flinched away from his half-winking, half-supercilious gaze, and fortifying himself with another gulp of wine, which Mr. Cardan a moment later unobtrusively made good from the flask, went on :

'Four of us,' he repeated. 'You can imagine it wasn't easy for my father. And my mother died when we were still children. Still, he managed to send us to a rather shabby specimen of the right sort of school, and we'd have gone on to the university if we could have got scholarships. But we didn't.' At this Mr. Elver, on whom the wine seemed quite suddenly to be making its effect, laughed loudly, as though he had made a very good joke. 'So my brother went into an engineering firm, and it was just being arranged, at goodness knows what sort of a sacrifice, that I should be turned into a solicitor, when pop ! my father falls down dead with heart failure. Well, he was all right rambling about the *Paradiso*. But I had to scramble into the nearest job available. That was how I came to be an advertisement canvasser. Oh Lord!' He put his hand over his eyes, as though to shut out some disgusting vision. 'Talk of the curse of not-having! For a monthly magazine it was—the sort of one with masses of little ads for indigestion cures; and electric belts to make you strong; and art by correspondence; and Why Wear a Truss? and superfluous hair-killers; and pills to enlarge the female figure; and labour-saving washing machines on the instalment system; and Learn to Play the Piano without Practising; and thirty-six reproductions of nudes from the Paris Salon for five bob; and drink cures in plain wrapper, strictly confidential, and all the rest. There were hundreds and hundreds of small advertisers. I used to spend all my days running round to shops and offices, cajoling old advertisers to renew or fishing for new ones. And, God! how horrible it was! Worming one's way in to see people who didn't want to see one and to whom one was only a nuisance, a sort of tiresome beggar on the hunt for money. How polite one had to be to insolent underlings, strong in their office and only too delighted to have an opportunity to play the bully in their turn! And then there was that terrible cheerful, frank, manly manner one had to keep up all the time. The "I put it to you, sir," straight from the shoulder business; the persuasive honesty, the earnestness and the frightful pretence one had to keep up so strenuously and continuously that one believed in what one was talking about, thought the old magazine a splendid proposition and regarded the inventor of advertisements as the greatest benefactor the human race has ever known. And what a presence one had to have! I could never achieve a presence, somehow. I could never even look neat. And you had to try and impress the devils as a keen, competent salesman. God, it was awful! And the way some of them would treat you. As the damnedest bore in the world—that was the best you could hope. But sometimes they treated you as a robber and a swindler. It was your fault if an insufficient number of imbeciles hadn't bought galvanic belly bands or learned to play like Busoni without practising. It was your fault; and they'd fly in a rage and curse at you, and you had to be courteous and cheery and tactful and always enthusiastic in the face of it. Good Lord, is there anything more horrible than having to face an angry man? I don't know why, but it's somehow so profoundly humiliating to take part in a squabble, even when one's the aggressor. One feels afterwards that one's no better than a dog. But when one's the victim of somebody else's anger—that's awful. That's simply awful,' he repeated, and brought his hand with a clap on to the table to emphasize his words. 'I'm not built for that sort of thing. I'm not a bully or a fighter. They used to make me almost ill, those scenes. I couldn't sleep, thinking of them—remembering those that were past and looking forward with terror to the ones that were coming. People talk about Dostoievsky's feelings when he was marched out into the barrack square, tied to a post with the firing party lined up in front of him, and then, at the very last second, when his eyes were already bandaged, reprieved. But I tell you I used to go through his experiences half a dozen times a day, nerving myself to face some inevitable interview, the very thought of which made me sick with apprehension. And for me there was no reprieve. The execution was gone through with, to the very end. Good Lord, how often I've hesitated at the door of some old bully's office, all in a bloody sweat, hesitating to cross the threshold. How often I've turned back at the last moment and turned into a pub for a nip of brandy to steady my nerves, or gone to a chemist for a pick-me-up! You can't imagine what I suffered then!' He emptied his glass, as though to drown the rising horror. 'Nobody can imagine,' he repeated, and his voice quivered with the anguish of his self-pity. 'And then how little one got in return! One suffered daily torture for the privilege of being hardly able to live. And all the things one might have done, if one had had capital! To know for an absolute certainty that—given ten thousand—one could turn them into a hundred thousand in two years; to have the whole plan worked out down to its smallest details, to have thought out exactly how one would live when one was rich, and meanwhile to go on living in poverty and squalor and slavery—that's the curse of not-having. That's what *I* suffered.' Overcome by wine and emotion, Mr. Elver burst into tears.

Mr. Cardan patted him on the shoulder. He was too tactful to offer the philosophical consolation that such suffering is the lot of nine-tenths of the human race. Mr. Elver, he could see, would never have forgiven such a denial of his dolorous uniqueness. 'You must have courage,' said Mr. Cardan, and pressing the glass into Mr. Elver's hand he added: 'Drink some of this. It'll do you good.'

Mr. Elver drank and wiped his eyes. 'But I'll make them smart for it one day,' he said, banging the table with his fist. The violent self-pity of a moment ago transformed itself into an equally violent anger. 'I'll make them all pay for what I suffered. When I'm rich.'

'That's the spirit,' said Mr. Cardan encouragingly.

'Thirteen years of it I had,' Mr. Elver went on. 'And two and a half years during the war, dressed in uniform and filling up forms in a wooden hut at Leeds; but that was better than touting for advertisements. Thirteen years. Penal servitude with torture. But I'll pay them, I'll pay them.' He banged the table again.

'Still,' said Mr. Cardan, 'you seem to have got out of it now all right. Living here in Italy is a sign of freedom; at least I hope so.'

At these words Mr. Elver's anger against 'them' suddenly

dropped. His face took on a mysterious and knowing expression. He smiled to himself what was meant to be a dark, secret and satanic smile, a smile that should be all but imperceptible to the acutest eye. But he found, in his tipsiness, that the smile was growing uncontrollably broader and broader; he wanted to grin, to laugh aloud. Not that what he was secretly thinking about was at all funny; it was not, at any rate when he was sober. But now the whole world seemed to swim in a bubbly sea of hilarity. Moreover, the muscles of his face, when he started to smile satanically, had all at once got out of hand and were insisting on expanding what should have been the expression of Lucifer's darkest and most fearful thoughts into a bumpkin's grin. Hastily Mr. Elver extinguished his face in his glass, in the hope of concealing from his guest that rebellious smile. He emerged again choking. Mr. Cardan had to pat him on the back. When it was all over, Mr. Elver reassumed his mysterious expression and nodded significantly. 'Perhaps,' he said darkly, not so much in response to anything Mr. Cardan had said as on general principles, so to speak, and to indicate that the whole situation was in the last degree dubious, dark and contingent—contingent on a whole chain of further contingencies.

Mr. Cardan's curiosity was roused by the spectacle of this queer pantomime; he refilled his host's glass. 'Still,' he insisted, 'if you hadn't freed yourself, how would you be staying here—' in this horrible marsh, he had almost added; but he checked himself and said 'in Italy' instead.

The other shook his head. 'I can't tell you,' he said darkly, and again the satanic smile threatened to enlarge itself to imbecility.

Mr. Cardan relapsed into silence, content to wait. From the expression on Mr. Elver's face he could see that the effort of keeping a secret would be, for his host, intolerably great.

The fruit must be left to ripen of itself. He said nothing and looked pensively into one of the dark corners of the tomb-like chamber as though occupied with his own thoughts.

Mr. Elver sat hunched up in his chair, frowning at the table in front of him. Every now and then he took a sip of wine. Tipsily mutable, his mood changed all at once from hilarious to profoundly gloomy. The silence, the darkness funereally tempered by the four unwavering candles, worked on his mind. What a moment since had seemed an uproarious joke now presented itself to his thoughts as appalling. He felt a great need to unburden himself, to transfer responsibilities on to other shoulders, to get advice that should confirm him in his course. Furtively, for a glimpse only, he looked at his guest. How abstractedly and regardlessly he was staring into vacancy! Not a thought, no sympathy for poor Philip Elver. Ah, if he only knew. . . .

He broke silence at last. 'Tell me,' he said abruptly, and it seemed to his drunken mind that he was displaying an incredible subtlety in his method of approaching the subject; 'do you believe in vivisection?'

Mr. Cardan was surprised by the question. 'Believe in it?' he echoed. 'I don't quite know how one can *believe* in vivisection. I think it useful, if that's what you mean.'

'You don't think it's wrong?'

'No,' said Mr. Cardan.

'You think it doesn't matter cutting up animals?'

'Not if the cutting serves some useful human purpose.'

'You don't think animals have got rights?' pursued Mr. Elver with a clarity and tenacity that, in a drunken man, surprised Mr. Cardan. This was a subject, it was clear, on which Mr. Elver must long have meditated. 'Just like human beings?'

'No,' said Mr. Cardan. 'I'm not one of those fools who

think that one life is as good as another, simply because it *is* a life ; that a grasshopper is as good as a dog and a dog as good as a man. You must recognize a hierarchy of existences.'

'A hierarchy,' exclaimed Mr. Elver, delighted with the word, 'a hierarchy—that's it. That's exactly it. A hierarchy. And among human beings too?' he added.

'Yes, of course,' Mr. Cardan affirmed. 'The life of the soldier who killed Archimedes isn't worth the life of Archimedes. It's the fundamental fallacy of democracy and humanitarian Christianity to suppose that it is. Though of course,' Mr. Cardan added pensively, 'one has no justifying reason for saying so, but only one's instinctive taste. For the soldier, after all, may have been a good husband and father, may have spent the non-professional, unsoldierly portions of his life in turning the left cheek and making two blades of grass grow where only one grew before. If, like Tolstoy, your tastes run to good fatherhood, left cheeks and agriculture, then you'll say that the life of the soldier is worth just as much as the life of Archimedes—much more, indeed ; for Archimedes was a mere geometrician, who occupied himself with lines and angles, curves and surfaces, instead of with good and evil, husbandry and religion. But if, on the contrary, one's tastes are of a more intellectual cast, then one will think as I think—that the life of Archimedes is worth the lives of several billion of even the most amiable soldiers. But as for saying which point of view is right——' Mr. Cardan shrugged his shoulders. 'Partner, I leave it to you.'

Mr. Elver seemed rather disappointed by the inconclusive turn that his guest's discourse had taken. 'But still,' he insisted, 'it's obvious that a wise man's better than a fool. There *is* a hierarchy.'

'Well, I personally should say there was,' said Mr. Cardan. 'But I can't speak for others.' He saw that he had been carried away by the pleasures of speculation into saying things his host did not want to hear. To almost all men, even when they are sober, a suspense of judgment is extraordinarily distasteful. And Mr. Elver was far from sober; moreover, Mr. Cardan began to suspect, this philosophic conversation was a tortuous introduction to personal confidences. If one wanted the confidences one must agree with the would-be confider's opinion. That was obvious.

'Good,' said Mr. Elver. 'Then you'll admit that an intelligent man is worth more than an imbecile, a moron; ha ha, a moron. . . .' And at this word he burst into violent and savage laughter, which, becoming more and more extravagant as it prolonged itself, turned at last into an uncontrollable screaming and sobbing.

His chair turned sideways to the table, his legs crossed, the fingers of one hand playing caressingly with his wine glass, the other manipulating his cigar, Mr. Cardan looked on, while his host, the tears streaming down his cheeks, his narrow face distorted almost out of recognition, laughed and sobbed, now throwing himself back in his chair, now covering his face with his hands, now bending forward over the table to rest his forehead on his arms, while his whole body shook and shook with the repeated and uncontrollable spasms. A disgusting sight, thought Mr. Cardan; and a disgusting specimen too. He began to have an inkling of what the fellow was up to. Translate 'intelligent man' and 'moron' into 'me' and 'my sister'—for the general, the philosophical in any man's conversation must always be converted into the particular and personal if you want to understand him—interpret in personal terms what he had said about vivisection, animal rights and the human hierarchy, and there appeared, as the plain transliteration of the cipher—what? Something that looked exceedingly villainous, thought Mr. Cardan.

'Then I suppose,' he said in a very cool and level voice, when the other had begun to recover from his fit, 'I suppose it's your sister who has the liberating cash.'

Mr. Elver glanced at him, with an expression of surprise, almost of alarm, on his face. His eyes wavered away from Mr. Cardan's steady, genial gaze. He took refuge in his tumbler. 'Yes,' he said, when he had taken a gulp. 'How did you guess?'

Mr. Cardan shrugged his shoulders. 'Purely at random,' he said.

'After my father died,' Mr. Elver explained, 'she went to live with her godmother, who was the old lady at the big house in our parish. A nasty old woman she was. But she took to Grace, she kind of adopted her. When the old bird died at the beginning of this year, Grace found she'd been left twenty-five thousand.'

For all comment, Mr. Cardan clicked his tongue against his palate and slightly raised his eyebrows.

'Twenty-five thousand,' the other repeated. 'A half-wit, a moron! What can she do with it?'

'She can take you to Italy,' Mr. Cardan suggested.

'Oh, of course we can live on the interest all right,' said Mr. Elver contemptuously. 'But when I think how I could multiply it.' He leaned forward eagerly, looking into Mr. Cardan's face for a second, then the shifty grey eyes moved away and fixed themselves on one of the buttons of Mr. Cardan's coat, from which they would occasionally dart upwards again to reconnoitre and return. 'I've worked it out, you see,' he began, talking so quickly that the words tumbled over one another and became almost incoherent. 'The Trade Cycle. . . . I can prophesy exactly what'll happen at any given moment. For instance . . .' He rambled on in a series of complicated explanations.

'Well, if you're as certain as all that,' said Mr. Cardan

when he had finished, 'why don't you get your sister to lend you the money?'

'Why not?' Mr. Elver repeated gloomily and leaned back again in his chair. 'Because that blasted old hag had the capital tied up. It can't be touched.'

'Perhaps she lacked faith in the Trade Cycle,' Mr. Cardan suggested.

'God rot her!' said the other fervently. 'And when I think of what I'd do with the money when I'd made really a lot. Science, art . . .'

'Not to mention revenge on your old acquaintances,' said Mr. Cardan, cutting him short. 'You've worked out the whole programme?'

'Everything,' said Mr. Elver. 'There'd never have been anything like it. And now this damned fool of an old woman goes and gives the money to her pet moron and makes it impossible for me to touch it.' He ground his teeth with rage and disgust.

'But if your sister were to die unmarried,' said Mr. Cardan, 'the money, I suppose, would be yours.'

The other nodded.

'It's a very hierarchical question, certainly,' said Mr. Cardan. In the vault-like room there was a prolonged silence.

Mr. Elver had reached the final stage of intoxication. Almost suddenly he began to feel weak, profoundly weary and rather ill. Anger, hilarity, the sense of satanic power —all had left him. He desired only to go to bed as soon as possible; at the same time he doubted his capacity to get there. He shut his eyes.

Mr. Cardan looked at the limp and sodden figure with an expert's eye, scientifically observing it. It was clear to him that the creature would volunteer no more; that it had come to a state when it could hardly think of anything but the gradually mounting nausea within it. It was time to change tactics. He leaned forward, and tapping his host's arm launched a direct attack.

'So you brought the poor girl here to get rid of her,' he said.

Mr. Elver opened his eyes and flashed at his tormentor a hunted and terrified look. His face became very pale. He turned away. 'No, no, not that.' His voice had sunk to an unsteady whisper.

'Not that?' Mr. Cardan echoed scornfully. 'But it's obvious. And you've as good as been telling me so for the last half-hour.'

Mr. Elver could only go on whispering: 'No.'

Mr. Cardan ignored the denial. 'How did you propose to do it?' he asked. 'It's always risky, whatever way you choose, and I shouldn't put you down as being particularly courageous. How, how?'

The other shook his head.

Mr. Cardan insisted, ruthlessly. 'Ratsbane?' he queried. 'Steel?—no, you wouldn't have the guts for that. Or did you mean that she should tumble by accident into one of those convenient ditches?'

'No, no. No.'

'But I insist on being told,' said Mr. Cardan truculently, and he thumped the table till the reflections of the candles in the brimming glasses quivered and rocked.

Mr. Elver put his face in his hands and burst into tears. 'You're a bully,' he sobbed, 'a dirty bully, like all the rest.'

'Come, come,' Mr. Cardan protested encouragingly. 'Don't take it so hardly. I'm sorry I upset you. You mustn't think,' he added, 'that I have any of the vulgar prejudices about this affair. I'm not condemning you. Far from it. I don't want to use your answers against you. I merely ask out of curiosity—pure curiosity. Cheer up, cheer up. Try a little more wine.'

But Mr. Elver was feeling too deplorably sick to be able to think of wine without horror. He refused it, shuddering. 'I didn't mean to do anything,' he whispered. 'I meant it just to happen.'

'Just to happen? Yours must be a very hopeful nature,' said Mr. Cardan.

'It's in Dante, you know. My father brought us up on Dante; I loathed the stuff,' he added, as though it had been castor oil. 'But things stuck in my mind. Do you remember the woman who tells how she died: "*Siena mi fe', disfecemi Maremma*"? Her husband shut her up in a castle in the Maremma and she died of fever. Do you remember?'

Mr. Cardan nodded.

'That was the idea. I had the quinine: I've been taking ten grains a day ever since I arrived—for safety's sake. But there doesn't seem to be any fever here nowadays,' Mr. Elver added. 'We've been here nine weeks. . . .'

'And nothing's happened!' Mr. Cardan leaned back in his chair and roared with laughter. 'Well, the moral of that,' he added, when he had breath enough to begin talking again, 'the moral of that is: See that your authorities are up to date.'

But Mr. Elver was past seeing a joke. He got up from his chair and stood unsteadily, supporting himself with a hand on the table. 'Would you mind helping me to my room?' he faintly begged. 'I don't feel very well.'

Mr. Cardan helped him first into the garden. 'You ought to learn to carry your liquor more securely,' he said, when the worst was over. 'That's another of the evening's morals.'

When he had lighted his host to bed, Mr. Cardan went to his appointed room and undressed. It was a long time before he fell asleep. The mosquitoes, partly, and partly his own busy thoughts, were responsible for his wakefulness.

Chapter VIII

NEXT morning Mr. Cardan was down early. The first thing he saw in the desolate garden before the house was Miss Elver. She was dressed in a frock cut on the same sack-like lines as her last night's dress, but made of a gaudy, large-patterned material that looked as though it had been designed for the upholstery of chairs and sofas, not of the human figure. Her beads were more numerous and more brilliant than before. She carried a parasol of brightly flowered silk.

Emerging from the house, Mr. Cardan found her in the act of tying a bunch of Michaelmas daisies to the tail of a large white maremman dog that stood, its mouth open, its pink tongue lolling out and its large brown eyes fixed, so it seemed, meditatively on the further horizon, waiting for Miss Elver to have finished the operation. But Miss Elver was very slow and clumsy. The fingers of her stubby little hands seemed to find the process of tying a bow in a piece of ribbon extraordinarily difficult. Once or twice the dog looked round with a mild curiosity to see what was happening at the far end of its anatomy. It did not seem in the least to resent the liberties Miss Elver was taking with its tail, but stood quite still, resigned and waiting. Mr. Cardan was reminded of that enormous tolerance displayed by dogs and cats of even the most fiendish children. Perhaps, in a flash of Bergsonian intuition, the beast had realized the childish essence of Miss Elver's character, had recognized the infant under the disguise of the full-grown woman. Dogs are good Bergsonians, thought Mr. Cardan. Men, on the other hand, are better Kantians. He approached softly.

Miss Elver had at last succeeded in tying the bow to her satisfaction; the dog's white tail was tipped with a rosette of purple flowers. She straightened herself up and looked admiringly at her handiwork. 'There!' she said at last, addressing herself to the dog. 'Now you can run away. Now you look lovely.'

The dog took the hint and trotted off, waving his flower-tipped tail.

Mr. Cardan stepped forward. '"Neat but not gaudy,"' he quoted, '"genteel but not expensive, like the gardener's dog with a primrose tied to his tail." Good-morning.' He took off his hat.

But Miss Elver did not return his salutation. Taken by surprise, she had stood, as though petrified, staring at him with stretched eyes and open mouth while he spoke. At Mr. Cardan's 'good-morning,' which was the first word of his that she had understood, the enchantment of stillness seemed to be lifted from her. She burst into a nervous laugh, covered her blushing face with her hands—for a moment only—then turned and ran down the path, ungainly as an animal moving in an element not its own, to take refuge behind a clump of rank bushes at the end of the garden. Seeing her run, the big dog came bounding after her, joyously barking. One Michaelmas daisy dropped to the ground, then another. In a moment they were all gone and the ribbon with them.

Slowly, cautiously, as though he were stalking a shy bird, and with a reassuring air of being absorbed in anything rather than the pursuit of a runaway, Mr. Cardan walked after Miss Elver down the path. Between the leaves of the bushes he caught glimpses of her bright frock; sometimes, with infinite circumspection, and certain, it was clear, that she was escaping all notice, she peeped at Mr. Cardan round the edge of the bush. Gambolling round her, the dog continued to bark.

Arrived within five or six yards of Miss Elver's hiding-place, Mr. Cardan halted. 'Come now,' he said cajolingly, 'what's there so frightening about me? Take a good look at me. I don't bite. I'm quite tame.'

The leaves of the bushes shook ; from behind them came a peal of shrill laughter.

'I don't even bark, like your stupid dog,' Mr. Cardan went on. 'And if you tied a bunch of flowers on to my tail I should never have the bad manners to get rid of them in the first two minutes like that rude animal.'

There was more laughter.

'Won't you come out?'

There was no answer.

'Oh, very well then,' said Mr. Cardan, in the tone of one who is deeply offended, 'I shall go away. Good-bye.' He retraced his steps for a few yards, then turned off to the right along a little path that led to the garden gate. When he was about three-quarters of the way along it, he heard the sound of hurrying footsteps coming up behind him. He walked on, pretending to notice nothing. There was a touch on his arm.

'Don't go. Please.' Miss Elver's voice spoke imploringly. He looked round, as though startled. 'I won't run away again. But you mustn't look at me like that.'

'Like what?' asked Mr. Cardan.

Miss Elver put up a screening hand and turned away. 'Like I don't know what,' she said.

Mr. Cardan thought he perfectly understood ; he pursued the subject no further. 'Well, if you promise not to run away,' he said, 'I won't go.'

Miss Elver's face shone with pleasure and gratitude. 'Thank you,' she said. 'Should we go and look at the chickens? They're round at the back.'

They went round to the back. Mr. Cardan admired the chickens. 'You like animals?' he asked.

'I should think so,' said Miss Elver rapturously, and nodded.

'Have you ever had a parrot of your own?'

'No.'

'Or a monkey?'

She shook her head.

'Not even a Shetland pony?' asked Mr. Cardan on a note of astonishment.

Miss Elver's voice trembled as she again had to answer 'No.' At the thought of all these enchanting things she had never possessed, the tears came into her eyes.

'In my house,' said Mr. Cardan, conjuring up fairy palaces as easily as Aladdin, 'there are hundreds of them. I'll give you some when you come to stay with me.'

Miss Elver's face became bright again. 'Will you?' she said. 'Oh, that would be nice, that would be nice. And do you keep bears?'

'One or two,' said Mr. Cardan modestly.

'Well . . .' Miss Elver looked up at him, her blank bright eyes opened to their fullest extent. She paused, drew a deep breath and let it slowly out again. 'It must be a nice house,' she added at last, turning away and nodding slowly at every word, 'a nice house. That's all I can say.'

'You'd like to come and stay?' asked Mr. Cardan.

'I should think I would,' Miss Elver replied decidedly, looking up at him again. Then suddenly she blushed, she put up her hands. 'No, no, no,' she protested.

'Why not?' asked Mr. Cardan.

She shook her head. 'I don't know.' And she began to laugh.

'Remember the bears,' said Mr. Cardan.

'Yes. But . . .' She left the sentence unfinished. The old woman came to the back door and rang the bell for breakfast. Ungainly as a diving-bird on land, Miss Elver scuttled into the house. Her companion followed more slowly. In the dining-room, less tomb-like in the bright morning light, breakfast was waiting. Mr. Cardan found his hostess already eating with passion, as though her life depended on it.

'I'm so hungry,' she explained with her mouth full. 'Phil's late,' she added.

'Well, I'm not surprised,' said Mr. Cardan, as he sat down and unfolded his napkin.

When he came down at last, it was in the guise of a cleric so obviously unfrocked, so deplorably seedy and broken-down that Mr. Cardan felt almost sorry for him.

'Nothing like good strong coffee,' he said cheerfully, as he filled his host's cup. Mr. Elver looked on, feeling too melancholy and too ill to speak. For a long time he sat motionless in his chair, without moving, lacking the strength to stretch out his hand to his cup.

'Why don't you eat, Phil?' asked his sister, as she decapitated her second egg. 'You generally eat such a lot.'

Goaded, as though by a taunt, Philip Elver reached for his coffee and swallowed down a gulp. He even took some toast and buttered it; but he could not bring himself to eat.

At half-past ten Mr. Cardan left the house. He told his host that he was going in search of his sculpture; and he comforted Miss Elver, who, seeing him put on his hat and take his walking stick, had begun to whimper, by assuring her that he would be back to luncheon. Following the old woman's directions, Mr. Cardan soon found himself on the shores of the shallow lake of Massaciuccoli. A mile away, on the further shore, he could see the clustering pink and whitewashed houses of the village in which, he knew, the grocer's brother lived and kept his treasure. But instead of proceeding directly to the goal of his pilgrimage, Mr. Cardan lighted a cigar and lay down on the grass at the side of the path. It was a bright clear day. Over the mountains floated great clouds, hard-edged against the sky, firm and massive as though carved from marble and seeming more solid than the marble mountains beneath. A breeze stirred the blue water of the lake into innumerable dazzling ripples. It rustled among the leaves of the poplars and the sound was like that of the sea heard from far off. In the midst of the landscape lay Mr. Cardan, pensively smoking his cigar ; the smoke of it drifted away along the wind.

Twenty-five thousand pounds, Mr. Cardan was thinking. If one were to invest them in the seven per cent. Hungarian Loan, they would bring in seventeen hundred and fifty a year. And if one lived in Italy that went a long way ; one could consider oneself rich on that. A nice house in Siena, or Perugia, or Bologna—Bologna he decided would be the best ; there was nothing to compare with Bolognese cooking. A car—one could afford to keep something handsome. Plenty of nice books, nice people to stay with one all the time, jaunts in comfort through Europe. A secure old age ; the horrors of decrepitude in poverty for ever averted. The only disadvantage—one's wife happened to be a harmless idiot. Still, she'd obviously be most devoted ; she'd do her best. And one would make her happy, one would even allow her a domesticated bear. In fact, Mr. Cardan assured himself, it was the poor creature's only chance of happiness. If she stayed with her brother, he'd find some substitute for the inefficient anopheles sooner or later. If she fell into the hands of an adventurer in need of her money, the chances were that he'd be a great deal more of a scoundrel than Tom Cardan. In fact, Mr. Cardan saw, he could easily make out a case for its being his bounden duty, for the poor girl's sake, to marry her. That would do very nicely for romantic spirits like Lilian Aldwinkle. For them, he'd be the gallant rescuer, the Perseus, the chivalrous St. George. Less enthusiastic souls might look at the twenty-five thousand and smile. But let them smile. After all, Mr. Cardan asked himself, a grin more or less—what does it matter ? No, the real problem, the real difficulty was himself. Could he do it? Wasn't it, somehow, a bit thick—an idiot? Wasn't it too—too Russian? Too Stavroginesque?

True, his motive would be different from the Russian's. He would marry his idiot for comfort and a placid old age—not for the sake of strengthening his moral fibres by hard exercise, not in the voluptuous hope of calling new scruples and finer remorses into existence, or in the religious hope of developing the higher consciousness by leading a low life. But on the other hand, nothing could prevent the life from being, in point of fact, thoroughly low; and he couldn't guarantee his conscience against the coming of strange qualms. Would seventeen hundred and fifty per annum be a sufficient compensation?

For more than an hour Mr. Cardan lay there, smoking, looking at the bright lake, at the ethereal fantastic mountains and the marbly clouds, listening to the wind among the leaves and the occasional far-away sounds of life, and pondering all the time. In the end he decided that seventeen hundred and fifty, or even the smaller income that would result from investment in something a little safer than seven per cent. Hungarian Loan, was a sufficient compensation. He'd do it. Mr. Cardan got up, threw away the stump of his second cigar and walked slowly back towards the house. As he approached it through the little plantation of poplar trees Miss Elver, who had been on the look-out for his return, came running out of the gate to meet him. The gaudy upholstery material blazed up as she passed out of the shade of the house into the sunlight, her coloured beads flashed. Uttering shrill little cries and laughing, she ran towards him. Mr. Cardan watched her as she came on. He had seen frightened cormorants bobbing their heads in a ludicrous anxiety from side to side. He had seen penguins waving their little flappers, scuttling along, undignified, on their short legs. He had seen vultures with trailing wings hobbling and hopping, ungainly, over the ground. Memories of all these sights appeared before his mind's eye as he watched Miss Elver's approach. He sighed profoundly.

'I'm so glad you've come back,' Miss Elver cried breathlessly, as she approached, 'I was really afraid you were going right away.' She shook his hand earnestly and looked up into his face. 'You've not forgotten about the monkeys and the Shetland ponies, have you?' she added, rather anxiously.

Mr. Cardan smiled. 'Of course not,' he answered; and he added gallantly: 'How could I forget anything that gives you pleasure?' He squeezed her hand and, bending down, kissed it.

Miss Elver's face flushed very red, then, the moment after, became exceedingly pale. Her breath came quickly and unsteadily. She shut her eyes. A shuddering ran through her; she wavered on her feet, she seemed on the point of falling. Mr. Cardan caught her by the arm and held her up. This was going to be worse, he thought, than he had imagined; more Stavroginesque. To faint when he kissed her hand—kissed it almost ironically—that was too much. But probably, he reflected, nothing of the kind had ever happened to her before. How many men had ever so much as spoken to her? It was understandable.

'My good child—really now.' He slightly shook her arm. 'Pull yourself together. If you're going to faint like this I shall never be able to trust you with a bear. Come, come.'

Still, the understanding of a thing does not alter it. It remains what it was when it was still uncomprehended. Seventeen hundred and fifty per annum—but at this rate it looked as though that would hardly be enough.

Miss Elver opened her eyes and looked at him. Into their

blankness had come that look of anxious, unhappy love with which a child looks at his mother when he thinks that she is going to leave him. Mr. Cardan could not have felt more remorseful if he had committed a murder.

> What every weakness, every vice?
> Tom Cardan, all were thine.

All the same, there were certain things the doing of which one felt to be an outrage. Still, one had to think of those seventeen hundred and fifty pounds; one had to think of old age in solitude and poverty.

Leaving Miss Elver to play by herself in the garden, Mr. Cardan went indoors. He found his host sitting behind closed jalousies in a greenish twilight, his head on his hand.

'Feeling better?' asked Mr. Cardan cheerfully; and getting no answer, he went on to tell a long, bright story of how he had searched for the grocer's brother, only to find, at last, that he was away from home and would be away till to-morrow. 'So I hope you won't mind,' he concluded, 'if I trespass on your charming hospitality for another night. Your sister has most kindly told me that I might.'

Mr. Elver turned on him a glance of concentrated loathing and averted his eyes. He said nothing.

Mr. Cardan drew up a chair and sat down. 'There's a most interesting little book,' he said, looking at his host with a genial twinkling expression, 'by a certain Mr. W. H. S. Jones called "Malaria: a factor in the history of Greece and Rome," or some such title. He shows how the disease may quite suddenly obtain a footing in countries hitherto immune and in the course of a few generations bring a whole culture, a powerful empire to the ground. Conversely he shows how it is got rid of. Drainage, quinine, wire-netting . . .' The other stirred uneasily in his chair; but Mr. Cardan went on ruthlessly. When the bell rang for luncheon he was talking to Mr. Elver about the only way in which the Yellow Peril might be permanently averted.

'First,' he said, laying the forefinger of his right hand against the thumb of his left, 'first you must introduce malaria into Japan. Japan's immune, so far; it's a crying scandal. You must start by remedying that. And secondly,' he moved on to the index, 'you must see that the Chinese never have a chance to stamp out the disease in their country. Four hundred million malarial Chinamen may be viewed with equanimity. But four hundred million healthy ones—that's a very different matter. The spread of malaria among the yellow races—there's a cause,' said Mr. Cardan, rising from his chair, 'a cause to which some good European might profitably devote himself. You, who take so much interest in the subject, Mr. Elver, you might find a much worse vocation. Shall we go into lunch?' Mr. Elver rose, totteringly. 'I have a tremendous appetite,' his guest went on, patting him on his bent back. 'I hope you have too.'

Mr. Elver at last broke silence. 'You're a damned bully,' he whispered in a passion of misery and futile rage, 'a damned stinking bully.'

'Come, come,' said Mr. Cardan. 'I protest against "stinking."'

Chapter IX

EARLY the next morning Mr. Cardan and his hostess left the house and walked rapidly away through the fields in the direction of the lake. They had told the old woman that they would be back to a late breakfast. Mr. Elver was not yet awake; Mr. Cardan had left instructions that he was not to be called before half-past nine.

The ground was still wet with dew when they set out;

the poplar trees threw shadows longer than themselves. The air was cool; it was a pleasure to walk. Mr. Cardan strode along at four miles an hour; and like a diver out of water, like a soaring bird reduced to walk the earth, Miss Elver trotted along at his side, rolling and hopping as she walked, as though she were mounted, not on feet, but on a set of eccentric wheels of different diameters. Her face seemed to shine with happiness; every now and then she looked at Mr. Cardan with shy adoration, and if she happened to catch his eyes she would blush, turn away her head and laugh. Mr. Cardan was almost appalled by the extent of his success and the ease with which it had been obtained. He might make a slave of the poor creature, might keep her shut up in a rabbit-hutch, and, provided he showed himself now and again to be worshipped, she would be perfectly happy. The thought made Mr. Cardan feel strangely guilty.

'When we're married,' said Miss Elver suddenly, 'shall we have some children?'

Mr. Cardan smiled rather grimly. 'The trouble about children,' he said, 'is that the bears might eat them. You can never be quite sure of bears. Remember Elisha's bears and those bad children.'

Miss Elver's face became thoughtful. She walked on for a long time in silence.

They came to the lake, lying placid and very bright under the pale early-morning sky. At the sight of it Miss Elver clapped her hands with pleasure; she forgot in an instant all her troubles. The fatal incompatibility between bears and children ceased to preoccupy her. 'What lovely water!' she cried, and bending down she picked up a pebble from the path and threw it into the lake.

But Mr. Cardan did not permit her to linger. 'There's no time to lose,' he said, and taking her arm he hurried her on.

'Where are we going to?' asked Miss Elver.

He pointed to the village on the further shore of the lake. 'From there,' he said, 'we'll take some sort of cab or cart.'

The prospect of driving in a cart entirely reconciled Miss Elver to parting at such short notice with the lake. 'That'll be lovely,' she declared, and trotted on so fast that Mr. Cardan had to quicken his pace in order to keep up with her.

While the little carriage was being made ready and the horse put in and harnessed—hastelessly, as these things are always done in Italy, with dignity and at leisure—Mr. Cardan went to visit the grocer's brother. Now that he had come so far it would be foolish to miss the opportunity of seeing the treasure. The grocer's brother was himself a grocer, and so like his relative that Mr. Cardan could almost fancy it was Miss Thriplow's virtuous and simple friend from the hill-top to whom he was now speaking in the plain. When Mr. Cardan explained his business the man bowed, wreathed himself in smiles, laughed and blew acetylene into his face just as his brother had done. He expatiated on the beauty and the antiquity of his treasure, and when Mr. Cardan begged him to make haste and show him the sculpture, he would not suffer himself to be interrupted, but went on lyrically with his description, repeating the same phrases again and again and gesticulating until he began to sweat. At last, when he considered Mr. Cardan worked up to a due state of preliminary enthusiasm, the grocer opened the door at the back of the shop and mysteriously beckoned to his visitor to follow him. They walked down a dark passage, through a kitchen full of tumbling children on whom one had to be careful not to tread, across a little yard and into a mouldering out-house. The grocer led the way, walking all the time on tip-toe and speaking only in a whisper—for what reason Mr. Cardan could not imagine, unless it was to impress him with the profound importance of the affair, and perhaps to suggest that the beauty and antiquity of the work of art were such that it was only barefoot and in silence that it should be approached.

'Wait there,' he whispered impressively, as they entered the out-house.

Mr. Cardan waited. The grocer tip-toed across to the further corner of the shed. Mysteriously draped in sacking, something that might have been an ambushed man stood motionless in the shadow. The grocer halted in front of it and, standing a little to one side so as to give Mr. Cardan an uninterrupted view of the marvel to be revealed, took hold of a corner of the sacking, and with a magnificently dramatic gesture whisked it off.

There emerged the marble effigy of what in the imagination of a monumental mason of 1830 figured as a Poet. A slenderer Byron with yet more hyacinthine hair and a profile borrowed from one of Canova's Greeks, he stood, leaning against a truncated column, his marble eyes turned upwards in pursuit of the flying Muse. A cloak hung lankly from his shoulders; a vine leaf was all the rest of his costume. On the top of the truncated column lay a half-opened marble scroll, which the Poet's left hand held down for fear it should be blown clean away by the wind of inspiration. His right, it was evident, had originally poised above the virgin page a stylus. But the hand, alas, and the whole forearm almost to the elbow were gone. At the base of the column was a little square tablet on which, if the figure had ever been put to its proper monumental use, should have been written the name and claims to fame of the poet upon whose tomb it was to stand. But the tablet was blank. At the time this statue was carved there had evidently been a dearth of lyrists in the principality of Massa Carrara.

'E bellissimo!' said the grocer's brother, standing back and looking at it with a connoisseur's enthusiasm.

'Davvero,' Mr. Cardan agreed. He thought sadly of his recumbent Etruscan, his sarcophagus by Jacopo della Quercia, his Romanesque demon. Still, he reflected, even a bas-relief by Giotto would hardly have brought him five-and-twenty thousand pounds.

Chapter X

Mr. Cardan returned to the palace of the Cybo Malaspina to find that the number of guests had been increased during his absence by the arrival of Mrs. Chelifer. Mrs. Aldwinkle had not been particularly anxious to have Chelifer's mother in the house, but finding that Chelifer was preparing to leave as soon as his mother should arrive, she peremptorily insisted on giving the lady hospitality.

'It's absurd,' she argued, 'to go down again to that horrible hotel at Marina di Vezza, stay there uncomfortably for a few days and then go to Rome by train. You must bring your mother here, and then, when it's time for Mr. Falx to go to his conference, we'll all go to Rome in the car. It'll be far pleasanter.'

Chelifer tried to object; but Mrs. Aldwinkle would not hear of objections. When Mrs. Chelifer arrived at the station of Vezza she found Francis waiting for her on the platform with Mrs. Aldwinkle, in yellow tussore and a floating white veil, at his side. The welcome she got from Mrs. Aldwinkle was far more effusively affectionate than that which she got from her son. A little bewildered, but preserving all her calm and gentle dignity, Mrs. Chelifer suffered herself to be led towards the Rolls-Royce.

'We all admire your son so enormously,' said Mrs. Aldwinkle. 'He's so—how shall I say?—so *post bellum*, so essentially one of *us*.' Mrs. Aldwinkle made haste to establish her position among the youngest of the younger generation. 'All that one only dimly feels he expresses. Can you be surprised at our admiration?'

So far Mrs. Chelifer was rather surprised by everything. It took her some time to get used to Mrs. Aldwinkle. Nor was the aspect of the palace calculated to allay her astonishment.

'A superb specimen of early baroque,' Mrs. Aldwinkle assured her, pointing with her parasol. But even after she knew the dates, it all seemed to Mrs. Chelifer rather queer.

Mrs. Aldwinkle remained extremely cordial to her new guest; but in secret she disliked Mrs. Chelifer extremely. There would have been small reason, in any circumstances, for Mrs. Aldwinkle to have liked her. The two women had nothing in common; their views of life were different and irreconcilable, they had lived in separate worlds. At the best of times Mrs. Aldwinkle would have found her guest *bourgeoise* and *bornée*. As things actually were she loathed her. And no wonder; for in his mother Chelifer had a permanent and unexceptionable excuse for getting away from Mrs. Aldwinkle. Mrs. Aldwinkle naturally resented the presence in her house of this cause and living justification of infidelity. At the same time it was necessary for her to keep on good terms with Mrs. Chelifer; for if she quarrelled with the mother, it was obvious that the son would take himself off. Inwardly chafing, Mrs. Aldwinkle continued to treat her with the same gushing affection as at first.

To Mrs. Aldwinkle's guests the arrival of Mrs. Chelifer was more welcome than to herself. Mr. Falx found in her a more sympathetic and comprehensible soul than he could discover in his hostess. To Lord Hovenden and Irene her arrival meant the complete cessation of Irene's duties as a spy; they liked her well enough, moreover, for her own sake.

'A nice old fing,' was how Lord Hovenden summed her up.

Miss Thriplow affected almost to worship her.

'She's so wonderfully good and simple and *integral*, if you understand what I mean,' Miss Thriplow explained to Calamy. 'To be able to be so undividedly enthusiastic about folk-songs and animals' rights and all that sort of thing —it's really wonderful. She's a lesson to us,' Miss Thriplow concluded, 'a lesson.' Mrs. Chelifer became endowed, for her, with all the qualities that the village grocer had unfortunately not possessed. The symbol of his virtues—if only he had possessed them—had been the white apron; Mrs. Chelifer's integrity was figured forth by her dateless grey dresses.

'She's one of Nature's Quakeresses,' Miss Thriplow declared. 'If only one could be born like that!' There had been a time, not so long ago, when she had aspired to be one of Nature's Guardswomen. 'I never knew that anything so good and dove-coloured existed outside of Academy subject-pictures of 1880. You know: "A Pilgrim Mother on Board the Mayflower," or something of that sort. It's absurd in the Academy. But it's lovely in real life.'

Calamy agreed.

But the person who most genuinely liked Mrs. Chelifer was Grace Elver. From the moment she set eyes on Mrs. Chelifer, Grace was her dog-like attendant. And Mrs. Chelifer responded by practically adopting her for the time being. When he learned the nature of her tastes and occupations, Mr. Cardan explained her kindness to himself by the hypothesis that poor Grace was the nearest thing to a stray dog or cat that Mrs. Chelifer could find. Conversely, Grace's love at first sight must be due to the realization by that cat-like mind that here was a born protector and friend. In any case, he was exceedingly grateful to Mrs. Chelifer for having made her appearance when she did. Her presence in the house made easy what would otherwise have been a difficult situation.

That Mrs. Aldwinkle would be impressed by the romantic story of Grace's abduction Mr. Cardan had always been certain. And when he told the story, she *was* impressed, though less profoundly than Mr. Cardan had hoped; she was too much preoccupied with her own affairs to be able to respond with her customary enthusiasm to what, at other times, would have been an irresistible appeal. About her reception of the story, then, Mr. Cardan had never entertained a doubt; he knew that she would find it romantic. But that was no guarantee that she would like the heroine of the story. From what he knew of her, which was a great deal, Mr. Cardan felt sure that she would very quickly find poor Grace exceedingly tiresome. He knew her lack of patience and her intolerance. Grace would get on her nerves; Lilian would be unkind, and goodness only knew what scenes might follow. Mr. Cardan had brought her to the palace meaning to stay only a day or two and then take his leave, before Mrs. Aldwinkle had had time to get poor Grace on her nerves. But the presence of Mrs. Chelifer made him change his mind. Her affectionate protection was a guarantee against Mrs. Aldwinkle's impatience; more important still, it had the best possible effect on Grace herself. In Mrs. Chelifer's presence she behaved quietly and sensibly, like a child doing its best to make a good impression. Mrs. Chelifer, moreover, kept a tenderly watchful eye on her appearance and her manners; kept her up to the mark about washing her hands and brushing her hair, dropped a gentle hint when she was not behaving as well as she ought to at table, and checked her propensity to eat too much of the things she liked and not enough of those she didn't like. Mrs. Chelifer, it was obvious, had the best possible influence over her. When they were married, Mr. Cardan decided, he would frequently invite Mrs. Chelifer to stay—preferably, though she was a very nice old thing, while he was away from home. Meanwhile, secure that his residence at the palace of the Cybo Malaspina would be marred by no disagreeable incidents, he wrote to his lawyer to make the necessary arrangements about his marriage.

For her part, Mrs. Chelifer was delighted to have found Grace. As Mr. Cardan had divined, she missed her cats and dogs, her poor children and traditional games. It was very reluctantly that she had at last given up the old Oxford house; very reluctantly, though the arguments that Francis had used to persuade her were unanswerable. It was too large for her, it was full of those mediaeval labour-creating devices of which Mr. Ruskin and his architectural followers were so fond, it cost more to keep up than she could afford; moreover, it was unhealthy, she was regularly ill there every winter; the doctors had been urging her for years past to get out of the Thames valley. Yes, the arguments were quite unanswerable; but it had been a long time before she had finally made up her mind to leave the place. Forty years of her life had been passed there; she was loth to part with all those memories. And then there were the dogs and the poor children, all her old friends and her charities. In the end, however, she had allowed herself to be persuaded. The house was sold; it was arranged that she should spend the winter in Rome.

'Now you're free,' her son had said.

But Mrs. Chelifer rather mournfully shook her head. 'I don't know that I very much like being free,' she answered. 'I shall be without occupation in Rome. I look forward to it almost with dread.'

Francis reassured her. 'You'll soon find something,' he said. 'Don't be afraid of that.'

'Shall I?' Mrs. Chelifer questioned doubtfully. They

were walking together in the little garden at the back of the house; looking round her at the familiar grass plot and flower beds, she sighed.

But Francis was right; dogs, poor children or their equivalents are fortunately not rare. At the end of the first stage of her journey Mrs. Chelifer had found, in Grace Elver, a compensation for what she had abandoned at Oxford. Attending to poor Grace she was happy.

For the rest of the party Miss Elver's arrival had no special or personal significance. For them she was just Mr. Cardan's half-wit; that was all. Even Mary Thriplow, who might have been expected to take an interest in so genuine a specimen of the simple soul, paid little attention to her. The fact was that Grace was really too simple to be interesting. Simplicity is no virtue unless you are potentially complicated. Mrs. Chelifer, being with all her simplicity a woman of intelligence, threw light, Miss Thriplow felt, on her own case. Grace was simple only as a child or an imbecile is simple; her didactic value was therefore nil. Miss Thriplow remained faithful to Mrs. Chelifer.

Chapter XI

It was night. Half undressed, Irene was sitting on the edge of her bed stitching away at an unfinished garment of pale pink silk. Her head was bent over her work and her thick hair hung perpendicularly down on either side, making an angle with her tilted face. The light clung richly to her bare arms and shoulders, was reflected by the curved and glossy surfaces of her tight-drawn stockings. Her face was extremely grave; the tip of her tongue appeared between her teeth. It was a difficult job.

Round her, on the walls of the enormous room which had once been the bedchamber of the Cardinal Alderano

Malaspina, fluttered an army of gesticulating shapes. Over the door sat God the Father, dressed in a blue crêpe de Chine tunic and enveloped in a mantle of red velvet, which fluttered in the divine afflatus as though it had been so much bunting. His right hand was extended ; and in obedience to the gesture a squadron of angels went flying down one of the side walls towards the window. At a *prie-Dieu* in the far corner knelt Cardinal Malaspina, middle-aged, stout, with a *barbiche* and moustache, and looking altogether, Irene thought, like the current British idea of a French chef. The Archangel Michael, at the head of his troop of Principalities and Powers, was hovering in the air above him, and with an expression on his face of mingled condescension and respect—condescension, inasmuch as he was the plenipotentiary of the *Padre Eterno*, and respect, in view of the fact that His Eminence was a brother of the Prince of Massa Carrara—was poising above the prelate's head the red symbolic hat that was to make him a Prince of the Church. On the opposite wall the Cardinal was represented doing battle with the powers of darkness. Dressed in scarlet robes he stood undaunted on the brink of the bottomless pit. Behind him was a carefully painted view of the Malaspina palace, with a group of retainers and handsome coaches in the middle distance and, immediately behind their Uncle, whom they gallantly supported by their prayers, the Cardinal's nephews. From the pit came up legions of hideous devils who filled the air with the flapping of their wings. But the Cardinal was more than a match for them. Raising a crucifix above his head, he conjured them to return to the flames. And the foiled devils, gnashing their teeth and trembling with terror, were hurled back towards the pit. Head foremost, tail foremost, in every possible position they came hurtling down towards the floor. When she lay in bed, Irene could see half a dozen devils diving down at her ; and when she woke up in the morning, a pair of plunging legs waved frantically within a foot of her opening eyes. In the wall space over the windows the Cardinal's cultured leisures were allegorically celebrated. Nine Muses and three Graces, attended by a troop of Hours, reclined or stood, or danced in studied postures; while the Cardinal himself, enthroned in the midst, listened to their conversation and proffered his own opinions without appearing to notice the fact that all the ladies were stark naked. No one but the most polished and accomplished man of the world could have behaved in the circumstances with such perfect *savoir-vivre.*

In the midst of the Cardinal's apotheosis and entirely oblivious of it, Irene stitched away at her pink chemise. Undressing, just now, she had caught sight of it lying here in her work-basket; she hadn't been able to resist the temptation of adding a touch or two there and then. It was going to be one of her masterpieces when it was done. She held it out in her two hands, at arm's length, and looked at it, lovingly and critically. It was simply too lovely.

Ever since Chelifer's arrival she had been able to do a lot of work on her underclothes. Mrs. Aldwinkle, absorbed by her unhappy passion, had completely forgotten that she had a niece who ought to be writing lyrics and painting in water-colours. Irene was free to devote all her time to her sewing. She did not neglect the opportunity. But every now and then her conscience would suddenly prick her and she would ask herself whether, after all, it was quite fair to take advantage of poor Aunt Lilian's mournful preoccupation to do what she did not approve of. She would wonder if she oughtn't, out of loyalty to Aunt Lilian, to stop sewing and make a sketch or write a poem. Once or twice in the first days she even acted on the advice of her conscience. But when in the evening she brought Aunt Lilian her sketch of the temple, and the lyric beginning ' O Moon, how calmly in the midnight sky . . .'—brought them with a certain triumph, a consciousness of virtuous actions duly performed —that distracted lady showed so little interest in these artistic tokens of niecely duty and affection that Irene felt herself excused henceforward from making any further effort to practise the higher life. She went on with her stitching. Her conscience, it is true, still troubled her at times ; but she did nothing about it.

This evening she felt no conscientious qualm. The garment was so lovely that even Aunt Lilian, she felt sure, would have approved of it. It was a work of art—a work of art that deserved that honourable title just as richly as ' O Moon, how calmly in the midnight sky ' ; perhaps even more richly.

Irene folded up the unfinished masterpiece in rose, put it away, and went on with her undressing. To-night, she decided, as she brushed her hair, she would tell Aunt Lilian how right she had been about Hovenden. That ought to please her. ' How grateful I am,' she would say. And she'd tell her how much she liked him—almost, almost in *that* way. Not quite yet. But soon ; she felt somehow that it might happen soon. And it would be the real thing. Real and solid. Not flimsy and fizzy and imaginary, like the episodes with Peter and Jacques and the rest of them.

She put on her dressing-gown and walked down the long corridor to Mrs. Aldwinkle's room. Cardinal Alderano was left alone with his devils and the obsequious angels, his nine naked Muses and the Eternal Father.

When Irene came in, Aunt Lilian was sitting in front of her looking-glass, rubbing skin food into her face.

' It appears,' she said, looking at herself in the glass, critically, as Irene had looked at her masterpiece of fine sewing, ' that there's such a wonderful electric massage machine. I forget who told me about it.'

' Was it Lady Belfry ? ' Irene suggested. The image of

Lady Belfry's face floated up before her mind's eye—smooth, pink, round, youthful looking, but with that factitious and terribly precarious youthfulness of beauty scientifically preserved.

'Perhaps it was,' said Mrs. Aldwinkle. 'I must certainly get one of them. Write to Harrods' about it to-morrow, will you, darling?'

Irene began the nightly brushing of her aunt's hair. There was a long silence. How should she begin about Hovenden? Irene was thinking. She must begin in some way that would show how really and genuinely serious it all was. She must begin in such a way that Aunt Lilian would have no possible justification for taking up a playful tone about it. At all costs, Aunt Lilian must not be allowed to talk to her in that well-known and dreaded vein of bludgeoning banter; on no account must she be given an opportunity for saying: 'Did she think then that her silly old auntie didn't notice?' or anything of that kind. But to find the completely fun-proof formula was not so easy. Irene searched for it long and thoughtfully. She was not destined to find it. For Aunt Lilian, who had also been thinking, suddenly broke the silence.

'I sometimes doubt,' she said, 'whether he takes any interest in women at all. Fundamentally, unconsciously, I believe he's a homosexualist.'

'Perhaps,' said Irene gravely. She knew her Havelock Ellis.

For the next half-hour Mrs. Aldwinkle and her niece discussed the interesting possibility.

Chapter XII

Miss Thriplow was writing in her secret note-book. 'There are people,' she wrote, 'who seem to have no capacity for feeling deeply or passionately about anything. It is a kind of emotional impotence for which one can only pity them profoundly. Perhaps there are more of these people nowadays than there were. But that's only an impression; one has no facts to go on, no justifying documents. But if it's the case, it's due, I suppose, to our intellectualizing education. One has to have a strong emotional constitution to be able to stand it. And then one lives so artificially that many of the profounder instincts rarely get an opportunity for displaying themselves. Fear, for example, and all the desperate passions evoked by the instinct of self-preservation in face of danger or hunger. Thousands of civilized people pass through life condemned to an almost complete ignorance of these emotions.'

Miss Thriplow drew a line under this paragraph and began again a little further down the page.

'To love primitively, with fury. To be no more civilized, but savage. No more critical, but whole-heartedly passionate. No more a troubled and dubious mind, but a young, healthy body certain and unwavering in its desires. The beast knows everything, says Uncle Yerochka in Tolstoy. Not everything; no. But he knows, at any rate, all the things the mind does not know. The strong complete spirit must know what the beast knows as well as what the mind knows.'

She drew another line.

'His hands are so strong and firm, and yet touch so softly. His lips are soft. Where his neck joins his body, in front, between the two strong tendons, where they converge towards the collar bone, is a boldly marked depression in the flesh that looks as though it had been made by the thumb of an artist god, so beautiful it is. So beautiful . . .'

It occurred to Miss Thriplow that there would be an excellent article to be written round the theme of masculine beauty. In the Song of Solomon it is described as lyrically as feminine beauty. It is rare to find modern poetesses expressing so frank an admiration. In the Paris Salons it is the female nude which prevails; the male is exceptional and, when complete, seems a little shocking. How different from the state of things in Pompeii! Miss Thriplow bit the end of her pen. Yes, decidedly, it would make a capital article.

'His skin is white and smooth,' she went on writing. 'How strong he is! His eyes are sleepy; but sometimes they seem to wake up and he looks at me so piercingly and commandingly that I am frightened. But I like being frightened—by him.'

Another line. Miss Thriplow would have written more on this subject; but she was always apprehensive that somebody might find her note-book and read it. She did not want that to happen till she was dead. Miss Thriplow made an asterisk by the side of the first of the evening's notes. In the margin of the blank page opposite she scratched a similar sign, to indicate that what she was going to write now was in the nature of an appendix or corollary to what she had written in the first note.

'Certain people,' she wrote, 'who have no natural capacity for profound feeling are yet convinced, intellectually, that they ought to feel profoundly. The best people, they think, have formidable instincts. They want to have them too. They are the emotional snobs. This type, I am sure, is new. In the eighteenth century people tried to make out that they were rational and polished. The cult of the emotions began in the nineteenth. It has had a new turn given to it by Bergsonism and Romain-Rollandism in the twentieth century. It is fashionable now to be exactly the opposite of what it was fashionable to be in the eighteenth century. So that you get emotionally impotent people simulating passion with their minds. Hypocrites of instinct, they often more than half deceive themselves. And, if they are intelligent, they completely deceive all but the most observant of those around them. They act the emotional part better than those who actually feel the emotions. It is Diderot's paradox of the comedian, in real life; the less you feel, the better you represent feeling. But while the comedian on the stage plays only for the audience in the theatre, those in real life perform as much for an inward as an outward gallery; they ask for applause also from themselves and, what is more, they get it; though always, I suppose, with certain secret reservations. What a curious type it is! I have known many specimens of it.'

Miss Thriplow stopped writing and thought of the specimens she had known. There was a surprisingly large number of them. Every human being is inclined to see his own qualities and weaknesses in others. Inevitably: since his own mental and moral attributes are the only ones of which he has any personal experience. The man who visualizes his multiplication table in a fantastic and definite picture imagines that all other men must do the same; the musician cannot conceive of a mind that is irresponsive to music. Similarly the ambitious man presumes that all his fellows are actuated by his own desire to achieve distinction and power. The sensualist sees sensuality everywhere. The mean man takes it for granted that everybody else is mean. But it must not be thought that the possessor of a vice who sees his own weakness in all his fellows therefore condones that weakness. We rarely give our own weaknesses their specific name, and are aware of them only in a vague and empirical fashion. The conscious and educated part of us condemns the vice to which we are congenitally subject. At the same time, our personal knowledge of the vice—a knowledge not conscious or intellectual, but obscure, practical and instinctive—tends to direct the attention of the superficial, educated part of the mind to manifestations of this particular weakness, tends even to make it detect such manifestations when they do not exist; so that we are constantly struck by the ludicrous spectacle of the avaricious passionately condemning avarice in others much more generous than themselves, of the lascivious crying out on lasciviousness, the greedy criticizing greed. Their education has taught them that these vices are blameworthy, while their personal and empirical knowledge of them causes them to take a special interest in these weaknesses and to see signs of them everywhere.

If the number of Miss Thriplow's friends who belonged to the type of the emotionally impotent was surprisingly large, the fact was due to a tendency in Miss Thriplow herself towards precisely this spiritual weakness. Being by nature a good deal more acute and self-analytic than most of the men and women who indignantly castigate their own inveterate sins, Miss Thriplow was not unaware, while she criticized others, of the similar defect in herself. She could not help suspecting, when she read Dostoievsky and Tchehov, that she was organized differently from these Russians. It seemed to her that she felt nothing so acutely, with such an intricate joy or misery as did they. And even before she had started reading the Russians, Miss Thriplow had come to the painful conclusion that if the Brontë sisters were emotionally normal, then she must be decidedly sub-normal. And even if they weren't quite normal, even if they were feverish, she desired to be like them; they seemed to her entirely admirable. It was the knowledge of her sub-normality (which she had come, however, to attribute to a lack of opportunities—we lead such sheltered, artificial lives—for the display of her potential passions and emotions) that had made Miss Thriplow so passionate an admirer of fine spontaneous feelings. It caused her at the same time to be willing and anxious to embrace every opportunity that presented itself for the testing of her reactions. It is experience that makes us aware of what we are; if it were not for contacts with the world outside ourselves we should have no emotions at all. In order to get to know her latent emotional self, Miss Thriplow desired to have as much experience, to make as many contacts with external reality as possible. When the external reality was of an unusual character and offered to be particularly fruitful in emotional revelations, she sought it with a special eagerness. Thus, a love affair with Calamy had seemed to her fraught with the most interesting emotional possibilities. She would have liked him well enough even if his drowsiness had concealed no inward fires. But the conviction that there was something 'queer,' as Mrs. Aldwinkle would say, and dangerous about the man made her imagine at every stage of their intimacy that she liked him better than she actually did; made her anxious to advance to further stages in the hope that, as he revealed himself, ampler and more interesting revelations of her own hidden soul might there be awaiting her. She had had her reward; Calamy had already genuinely frightened her, had revealed himself as excitingly brutal.

'You exasperate me so much,' he had said, 'that I could wring your neck.'

And there were moments when she half believed that he really would kill her. It was a new kind of love. She abandoned herself to it with a fervour which she found, taking its temperature, very admirable. The flood of passion carried her along; Miss Thriplow took notes of her sensations on the way and hoped that there would be more and intenser sensations to record in the future.

Chapter XIII

Calamy lay on his back, quite still, looking up into the darkness. Up there, he was thinking, so near that it's only a question of reaching out a hand to draw back the curtaining darkness that conceals it, up there, just above me, floats the great secret, the beauty and the mystery. To look into the depths of that mystery, to fix the eyes of the spirit on that bright and enigmatic beauty, to pore over the secret until its symbols cease to be opaque and the light filters through from beyond—there is nothing else in life, for me at any rate, that matters; there is no rest or possibility of satisfaction in doing anything else.

All this was obvious to him now. And it was obvious, too, that he could not do two things at once; he couldn't at the same time lean out into the silence beyond the futile noise and bustle—into the mental silence that lies beyond the body—he couldn't at the same time do this and himself partake in the tumult; and if he wanted to look into the depths of mind, he must not interpose a preoccupation with his bodily appetites.

He had known all this so well and so long; and still he went on in the same way of life. He knew that he ought to change, to do something different, and he profoundly resented this knowledge. Deliberately he acted against it. Instead of making an effort to get out of the noise and bustle, to break away from his enslavement and do what he ought to do, what he knew that, really and profoundly, he wanted to do, he had more than once, when his bonds had seemed on the point of falling away of themselves, deliberately tightened them. He resented this necessity of changing, even though it was a necessity imposed on him, not from without, but by what he knew to be the most intelligent part of his own being. He was afraid, too, that if he changed he would be making himself ridiculous. It was not that he desired to live as he had until a year ago. That dreary and fatiguing routine of pleasure had become intolerable; he had broken definitely with that. No; he pictured a sort of graceful Latin compromise. An Epicurean cultivation of mind and body. Breakfast at nine. Serious reading from ten till one. Luncheon prepared by an excellent French cook. In the afternoon a walk and talk with intelligent friends. Tea with crumpets and the most graceful of female society. A frugal but exquisite supper. Three hours' meditation about the Absolute, and then bed, not unaccompanied. . . . It sounded charming. But somehow it wouldn't do. To the liver of this perfect Life of Reason the secret, the mystery and the beauty, though they might be handled and examined, refused to give up their significance. If one really wanted to know about them, one must do more than meditate upon them of an evening between the French chef's masterpiece of maigre cooking and the night's rest, not in solitude. In these delightful Latin circumstances the secret, the mystery and the beauty reduced themselves to nothing. One thought of them only because they were amusing and to pass the time; they were really no more important than the tea with crumpets, the vegetarian supper and the amorous repose. If one wanted them to be more than these, one must abandon oneself completely to the contemplation of them. There could be no compromise.

Calamy knew this. But all the same he had made love to Mary Thriplow, not because he had felt an overwhelming passionate necessity to do so; but because she amused him, because her prettiness, her air of unreal innocence exasperated his senses, more than all because he felt that a love affair with Mary Thriplow would keep him thoroughly occupied and prevent him from thinking about anything else. It had not. The beauty and the mystery still hung just above him when he lay alone in the darkness. They were still there; his affair with Mary Thriplow merely prevented him from approaching them.

Down in the valley a clock struck one. The sound reminded him that he had promised to go to her to-night. He found himself thinking of what would happen when they met, of the kisses, the caresses given and received. Angrily he tried to turn his thoughts to other themes; he tried to think of the mystery and the beauty that floated there, above him, on the further side of the curtaining darkness. But however vehemently he strove to expel them, the charnel images kept returning again and again to his mind.

'I won't go,' he said to himself; but he knew while he was saying it that he would. With an extraordinary vividness he imagined her lying on the crook of his arm, extenuated, limp and shuddering, like one who has been tormented on the rack. Yes, he knew that he would go.

The notion of torture continued to haunt his mind. He thought of those poor wretches who, accused of sorcery, admitted after the third day's torment that they had indeed flown along the wind, passed through keyholes, taken the form of wolves and conjoined themselves with incubi; who would admit, not only these things, but also, after another hour on the rack, that they had accomplices, that this man, that woman, that young child were also sorcerers and servants of the devil. The spirit is willing, but the flesh is weak. Weak in pain, but weaker still, he thought, more inexcusably weak, in pleasure. For under the torments of pleasure, what cowardices, what betrayals of self and of others will it not commit! How lightly it will lie and perjure itself! How glibly, with a word, condemn others to suffer! How abjectly it will surrender happiness and almost life itself for a moment's prolongation of the delicious torture! The shame that follows is the spirit's resentment, its sad indignation at its bondage and humiliation.

Under the torment of pleasure, he thought, women are weaker than men. Their weakness flatters their lover's consciousness of strength, gratifies his desire for power. On one of his own sex a man will vent his love of power by making him suffer; but on a woman by making her enjoy. It is more the pleasurable torment he inflicts than what is inflicted upon him that delights the lover.

And since man is less weak, Calamy went on thinking, since pleasure with him is never so annihilating that he cannot take greater pleasure in the torment of his tormentor, is he not therefore the less excusable for breaking faith with himself or others under the delicious torture or the desire and anticipation of it? Man has less physical justification for his weakness and his enslavement. Woman is made by nature to be enslaved—by love, by children. But every now and then a man is born who ought to be free. For such a man it is disgraceful to succumb under the torture.

If I could free myself, he thought, I could surely do something; nothing useful, no doubt, in the ordinary sense, nothing that would particularly profit other people; but something that for me would be of the last importance. The mystery floats just above me. If I were free, if I had time, if I could think and think and slowly learn to plumb the silences of the spirit . . .

The image of Mary Thriplow presented itself again to his mind's eye. Limply she lay in the crook of his arm, trembling as though after torment. He shut his eyes; angrily he shook his head. The image would not leave him. If I were free, he said to himself, if I were free . . .

In the end he got out of bed and opened the door. The corridor was brightly illumined; an electric light was left burning all night. Calamy was just about to step out, when another door a little further down the passage was violently thrown open and Mr. Falx, his legs showing thin and hairy below the hem of a night-shirt, impetuously emerged. Calamy retired into the shadowed embrasure of his door. With the anxious, harrowed expression on his face of one who suffers from colic, Mr. Falx hurried past, looking neither to the left hand nor to the right. He turned down another passage which entered the main corridor a few yards away and disappeared; a door slammed. When he was out of sight, Calamy walked softly and rapidly down the corridor, opened the fourth door on the left and disappeared into the darkness. A little later Mr. Falx returned, at leisure, to his room.

PART IV

THE JOURNEY

Chapter I

LORD HOVENDEN detached from his motor-car was an entirely different being from the Lord Hovenden who lounged with such a deceptive air of languor behind the steering-wheel of a Vauxhall Velox. Half an hour spent in the roaring wind of his own speed transformed him from a shy and diffident boy into a cool-headed hero, daring not merely in the affairs of the road, but in the affairs of life as well. The fierce wind blew away his diffidence; the speed intoxicated him out of his self-consciousness. All his victories had been won while he was in the car. It was in the car—eighteen months ago, before he came of age—that he had ventured to ask his guardian to increase his allowance; and he had driven faster and faster until, in sheer terror, his guardian had agreed to do whatever he wished. It was on board the Velox that he had ventured to tell Mrs. Terebinth, who was seventeen years older than he, had four children and adored her husband, that she was the most beautiful woman he had ever seen; he had bawled it at her while they were doing seventy-five on the Great North Road. At sixty, at sixty-five, at seventy, his courage had still been inadequate to the achievement; but at seventy-five it reached the sticking-point: he had told her. And when she laughed and told him that he was an impudent young shrimp, he felt not a whit abashed, but laughed back, pressed the accelerator down a little further, and when the needle of the speedometer touched eighty, shouted through the wind and the noise of the engine: 'But I love you.' Unfortunately, however, the drive came to an end soon after; all drives must come to an end, sooner or later. The *affaire* Terebinth went no further. If only, Lord Hovenden regretfully sighed, if only one could spend all one's life in the Velox! But the Velox had its disadvantages. There were occasions when the heroic, speed-intoxicated self had got the timorous pedestrian into awkward scrapes. There was that time, for example, when, rolling along at sixty, he had airily promised one of his advanced political friends to make a speech at a meeting. The prospect, while one was doing sixty, had seemed not merely unalarming, but positively attractive. But what agonies he suffered when he was standing on the solid earth again, at his journey's end! How impossibly formidable the undertaking seemed! How bitterly he cursed himself for his folly in having accepted the invitation! In the end he was reduced to telegraphing that his doctor had ordered him peremptorily to the south of France. He fled, ignominiously.

To-day the Velox had its usual effect on him. At Vezza, when they started, he was all shyness and submission. He assented meekly to all the arrangements that Mrs. Aldwinkle made and re-made every five minutes, however contradictory and impossible. He did not venture to suggest that Irene should come in his car; it was through no good management of his own, but by the mere luck of Mrs. Aldwinkle's final caprice before the actual moment of starting, that he did in fact find her sitting next him when at last they moved off from before the palace doors. At the back sat Mr. Falx, in solitude, surrounded by suit-cases. To him Lord Hovenden had even dutifully promised that he would never go more than five-and-twenty miles an hour. Pedestrian slavishness could hardly go further.

Heavily loaded, Mrs. Aldwinkle's limousine started first. Miss Elver, who had begged to be granted this special favour, sat in front, next the chauffeur. An expression of perfect and absolute bliss irradiated her face. Whenever the car passed any one by the roadside, she made a shrill hooting noise and waved her handkerchief. Luckily she was unaware of the feelings of disgust and indignation which her conduct aroused in the chauffeur; he was English and enormously genteel, he had the reputation of his country and his impeccable car to keep up. And this person waved handkerchiefs and shouted as though she were on a char-à-banc. Miss Elver even waved at the cows and horses, she shouted even to the cats and the chickens.

In the body of the car sat Mrs. Aldwinkle, Mrs. Chelifer, Chelifer and Mr. Cardan. Calamy and Miss Thriplow had decided that they had no time to go to Rome and had been left—without a word of objection on Mrs. Aldwinkle's part—at the palace. The landscape slid placidly past the windows. Mr. Cardan and Mrs. Chelifer talked about traditional games.

Meanwhile, a couple of hundred yards behind, Lord Hovenden disgustfully sniffed the dusty air. 'How intolerably slowly old Ernest drives!' he said to his companion.

'Aunt Lilian doesn't allow him to do more than thirty miles an hour,' Irene explained.

Hovenden snorted derisively. 'Firty! But must we eat veir filthy dust all ve way?'

'Perhaps you might drop back a bit,' Irene suggested.

'Or perhaps we might pass vem?'

'Well . . .' said Irene doubtfully. 'I don't think we ought to make poor Aunt Lilian eat our dust.'

'She wouldn't eat it for long, if old Ernest is only allowed to do firty.'

'Well, in that case,' said Irene, feeling that her duty towards Aunt Lilian had been done, 'in that case . . .'

Lord Hovenden accelerated. The road was broad, flat and straight. There was no traffic. In two minutes Mrs. Aldwinkle had eaten her brief, unavoidable meal of dust;

the air was clear again. Far off along the white road, a rapidly diminishing cloud was all that could be seen of Lord Hovenden's Velox.

'Well, fank God,' Lord Hovenden was saying in a cheerful voice, 'now we can get along at a reasonable rate.' He grinned, a young ecstatic giant.

Irene also found the speed exhilarating. Under her grey silk mask, with its goggling windows for the eyes, her short lip was lifted in a joyful smile from the white small teeth. 'It's lovely,' she said.

'I'm glad you like it,' said Hovenden. 'Vat's splendid.'

But a tap on his shoulder reminded him that there was somebody else in the car besides Irene and himself. Mr. Falx was far from finding the present state of affairs splendid. Blown by the wind, his white beard shook and fluttered like a living thing in a state of mortal agitation. Behind the goggles, his dark eyes had an anxious look in them. 'Aren't you going rather fast?' he shouted, leaning forward, so as to make himself heard.

'Not a bit,' Hovenden shouted back. 'Just ve usual speed. Perfectly safe.' His ordinary pedestrian self would never have dreamed of doing anything contrary to the wishes of the venerated master. But the young giant who sat at the wheel of the Velox cared for nobody. He went his own way.

They passed through the sordid outskirts of Viareggio, through the pinewoods beyond, solemn with dark green shadow, and aromatic. Islanded in their grassy meadow within the battlemented walls, the white church, the white arcaded tower miraculously poised on the verge of falling, the round white baptistery seemed to meditate in solitude of ancient glories—Pisan dominion, Pisan arts and thoughts—of the mysteries of religion, of inscrutable fate and unfathomed godhead, of the insignificance and the grandeur of man.

'Why ve deuce it shouldn't fall,' said Hovenden, as the Leaning Tower came in sight, 'I can't imagine.'

They drove past the house on the water, where Byron had bored himself through an eternity of months, out of the town. After Pontedera the road became more desolate. Through a wilderness of bare, unfertile hills, between whose yellowing grasses showed a white and ghastly soil, they mounted towards Volterra. The landscape took on something of an infernal aspect; a prospect of parched hills and waterless gulleys, like the undulations of a petrified ocean, expanded interminably round them. And on the crest of the highest wave, the capital of this strange hell, stood Volterra—three towers against the sky, a dome, a line of impregnable walls, and outside the walls, still outside but advancing ineluctably year by year towards them, the ravening gulf that eats its way into the flank of the hill, devouring the works of civilization after civilization, the tombs of the Etruscans, Roman villas, abbeys and mediaeval fortresses, renaissance churches and the houses of yesterday.

'Must be a bit slow, life in a town like vis,' said Hovenden, racing round the hairpin turns with an easy virtuosity that appalled Mr. Falx.

'Think if one had been born there,' said Irene.

'Well, if we'd both been born vere,' replied Lord Hovenden, flushed with insolence and speed, 'it wouldn't have been so bad.'

They left Volterra behind them. The hellish landscape was gradually tempered with mundane greenness and amenity. They descended the headlong street of Colle. The landscape became once more completely earthly. The soil of the hills was red, like that from which God made Adam. In the steep fields grew rows of little pollard trees, from whose twisted black arms hung the festooned vines. Here and there between the trees shuffled a pair of white oxen, dragging a plough.

'Excellent roads, for a change,' said Lord Hovenden. On one straight stretch he managed to touch eighty-eight. Mr. Falx's beard writhed and fluttered with the agonized motions of some captive animal. He was enormously thankful when they drew up in front of the hotel at Siena.

'Wonderful machine, don't you fink?' Lord Hovenden asked him, when they had come to a standstill.

'You go much too fast,' said Mr. Falx severely.

Lord Hovenden's face fell. 'I'm awfully sorry,' he apologized. The young giant in him was already giving place to the meek pedestrian. He looked at his watch. 'The others won't be here for another three-quarters of an hour, I should fink,' he added, in the hope that Mr. Falx would be mollified by the information.

Mr. Falx was not mollified, and when the time came, after lunch, for setting out on the Perugia road, he expressed a decided preference for a seat in Mrs. Aldwinkle's limousine. It was decided that he should change places with Miss Elver.

Miss Elver had no objection to speed; indeed, it excited her. The faster they went, the more piercing became her cries of greeting and farewell, the more wildly she waved her handkerchief at the passing dogs and children. The only trouble about going so fast was that the mighty wind was always tearing the handkerchiefs from between her fingers and whirling them irretrievably into receding space. When all the four handkerchiefs in her reticule had been blown away, Miss Elver burst into tears. Lord Hovenden had to stop and lend her his coloured silk bandana. Miss Elver was enchanted by its gaudy beauty; to secure it against the assaults of the thievish wind, she made Irene tie one corner of it round her wrist.

'Now it'll be all right,' she said triumphantly; lifting her goggles, she wiped away the last traces of her recent grief.

Lord Hovenden set off again. On the sky-line, lifted high

above the rolling table-land over which they were travelling, the solitary blue shape of Monte Amiata beckoned from far away. With every mile to southward the horns of the white oxen that dragged the carts became longer and longer. A sneeze—one ran the risk of a puncture; a sideways toss of the head—one might have been impaled on the hard and polished points. They passed through San Quirico; from that secret and melancholy garden within the walls of the ruined citadel came a whiff of sun-warmed box. In Pienza they found the Platonic idea of a city, the town with a capital T; walls with a gate in them, a short street, a piazza with a cathedral and palaces round the other three sides, another short street, another gate and then the fields, rich with corn, wine and oil; and the tall blue peak of Monte Amiata looking down across the fertile land. At Montepulciano there were more palaces and more churches; but the intellectual beauty of symmetry was replaced by a picturesque and precipitous confusion.

'Gosh!' said Lord Hovenden expressively, as they slid with locked wheels down a high street that had been planned for pack-asses and mules. From pedimented windows between the pilasters of the palaces, curious faces peered out at them. They tobogganed down, through the high renaissance, out of an arch of the Middle Ages, into the dateless and eternal fields. From Montepulciano they descended on to Lake Trasimene.

'Wasn't there a battle here, or something?' asked Irene, when she saw the name on the map.

Lord Hovenden seemed to remember that there had indeed been something of the kind in this neighbourhood. 'But it doesn't make much difference, does it?'

Irene nodded; it certainly didn't seem to make much difference.

'Nofing makes any difference,' said Lord Hovenden,

making himself heard with difficulty in the teeth of a wind which his speedometer registered as blowing at forty-five miles an hour. 'Except'—the wind made him bold—'except you.' And he added hastily, in case Irene might try to be severe. 'Such a bore going down-hill on a twiddly road like vis. One can't risk ve slightest speed.'

But when they turned into the flat highway along the western shore of the lake, his face brightened. 'Vis is more like it,' he said. The wind in their faces increased from a capful to half a gale, from half a gale to a full gale, from a full gale very nearly to a hurricane. Lord Hovenden's spirits rose with the mounting speed. His lips curved themselves into a smile of fixed and permanent rapture. Behind the glass of his goggles his eyes were very bright. 'Pretty good going,' he said.

'Pretty good,' echoed Irene. Under her mask, she too was smiling. Between her ears and the flaps of her leather cap the wind made a glorious roaring. She was happy.

The road swung round to the left following the southern shore of the lake.

'We shall soon be at Perugia,' said Hovenden regretfully. 'What a bore!'

And Irene, though she said nothing, inwardly agreed with him.

They rushed on, the gale blew steadily in their faces. The road forked; Lord Hovenden turned the nose of his machine along the leftward branch. They lost sight of the blue water.

'Good-bye, Trasimene,' said Irene regretfully. It was a lovely lake; she wished she could remember what had happened there.

The road began to climb and twist; the wind abated to a mere half-gale. From the top of the hill, Irene was surprised to see the blue waters, which she had just taken leave of for ever, sparkling two or three hundred feet below on the left. At the joyous sight Miss Elver clapped her hands and shouted.

'Hullo,' Irene said, surprised. 'That's odd, isn't it?'

'Taken ve wrong road,' Hovenden explained. 'We're going norf again up ve east side of ve lake. We'll go right round. It's too much bore to stop and turn.'

They rushed on. For a long time neither of them spoke. Behind them Miss Elver hooted her greetings to every living creature on the road.

They were filled with happiness and joy; they would have liked to go on like this for ever. They rushed on. On the north shore of the lake the road straightened itself out and became flat again. The wind freshened. Far off on their respective hills Cortona and Montepulciano moved slowly, as they rushed along, like fixed stars. And now they were on the west shore once more. Perched on its jutting peninsula Castiglione del Lago reflected itself complacently in the water. 'Pretty good,' shouted Lord Hovenden in the teeth of the hurricane. 'By the way,' he added, 'wasn't it Hannibal or somebody who had a battle here? Wiv elephants, or somefing.'

'Perhaps it was,' said Irene.

'Not vat it matters in ve least.'

'Not in the least.' She laughed under her mask.

Hovenden laughed too. He was happy, he was joyful, he was daring.

'Would you marry me if I asked you?' he said. The question followed naturally and by a kind of logic from what they had been saying about Hannibal and his elephants. He did not look at her as he asked the question; when one is doing sixty-seven one must keep one's eyes on the road.

'Don't talk nonsense,' said Irene.

'I'm not talking nonsense,' Lord Hovenden protested.

'I'm asking a straightforward question. Would you marry me?'

'No.'

'Why not?'

'I don't know,' said Irene.

They had passed Castiglione. The fixed stars of Montepulciano and Cortona had set behind them.

'Don't you like me?' shouted Lord Hovenden. The wind had swelled into a hurricane.

'You know I do.'

'Ven why not?'

'Because, because . . . Oh, I don't know. I wish you'd stop talking about it.'

The machine rushed on. Once more they were running along the southern shore. A hundred yards before the forking of the roads, Lord Hovenden broke silence. 'Will you marry me?' he asked.

'No,' said Irene.

Lord Hovenden turned the nose of his machine to the left. The road climbed and twisted, the wind of their speed abated.

'Stop,' said Irene. 'You've taken the wrong turn again.'

But Hovenden did not stop. Instead, he pressed down the accelerator. If the car got round the corners it was more by a miracle than in obedience to the laws of Newton or of nature.

'Stop!' cried Irene again. But the car went on.

From the hill-top they looked down once more upon the lake.

'Will you marry me?' Lord Hovenden asked again. His eyes were fixed on the road in front of him. Rapturously, triumphantly he smiled. He had never felt happier, never more daring, more overflowing with strength and power. 'Will you marry me?'

'No,' said Irene. She felt annoyed; how stupidly he was behaving!

They were silent for several minutes. At Castiglione del Lago he asked again. Irene repeated her answer.

'You're not going to do this clown's trick again, are you?' she asked as they approached the bifurcation of the roads.

'It depends if you're going to marry me,' he answered. This time he laughed aloud; so infectiously that Irene, whose irritation was something laid on superficially over her happiness, could not help laughing too. '*Are* you going to?' he asked.

'No.'

Lord Hovenden turned to the left. 'It'll be late before we get to Perugia,' he said.

'Oo-ooh!' cried Miss Elver, as they topped the long hill. 'How lovely!' She clapped her hands. Then, leaning forward, she touched Irene's shoulder. 'What a lot of lakes there are here!' she said.

On the north shore Lord Hovenden asked again. Cortona and Montepulciano presided at the asking.

'I don't see why I should be bullied,' said Irene. Lord Hovenden found the answer more promising than those which had gone before.

'But you're not being bullied.'

'I am,' she insisted. 'You're trying to force me to answer all at once, without thinking.'

'Now really,' said Hovenden, 'I call vat a bit fick. Forcing you to answer all at once! But vat's exactly what I'm not doing. I'm giving you time. We'll go round ve lake all night, if you like.'

A quarter of a mile from the forking of the road, he put the question yet once more.

'You're a beast,' said Irene.

'Vat's not an answer.'

'I don't want to answer.'

'You needn't answer definitely if you don't want to,' he conceded. 'I only want you to say vat you'll fink of it. Just say perhaps.'

'I don't want to,' Irene insisted. They were very close, now, to the dividing of ways.

'Just perhaps. Just say you'll fink of it.'

'Well, I'll think,' said Irene. 'But mind, it doesn't commit . . .'

She did not finish her sentence; for the car, which had been heading towards the left, swerved suddenly to the right with such violence that Irene had to clutch at the arm of her seat to prevent herself from being thrown sideways bodily out of the machine. 'Goodness!'

'It's all right,' said Lord Hovenden. They were running smoothly now along the right-hand road. Ten minutes later, from the crest of a little pass, they saw Perugia on its mountain, glittering in the sunlight. They found, when they reached the hotel, that the rest of the party had long since arrived.

'We took ve wrong turning,' Lord Hovenden explained. 'By ve way,' he added, turning to Mr. Cardan, 'about vat lake we passed—wasn't it Hannibal or some one . . .'

'Such a lot of lakes,' Miss Elver was telling Mrs. Chelifer. 'Such a lot!'

'Only one, surely, my dear,' Mrs. Chelifer mildly insisted.

But Miss Elver wouldn't hear of it. 'Lots and lots.'

Mrs. Chelifer sighed compassionately.

Before dinner Irene and Lord Hovenden went for a stroll in the town. The huge stone palaces lowered down at them as they passed. The sun was so low that only their highest windows, their roofs and cornices took the light. The world's grey shadow was creeping up their flanks; but their crests were tipped with coral and ruddy gold.

'I like vis place,' said Lord Hovenden. In the circumstances he would have liked Wigan or Pittsburg.

'So do I,' said Irene. Through the window in her thick hair her face looked smiling out, merry in its childishness.

Leaving the stately part of the town, they plunged into the labyrinth of steep alleys, of winding passage-ways and staircases behind the cathedral. Built confusedly on the hill-side, the tall houses seemed to grow into one another, as though they were the component parts of one immense and fantastical building, in which the alleys served as corridors. The road would burrow through the houses in a long dark tunnel, to widen out into a little well-like courtyard, open to the sky. Through open doors, at the head of an outside staircase, one saw in the bright electric light a family sitting round the soup tureen. The road turned into a flight of stairs, dipped into another tunnel, made cheerful by the lights of a subterranean wine shop opening into it. From the mouth of the bright cavern came up the smell of liquor, the sound of loud voices and reverberated laughter.

And then, suddenly emerging from under the high houses, they found themselves standing on the edge of an escarped slope, looking out on to a huge expanse of pale evening sky, scalloped at its fringes by the blue shapes of mountains, with the round moon, already bright, hanging serene and solemn in the midst. Leaning over the parapet, they looked down at the roofs of another quarter of the city, a hundred feet below. The colours of the world still struggled against the encroaching darkness; but a lavish municipality had already beaded the streets with yellow lights. A faint smell of wood-smoke and frying came up through the thin pure air. The silence of the sky was so capacious, so high and wide, that the noises of the town—like so many small, distinctly seen objects in the midst of an immense blank prairie—served but to intensify the quiet, to make the listener more conscious of its immensity in comparison with the trivial clatter at its heart.

'I like vis place,' Lord Hovenden repeated.

They stood for a long time, leaning their elbows on the parapet, saying nothing.

'I say,' said Hovenden suddenly, turning towards his companion a face on which all the shyness, the pedestrian's self-deprecation had reappeared, 'I'm most awfully sorry about vat silly business of going round vat beastly lake.' The young giant who sat at the wheel of the Vauxhall Velox had retired with the machine into the garage, leaving a much less formidable Hovenden to prosecute the campaign which he had so masterfully begun. The moon, the enchanting beauty of the face that looked out so pensively through its tress-framed window, the enormous silence with the little irrelevant noises at its heart, the smell of wood-smoke and fried veal cutlets—all these influences had conspired to mollify Lord Hovenden's joyous elation into a soft and sugary melancholy. His actions of this afternoon seemed to him now, in his changed mood, reprehensibly violent. He was afraid that his brutality might have ruined his cause. Could she ever forgive him for such behaviour? He was overwhelmed by self-reproach. To beg forgiveness seemed to be his only hope. 'I'm awfully sorry.'

'Are you?' Irene turned and smiled at him. Her small white teeth showed beneath the lifted lip; in the wide-set, childish eyes there was a shining happiness. 'I'm not. I didn't mind a bit.'

Lord Hovenden took her hand. 'You didn't mind? Not at all?'

She shook her head. 'You remember that day under the olive trees?'

'I was a beast,' he whispered remorsefully.

'I was a goose,' said Irene 'But I feel different now.'

'You don't mean . . .'

She nodded. They walked back to their hotel hand in hand. Hovenden never stopped talking and laughing all the way. Irene was silent. The kiss had made her happy too, but in a different way.

Chapter II

TIME and space, matter and mind, subject, object—how inextricably they got mixed, next day, on the road to Rome! The simple-minded traveller who imagines himself to be driving quietly through Umbria and Latium finds himself at the same time dizzily switchbacking up and down the periods of history, rolling on top gear through systems of political economy, scaling heights of philosophy and religion, whizzing from aesthetic to aesthetic. Dimensions are bewilderingly multiplied, and the machine which seems to be rolling so smoothly over the roads is travelling, in reality, as fast as forty horses and the human minds on board can take it, down a score of other roads, simultaneously, in all directions.

The morning was bright when they left Perugia. In the blue sky above Subasio floated a few large white clouds. Silently they rolled away down the winding hill. At the foot of the mountain, secure from the sunlight in the delicious cool of their family vault, the obese Volumni reclined along the lids of their marble ashbins, as though on couches round the dinner-table. In an eternal anticipation of the next succulent course they smiled and for ever went on smiling. We enjoyed life, they seemed to say, and considered death without horror. The thought of death was the seasoning which made our five and twenty thousand dinners upon this earth yet more appetizing.

A few miles further on, at Assisi, the mummy of a she-saint lies in a glass case, brilliantly illumined by concealed electric lights. Think of death, says the she-saint, ponder incessantly on the decay of all things, the transience of this sublunary life. Think, think; and in the end life itself will lose all its savour; death will corrupt it; the flesh will seem a shame and a disgustfulness. Think of death hard enough and you will come to deny the beauty and the holiness of life; and, in point of fact, the mummy was once a nun.

'When Goethe came to Assisi,' said Mr. Cardan, as they emerged from the vaults of St. Clare, 'the only thing he looked at was the portico of a second-rate Roman temple. Perhaps he wasn't such a fool as we think him.'

'An admirable place for playing halma,' said Chelifer, as they entered the Teatro Metastasio.

Upon that rococo stage art was intended to worship itself. Everywhere now, for the last two hundred years and more, it has been worshipping itself.

But in the upper and the lower churches of St. Francis, Giotto and Cimabue showed that art had once worshipped something other than itself. Art there is the handmaid of religion—or, as the psycho-analysts would say, more scientifically, anal-erotism is a frequent concomitant of incestuous homosexuality.

'I wonder,' said Mr. Cardan pensively, 'if St. Francis really managed to make poverty seem so dignified, charming and attractive as they make out. I know very few poor people nowadays who cut a particularly graceful figure.' He looked at Miss Elver, who was waddling along the road like a water-bird on land, a few yards ahead. The end of one of Lord Hovenden's bright bandanas trailed behind her in the dust; it was tied by one corner to her wrist and she had forgotten its existence. Twenty-five thousand pounds, thought Mr. Cardan, and sighed. St. Francis, Gotama

Buddha—they managed their affairs rather differently. But it was difficult nowadays to beg with any degree of dignity.

They got into the cars once more; waving the red bandana, Miss Elver said good-bye to the saints who thought so much of death that they were forced to mortify their lives. In their cool summer-house the obese Volumni smiled contemptuously. We thought not of death, we begat children, multiplied our flocks, added acre to acre, glorified life. . . . Lord Hovenden accelerated; the two wisdoms, the new and the ancient law, receded into the distance.

Spello came tumbling down the hill to look at them. In Foligno it was market day. There were so many people that Miss Elver exhausted herself in continuous wavings and greetings. Trevi on its conical mountain was like the picture of a city in an illuminated book. By the side of the road, in the rich plain, stood factories; their tall chimneys were the slenderer repetitions of the castle towers perched high on the slopes of the hills above. In these secure and civilized times the robbers come down from their mountain fastnesses and build their watch-towers in the valleys. They were driving through progress; through progress at a mile a minute. And suddenly the cool and sparkling miracle of Clitumnus was at their right hand. The sacred spring came rushing out of the flank of the hill into a brimming pool. The banks were green with an almost English grass. There were green islands in the midst; and the weeping willow trees drooping over the water, the little bridges, transformed the Roman site into the original landscape from which a Chinese artist first drew a willow pattern.

'More lakes,' cried Miss Elver.

At Spoleto they stopped for lunch and the frescoes of Filippo Lippi, a painter Mrs. Aldwinkle particularly admired for having had the strength of mind, though a friar, to run off with a young girl at a Convent School. The shadowy apse was melodious with pious and elegant shapes and clear, pure colours. Anal-erotism was still the handmaid of incestuous homosexuality, but not exclusively. There was more than a hint in these bright forms of anal-erotism for anal-erotism's sake. But the designer of that more than Roman *cinquecento* narthex at the west end of the church, he surely was a pure and unmixed coprophilite. How charming is divine philosophy! Astrology, alchemy, phrenology and animal magnetism, the N-rays, ectoplasm and the calculating horses of Elberfield—these have had their turn and passed. We need not regret them; for we can boast of a science as richly popular, as easy and as all-explanatory as ever were phrenology or magic. Gall and Mesmer have given place to Freud. Filippo Lippi once had a bump of art. He is now an incestuous homosexualist with a bent towards anal-erotism. Can we doubt any longer that human intelligence progresses and grows greater? Fifty years hence, what will be the current explanation of Filippo Lippi? Something profounder, something more fundamental even than faeces and infantile incestuousness; of that we may be certain. But what, precisely what, God alone knows. How charming is divine philosophy!

'I like vese paintings,' Lord Hovenden whispered to Irene.

They set out again. Over the pass of the Somma, down the long winding gorge to Terni.

On across the plain (the mountains bristling jaggedly all round) and up the hill to Narni; Narni that hangs precariously on the brink of its deep precipitous valley; on into the Sabine hills.

Sabine, Sabine—how wildly the mere word deviated the machine from its course! *Eheu, fugaces*, how the days draw in—was not that first said, first elegantly and compellingly said, in a Sabine farm? And the Sabine women! Only

Rubens knew what they looked like and how they ought to be raped. How large and blonde they were! What glossy satin dresses they had on, what pearls! And their Roman ravishers were tanned as brown as Indians. Their muscles bulged; their eyes, their polished armour flashed. From the backs of their prancing horses they fairly dived into the foaming sea of female flesh that splashed and wildly undulated around them. The very architecture became tumultuous and orgiastic. Those were the high old times. Climbing from Narni, they drove into the heart of them.

But other artists than Peter Paul had passed this way. He painted only the Sabine name; they, the scene. An ancient shepherd, strayed from one of Piranesi's ruins, watched them from a rock above the road, leaning on his staff. A flock of goats, kneeling ruminatively in the shade of an oak tree, their black bearded faces, their twisted horns sharply outlined against the bright blue sky, grouped themselves professionally —good beasts! they had studied the art of pictorial composition under the best masters—in momentary expectation of Rosa da Tivoli's arrival. And the same Italianizing Dutchman was surely responsible for that flock of dusty sheep, those dogs, those lads with staves and that burly master shepherd, dressed like a capripede in goatskin breeches and mounted on the back of a little donkey, whose smallness contributed by contrast to the portly dignity of its rider. Nor were Dutchmen and Flemings the only foreign painters in this Italian scene. There were trees, there were glades in the woods, there were rocks that belonged by right of conquest to Nicolas Poussin. Half close the eyes, and that grey stone becomes a ruined sepulchre: *Et ego in Arcadia* . . .; the village there, on the hill-top, across the valley, flowers into a little city of colonnades and cupolas and triumphal arches, and the peasants working in the fields are the people of a transcendental Arcadia gravely and soberly engaged in pursuing the True, the rationally Good and Beautiful. So much for the foreground and the middle distance. But suddenly, from the crest of a long descent, the remote wide background of Poussin's ideal world revealed itself: the vale of the Tiber, the broken plain of the Campagna, and in the midst—fantastic, improbable—the solitary cone of Mount Soracte, dim and blue against the blue of the sky.

Chapter III

FROM the heights of the Pincio Mr. Falx denounced the city that lay spread out below him.

'Marvellous, isn't it?' Mrs. Aldwinkle had said. Rome was one of her private properties.

'But every stone of it,' said Mr. Falx, 'raised by slave labour. Every stone! Millions of wretches have sweated and toiled and died'—Mr. Falx's voice rose, his language became richer and richer, he gesticulated as though he were addressing a public meeting—'in order that these palaces, these stately churches, these forums, amphitheatres, cloaca maximas and what-nots might be here to-day to gratify your idle eyes. Is it worth it, I ask you? Is the momentary gratification of a few idlers a sufficient reason for the secular oppression of millions of human beings, their brothers, their equals in the eyes of God? Is it, I ask again? No, a thousand times no.' With his right fist Mr. Falx thumped the open palm of his left hand. 'No!'

'But you forget,' said Mr. Cardan, 'there's such a thing as a natural hierarchy.' The words seemed to remind him of something. He looked round. At one of the little tea-tables grouped round the band-stand at the other side of the road, Miss Elver, dressed in her sack of flowered upholstery, was eating chocolate éclairs and meringues, messily, with an expression of rapture on her cream-smeared face. Mr. Cardan turned back and continued: 'There are a few choice Britons who never never will be slaves, and a great many who not only will be slaves, but would be utterly lost if they were made free. Isn't it so?'

'Specious,' said Mr. Falx severely. 'But does the argument justify you in grinding the life out of a million human beings for the sake of a few works of art? How many thousand workmen and their wives and children lived degraded lives in order that St. Peter's might be what it is?'

'Well, as a matter of fact, St. Peter's isn't much of a work of art,' said Mrs. Aldwinkle scornfully, feeling that she had scored a decided point in the argument.

'If it's a question of degraded lives,' put in Chelifer, 'let me make a claim for the middle classes rather than the workers. Materially, perhaps, they may live a little better; but morally and spiritually, I assure you, they stand at the very heart of reality. Intellectually, of course, they are indistinguishable from the workers. All but a negligible, freakish minority in both classes belong to the three lowest Galtonian categories. But morally and spiritually they are worse off; they suffer from a greater reverence for public opinion, they are tortured by snobbery, they live perpetually in the midst of fear and hate. For if the workers are afraid of losing their jobs, so too are the burgesses, and with almost better reason—for they have more to lose, have further to fall. They fall from a precarious heaven of gentility into the abysses of unrelieved poverty, into the workhouse and the glutted labour exchanges; can you wonder that they live in fear? And as for hate—you can talk about the hate of the proletariat for the bourgeoisie, but it's nothing, I assure you, to the hate that the bourgeoisie feel for the proletariat. Your burgess loathes the worker because he is afraid of him; he is terrified of the revolution that may pull him down from his genteel heaven into hell. How enviously, with what a bitter resentment, your burgess regards the slightest amelioration of the worker's existence! To him it always seems an amelioration made at his expense. Do you remember, during the war, and in the prosperous time immediately following, when the workers for the first time in history were paid a wage that enabled them to live in something like comfort, do you remember how furiously, with what a black atrabilious overflow of hatred, the middle classes denounced the riotous excesses of the idle poor? Why, the monsters even bought pianos—pianos! The pianos have all been sold again, long since. The spare furniture has gone the way of all superfluities. Even the winter overcoat is pawned. The burgess, for all that the times are hard for him too, feels happier; he is revenged. He can live in a comparative tranquillity. And what a life! He lives according to his lusts, but timorously and in a conventional way; his diversions are provided for him by joint stock companies. He has no religion, but a great respect for genteel conventions which have not even the justification of a divine origin. He has heard of art and thought, and respects them because the best people respect them; but his mental capacities and his lack of education do not allow him to get any real satisfaction out of them. He is thus poorer than the savage, who, if he has never heard of art or science, is yet rich in religion and traditional lore. The life of a wild animal has a certain dignity and beauty; it is only the life of a domesticated animal that can be called degraded. The burgess is the perfectly domesticated human animal. That is why,' added Chelifer, 'that is why any one who wants to live really at the heart of human reality must live in the midst of burgessdom. In a little while, however, it won't be necessary to make any invidious distinctions between the classes. Every one will soon be bourgeois. The charm of the lower classes in the past consisted in the fact that they were composed of human animals in a state of relative wildness. They had a traditional wisdom and a traditional superstition; they had ancient and symbolical diversions of their own. My mother can tell you all about those,' he put in parenthetically. 'That Tolstoy should have preferred the Russian peasants to his rich and literary friends is very comprehensible. The peasants were wild; the others, just as brutish at bottom, were disgustingly tame. Moreover, they were lap-dogs of a perfectly useless breed; the peasants at any rate did something to justify their existence. But in the other countries of Europe and the New World the wild breed is rapidly dying out. Million-sale newspapers and radios are domesticating them at a prodigious rate. You can go a long way in England nowadays before you find a genuine wild human animal. Still, they do exist in the country and even in the more fetid and savage parts of towns. That's why, I repeat, one must live among the suburban bourgeoisie. The degraded and domesticated are the typical human animals of the present time; it's they who will inherit the earth in the next generation; they're the characteristic modern reality. The wild ones are no longer typical; it would be ludicrous to be a Tolstoyan now, in western Europe. And as for the genuine men and women, as opposed to the human animals, whether wild or tame—they're so fabulously exceptional that one has no right to think of them at all. That cupola,' he pointed to the silhouette of St. Peter's, rising high above the houses on the other side of the city, 'was designed by Michelangelo. And very nice too. But what has it or he to do with us?'

'Blasphemy!' cried Mrs. Aldwinkle, flying to the defence of Buonarroti.

Mr. Falx harked back to an earlier grievance. 'You malign human nature,' he said.

'All very true and indeed obvious,' was Mr. Cardan's comment. 'But I can't see why you shouldn't allow us to amuse ourselves with Michelangelo if we want to. God knows, it's hard enough for a man to adapt himself to circumstances; why should you deprive him of his little assistants in the difficult task? Wine, for example, learning, cigars and conversation, art, cooking, religion for those that like it, sport, love, humanitarianism, hashish and all the rest. Every man has his own recipe for facilitating the process of adaptation. Why shouldn't he be allowed to indulge in his dope in peace? You young men are all so damned intolerant. How often have I had occasion to say it? You're nothing but a set of prohibitionists, the whole lot of you.'

'Still,' said Mrs. Chelifer in her gentle and musical voice, 'you can't deny that prohibition has done a great deal of good in America.'

They strolled back to the tea-table, which they had left a few minutes before to look at the view. Miss Elver was just finishing an éclair. Two empty dishes stood in front of her.

'Had a good tea?' asked Mr. Cardan.

Miss Elver nodded; her mouth was too full to speak.

'Perhaps you'd like some more cakes?' he suggested.

Miss Elver looked at the two empty dishes, then at Mr. Cardan. She seemed on the point of saying yes. But Mrs. Chelifer, who had taken the chair next hers, laid a hand on her arm.

'I don't think Grace really wants any more,' she said.

Grace turned towards her; a look of disappointment and melancholy came into her eyes, but it gave place after a moment to a happier expression. She smiled, she took Mrs. Chelifer's hand and kissed it.

'I like you,' she said.

On the back of Mrs. Chelifer's hand her lips had left a brown print of melted chocolate. 'I think you'd better just give your face a little wipe with your napkin,' Mrs. Chelifer suggested.

'Perhaps if you dipped the corner of it first into the hot water . . .'

There was a silence. From the open-air dancing-floor, a hundred yards away beneath the trees, came the sound, a little dimmed by the intervening distance and the pervading Roman noise, of the jazz band. Monotonously, unceasingly, the banjos throbbed out the dance rhythms. An occasional squeak indicated the presence of a violin. The trumpet could be heard tooting away with a dreary persistence at the tonic and dominant; and clear above all the rest the saxophone voluptuously caterwauled. At this distance every tune sounded exactly the same. Suddenly, from the bandstand of the tea-garden a pianist, two fiddlers and a 'cellist began to play the Pilgrims' Chorus out of *Tannhäuser*.

Irene and Lord Hovenden, locked in one another's arms, were stepping lightly, meanwhile, lightly and accurately over the concrete dance-floor. Obedient to the music of the jazz band, forty other couples stepped lightly round them. Percolating insidiously through the palisade that separated the dance-floor from the rest of the world, thin wafts of the Pilgrims' Chorus intruded faintly upon the jazz.

'Listen,' said Hovenden. Dancing, they listened. 'Funny it sounds when you hear bof at ve same time!'

But the music from beyond the palisade was not strong enough to spoil their rhythm. They listened for a little, smiling at the absurdity of this other music from outside; but they danced on uninterruptedly. After a time they did not even take the trouble to listen.

Chapter IV

Mr. Falx had expected to find no difficulty, once they were arrived in Rome, in recalling his pupil to what he considered a better and more serious frame of mind. In the bracing atmosphere of an International Labour Conference Lord Hovenden, he hoped, would recover his moral and intellectual tone. Listening to speeches, meeting foreign comrades, he would forget the corrupting charms of life under Mrs. Aldwinkle's roof and turn to nobler and more important things. Moreover, on a young and generous spirit like his the prospect of possible persecution at the hands of the Fascists might be expected to act as a stimulant; the fact of being in opposition ought to make him feel the more ardently for the unpopular cause. So Mr. Falx calculated.

But it turned out in the event that he had calculated badly. Arrived in Rome, Lord Hovenden seemed to take even less interest in advanced politics than he had during the last two or three weeks at Vezza. He suffered himself, but with a reluctance that was only too obvious to Mr. Falx, to be taken to a few of the meetings of the conference. Their bracing intellectual atmosphere had no tonic effect upon him whatsoever, and he spent his time at the meetings yawning and looking with an extraordinary frequency at his watch. In the evenings, when Mr. Falx wanted to take him to see some distinguished comrade, Lord Hovenden either made some vague excuse or, more frequently, was simply undiscoverable. The next day Mr. Falx learned with distress that he had passed half the night at a Dancing Club with Irene Aldwinkle. He could only look forward hopefully to the date of Mrs. Aldwinkle's return journey. Lord Hovenden—it had been arranged before they left England—would stay on with him in Rome till the end of the conference. With the removal of all temptations to frivolity he might be relied upon to re-become his better self.

Lord Hovenden's conscience, meanwhile, occasionally troubled him.

'I sometimes feel I've raver left old Mr. Falx in ve lurch,' he confided uneasily to Irene on the evening of their second day in Rome. 'But still, he can't really expect me to spend all ve day wiv him, can he?'

Irene agreed that he really couldn't.

'Besides,' Lord Hovenden went on, reassuring himself, 'I'd really be raver out of it wiv his friends. And it's not as if he were lonely. Vere's such a lot of people he wants to talk to. And, you know, I fink I'd really be in ve way more van anyfing.'

Irene nodded. The band struck up again. Simultaneously the two young people got up and, united, stepped off on to the floor. It was a sordid and flashy cabaret, frequented by the worst sort of international and Italian public. The women were mostly prostitutes; a party of loud and tipsy young Englishmen and Americans were sitting in one corner with a pair of swarthy young natives who looked altogether too sober; the couples who took the floor danced with an excessive intimacy. Irene and Lord Hovenden were discussing the date of their wedding; they thought the cabaret delightful.

In the day-time, when Hovenden could get off going to the conferences, they wandered about the town buying what they imagined to be antiques for their future home. The process was a little superfluous. For, absorbed in the delights of shopping, they forgot that their future home was also a highly ancestral home.

'Vat looks an awfully nice dinner-service,' Lord Hovenden would say; and darting into the shop they would buy it out of hand. 'A bit chipped'—he shook his head. 'But never mind.' Among the twenty-three valuable dinner-services with which their future home was already supplied was one of solid gold and one of silver gilt for less important occasions. Still, it was such fun buying, such fun to poke about in the shops ! Under the pale blue sky of autumn the city was golden and black—golden where the sunlight fell on walls of stucco or travertine, black in the shadows, deeply black under archways, within the doors of churches, glossily black where the sculptured stone of fountains shone wet with the unceasing gush of water. In the open places the sun was hot; but a little wind from the sea blew freshly, and from the mouth of narrow alleys, sun-proof these thousand years, there breathed forth wafts of a delicious vault-like coolness. They walked for hours without feeling tired.

Mrs. Aldwinkle meanwhile went the round of the sights with Chelifer. She had hopes that the Sistine Chapel, the Appian Way at sunset, the Coliseum by moonlight, the gardens of the Villa d'Este might arouse in Chelifer's mind emotions which should in their turn predispose him to feel romantically towards herself. The various emotions, she knew by experience, are not boxed off from one another in separate pigeon-holes; and when one is stimulated it is likely that its neighbours will also be aroused. More proposals are made in the taxi, on the way home from a Wagner opera, in the face of an impressive view, within the labyrinth of a ruined palace, than in drab parlours or the streets of West Kensington. But the Appian Way, even when the solitary pine trees were black against the sunset and the ghosts were playing oboes, not for the sensual ear, in the ruined sepulchres; the Coliseum, even under the moon; the cypresses, the cascades and the jade-green pools of Tivoli —all were ineffective. Chelifer never committed himself; his behaviour remained perfectly courteous.

Seated on a fallen column in the ruins of Hadrian's Villa,

Mrs. Aldwinkle even went so far as to tell him about certain amorous passages in her past life. She told him, with various little modifications of the facts, modifications in which she herself had long ago come implicitly to believe, the story of the affair with Elzevir, the pianist—such an artist ! to his finger-tips ; with Lord Trunion—such a *grand seigneur* of the old school ! But concerning Mr. Cardan she was silent. It was not that Mrs. Aldwinkle's mythopoeic faculties were not equal to making something very extraordinary and romantic out of Mr. Cardan. No, no ; she had often described the man to those who did not know him ; he was a sort of village Hampden, a mute inglorious What's-his-name, who might have done anything—but anything—if he had chosen to give himself the trouble. He was a great Don Juan, actual in this case, not merely potential. He was a mocking devil's advocate, he was even a devil. But that was because he was misunderstood—misunderstood by everybody but Mrs. Aldwinkle herself. Secretly he was so sensitive and kind-hearted. But one had to be gifted with intuition to find it out. And so on ; she had made a capital mythical figure out of him. But an instinct of caution restrained her from showing off her myths too freely before people who were well acquainted with the originals. Chelifer had never met Lord Trunion or the immortal Elzevir. He *had* met Mr. Cardan.

But the effect of the confidences was as small as that of the romantic scenery and the stupendous works of art. Chelifer was not encouraged by them either to confide in return or to follow the example of Elzevir and Lord Trunion. He listened attentively, gave vent, when she had finished, to a few well-chosen expressions of sympathy, such as one writes to acquaintances on the deaths of their aged grandmothers, and after a considerable silence, looking at his watch, said he thought it was time to be getting back : he had promised to meet his mother for tea, and after tea, he added, he was going to take her to look at *pensions*. Seeing that she was going to stay in Rome the whole winter, it was worth taking some trouble about finding a nice room. Wasn't it? Mrs. Aldwinkle was forced to agree. They set off through the parched Campagna towards the city. Mrs. Aldwinkle preserved a melancholy silence all the way.

On their way from the hotel to the tea-shop in the Piazza Venezia Mrs. Chelifer, Miss Elver and Mr. Cardan passed through the forum of Trajan. The two little churches lifted their twin domes of gold against the sky. From the floor of the forum, deep-sunk beneath the level of the road—a foot for every hundred years—rose the huge column, with tumbled pillars and blocks of masonry lying confusedly round its base. They paused to look round.

'I've always been a Protestant,' said Mrs. Chelifer after a moment's silence; 'but all the same I've always felt, whenever I came here, that Rome was somehow a special place; that God had marked it out in some peculiar way from among other cities as a place where the greatest things should happen. It's a significant place, a portentous place—though I couldn't tell you exactly why. One just feels that it is portentous; that's all. Look at this piazza, for example. Two florid little counter-Reformation churches, all trumpery pretentiousness and no piety; a mixed lot of ordinary houses all round, and in the hole in the middle a huge heathen memorial of slaughter. And yet for some reason it all seems to me to have a significance, a spiritual meaning; it's important. And the same applies to everything in this extraordinary place. You can't regard it with indifference as you can an ordinary town.'

'And yet,' said Mr. Cardan, 'a great many tourists and all the inhabitants contrive to do so with complete success.'

'That's only because they've never looked at the place,' said Mrs. Chelifer. 'Once you've really looked . . .'

She was interrupted by a loud whoop from Miss Elver, who had wandered away from her companions and was looking over the railing into the sunken forum.

'What is it?' called Mr. Cardan. They hurried across the street towards her.

'Look,' cried Miss Elver, pointing down, 'look. All the cats!'

And there they were. On the sun-warmed marble of a fallen column basked a large tabby. A family of ginger kittens were playing on the ground below. Small tigers stalked between the blocks of masonry. A miniature black panther was standing up on its hind legs to sharpen its claws on the bark of a little tree. At the foot of the column lay an emaciated corpse.

'Puss, puss,' Miss Elver shrilly yelled.

'No good,' said Mr. Cardan. 'They only understand Italian.'

Miss Elver looked at him. 'Perhaps I'd better learn a little, then,' she said. 'Cat's Italian.'

Mrs. Chelifer meanwhile was looking down very earnestly into the forum. 'Why, there are at least twenty,' she said. 'How do they get there?'

'People who want to get rid of their cats just come and drop them over the railing into the forum,' Mr. Cardan explained.

'And they can't get out?'

'So it seems.'

An expression of distress appeared on Mrs. Chelifer's gentle face. She made a little clicking with her tongue against her teeth and sadly shook her head. 'Dear, dear,' she said, 'dear, dear. And how do they get fed?'

'I've no idea,' said Mr. Cardan. 'Perhaps they feed on

one another. People throw things down from time to time, no doubt.'

'There's a dead one there, in the middle,' said Mrs. Chelifer; and a note of something like reproach came into her voice, as though she found that Mr. Cardan was to blame for the deadness of the little corpse at the foot of the triumphal column.

'Very dead,' said Mr. Cardan.

They walked on. Mrs. Chelifer did not speak; she seemed preoccupied.

Chapter V

'*AN pris caruns flucuthukh*'; Mr. Cardan beckoned to the guide. 'Bring the lamp a little nearer,' he said in Italian, and when the light had been approached, he went on slowly spelling out the primitive Greek writing on the wall of the tomb: '*flucuthukh nun tithuial khues khathc anulis mulu vizile ziz riin puiian acasri flucuper pris an ti ar vus ta aius muntheri flucuthukh.*' He straightened himself up. 'Charming language,' he said, 'charming! Ever since I learned that the Etruscans used to call the god of wine Fufluns, I've taken the keenest interest in their language. Fufluns—how incomparably more appropriate that is than Bacchus, or Liber, or Dionysos! Fufluns, *Fufluns*,' he repeated with delighted emphasis. 'It couldn't be better. They had a real linguistic genius, those creatures. What poets they must have produced! "When Fufluns *flucuthukhs* the *ziz*"—one can imagine the odes in praise of wine which began like that. You couldn't bring together eight such juicy, boozy syllables as that in English, could you?'

'What about "Ale in a Saxon rumkin" then?' suggested Chelifer.

Mr. Cardan shook his head. 'It doesn't compare with

the Etruscan,' he said. 'There aren't enough consonants. It's too light, too fizzy and trivial. Why, you might be talking about soda water.'

'But for all you know,' said Chelifer, '*flucuthukh* in Etruscan may mean soda water. Fufluns, I grant you, is apposite. But perhaps it was just a fluke. You have no evidence to show that they fitted sound to sense so aptly in other words. "When Fufluns *flucuthukhs* the *ziz*" may be the translation of "When Bacchus drowns the hock with soda." You don't know.'

'You're quite right,' Mr. Cardan agreed. 'I don't. Nor does any one else. My enthusiasm for Fufluns carried me away. *Flucuthukh* may not have the fruity connotation that a word with a sound like that ought to have; it may even, as you say, mean soda water. Still, I continue to hope for the best; I believe in my Etruscans. One day, when they find the key to this fossilized language, I believe I shall be justified; *flucuthukh* will turn out to be just as appropriate as Fufluns—you mark my words! It's a great language, I insist; a great language. Who knows? A couple of generations hence some new Busby or Keat may be drumming Etruscan syntax and Etruscan prosody into the backsides of British boyhood. Nothing would give me greater satisfaction. Latin and Greek have a certain infinitesimal practical value. But Etruscan is totally and absolutely useless. What better basis for a gentleman's education could possibly be discovered? It's the great dead language of the future. If Etruscan didn't exist, it would be necessary to invent it.'

'Which is precisely what the pedagogues will have to do,' said Chelifer, 'there being no Etruscan literature beyond the inscriptions and the rigmarole on the mummy-wrappings at Agram.'

'So much the better,' replied Mr. Cardan. 'If we wrote

it ourselves, we might find Etruscan literature interesting. Etruscan literature composed by Etruscans would be as boring as any other ancient literature. But if the epics were written by you, the Socratic dialogues by me, the history by some master of fiction like Miss Thriplow—then we'd possess a corpus in which the rare schoolboys who can derive some profit from their education could take a real interest. And when, a generation hence, we have become as much out of date in our ideas as Tully or Horace, the literature of Etruria will be rewritten by our descendants. Each generation will use the dead language to express its own ideas. And expressed in so rich an idiom as I take Etruscan to be, the ideas will seem the more significant and memorable. For I have often noticed that an idea which, expressed in one's native language, would seem dull, commonplace and opaque, becomes transparent to the mind's eye, takes on a new significance when given a foreign and unfamiliar embodiment. A cracker-motto in Latin sounds much weightier and truer than the same motto in English. Indeed, if the study of dead languages has any use at all, which I should be sorry to admit, it consists in teaching us the importance of the verbal medium in which thoughts are expressed. To know the same thing in several languages is to know it (if you have any sense at all) more profoundly, more richly, than if it were known only in one. The youth who learns that the god of wine is called, in Etruscan, Fufluns has a profounder knowledge of the attributes of that divine personality than the youth who only knows him under the name of Bacchus. If I desire that archaeologists should discover the key to the Etruscan language, it is merely in order that I may have a deeper insight into the thing or idea connoted by such sumptuous words as *flucuthukh* or *khathc*. For the rest I care nothing. That they should discover the meaning of these inscriptions is a matter to me of the most complete indifference. For after all, what would they discover? Nothing that we don't already know. They would discover that before the Romans conquered Italy men ate and drank, made love, piled up wealth, oppressed their weaker neighbours, diverted themselves with sports, made laws and so on. One could have divined as much by walking down Piccadilly any day of the week. And besides, we have their pictures.' He threw out his hand. The guide, who had been listening patiently to the incomprehensible discourse, responded to the gesture by raising his acetylene lamp. Called magically into existence by the bright white light, a crowd of gaily coloured forms appeared on the walls of the vault in which they were standing. Set in a frame of conventionalized trees, a pair of red-brown wrestlers with Egyptian eyes and the profiles of the Greeks who disport themselves round the flanks of the earliest vases were feeling for a hold. On either side of them, beyond the trees, stood two couples of long-legged black horses. Above them, in the segment of a circle between the upper line of this band of paintings and the vaulted roof, a great leopard lay couchant, white-skinned, with a pattern of black spots arranged like those on the china dogs and cats of a later age. On the wall to the left they were feasting: red-brown Etruscans reclined on couches; porcelain-white women, contrasting as voluptuously with their tanned companions as the pale, plump nymphs of Boucher with their brown pastoral lovers, sat by their sides. With hieratic gestures of mutual love they pledged one another in bowls of wine. On the opposite wall the fowlers were busy—here with slings, there with nets. The sky was alive with birds. In the blue sea below they were spearing fish. A long inscription ran from right to left across the wall. The vaulted roof was painted with chequers, red, black and white. Over the low, narrow door that led from the tomb into the ante-chamber there knelt a benevolent white bull. Two thousand five hundred years ago they had wept here over the newly dead.

'You see them,' continued Mr. Cardan, 'hunting, drinking, playing, making love. What else could you expect them to do? This writing will tell us no more than we know already. True, I want to know what it means, but only because I hope that the brown man may be saying to the white lady: "*Flucuthukh* to me only with thine eyes," or words to that effect, "and I will *flucuthukh* with mine." If that was what they really were saying, it would throw an entirely new light on the notion of drinking. An entirely new light.'

'It would throw no new light on love, if lovers they are,' said Mrs. Aldwinkle mournfully.

'Wouldn't it?' Mr. Cardan queried. 'But imagine if *flucuthukh* turned out to mean, not drink, but love. I assure you that the feelings denoted by such a word would be quite different from those we sum up by "love." You can make a good guess from the sound of the word in any language what the people who speak it mean when they talk of love. *Amour*, for example—that long ou sound with the rolled r at the end of it, how significant it is! Ou—you have to push your lips into a snout-like formation, as though you were going to kiss. Then, briskly, rrr—you growl like a dog. Could anything be more perfectly expressive of the matter-of-fact lasciviousness which passes for love in nine-tenths of French fiction and drama? And *Liebe*—what a languishing, moonlit, sentimental sound the long ie has! And how apt, too, is the bleating labial by which it is followed!—be,—be. It is a sheep whose voice is choked by emotion. All German romanticism is implied in the sound of the word. And German romanticism, a little *détraqué*, turns quite logically into expressionismus and the wild erotic extravagance of contemporary German fiction. As for our *love*—that's characteristically non-committal and diffident. That dim little monosyllable illustrates our English reluctance to call a spade a spade. It is the symbol of our national repressions. All our hypocrisy and all the beautiful platonism of our poetry is there. Love . . .' Mr. Cardan whispered the word, and holding up his finger for silence cocked his ear to catch the faint echoes of his voice reverberating from wall to wall under the sepulchral vault. 'Love. . . . How utterly different is our English emotion from that connoted by *amore* ! *Amore*—you fairly sing the second syllable, in a baritone voice, from the chest, with a little throaty tremolo on the surface to make it sound more palpitating. *Amore*—it's the name of the quality that Stendhal so much admired in the Italians and the absence of which in his own countrymen, and more especially countrywomen, made him rank Paris below Milan or Rome—it's the apt and perfectly expressive name of passion.'

'How true !' said Mrs. Aldwinkle, brightening for a moment through her gloom. This compliment to her Italian language and Italian character touched and pleased her. 'The very sound of *amore* is passionate. If the English knew what passion meant, they'd have found a more expressive word than love. That's certain. But they don't know.' She sighed.

'Quite so,' said Mr. Cardan. '*Amore*, we see, can mean nothing else than Southern passion. But now, suppose that *flucuthukh* should turn out to be the Etruscan for love—what then ? *Amour* connotes lasciviousness, *Liebe* sentiment, *amore* passion. To what aspect of the complex phenomenon of love can *flucuthukh* refer ? The microbe Staphylococcus pyogenes produces in some patients boils, in others sties in the eye ; in certain cases it is even responsible for *keratitis punctata*. It is the same with love. The symptoms vary in different individuals. But owing to the boundless suggestibility and imitativeness of man, the commonest symptoms at any given period tend to become universal in any one society. Whole peoples take the disease in the same way; one suffers from *amour*, another from *Liebe* and so on. But now imagine a people to whom love was *flucut-hukh*. What can have been the particular symptoms of the general amorous disease to which such a name was given? One cannot guess. But at least it is fascinating to speculate.'

One after the other the party filed out through the narrow door into the ante-room of the sepulchre and up the steep flight of steps leading to the surface of the ground. Blinking in the bright afternoon light, they stepped out on to the bare and windy down.

It was a solitary place. The arches of a ruined aqueduct went striding along the ridge, and following their long recession the eye came at last to rest on the walls and tall towers of Corneto. To the left the hog-backed down sloped seawards; on the further side of the narrow plain at its foot stretched the Mediterranean. On the right lay a deep valley, shut in on the further side by a great round hill. Its grassy flanks were furrowed and pitted with what had once been the works of man. Once, on that hill, had stood the sacred city, Tarquinii of the Etruscans. The long bare down on which they were standing had been, through how many centuries? its necropolis. In little houses hollowed out of the chalky stone slept the innumerable dead. Here and there the top of a vault was broken through; from the hollow darkness within came up even at high summer an immemorial coolness. Here and there the surface of the down swelled up into round grass-grown barrows. It was from the heart of one of these tumuli that they had now emerged. The guide put out his lamp and shut the door upon the Etruscan ghosts. They walked for a few hundred yards through geological time—between the sea and the hills, under the floating clouds; on the sky-line the Middle Ages pricked up their towers; the smudged and flattened relics of Etruria undulated almost imperceptibly under the grass; from the Roman road in the plain below came up the distant hooting of a motor-car.

The sound of the motor-horn aroused Irene from the thoughtful trance in which, sad-faced and childish, this time, pathetically, she was walking. She had been silent and melancholy ever since, yesterday morning, they had left Rome; Lord Hovenden had stayed behind with Mr. Falx. The long-drawn hooting of the electric horn seemed to remind her of something. She looked down towards the sea-board plain. A cloud of white dust was advancing along the Maremman road from the direction of Civita Vecchia. It hung, opaque, over half a mile of road, fading slowly to transparency towards the tail. At the head, where the dust was thickest, a small black object moved like a rapidly crawling insect across the map-like expanse of plain, drawing the cloud after it. From the opposite direction came another black-headed comet of dust. Like two white serpents they approached one another as though rushing to battle. Nearer, nearer they came. Irene stopped still to look at them. She was filled with a horrible apprehension. It seemed impossible that they should not crash together. Nearer, nearer. The heads of the two serpents seemed almost to be touching one another. Suppose, just suppose that one of the cars was his. . . . Inevitably they must collide. Crash and smash—oh, the horror of it! Irene shut her eyes. A few seconds later she opened them. The two white snakes had merged together into one very thick opaque snake. It was impossible to see the little black heads at all. For one horrible moment she thought that they must have destroyed one another. But they reappeared after a little, receding now one from the other, no more approaching. The two serpents were still one serpent, but two-headed, a long amphisbaena. Then, gradually, the middle of the amphisbaena began to grow thin, to fade; a little clump of trees showed through it, dimly at first, mistily, then clearly. The amphisbaena had fallen in half and the two white snakes crawled on, one northwards, the other towards the south, and between their fading tails was a wide and ever wider gap. Irene heaved a deep sigh of relief and ran on after the others. It seemed to her that she had been the witness of a catastrophe miraculously averted. She felt much happier than she had felt all day. On a wide road two automobiles had passed one another. That was all.

The guide was unlocking the door that gave entrance to another excavated barrow. He relit his lamp and led the way down the steep steps into the tomb. On one wall they were horse-racing and wrestling, hieratically, all in profile. A goddess—or perhaps it was merely the Lady Mayoress of the city—wearing that high bonnet-shaped coiffure which the Roman matrons were afterwards to borrow from their neighbours, was distributing the prizes. On the other walls they were feasting. The red-brown men, the white-skinned ladies reclined along their couches. A musician stood by, playing on his double flute, and a female dancer, dressed in what looked rather like a Persian costume, was dancing a shawl dance for the diversion of the diners.

'They seem to have had simple tastes,' said Mr. Cardan. 'There's nothing very sophisticated or *fin de siècle* here—no bull-baiting by naked female acrobats, as at Cnossos; no gladiatorial fights, no wholesale butchering of animals, no boxing matches with brass knuckle-dusters, as in the Roman arenas. A nice schoolboyish sort of people, it looks to me. Not quite civilized enough to be *exigeant* about their pleasures.'

'And not yet quite civilized enough,' added Chelifer, 'to be really vulgar. In that respect they fall a long way behind the later Romans. Do you know that huge mosaic in the Lateran museum? It comes from one of the Imperial baths, I forget which, and consists of portraits of the principal sporting heroes of the epoch—boxers and wrestlers—with their trainers and backers. These last are treated very respectfully by the mosaic-maker, who represents them wearing togas and standing in the noblest attitudes. One sees at a glance that they are the *gens bien*, the sportsmen, the amateurs—in a word, the monied interest. The athletes are portrayed in a state of nature, and are indeed so excessively natural that one could easily mistake the heavy-weight boxers for gorillas peeled of their superfluous hair. Under each portrait is a caption with the name of the hero represented. The whole thing reminds one very much of the sporting page in a picture paper—only it is a page that is forty feet long by thirty wide, and made, not of wood-pulp, but of the most durable materials ever devised by the ingenuity of man for the embodiment and visible eternization of his thoughts. And it is, I think, precisely the size and everlastingness of the frightful thing that makes it so much worse than the similar page from our picture papers. To make ephemeral heroes of professional sportsmen and prize-fighters is bad enough; but that a people should desire to immortalize their fame is surely indicative of a profounder vulgarity and abjection. Like the Roman mob, the mobs of our modern capitals delight in sports and exercises which they themselves do not practise; but at any rate, the fame of our professionals lasts only a day after their triumph. We do not print their effigies on marble pavements made to live down a hundred generations of men. We print them on wood-pulp, which is much the same as printing them on water. It is comforting to think that by the year two thousand one hundred the whole of contemporary journalism, literature and thought will have crumbled to dust. The mosaic, however, will still be in its present state of perfect preservation. Nothing short of dynamite or an earthquake will ever totally destroy the effigies of those Imperial boxers. And a very good thing, too, for the future historians of Rome. For no man can claim that he has really understood the Roman empire till he has studied that mosaic. That pavement is a vessel filled with the quintessence of Roman reality. A drop of that reality is enough to shrivel up all the retrospective Utopias that historians have ever made or ever can make out of the chronicles of ancient Rome. After looking at that mosaic a man can have no more generous illusions about the people who admired it or the age in which it was made. He will realize that Roman civilization was not merely just as sordid as ours, but if anything more sordid. But in these Etruscan vaults,' Chelifer added, looking round at the frescoed walls, 'one gets no such impression of organized and efficient beastliness as one gets from the Roman mosaic. There's a freshness, as you say, Mr. Cardan, a certain jolly schoolboyishness about all the fun they represent. But I have no doubt, of course, that the impression is entirely fallacious. Their art has a certain archaic charm; but the artists were probably quite as sophisticated and quite as repulsive as their Roman successors.'

'Come, come,' said Mr. Cardan, 'you forget that they called Bacchus Fufluns. Give them at least the credit that is due to them.'

'But the Romans too had a fine language,' Chelifer objected. 'And yet they laid down immense enlargements of the sporting page of the *Daily Sketch* in marble tesserae on a foundation of cement.'

They climbed again towards the light. The steps were so high and her legs so short that Miss Elver had to be helped up. The tomb resounded with her laughter and shrill whooping. They emerged at last out of the ground.

On the top of a high barrow some two or three hundred yards away stood the figure of a man, distinct against the sky. He was shading his eyes with his hand and seemed to be looking for something. Irene suddenly became very red.

'Why, I believe it's Hovenden,' she said in a voice that was as casual as she could make it.

Almost simultaneously the man turned his face in their direction. The shading hand went up in a gesture of greeting. A glad 'Hullo!' sounded across the tombs; the man skipped down from his barrow and came running across the down towards them. And Hovenden it was; Irene had seen aright.

'Been looking for you all over ve place,' he explained breathlessly as he came up. With the greatest heartiness, he shook the hands of all present except—diplomatically—Irene's. 'Vey told me in ve town vat a party of foreigners was out here looking at ve cemetery or somefing. So I buzzed after you till I saw old Ernest wiv ve car at ve side of ve road. Been underground, have you?' He looked into the dark entrance of the tomb. 'No wonder I couldn't . . .'

Mrs. Aldwinkle cut him short. 'But why aren't you in Rome with Mr. Falx?' she asked.

Lord Hovenden's boyish, freckled face became all at once exceedingly red. 'Ve fact is,' he said, looking at the ground, 'vat I didn't feel very well. Ve doctor said I ought to get away from Rome at once. Country air, you know. So I just left a note for Mr. Falx and . . . and here I am.' He looked up again, smiling.

Chapter VI

'BUT at Montefiascone,' said Mr. Cardan, concluding the history of the German bishop who gave the famous wine of Montefiascone its curious name, 'at Montefiascone Bishop Defuk's servant found good wine at every shop and tavern;

so that when his master arrived he found the prearranged symbol chalked up on a hundred doors. *Est, Est, Est*—the town was full of them. And the Bishop was so much enraptured with the drink that he decided to settle in Montefiascone for life. For life—but he drank so much that in a very short time it turned out that he had settled here for death. They buried him in the lower church, down there. On his tombstone his servant engraved the Bishop's portrait with this brief epitaph: "*Est Est Jo Defuk. Propter nimium hic est. Dominus meus mortuus est.*" Since when the wine has always been called Est Est Est. We'll have a flask of it dry for serious drinking. And for the frivolous and the feminine, and to sip with the dessert, we'll have a bottle of the sweet *moscato*. And now let's see what there is to eat.' He picked up the menu and holding it out at arm's length—for he had the long sight of old age—read out slowly, with comments, the various items. It was always Mr. Cardan who ordered the dinner (although it was generally Lord Hovenden or Mrs. Aldwinkle who paid), always Mr. Cardan; for it was tacitly admitted by every one that Mr. Cardan was the expert on food and wine, the professional eater, the learned and scholarly drinker.

Seeing Mr. Cardan busy with the bill of fare, the landlord approached, rubbing his hands and cordially smiling—as well he might on a Rolls-Royce-full of foreigners—to take orders and give advice.

'The fish,' he confided to Mr. Cardan, 'the fish is something special.' He put his fingers to his lips and kissed them. 'It comes from Bolsena, from the lake, down there.' He pointed out of the window at the black night. Somewhere, far down through the darkness, lay the Lake of Bolsena.

Mr. Cardan held up his hand. 'No, no,' he objected with decision and shook his head. 'Don't talk to me of fish. Never safe in these little places,' he explained to his companions. 'Particularly in such hot weather. And then, imagine eating fish from Bolsena—a place where they have miracles, where holy wafers bleed for the edification of the pious and as a proof of the fact of transubstantiation. No, no,' Mr. Cardan repeated, 'fishes from Bolsena are altogether too fishy. Let's stick to fried eggs with fillet of veal to follow. Or a little roast capon . . .'

'I want fish,' said Miss Elver. The passionate earnestness of her tone contrasted strikingly with the airiness of Mr. Cardan's banter.

'I really wouldn't, you know,' said Mr. Cardan.

'But I like fish.'

'But it may be unwholesome. You never can tell.'

'But I want it,' Miss Elver insisted. 'I love fish.' Her large lower lip began to tremble, her eyes filled with tears. 'I *want* it.'

'Well, then, of course you shall have it,' said Mr. Cardan, making haste to console her. 'Of course, if you really like it. I was only afraid that it mightn't perhaps be good. But it probably will be.'

Miss Elver took comfort, blew her long nose and smiled. 'Thank you, Tommy,' she said, and blushed as she pronounced the name.

After dinner they went out into the piazza for coffee and liqueurs. The square was crowded and bright with lights. In the middle the band of the local Philharmonic Society was giving its Sunday evening concert. Planted on the rising ground above the piazza Sammicheli's great church solemnly impended. The lights struck up, illuminating its pilastered walls. The cupola stood out blackly against the sky.

'The choice,' said Mr. Cardan, looking round the piazza, 'seems to lie between the Café Moderno and the Bar Ideale. Personally, I should be all for the ideal rather than the real if it wasn't for the disagreeable fact that in a bar one has to stand. Whereas in a café, however crassly materialistic, one can sit down. I'm afraid the Moderno forces itself upon us.'

He led the way in the direction of the café.

'Talking of Bars,' said Chelifer, as they sat down at a little table in front of the café, 'has it ever occurred to you to enumerate the English words that have come to have an international currency? It's a somewhat curious selection, and one which seems to me to throw a certain light on the nature and significance of our Anglo-Saxon civilization. The three words from Shakespeare's language that have a completely universal currency are Bar, Sport and W.C. They're all just as good Finnish now as they are good English. Each of these words possesses what I may call a family. Round the idea "Bar" group themselves various other international words, such as Bitter, Cocktail, Whiskey and the like. "Sport" boasts a large family—Match, for example, Touring Club, the verb to Box, Cycle-Car, Performance (in the sporting sense) and various others. The idea of hydraulic sanitation has only one child that I can think of, namely Tub. Tub—it has a strangely old-world sound in English nowadays; but in Yugo-Slavia, on the other hand, it is exceedingly up-to-date. Which leads us on to that very odd class of international English words that have never been good English at all. A Smoking for example, a Dancing, a Five-o'clock—these have never existed except on the continent of Europe. As for High-Life, so popular a word in Athens, where it is spelt iota, gamma, lambda, iota, phi—that dates from a remote, mid-Victorian epoch in the history of our national culture.'

'And Spleen,' said Mr. Cardan, 'you forget Spleen. That comes from much further back. A fine aristocratic word, that; we were fools to allow it to become extinct. One has to go to France to hear it uttered now.'

'The word may be dead,' said Chelifer, 'but the emotion,

I fancy, has never flourished more luxuriantly than now. The more material progress, the more wealth and leisure, the more standardized amusements—the more boredom. It's inevitable, it's the law of Nature. The people who have always suffered from spleen and who are still the principal victims, are the prosperous, leisured and educated. At present they form a relatively small minority; but in the Utopian state where everybody is well off, educated and leisured, everybody will be bored; unless for some obscure reason the same causes fail to produce the same effects. Only two or three hundred people out of every million could survive a lifetime in a really efficient Utopian state. The rest would simply die of spleen. In this way, it may be, natural selection will work towards the evolution of the super-man. Only the intelligent will be able to bear the almost intolerable burden of leisure and prosperity. The rest will simply wither away, or cut their throats—or, perhaps more probably, return in desperation to the delights of barbarism and cut one another's throats, not to mention the throats of the intelligent.'

'That certainly sounds the most likely and natural ending,' said Mr. Cardan. 'If of two possible alternatives one is in harmony with our highest aspirations and the other is, humanly speaking, absolutely pointless and completely wasteful, then, you may be sure, Nature will choose the second.'

At half-past ten Miss Elver complained that she did not feel very well. Mr. Cardan sighed and shook his head. 'These miraculous fishes,' he said. They went back to the hotel.

'Luckily,' said Mrs. Aldwinkle that evening while Irene was brushing her hair, 'luckily I never had any babies. They spoil the figure so frightfully.'

'Still,' Irene ventured to object, 'still . . . they must be rather fun, all the same.'

Mrs. Aldwinkle pretexted a headache and sent her to bed

almost at once. At half-past two in the morning Irene was startled out of her sleep by a most melancholy groaning and crying from the room next to hers. 'Oo, Oo! Ow!' It was Grace Elver's voice. Irene jumped out of bed and ran to see what was the matter. She found Miss Elver lying in a tumbled bed, writhing with pain.

'What is it?' she asked.

Miss Elver made no articulate answer. 'Oo, Oo,' she kept repeating, turning her head from side to side as though in the hope of escaping from the obsessing pain.

Irene ran to her aunt's bedroom, knocked at the door and, getting no answer, walked in. 'Aunt Lilian,' she called in the darkness, and louder, 'Aunt Lilian!' There was still no sound. Irene felt for the switch and turned on the light. Mrs. Aldwinkle's bed was empty. Irene stood there for a moment looking dubiously at the bed, wondering, speculating. From down the corridor came the repeated 'Oo, Oo!' of Grace Elver's inarticulate pain. Roused by the sound from her momentary inaction, Irene turned, stepped across the passage and began knocking at Mr. Cardan's door.

Chapter VII

SELECTIONS FROM FRANCIS CHELIFER

In the sporting calendar the most interesting events are booked for the autumnal months. There is no hunting in the spring. And even in Italy there is a brief close season for song-birds that lasts from the coming of the nightingales to the departure of the last swallow. The fun, the real fun, starts only in the autumn. Grouse-shooting, partridge-shooting—these are the gay preliminaries. But the great day is the First of October, when the massacre of the gaudy pheasant begins. Crack! crack!—the double barrels make music in the fading woods. And a little later the harmonious dogs join in and the hoof, as the Latin poet so aptly puts it, the hoof shakes the putrid field with quadrupedantical sound. Winter is made gay with the noise of hunting.

It is the same in the greater year of certain feminine lives. . . . Pop ! pop !—on the First of October they go out to shoot the pheasant. A few weeks later, tally-ho, they hunt the fox. And on Guy Fawkes's day the man-eating season begins. My hostess, when she picked me up on the beach of Marina di Vezza, had reached a point in her year somewhere between pheasant-shooting and man-eating. They say that foxes enjoy being hunted ; but I venture to doubt the truth of this comforting hypothesis. Experientia does it, as Mrs. Micawber's papa (ha ha ! from Mr. Toft) . . . Etcetera.

If loving without being loved in return may be ranked as one of the most painful of experiences, being loved without loving is certainly one of the most boring. Perhaps no experience is better calculated to make one realize the senselessness of the passion. The spectacle of some one making a fool of himself arouses only laughter. When one is playing the fool oneself, one weeps. But when one is neither the active imbecile nor the disinterested spectator, but the unwilling cause of somebody else's folly—then it is that one comes to feel that weariness and that disgust which are the proper, the human reaction to any display of the deep animal stupidity that is the root of all evil.

Twice in my life have I experienced these salutary horrors of boredom—once by my own fault, because I asked to be loved without loving ; and once because I had the misfortune to be picked up on the beach, limp as sea-weed, between the First of October and Guy Fawkes's day. The experiences were disagreeable while they lasted ; but on the other hand, they were highly didactic. The first of them rounded off, so to speak, the lesson I had learned from Barbara. The second episode was staged by Providence, some few years later, to remind me of the first and to print what the Americans would call its ' message ' still more indelibly upon my mind. Providence has been remarkably persistent in its efforts to sober me. To what end I cannot imagine.

Poor Miss Masson ! She was a very good secretary. By the end of 1917 she knew all that it was possible to know about rubber tubing and castor oil. It was unfortunate for every one concerned that Providence should have destined her to instruct me yet more deeply in the fearful mysteries of love. True, I brought it on myself. Providence, on that occasion, elected to act indirectly and threw the blame on me. I accept it all—all the more willingly since my act shows in the most illuminating manner what are the consequences, the frightful consequences, of stupidity. There is a certain satisfaction to be derived from having personally proved the truth of one's own wisdom by acting in defiance of its precepts.

Yes, I brought it on myself. For it was I who made the first advances. It was I who, out of pure wantonness, provoked the sleeping, or at least well-disciplined tiger that lay hidden in Dorothy Masson's heart—put my walking-stick between the bars and, against all the rules, poked it rudely in the ribs. I got what I asked for.

I was like that wanton Blackamoor in one of old Busch's misanthropically comic picture-books.

> Ein Mohr aus Bosheit und Pläsier
> Schiesst auf das Elefantentier.

With his little arrow he punctures the placid pachyderm ; and the pachyderm takes his revenge, elaborately, through fourteen subsequent woodcuts.

My only excuse—the recentness of that ludicrous catastrophe with which the tragedy of Barbara had concluded—

was an excuse that might equally have served as an additional reason against doing what I did ; I ought, after having once been bitten, to have shown myself twice shy. But in the state of misery in which I found myself I hoped that a second bite might distract my attention from the anguish of the first. And even this is not precisely accurate ; for I never anticipated that the second would really be a bite at all. I looked forward merely to a kind of playful diversion, not to anything painful. True, when I found how serious the affair threatened to become for Dorothy Masson, I might have guessed that it would soon be serious also for myself, and have drawn back. But, inspired by that high-spirited irresponsibility which I have come since then so highly to admire in the natural, brutish human specimen, I refused to consider possible consequences and went on in the course I had begun. I was not in the least in love with the woman ; nor did her person inspire me with any specific desire. My motive forces were misery, mingled with a kind of exasperation, and the vague itch of recurrent appetite. More than half of the world's 'affairs' have no more definite reasons for occurring. Ennui and itch are their first causes. Subsequently imagination may come into play and love will be born. Or experience may beget specific desires and in so doing may render one party necessary to the happiness of the other, or each to each. Or perhaps there will be no development at all and the affair will end placidly as it began, in itch and ennui.

But there are cases, of which mine was one, where one party may be inspired by the mere indefinite wantonness I have been describing, while the other is already imagination-ridden and in love. Poor Dorothy ! There came into her eyes when I kissed her a look such as I had never seen in any other human eyes before or since. It was the look one sees in the eyes of a dog when its master is angry and raises his whip—a look of absolute self-abasement mingled with terror. There was something positively appalling in seeing those eyes staring at one out of a woman's face. To see a human being reduced in one's arms to the condition of a frightened and adoring dog is a shocking thing. And the more so in this case since it was completely indifferent to me whether she was in my arms or not. But when she raised her face and looked at me for a moment with those abject and terrified eyes of hers, it was not merely indifferent to me; it was even positively distasteful. The sight of those large-pupilled eyes, in which there was no glimmer of a human rational soul, but only an animal's terror and abasement, made me feel at once guilty and, complementarily, angry, resentful and hostile.

'Why do you look at me like that?' I asked her once. 'As though you were frightened of me.'

She did not answer; but only hid her face against my shoulder, and pressed me more closely in her arms. Her body shook with involuntary startings and tremblings. Casually, from force of habit, I caressed her. The trembling became more violent. 'Don't,' she implored me in a faint hoarse whisper, 'don't.' But she pressed me still closer.

She was frightened, it seemed, not of me but of herself, of that which lay sleeping in the depths of her being and whose awakening threatened to overwhelm, to blot for a moment out of existence that well-ordered, reasonable soul which was the ruler at ordinary times of her life. She was afraid of the power within her that could make her become something other than her familiar self. She was fearful of losing her self-mastery. And at the same time there was nothing else that she desired. The sleeping power within her had begun to stir and there was no resisting it. Vainly, hopelessly, she continued to attempt the impossible. She went on trying to resist, and her resistance quickened her desire to yield.

She was afraid and yet invited my awakening kisses. And while she whispered to me imploringly, like one who begs for mercy, she pressed me in her arms. I, meanwhile, had begun to realize all the potentialities for boredom implicit in the situation. And how boring it did in fact turn out to be! To be pursued by restless warmth when all that one desires is cool peace; to be perpetually and quite justly accused of remissness in love and to have to deny the accusation, feebly, for the sake of politeness; to be compelled to pass hours in tedious company—what an affliction, what a martyrdom it is! I came to feel extremely sorry for those pretty women who are perpetually being courted by a swarm of men. But the pretty women, I reflected, had this advantage over me: that they were by nature a good deal more interested in love than I. Love is their natural business, the reason of their existence; however distasteful their suitors may personally be to them, they cannot find them as completely boring and insufferable as would, placed in similar circumstances, a person to whom love as such is fundamentally rather uninteresting. The most tedious lover atones a little, in the eyes of the courted lady, for his personal insupportableness by the generic fact of being a lover. Lacking a native enthusiasm for love, I found it more difficult to support the martyrdom of being loved by Miss Masson.

But such an affair, you will object, is a typical piece of reality. True; but at that time I was not quite such a believer in the real and earnest side of life as I am now. And even now I should regard it as something of a work of supererogation to associate with realities of so exceptionally penetrative a nature. A sober man, if he is logical and courageous, is bound to pass his life between Gog's Court and Miss Carruthers's. But he is not bound to make love to Miss Carruthers or to provoke the clinging affections of Fluffy. That would be too much—so it seems to me, at any rate at present; though perhaps the time may come when I shall feel strong enough to take my reality in these stiff doses. There is an electric machine used by masseurs for driving iodine into stiffened joints. Love acts like this machine; it serves to drive the lover's personality into the mind of the beloved. I am strong enough at present to be able to bathe in the personalities of ordinary human animals; but I should be suffocated, I should faint away, if the muddy swill were to be pumped into my spiritual system by the penetrating electricity of love.

Miss Masson stood one Galtonian class higher than Miss Carruthers or Fluffy. One out of every four people is a Fluffy; only one out of every six is a Dorothy Masson. It makes a slight but perceptible difference. None the less, how much I suffered! When I brought her a few orchids as a present, remarking as I gave them to her that they looked so delightfully like artificial flowers, she would thank me and say she adored orchids, adding after a moment's pause for thought that she liked them because they looked so like artificial flowers. And she laughed softly to herself, she looked up at me for confirmatory applause. For that little habit alone I sometimes felt that I could have murdered her. But her solicitude, her reproaches, expressed or more often mute (for she rarely made scenes, but only looked at me with those sad brown eyes), her incessant desire to be close to me, to touch me, to kiss and be kissed—these were almost enough to drive me to suicide. It lasted for more than a year, an eternity. And technically it still lasts; for I never broke with her, never dramatically quitted her, but only quietly and gradually faded out of her life like the Cheshire Cat. Sometimes, even, we still meet. And still, as though nothing had happened, I take her in my arms and kiss her, till that strange expression of abject terror comes again into her eyes, till she implores me, in a voice made faint with excessive desire, to spare her well-disciplined everyday soul and not deliver it into the power of the fearful thing that is waking darkly within her. And still as she speaks she presses me closer, she offers her stretched throat to my kisses. And before and after, we talk about politics and common friends. And still as of old she echoes the last phrase I have spoken, still softly laughs and still expects me to admire her original thoughts. Finally I take my leave.

'You'll come again soon?' she asks, looking up into my face with eyes that are full of sadness and apprehension, of questions unuttered, of unexpressed reproaches. I kiss her hand. 'Of course,' I say. And I go away, taking pains as I walk down the street not to speculate on the subject of her thoughts.

But Providence seems to have thought my connection with Dorothy inadequately instructive. Dorothy, after all, was only twenty-six when the episode began. Hers was that vernal and flowery season during which, even in Italy, warblers are not shot. It would be another twenty years before she reached her First of October; thirty, perhaps, before the man-eating season should begin. And it was I who had made the first advances. But for my exhibition of *Bosheit und Pläsier* the boring history would never have unrolled itself. But Providence, anxious, for some inscrutable reason, to teach me a yet more memorable lesson, went so far as almost to drown me, so determined was it that I should fall into the hands of the suitable schoolmistress. I was to learn how ludicrously dreadful, as well as how boring, love can be.

I made no advances on this occasion. From the first I did nothing but retreat. Mrs. Aldwinkle's blue danger signals bore down on me; like an agile pedestrian in the London traffic, I stepped aside. When she asked what women had inspired me, I answered that nothing inspired me but the London slums and the vulgarity of Lady Giblet.

When she said that one could see by my face that I had been unhappy, I said that that was odd ; I had always been perfectly happy. When she talked about experience, meaning, as women generally do when they use that word, merely love, I replied with a discussion of experience in relation to the Theory of Knowledge When she accused me of wearing a mask, I protested that I paraded my naked soul for every one to see. When she asked if I had ever been in love, I shrugged my shoulders and smiled : not to speak of. And when she asked, at very close range, if I had ever been loved, I answered quite truthfully that I had, but that it bored me.

But still, indomitably, she renewed the attack. There might have been something grand about her unwavering determination—something grand, if it had not been grotesque. Providence was teaching me yet once more that the unsapient life is a dreary and hopeless business, and that it is, for all practical purposes, the only life—lived everywhere by all but a negligibly few exceptions. At least I presume that that is what Providence was trying to impress on me. But in the process it was using Mrs. Aldwinkle, I thought, rather hardly. I felt sorry for the poor lady. Some hidden irrational force within herself was compelling her to cut these capers, throw herself into these ludicrous postures, say these stupid words and contort her face into these grimaces ; she was helpless. She just obeyed orders and did her best ; but her best was ludicrous. And not merely ludicrous but appalling. She was like a buffoon carrying a skull.

Unflaggingly she played the deplorable part assigned to her. Every day she brought me flowers. 'I want them to blossom in your verses,' she said. I assured her that the only scent which provoked me to write was that of the butchers' shops on a winter's evening along the Harrow Road. She smiled at me. 'Don't think I can't understand you,' she said. 'I do. I do.' She leaned forward ; her eyes shone, her perfume enveloped me, she breathed heliotrope in my face. I could see with extraordinary distinctness the little wrinkles round her eyes, the careless smear of rouge at the corners of the mouth. 'I do understand you,' she repeated.

She did understand me. . . . One night (it was at Montefiascone, on our way back from Rome), when I was reading in bed, I heard a sound ; I looked up, and saw Mrs. Aldwinkle carefully closing the door behind her. She was wearing a dressing-gown of sea-green silk. Her hair hung in two thick plaits over her shoulders. When she turned round, I saw that her face had been coloured and powdered with more than ordinary care. In silence she advanced across the room, she sat down on the edge of my bed. An aura of ambergris and heliotrope surrounded her.

I smiled politely, closed my book (keeping a finger, however, between the pages to mark my place) and slightly raised my eyebrows in interrogation. To what, I made my face inquire, do I owe the honour ? . . .

I owed it, it seemed, to my hostess's urgently felt need to tell me yet once more that she understood me.

'I couldn't bear,' she said breathlessly, 'couldn't bear to think of you here alone. With your secret misery.' And when I made as though to protest, she held up her hand. 'Oh, don't think I haven't seen through your mask. Alone with your secret misery . . .'

'No, really . . .' I managed to put in. But Mrs. Aldwinkle would not suffer herself to be interrupted.

'I couldn't bear to think of your terrible loneliness,' she went on. 'I wanted you to know there was at least one person who understood.' She leaned towards me, smiling, but with lips that trembled. All at once her eyes filled with tears, her face contorted itself into the terrible grimace of misery. She made a little moaning noise and, letting herself fall forward, she hid her face against my knees. 'I love you, I love you,' she repeated in a muffled voice. Her body was shaken by recurrent spasms of sobbing. I was left wondering what to do. This was not in the programme. When one goes out man-eating or pheasant-shooting, one has no business to weep over the victim. But the trouble is, of course, that the man-eater sees herself as the victim. *Hinc illae lacrimae.* It is impossible for two human beings to agree completely about anything. *Quot homines*, for now that the Dictionary of Familiar Quotations has been opened I may as well continue to make use of it, *quot homines, tot disputandum est.* There is no agreement even about the truths of science. One man is a geometrician; the other can only understand analysis. One is incapable of believing in anything of which he cannot make a working model; the other wants his truth as abstract as it is possible to make it. But when it comes to deciding which of two people is the victim and which the man-eater, there is nothing to be done but abandon the attempt. Let each party stick to his own opinion. The most successful men are those who never admit the validity of other people's opinions, who even deny their existence.

'My dear Lilian,' I said (she had insisted on my calling her Lilian within a day or two of my arrival), 'my dear Lilian . . .' I could find nothing more to say. A successful man, I suppose, would have said something frankly brutal, something that would have made it clear to Mrs. Aldwinkle which of the two, in his opinion, was the victim and which the carnivore. I lacked the force. Mrs. Aldwinkle went on sobbing.

'I love you. Couldn't you love me a little? A little only? I would be your slave. Your slave; I'd be your slave,' she kept repeating.

What things she said! I listened to her, feeling pity—yes, pity no doubt—but still more, a profound embarrassment, and with it anger against the person who had thrust me into this untenable position.

'It's no good,' I protested. 'It's impossible.'

She only began again, desperately.

How much further the scene might have prolonged itself and what might have happened if it had been protracted, I do not know. Luckily, however, an extraordinary commotion suddenly broke loose in the hotel. Doors slammed, voices were raised, there was the noise of feet along the corridors and on the stairs. Startled and alarmed, Mrs. Aldwinkle got up, went to the door, opened it a crack and looked into the passage. Some one hurried past; hastily she closed it again. When the coast was clear, she slipped out into the passage and tip-toed away, leaving me alone.

The commotion was caused by the beginning of Miss Elver's death-agony. Providence, having decided that my education had gone far enough, had broken off the lesson. The means it employed were, I must say, rather violent. A vain man might have been gratified by the reflection that one woman had been made miserable in order that he might be taught a lesson, while another had died—like King John, of a surfeit of lampreys—in order that the lesson might be interrupted before it was carried too disagreeably far. But as it happens, I am not particularly vain.

Chapter VIII

FROM the first nobody put very much faith in the local doctor; the mere look of him was enough to inspire mistrust. But when across the patient's prostrate and comatose body he chattily confided that he had taken his degree at the University of Siena, Mr. Cardan decided that it was time to send for somebody else.

'Siena's notorious,' he whispered. 'It's the place where the imbeciles who can't get their degrees at Bologna, or Rome, or Pisa go and have themselves made doctors.'

Mrs. Aldwinkle, who in the middle of the tumult had suddenly reappeared (Irene did not know from where), expressed her horror. Doctors were one of her specialities; she was very particular about doctors. Mrs. Aldwinkle had had a number of interesting maladies in the course of her life —three nervous break-downs, an appendicitis, gout and various influenzas, pneumonias and the like, but all of them aristocratic and avowable diseases; for Mrs. Aldwinkle distinguished sharply between complaints that are vulgar and complaints of a gentlemanly sort. Chronic constipation, hernia, varicose veins (' bad legs ' as the poor so gruesomely call them)—these, obviously, were vulgar diseases which no decent person could suffer from, or at any rate, suffering, talk about. Her illnesses had all been extremely refined and correspondingly expensive. What she did not know about doctors, English, French, Swiss, German, Swedish and even Japanese, was not worth knowing. Mr. Cardan's remarks about the University of Siena impressed her profoundly.

' The only thing to do,' she said decisively, ' is for Hovenden to drive straight back to Rome and bring back a specialist. At once.' She spoke peremptorily. It was a comfort for her, in her present distress of mind, to be able to do something, to make arrangements, to order people about, even herself to carry and fetch. ' The Principessa gave me the name of a wonderful man. I've got it written down somewhere. Come.' And she darted off to her room.

Obediently Lord Hovenden followed her, wrote down the talismanic name and took himself off. Chelifer was waiting for him at the bottom of the stairs.

' I may as well come with you, if you don't mind,' he said. ' I think I should only be in the way here.'

It was nearly half-past five when they started. The sun had not yet risen, but it was already light. The sky was pale grey with dark clouds low down on the horizon. There were mists in the valleys and the Lake of Bolsena was hidden from view under what seemed the waters of a milky sea. The air was cold. Driving out of the town, they met a train of pack mules climbing slowly, in the midst of a jingle of bells, up the steep street towards the market-place.

Viterbo was still asleep when they drove through. From the crest of the Ciminian mountains they first saw the sun. By seven o'clock they were in Rome. The sun-tipped obelisks, the gilded roofs and cupolas reached up out of shadow into the pale blue sky. They drove up the Corso. In the Piazza di Venezia they stopped at a café, ordered some coffee, and while it was being brought looked up in a directory the address of Mrs. Aldwinkle's doctor. He lived, they found, in the new quarter near the station.

'I leave all ve talking to you,' said Hovenden, as they sipped their coffee. 'I'm no good at ve language.'

'How did you manage the other day when you had to see the doctor yourself?' Chelifer inquired.

Lord Hovenden blushed. 'Well,' he said, 'as a matter of fact, ve doctor I saw was English. But he's gone away now,' he added hastily, for fear that Chelifer might suggest their bringing the English doctor along too; 'gone to Naples,' he further specified, hoping by the accumulation of circumstantial details to give greater verisimilitude to his story, 'for an operation.'

'He was a surgeon, then?' Chelifer raised his eyebrows.

Hovenden nodded. 'A surgeon,' he echoed, and buried his face in his coffee-cup.

They drove on. As they turned out of the Piazza into Trajan's Forum, Chelifer noticed a little crowd, mostly of street boys, pressing against the railings on the further side of the forum. At its centre stood a pale thin woman in dove-grey clothes whom even at this distance one could not fail to recognize as English, or at any rate definitely not Italian.

The lady in grey was leaning over the railings, lowering very carefully at the end of a string, to which it was ingeniously attached by four subsidiary strings passed through holes bored in the rim, a large aluminium pannikin filled with milk. Slowly revolving as it went down, the pannikin was lowered to the floor of the sunken forum. Hardly had it touched the ground when, with simultaneous mewings and purrings, half a dozen thirsty cats came running up to it and began to lap at the white milk. Others followed; every cranny gave up its cat. Lean toms jumped down from their marble pedestals and trotted across the open with the undulating, bounding gait of a running leopard. Month-old kittens staggered up on tottering legs. In a few seconds the pannikin was besieged by a horde of cats. The street boys whooped with delight.

'Well, I'm blowed,' said Lord Hovenden, who had slowed up to watch the curious scene. 'I believe it's your mover.'

'I think it is,' said Chelifer, who had recognized her long ago.

'Would you like me to stop?' asked Hovenden.

Chelifer shook his head. 'I think we'd better get to the doctor as quickly as possible,' he said.

Looking back as they drove out of the forum, Chelifer saw that his mother, faithful to her vegetarian principles, was throwing down into the den of cats bread and cold potatoes. In the evening he imagined she would come again. She had not taken long to find her Roman occupation.

Chapter IX

THE funeral was not due to take place before sunset. The bearers, the choristers, the sexton, the priest himself, most likely, were all in the fields, picking the grapes. They had something more important to do, while the light lasted, than to bury people. Let the dead bury their dead. The living were there to make wine.

Mr. Cardan sat alone in the empty church. Alone; what had once been Grace Elver lay, coffined, on a bier in the middle of the aisle. That did not count as company; it was just so much stuff in a box. His red knobbly face was as though frozen into stillness, all its gaiety, its twinkling mobility were gone. It might have been the face of a dead man, of one of the dead whose business it is to bury the dead. He sat there grim and stony, leaning forward, his chin in his hand, his elbow on his knee.

Three thousand six hundred and fifty days more, he was thinking; that is, if I live another ten years. Three thousand six hundred and fifty, and then the end of everything, the tunnelling worms.

There are such horrible ways of dying, he thought. Once, years ago, he had a beautiful grey Angora cat. She ate too many black-beetles in the kitchen and died vomiting shreds of her shard-torn stomach. He often thought of that cat. One might die like that oneself, coughing up one's vitals.

Not that one eats many black-beetles, of course. But there is always putrid fish. The effects are not so very different. Wretched moron! he thought, looking at the coffin. It had been a disgusting sort of death. Pains, vomiting, collapse, coma, then the coffin—and now the busy ferments of putrefaction and the worms. Not a very dignified or inspiring conclusion. No speeches, no consoling serenities, no Little Nells or Paul Dombeys. The nearest approach to the Dickensian had been when, in a brief spell of lucidity, she asked him about the bears he was going to give her after they were married.

'Will they be grown up?' she asked. 'Or puppies?'

'Puppies,' he answered, and she had smiled with pleasure.

Those had been almost the only articulate words she had uttered. Through that long death-agony they were the only witnesses to the existence of her soul. For the rest of the time she had been no more than a sick body, mindlessly crying and muttering. The tragedy of bodily suffering and extinction has no catharsis. Punctually it runs its dull, degrading course, act by act to the conclusion. It ennobles neither the sufferer nor the contemplator. Only the tragedy of the spirit can liberate and uplift. But the greatest tragedy of the spirit is that sooner or later it succumbs to the flesh. Sooner or later every soul is stifled by the sick body; sooner or later there are no more thoughts, but only pain and vomiting and stupor. The tragedies of the spirit are mere struttings and posturings on the margin of life, and the spirit itself is only an accidental exuberance, the products of spare vital energy, like the feathers on the head of a hoopoo or the innumerable populations of useless and foredoomed spermatozoa. The spirit has no significance; there is only the body. When it is young, the body is beautiful and strong. It grows old, its joints creak, it becomes dry and smelly; it breaks down, the life goes out of it and it rots away. However lovely the feathers on a bird's head, they perish with it; and the spirit, which is a lovelier ornament than any, perishes too. The farce is hideous, thought Mr. Cardan, and in the worst of bad taste.

Fools do not perceive that the farce is a farce. They are the more blessed. Wise men perceive it and take pains not to think about it. Therein lies their wisdom. They indulge themselves in all the pleasures, of the spirit as of the body—and especially in those of the spirit, since they are by far the more varied, charming and delightful—and when the time comes they resign themselves with the best grace they can muster to the decay of the body and the extinction of its spiritual part. Meanwhile, however, they do not think too much of death—it is an unexhilarating theme; they do not insist too much upon the farcical nature of the drama in which they are playing, for fear that they should become too much disgusted with their parts to get any amusement out of the piece at all.

The most ludicrous comedies are the comedies about people who preach one thing and practise another, who make imposing claims and lamentably fail to fulfil them. We preach immortality and we practise death. Tartuffe and Volpone are not in it.

The wise man does not think of death lest it should spoil his pleasures. But there are times when the worms intrude too insistently to be ignored. Death forces itself sometimes upon the mind, and then it is hard to take much pleasure in anything.

This coffin, for instance—how can a man take pleasure in the beauty of the church in which this boxful of decaying stuff is lying? What can be more delightful than to look up the aisle of a great church and see at the end of a long dark vista of round-headed arches a brightly illumined segment of the drum of the cupola—the horizontal circle contrasting harmoniously with the perpendicular half-circles of the arches? There is nothing lovelier among all the works of man. But the coffin lies here under the arches, reminding the connoisseur of beauty that there is nothing but the body and that the body suffers degradingly, dies and is eaten by maggots.

Mr. Cardan wondered how he would die. Slowly or suddenly? After long pain? Intelligent, still human? Or an idiot, a moaning animal? He would die poor, now, in any case. Friends would club together and send him a few pounds every now and then. Poor old Cardan, can't let him die in the workhouse. Must send him five pounds. What a bore! Extraordinary how he manages to last so long! But he was always a tough old devil. Poor old Cardan!

A door banged; in the hollow echoing church there was a sound of footsteps. It was the sacristan. He came to tell Mr. Cardan that they would soon be ready to begin. They had hurried back from the fields on purpose. The grapes were not so plentiful nor of quite such good quality as they had been last year. But still, one thanked God for His mercies, such as they were.

Blessed are the fools, thought Mr. Cardan, for they shall see nothing. Or perhaps they do see and, seeing, nevertheless comfortingly believe in future compensations and the justice of eternity. In either case—not seeing, or seeing but believing—they are fools. Still, believing is probably the best solution of all, Mr. Cardan went on to reflect. For it allows one to see and not to ignore. It permits one to accept the facts and yet justify them. For a believer the presence of a coffin or two would not interfere with the appreciation of Sammicheli's architecture.

The bearers filed in, bringing with them from the fields a healthy smell of sweat. They were dressed for the occasion in garments that ought, no doubt, to have been surplices, but which were, in point of fact, rather dirty and crumpled white dust-coats. They looked like a cricket eleven entirely composed of umpires. After the bearers came the priest, followed by a miniature umpire in a dust-coat so short that it did not hide his bare knees. The service began. The priest reeled off his Latin formulas as though for a wager; the bearers, in ragged and tuneless unison, bawled back at him the incomprehensible responses. During the longer prayers they talked to one another about the vintage. The boy scratched first his head, then his posterior, finally picked his nose. The priest prayed so fast that all the words fused together and became one word. Mr. Cardan wondered why the Catholic Church did not authorize prayer wheels. A simple little electric motor doing six or eight hundred revolutions a minute would get through a quite astonishing amount of pious work in a day and cost much less than a priest.

'Baa baba, baa baa, Boo-oo-baa,' bleated the priest.

'Boooo-baa,' came back from the bawling flock.

Not ceasing for a moment to pick his nose, the diminutive

umpire, who seemed to know his part as perfectly as a trained dog in a music hall, handed the priest a censer. Waving it as he went, and rattling off his pious Latin, he walked round and round the bier. Symbolic and religious perfume ! It had smoked in the stable of Bethlehem, in the midst of the ammoniac smell of the beasts, the sign and symbol of the spirit. The blue smoke floated up and was lost along the wind. On the surface of the earth the beasts unremittingly propagate their kind ; the whole earth is a morass of living flesh. The smell of it hangs warm and heavy over all. Here and there the incense burns ; its smoke soon vanishes. The smell of the beasts remains.

'Baa baba,' went the priest.

'Baa,' the choristers retorted, a fifth lower down the scale.

The boy produced water and a kind of whisk. Once more the priest walked round the bier, sprinkling the water from the end of the wetted whisk ; the little umpire followed in his train, holding up the tail of his outer garment. The bearers, meanwhile, talked to one another in serious whispers about the grapes.

Sometimes, Mr. Cardan thought, the spirit plays its part so solemnly and well that one cannot help believing in its reality and ultimate significance. A ritual gravely performed is overwhelmingly convincing, for the moment at any rate. But let it be performed casually and carelessly by people who are not thinking of what the rite is meant to symbolize ; one perceives that there is nothing behind the symbols, that it is only the acting that matters—the judicious acting of the body—and that the body, the doomed, decaying body, is the one, appalling fact.

The service was over ; the bearers picked up the coffin and carried it to the hearse that stood at the church door. The priest beckoned to Mr. Cardan to follow him into the sacristy. There, while the little umpire put away his censer and the whisk, he presented his bill. Mr. Cardan paid.

PART V

CONCLUSIONS

Chapter I

'WHAT are you thinking of?'

'Nothing,' said Calamy.

'Yes, you were. You must have been thinking about something.'

'Nothing in particular,' he repeated.

'Tell me,' Mary insisted. 'I want to know.'

'Well, if you really want to know,' Calamy began slowly . . .

But she interrupted him. 'And why did you hold up your hand like that? And spread out the fingers? I could see it, you know; against the window.' Pitch dark it was in the room, but beyond the unshuttered windows was a starlit night.

Calamy laughed—a rather embarrassed laugh. 'Oh, you saw it, did you—the hand? Well, as a matter of fact, it was precisely about my hand that I was thinking.'

'About your hand?' said Mary incredulously. 'That seems a queer thing to think about.'

'But interesting if you think about it hard enough.'

'Your hands,' she said softly, in another voice, 'your hands. When they touch me . . .' With a feminine movement of gratitude, of thanks for a benefit received, she pressed herself more closely against him; in the darkness she kissed him. 'I love you too much,' she whispered, 'too much.' And at the moment it was almost true. The strong complete spirit, she had written in her note-book, must be able to love with fury, savagely, mindlessly. Not without pride, she had found herself complete and strong. Once, at a dinner party, she had been taken down by a large black and lemon coloured Argentine; unfolding his napkin, he had opened the evening's conversation, in that fantastic trans-Pyrenean French which was his only substitute for the Castilian, by saying, with a roll of his black eyes and a flashing ivory smile: 'Jé vois qué vous avez du temmperramenk.' 'Oh, à revendre,' she had answered gaily, throwing herself into the light Parisian part. How marvellously amusing! But that was Life—Life all over. She had brought the incident into a short story, long ago. But the Argentine had looked with an expert's eye; he was right. 'I love you too much,' she whispered in the darkness. Yes, it was true, it was nearly true, at the moment, in the circumstances. She took his hand and kissed it. 'That's all *I* think about your hand,' she said.

Calamy allowed his hand to be kissed, and as soon as it was decently possible gently withdrew it. Invisibly, in the darkness, he made a little grimace of impatience. He was no longer interested in kisses, at the moment. 'Yes,' he said meditatively, 'that's one way of thinking of my hand, that's one way in which it exists and is real. Certainly. And that was what I was thinking about—all the different ways in which these five fingers'—he held them up again, splayed out, against the window's oblong of paler darkness—'have reality and exist. All the different ways,' he repeated slowly. 'If you think of that, even for five minutes, you find yourself plunged up to the eyes in the most portentous mysteries.' He was silent for a moment; then added in a very serious voice. 'And I believe that if one could stand the strain of thinking really hard about one thing—this hand, for example—really hard for several days, or weeks, or months, one might be able to burrow one's way right through the mystery and really get at something—some kind of truth, some explanation.' He paused, frowning. Down and down, through the obscurity, he was thinking. Slowly, painfully, like Milton's Devil, pushing his way through chaos; in the end, one might emerge into the light, to see the universe, sphere within sphere, hanging from the floor of heaven. But it would be a slow, laborious process; one would need time, one would need freedom. Above everything, freedom.

'Why don't you think about me?' Mary Thriplow asked. She propped herself up on one elbow and leaned over him; with her other hand she ruffled his hair. 'Don't I bear thinking about?' she asked. She had a fistful of his thick hair in her hand; softly she tugged at it, testingly, as though she were preparing for something worse, were assuring her grip for a more violent pull. She felt a desire to hurt him. Even in her arms, she was thinking, he escaped her, he simply wasn't there. 'Don't I bear thinking about?' she repeated, tugging a little harder at his hair.

Calamy said nothing. The truth was, he was reflecting, that she didn't bear thinking about. Like a good many other things. All one's daily life was a skating over thin ice, was a scampering of water-beetles across the invisible skin of depths. Stamp a little too hard, lean a shade too heavily and you were through, you were floundering in a dangerous and unfamiliar element. This love business, for example—it simply couldn't be thought of; it could only support one on condition that one never stopped to think. But it was necessary to think, necessary to break through and sink into the depths. And yet, insanely and desperately, one still went skating on.

'Do you love me?' asked Mary.

'Of course,' he said; but the tone of his voice did not carry much conviction.

Menacingly she tugged at the tuft of hair she held twined round her fingers. It angered her that he should escape her, that he should not give himself up completely to her. And this resentful feeling that he did not love her enough produced in her a complementary conviction that she loved him too much. Her anger combined with her physical gratitude to make her feel, for the moment, peculiarly passionate. She found herself all at once playing the part of the *grande amoureuse*, the impassioned de Lespinasse, playing it spontaneously and without the least difficulty. 'I could hate you,' she said resentfully, 'for making me love you so much.'

'And what about me?' said Calamy, thinking of his freedom. 'Haven't I a right to hate too?'

'No. Because you don't love so much.'

'But that's not the question,' said Calamy, neglecting to record his protest against this damning impeachment. 'One doesn't resent love for its own sake, but for the sake of what it interferes with.'

'Oh, I see,' said Mary bitterly. She was too deeply wounded even to desire to pull his hair. She turned her back on him. 'I'm sorry I should have got in the way of your important occupations,' she said in her most sarcastic voice. 'Such as thinking about your hand.' She laughed derisively. There was a long silence. Calamy made no attempt to break it; he was piqued by this derisive treatment of a subject which, for him, was serious, was in some sort sacred. It was Mary who first spoke.

'Will you tell me, then, what you were thinking?' she asked submissively, turning back towards him. When one loves, one swallows one's pride and surrenders. 'Will you tell me?' she repeated, leaning over him. She took one of his hands and began to kiss it, then suddenly bit one of his fingers so hard that Calamy cried out in pain.

'Why do you make me so unhappy?' she asked between clenched teeth. She saw herself, as she spoke the words, lying face downward on her bed, desperately sobbing. It needs a great spirit to be greatly unhappy.

'Make you unhappy?' echoed Calamy in a voice of irritation; he was still smarting with the pain of that bite. 'But I don't. I make you uncommonly happy.'

'You make me miserable,' she answered.

'Well, in that case,' said Calamy, 'I'd better go away and leave you in peace.' He slipped his arm from under her shoulders, as though he were really preparing to go.

But Mary enfolded him in her arms. 'No, no,' she implored. 'Don't go. You mustn't be cross with me. I'm sorry. I behaved abominably. Tell me, please, what you were thinking about your hand. I really am interested. Really, really.' She spoke eagerly, childishly, like the little girl at the Royal Institution lecture.

Calamy couldn't help laughing. 'You've succeeded in rather damping my enthusiasm for that subject,' he said. 'I'd find it difficult to begin now, in cold blood.'

'Please, please,' Mary insisted. Wronged, it was she who asked pardon, she who cajoled. When one loves . . .

'You've made it almost impossible to talk anything but nonsense,' Calamy objected. But in the end he allowed himself to be persuaded. Embarrassed, rather awkwardly—for the spiritual atmosphere in which these ideas had been ruminated was dissipated, and it was in the void, so to speak, in the empty cold that his thoughts now gasped for breath—he began his exposition. But gradually, as he spoke, the mood returned; he became at home once more with what he was saying. Mary listened with a fixed attention of which, even in the darkness, he was somehow conscious.

'Well, you see,' he started hesitatingly, 'it's like this. I was thinking of all the different ways a thing can exist—my hand, for example.'

'I see,' said Mary Thriplow sympathetically and intelligently. She was almost too anxious to prove that she was listening, that she was understanding everything; she saw before there was anything to see.

'It's extraordinary,' Calamy went on, 'what a lot of different modes of existence a thing has, when you come to think about it. And the more you think, the more obscure and mysterious everything becomes. What seemed solid vanishes; what was obvious and comprehensible becomes utterly mysterious. Gulfs begin opening all around you—more and more abysses, as though the ground were splitting in an earthquake. It gives one a strange sense of insecurity, of being in the dark. But I still believe that, if one went on thinking long enough and hard enough, one might somehow come through, get out on the other side of the obscurity. But into what, precisely into what? That's the question.' He was silent for a moment. If one were free, he thought, one could go exploring into that darkness. But the flesh was weak; under the threat of that delicious torture it turned coward and traitor.

'Well?' said Mary at last. She moved closer to him, lightly, her lips brushed across his cheek. She ran her hand softly over his shoulder and along his arm. 'Go on.'

'Very well,' he said in a business-like voice, moving a little away from her as he spoke. He held up his hand once more against the window. 'Look,' he said. 'It's just a shape that interrupts the light. To a child who has not yet learned to interpret what he sees, that's all it would be, just a shaped blotch of colour, no more significant than one of those coloured targets representing a man's head and shoulders that one learns shooting on. But now, suppose I try to consider the thing as a physicist.'

'Quite,' said Mary Thriplow; and from the movement of a floating tress of her hair which brushed against his shoulder he knew that she was nodding her head.

'Well then,' Calamy went on, 'I have to imagine an almost inconceivable number of atoms, each consisting of a greater or lesser number of units of negative electricity whirling several million times a minute round a nucleus of positive electricity. The vibrations of the atoms lying near the surface sift out, so to speak, the electro-magnetic radiations which fall upon them, permitting only those waves to reach our eyes which give us the sensation of a brownish-pink colour. In passing it may be remarked that the behaviour of light is satisfactorily explained according to one theory of electro-dynamics, while the behaviour of the electrons in the atom can only be explained on a theory that is entirely inconsistent with it. Inside the atom, they tell us now, electrons move from one orbit to another without taking any time to accomplish their journey and without covering any space. Indeed, within the atom there is neither space nor time. And so on and so on. I have to take most of this on trust, I'm afraid, for I understand next to nothing about these things. Only enough to make me feel rather dizzy when I begin to think about them.'

'Yes, dizzy,' said Mary, 'that's the word. Dizzy.' She made a prolonged buzzing over the z's.

'Well then, here are two ways already in which my hand exists,' Calamy went on. 'Then there's the chemical way. These atoms consisting of more or fewer electrons whizzing round a nucleus of greater or lesser charge are atoms of different elements that build themselves up in certain architectural patterns into complicated molecules.'

Sympathetic and intelligent, Mary echoed: 'Molecules.'

'Now if, like Cranmer, I were to put my right hand into the fire, to punish it for having done something evil or unworthy (words, by the way, which haven't much in common with chemistry), if I were to put my hand in the fire, these molecules would uncombine themselves into their constituent atoms, which would then proceed to build themselves up again into other molecules. But this leads me on at once to a set of entirely different realities. For if I were to put my hand in the fire, I should feel pain; and unless, like Cranmer, I made an enormous effort of will to keep it there, I should withdraw it; or rather it would withdraw itself almost without my knowledge and before I was aware. For I am alive, and this hand is part of a living being, the first law of whose existence is to preserve its life. Being alive, this hand of mine, if it were burnt, would set about trying to repair itself. Seen by a biologist, it reveals itself as a collection of cells, having each its appointed function, and existing harmoniously together, never trespassing upon one another, never proliferating into wild adventures of growth, but living, dying and growing to one end—that the whole which they compose may fulfil its purpose—and as though in accordance with a preordained plan. Say that the hand is burnt. From all round the burn the healthy cells would breed out of themselves new cells to fill in and cover the damaged places.'

'How wonderful life is!' said Mary Thriplow. 'Life . . .'

'Cranmer's hand,' Calamy went on, 'had done an ignoble thing. The hand is part, not merely of a living being, but of a being that knows good and evil. This hand of mine can do good things and bad things. It has killed a man, for example; it has written all manner of words; it has helped a man who was hurt; it has touched your body.' He laid his hand on her breast; she started, she trembled involuntarily under his caress. He ought to think that rather flattering, oughtn't he? It was a symbol of his power over her—of her power, alas, over him. 'And when it touches your body,' he went on, 'it touches also your mind. My hand moves like this, and it moves through your consciousness as well as here, across your skin. And it's my mind that orders it to move; it brings your body into my mind. It exists in mind; it has reality as a part of my soul and a part of yours.'

Miss Thriplow couldn't help reflecting that there was, in all this, the stuff for a very deep digression in one of her novels. 'This thoughtful young writer . . .' would be quoted from the reviewers on the dust-cover of her next book.

'Go on,' she said.

Calamy went on. 'And so these,' he said, 'are some of the ways—and there are plenty more, of course, besides—these are some of the ways in which my hand exists and is real. This shape which interrupts the light—it is enough to think of it for five minutes to perceive that it exists simultaneously in a dozen parallel worlds. It exists as electrical charges; as chemical molecules; as living cells; as part of a moral being, the instrument of good and evil; in the physical world and in mind. And from this one goes on to ask, inevitably, what relationship exists between these different modes of being. What is there in common between life and chemistry; between good and evil and electrical charges; between a collection of cells and the consciousness of a caress? It's here that the gulfs begin to open. For there isn't any connection—that one can see, at any rate. Universe lies on the top of universe, layer after layer, distinct and separate . . .'

'Like a Neapolitan ice,' Mary's mind flew at once to the fantastic and unexpected comparison. 'This witty young writer . . .' That was already on her dust-covers.

Calamy laughed. 'All right,' he agreed. 'Like a Neapolitan ice, if you like. What's true in the chocolate layer, at the bottom of the ice, doesn't hold in the vanilla at the top. And a lemon truth is different from a strawberry truth. And each one has just as much right to exist and to call itself real as every other. And you can't explain one in terms of the others. Certainly you can't explain the vanilla in terms of any of the lower layers—you can't explain mind as mere life, as chemistry, as physics. That at least is one thing that's perfectly obvious and self-evident.'

'Obvious,' Mary agreed. 'And what's the result of it all? I really don't see.'

'Neither do I,' said Calamy, speaking through an explosion of melancholy laughter. 'The only hope,' he went on slowly, 'is that perhaps, if you went on thinking long enough and hard enough, you might arrive at an explanation of the chocolate and the lemon by the vanilla. Perhaps it's really all vanilla, all mind, all spirit. The rest is only apparent, an illusion. But one has no right to say so until one has thought a long time, in freedom.'

'In freedom?'

'The mind must be open, unperturbed, empty of irrelevant things, quiet. There's no room for thoughts in a half-shut, cluttered mind. And thoughts won't enter a noisy mind; they're shy, they remain in their obscure hiding-places below the surface, where they can't be got at, so long as the mind is full and noisy. Most of us pass through life without knowing that they're there at all. If one wants to lure them out, one must clear a space for them, one must open the mind wide and wait. And there must be no irrelevant preoccupations prowling around the doors. One must free oneself of those.'

'I suppose I'm one of the irrelevant preoccupations,' said Mary Thriplow, after a little pause.

Calamy laughed, but did not deny it.

'If that's so,' said Mary, 'why did you make love to me?'

Calamy did not reply. Why indeed? He had often asked that question himself.

'I think it would be best,' she said, after a silence, 'if we were to make an end.' She would go away, she would grieve in solitude.

'Make an end?' Calamy repeated. He desired it, of course, above everything—to make an end, to be free. But he found himself adding, with a kind of submarine laughter below the surface of his voice: 'Do you think you *can* make an end?'

'Why not?'

'Suppose I don't allow you to?' Did she imagine, then, that she wasn't in his power, that he couldn't make her obey his will whenever he desired? 'I *don't* allow you,' he said, and his voice quivered with the rising mirth. He bent over her and began to kiss her on the mouth; with his hands he held and caressed her. What an insanity, he said to himself.

'No, no.' Mary struggled a little; but in the end she allowed herself to be overcome. She lay still, trembling, like one who has been tortured on the rack.

Chapter II

ON their return, somewhat low-spirited, from Montefiascone, Mrs. Aldwinkle and her party found Mary Thriplow alone in the palace.

'And Calamy?' Mrs. Aldwinkle inquired.

'He's gone into the mountains,' said Miss Thriplow in a serious, matter-of-fact voice.

'Why?'

'He felt like that,' Mary answered. 'He wanted to be alone to think. I understand it so well. The prospect of your return filled him almost with terror. He went off two or three days ago.'

'Into the mountains?' echoed Mrs. Aldwinkle. 'Is he sleeping in the woods, or in a cave, or something of that kind?'

'He's taken a room in a peasant's cottage on the road up to the marble quarries. It's a lovely place.'

'This sounds most interesting,' said Mr. Cardan. 'I must really climb up and have a look at him.'

'I'm sure he'd rather you didn't,' said Miss Thriplow. 'He wants to be left alone. I understand it so well,' she repeated.

Mr. Cardan looked at her curiously; her face expressed a bright and serious serenity. 'I'm surprised that you too don't retire from the world,' he said, twinkling. He had not felt as cheerful as this since before the dismal day of poor Grace's funeral.

Miss Thriplow smiled a Christian smile. 'You think it's a joke,' she said, shaking her head. 'But it isn't really, you know.'

'I'm sure it isn't,' Mr. Cardan made haste to protest. 'And believe me, I never meant to imply that it was. Never, on my word. I merely said—quite seriously, I assure you. —that I was surprised that you too . . .'

'Well, you see, it doesn't seem to me necessary to go away bodily,' Miss Thriplow explained. 'It's always seemed to me that one can live the hermit's life, if one wants to, in the heart of London, anywhere.'

'Quite,' said Mr. Cardan. 'You're perfectly right.'

'I think he might have waited till I came back,' said Mrs. Aldwinkle rather resentfully. 'The least he could have done was to leave a note.' She looked at Miss Thriplow angrily, as though it were she who were to blame for Calamy's impoliteness. 'Well, I must go and get out of my dusty clothes,' she added crossly, and walked away to her room. Her irritation was the disguise and public manifestation of a profound depression. They're all going, she was thinking, they're all slipping away. First Chelifer, now Calamy. Like all the rest. Mournfully she looked back over her life.

Everybody, everything had always slipped away from her. She had always missed all the really important, exciting things; they had invariably happened, somehow, just round the corner, out of her sight. The days were so short, so few now. Death approached, approached. Why had Cardan brought that horrible imbecile creature to die in front of her like that? She didn't want to be reminded of death. Mrs. Aldwinkle shuddered. I'm getting old, she thought; and the little clock on the mantel-piece, ticking away in the silence of her huge room, took up the refrain: Getting old, getting old, getting old, it repeated again and again, endlessly. Getting old—Mrs. Aldwinkle looked at herself in the glass—and that electric massage machine hadn't arrived. True, it was on its way; but it would be weeks before it got here. The posts were so slow. Everything conspired against her. If she had had it before, if she'd looked younger . . . who knew? Getting old, getting old, repeated the little clock. In a couple of days from now Chelifer would be going back to England; he'd go away, he'd live apart from her, live such a wonderful, beautiful life. She'd miss it all. And Calamy had already gone; what was he doing, sitting there in the mountains? He was thinking wonderful thoughts, thoughts that might hold the secret she had always been seeking and had never found, thoughts that might bring the consolation and tranquillity of which she always so sorely stood in need. She was missing them, she'd never know them. Getting old, getting old. She took off her hat and tossed it on to the bed. It seemed to her that she was the unhappiest woman in the world.

That evening, while she was brushing Mrs. Aldwinkle's hair, Irene, braving the dangers of Aunt Lilian's terrifying fun, screwed up her courage to say: 'I can never be grateful enough to you, Auntie, for having talked to me about Hovenden.'

'What about him?' asked Mrs. Aldwinkle, from whose mind the painful events of the last few weeks had quite obliterated such trivial memories.

Irene blushed with embarrassment. This was a question she had not anticipated. Was it really possible that Aunt Lilian could have forgotten those momentous and epoch-making words of hers? 'Why,' she began stammering, 'what you said about . . . I mean . . . when you said that he looked as though . . . well, as though he liked me.'

'Oh yes,' said Mrs. Aldwinkle without interest.

'Don't you remember?'

'Yes, yes,' Mrs. Aldwinkle nodded. 'What about it?'

'Well,' Irene went on, still painfully embarrassed, 'you see . . . that made me . . . that made me pay attention, if you understand.'

'Hm,' said Mrs. Aldwinkle. There was a silence. Getting old, getting old, repeated the little clock remorselessly.

Irene leaned forward and suddenly boiled over with confidences. 'I love him so much, Aunt Lilian,' she said, speaking very rapidly, 'so much, so much. It's the real thing this time. And he loves me too. And we're going to get married at the New Year, quite quietly; no fuss, no crowds shoving in on what isn't their business; quietly and sensibly in a registry office. And after that we're going in the Velox to . . .'

'What are you talking about?' said Mrs. Aldwinkle in a furious voice, and she turned round on her niece a face expressive of such passionate anger that Irene drew back, not merely astonished, but positively afraid. 'You don't mean to tell me,' Mrs. Aldwinkle began; but she could not find the words to continue. 'What have you two young fools been thinking about?' she got out at last.

. . . old, getting old; the remorseless ticking made itself heard in every silence.

From being merry and excited in its childishness Irene's face had become astonished and miserable. She was pale, her lips trembled a little as she spoke. 'But I thought you'd be glad, Aunt Lilian,' she said. 'I thought you'd be glad.'

'Glad because you're making fools of yourselves?' asked Mrs. Aldwinkle, savagely snorting.

'But it was you who first suggested,' Irene began.

Mrs. Aldwinkle cut her short, before she could say any more, with a brusqueness that might have revealed to a more practised psychologist than Irene her consciousness of being in the wrong. 'Absurd,' she said. 'I suppose you're going to tell me,' she went on sarcastically, 'that it was I who told you to marry him.'

'I know you didn't,' said Irene.

'There!' Mrs. Aldwinkle's tone was triumphant.

'But you did say you wondered why I wasn't in love . . .'

'Bah,' said Aunt Lilian, 'I was just making fun. Calf loves . . .'

'But why shouldn't I marry him?' asked Irene. 'If I love him and he loves me. Why shouldn't I?'

Why shouldn't she? Yes, that was an awkward question. Getting old, getting old, muttered the clock in the brief ensuing silence. Perhaps that was half the answer. Getting old! they were all going; first Chelifer, then Calamy, now Irene. Getting old, getting old; soon she'd be quite alone. And it wasn't only that. It was also her pride that was hurt, her love of dominion that suffered. Irene had been her slave; had worshipped her, taken her word as law, her opinions as gospel truth. Now she was transferring her allegiance. Mrs. Aldwinkle was losing a subject—losing her to a more powerful rival. It was intolerable. 'Why shouldn't you marry him?' Mrs. Aldwinkle repeated the phrase ironically two or three times, while she hunted for the answer. 'Why shouldn't you marry him?'

'Why shouldn't I?' Irene asked again. There were tears in her eyes; but however unhappy she might look, there was something determined and indomitable in her attitude, something obstinate in her expression and her tone of voice. Mrs. Aldwinkle had reason to fear her rival.

'Because you're too young,' she said at last. It was a very feeble answer; but she had been unable to think of a better one.

'But, Aunt Lilian, don't you remember? You always said that people ought to marry young. I remember so well, one time, when we talked about Juliet being only fourteen when she first saw Romeo, that you said . . .'

'That has nothing to do with it,' said Mrs. Aldwinkle, cutting short her niece's mnemonic display. Irene's memory, Mrs. Aldwinkle had often had reason to complain, was really too good.

'But if you said . . .' Irene began again.

'Romeo and Juliet have nothing to do with you and Hovenden,' retorted Mrs. Aldwinkle. 'I repeat: you're too young.'

'I'm nineteen.'

'Eighteen.'

'Practically nineteen,' Irene insisted. 'My birthday's in December.'

'Marry in haste and repent at leisure,' said Mrs. Aldwinkle, making use of any missile, even a proverb, that came ready to hand. 'At the end of six months you'll come back howling and complaining and asking me to get you out of the mess.'

'But why should I?' asked Irene. 'We love one another.'

'They all say that. You don't know your own minds.'

'But we do.'

Mrs. Aldwinkle suddenly changed her tactics. 'And

what makes you so anxious all at once to run away from me?' she asked. 'Can't you bear to stay with me a moment longer? Am I so intolerable and odious and . . . and . . . brutal and . . .' She clawed at the air. 'Do you hate me so much that . . .'

'Aunt Lilian!' protested Irene, who had begun to cry in earnest.

Mrs. Aldwinkle, with that tactlessness, that lack of measure that were characteristic of her, went on piling question upon rhetorical question, until in the end she completely spoiled the effect she had meant to achieve, exaggerating into ludicrousness what might otherwise have been touching. 'Can't you bear me? Have I ill-treated you? Tell me. Have I bullied you, or scolded you, or . . . or not given you enough to eat? Tell me.'

'How can you talk like that, Aunt Lilian?' Irene dabbed her eyes with a corner of her dressing-gown. 'How can you say that I don't love you? And you were always telling me that I ought to get married,' she added, breaking out into fresh tears.

'How can I say that you don't love me?' echoed Mrs. Aldwinkle. 'But is it true that you're longing to leave me as soon as possible? Is that true or not? I merely ask what the reason is, that's all.'

'But the reason is that we want to get married; we love each other.'

'Or that you hate me,' Mrs. Aldwinkle persisted.

'But I don't hate you, Aunt Lilian. How can you say such a thing? You know I love you.'

'And yet you're anxious to run away from me as fast as you possibly can,' said Mrs. Aldwinkle. 'And I shall be left all alone, all alone.' Her voice trembled; she shut her eyes, she contorted her face in an effort to keep it closed and rigid. Between her eyelids the tears came welling out.

'All alone,' she repeated brokenly. Getting old, said the little clock on the mantel-piece, getting old, getting old.

Irene knelt down beside her, took her hands between her own and kissed them, pressed them against her tear-wet face. 'Aunt Lilian,' she begged, 'Aunt Lilian.'

Mrs. Aldwinkle went on sobbing.

'Don't cry,' said Irene, crying herself. She imagined that she alone was the cause of Aunt Lilian's unhappiness. In reality, she was only the pretext; Mrs. Aldwinkle was weeping over her whole life, weeping at the approach of death. In that first moment of agonized sympathy and self-reproach, Irene was on the point of declaring that she would give up Hovenden, that she would spend all her life with her Aunt Lilian. But something held her back. Obscurely she was certain that it wouldn't do, that it was impossible, that it would even be wrong. She loved Aunt Lilian and she loved Hovenden. In a way she loved Aunt Lilian more than Hovenden, now. But something in her that looked prophetically forward, something that had come through innumerable lives, out of the obscure depths of time, to dwell within her, held her back. The conscious and individual part of her spirit inclined towards Aunt Lilian. But consciousness and individuality—how precariously, how irrelevantly almost, they flowered out of that ancient root of life planted in the darkness of her being! The flower was for Aunt Lilian, the root for Hovenden.

'But you won't be all alone,' she protested. 'We shall constantly be with you. You'll come and stay with us.'

The assurance did not seem to bring much consolation to Mrs. Aldwinkle. She went on crying. The clock ticked away as busily as ever.

Chapter III

In the course of the last few days the entries in Miss Thriplow's note-book had changed their character. From being amorous they had turned mystical. Savage and mindless passion was replaced by quiet contemplation. De Lespinasse had yielded to de Guyon.

'Do you remember, darling Jim,' she wrote, 'how, when we were ten, we used to discuss what was the sin against the Holy Ghost? I remember we agreed that using the altar as a W.C. was probably the unforgivable sin. It's a great pity that it isn't, for then it would be so extremely easy to avoid committing it. No, I'm afraid it's not quite so straightforward as that, the sin against the Holy Ghost. And it's most perilously easy to fall into it. Stifling the voices inside you, filling the mind with so much earthy rubbish that God has no room to enter it, not giving the spirit its fair chance —that's the sin against the Holy Ghost. And it's unforgivable because it's irremediable. Last-minute repentances are no good. The sin and the corresponding virtue are affairs of a lifetime. And almost everybody commits the sin; they die unforgiven, and at once they begin again another life. Only when they've lived in the virtue of the Holy Ghost are they forgiven, let off the pains of life and allowed to sink into unity with All. Isn't that the meaning of the text? It's terribly difficult not to commit the sin. Whenever I stop to think, I am appalled by the badness of my own life. Oh, Jim, Jim, how easily one forgets, how unthinkingly one allows oneself to be buried under a mountain of little earthy interests! The voices are muffled, the mind is blocked up, there's no place for the spirit of God. When I'm working, I feel it's all right; I'm living in the virtue of the Holy Ghost. For then I'm doing the best I can. But the rest of the time, that's when I go wrong.

One can't be doing all the time, one can't always give out. One must also be passive, must receive. That's what I fail to do. I flutter about, I fill my mind with lumber, I make it impossible for myself to receive. One can't go on like this; one can't go on sinning against the Holy Ghost—not if one once realizes it.'

There was a line. The next note began: 'To think steadily and intensely of one thing is a wonderful mental exercise; it serves to open up the mysteries that lie below the commonplace surface of existence; and perhaps, if one went on thinking long enough and hard enough, one might get through the mystery to its explanation. When I think, for example, of my hand . . .' The note was a long one; it covered, in Miss Thriplow's clear, cultured writing, more than two pages of the book.

'Recently,' she had written after that, 'I have been saying my prayers again, as I used to when I was a child. Our Father which art in heaven—the words help to clear out one's mind, to rid it of the lumber and leave it free for the coming of the spirit.'

The next three notes had got there by mistake. Their place was not in the secret, personal book, but in the other volume, wherein she recorded little snippets that might come in useful for her novels. Not, of course, that the entries in the secret book didn't also come in useful for her fiction sometimes; but they were not recorded expressly for that purpose.

'A man in riding breeches,' the first note ran: 'he makes a little creaking noise as he walks along, whipcord rubbing against whipcord, that is like the creaking noise that swans make, flying, when they move their big white wings.'

Then followed two lines of comic dialogue.

'*Me.* I find the *Fall of the House of Usher* a most blood-curdling story.

'*Frenchman.* Yes, yes, she bloods my curdle also.'

The third note recorded that 'moss after a shower on a sultry day is like a sponge still damp from the hot bath.'

There followed a corollary to the note on prayer. 'There is no doubt,' she had written, 'that the actual technique of prayer—the kneeling, the hiding the face in the hands, the uttering of words *in an audible voice*, the words being addressed into empty space—helps by its mere dissimilarity from the ordinary actions of everyday life to put one into a devout frame of mind. . . .'

To-night she sat for some time in front of the open book, pen in hand, without writing anything. She frowned pensively and bit the end of her pen. In the end she put it on record that 'St. Augustine, St. Francis and St. Ignatius Loyola lived dissolute lives before their conversions.' Then, opening her other, her un-secret note-book, she wrote: 'X and Y are old friends from childhood. X dashing, Y timid; Y admires X. Y marries, while X is at the war, a passionate creature who takes Y more out of pity (he is wounded) than from love. There is a child. X returns, falls in love with Y's wife, A. Great passion amid growing anguish of mind —on her part because she is deceiving Y, whom she likes and respects, and daren't undeceive him for fear of losing the child; on his part because he feels that he ought to give up all this sort of thing and devote himself to God, etc.; in fact, he feels the premonitions of conversion. One night they decide that the time has come to part; it can't go on—she because of the deception, he because of mysticism, etc. It is a most touching scene, lasting all a last chaste night. Unfortunately Y finds out for some reason—baby ill, or something of the kind—that A is not staying at her mother's as she said, but is elsewhere. Early in the morning Y comes to X's flat to ask him to help in the search for A. Sees A's coat and hat lying on the drawing-room sofa; understands all. In a fury flies at X, who, defending himself, kills him. The end. Question, however; doesn't it end with too much of a click? too epigrammatically, so to speak? I wonder whether in this twentieth century one can permit oneself the luxury of such effective dramatic devices. Oughtn't one to do it more *flatly*, somehow? More terre-à-terreishly, more real-lifeishly? I feel that a conclusion like that is almost an unfair advantage taken at the reader's expense. One ought to arrange it differently. But the question is, how? Can one let them separate and show them living, she *en bonne mère de famille*, he as a coenobite? It would drag it out terribly, wouldn't it? Must think of this carefully.'

She shut the book and put the cap on her fountain pen, feeling that she had done a good evening's work. Calamy was now safely laid down in pickle, waiting to be consumed whenever she should be short of fictional provisions.

After having undressed, washed, brushed her hair, polished her nails, greased her face and cleaned her teeth, Miss Thriplow turned out the light, and kneeling down by the side of her bed said several prayers, aloud. She then got into bed, and lying on her back, with all her muscles relaxed, she began to think about God.

God is a spirit, she said to herself, a spirit, a spirit. She tried to picture something huge and empty, but alive. A huge flat expanse of sand, for example, and over it a huge blank dome of sky; and above the sand everything should be tremulous and shimmering with heat—an emptiness that was yet alive. A spirit, an all-pervading spirit. God is a spirit. Three camels appeared on the horizon of the sandy plain and went lolloping along in an absurd ungainly fashion from left to right. Miss Thriplow made an effort and dismissed them. God is a spirit, she said aloud. But of all animals camels are really almost the queerest; when one thinks of their frightfully supercilious faces, with their protruding under lips like the last Hapsburg kings of Spain . . . No, no; God is a spirit, all-pervading, everywhere. All the universes are made one in him. Layer upon layer . . . A Neapolitan ice floated up out of the darkness. She had never liked Neapolitan ices since that time, at the Franco-British exhibition, when she had eaten one and then taken a ride on Sir Hiram Maxim's Captive Flying Machines. Round and round and round. Lord, how she had been sick, afterwards, in the Blue Grotto of Capri! 'Sixpence each, ladies and gentlemen, only sixpence each for a trip to the celebrated Blue Grotto of Capri, the celebrated Blue Grotto, ladies and gentlemen. . . .' How sick! It must have been most awkward for the grown-ups. . . . But God is a spirit. All the universes are one in the spirit. Mind and matter in all their manifestations—all one in the spirit. All one—she and the stars and the mountains and the trees and the animals and the blank spaces between the stars and . . . and the fish, the fish in the Aquarium at Monaco. . . . And what fish! What extravagant fantasies! But no more extravagant or fantastic, really, than the painted and jewelled old women outside. It might make a very good episode in a book—a couple of those old women looking through the glass at the fishes. Very beautifully and discreetly described; and the fundamental similarity between the creatures on either side of the glass would just be delicately implied—not stated, oh, not stated; that would be too coarse, that would spoil everything, but just implied, by the description, so that the intelligent reader could take the hint. And then in the Casino . . . Miss Thriplow brusquely interrupted herself. God is a spirit. Yes. Where was she? All things are one, ah yes, yes. All, all, all, she repeated. But to arrive at the realization of their oneness one must climb up into the spirit. The body separates, the spirit unites. One must give up the body, the self; one must lose one's life to gain it. Lose one's life, empty oneself of the separating Me. She clasped her hands tightly together, tighter, tighter, as though she were squeezing out her individual life between them. If she could squeeze it all out, make herself quite empty, then the other life would come rushing in to take its place.

Miss Thriplow lay quite still, hardly breathing. Empty, she said to herself every now and then, quite empty. She felt wonderfully tranquil. God was surely very near. The silence grew more profound, her spirit became calmer and emptier. Yes, God was very near.

Perhaps it was the distant roaring of a train in the valley far below that reminded her of the noise of the whirling drill; or perhaps the thin bright line of light that came in, through a chink in the top of the rickety old door, from the illuminated corridor, to reach half across the ceiling above her—perhaps it was this long sharp probe of brightness that reminded her of a surgical instrument. Whatever may have been the cause, Miss Thriplow suddenly found herself thinking of her dentist. Such a charming man; he had a china bull-dog on the mantel-piece of his consulting-room and a photograph of his wife and twins. His hair wouldn't lie down. He had such kind grey eyes. And he was an enthusiast. 'This is an instrument of which I'm particularly fond, Miss Thriplow,' he used to say, picking out a little curved harpoon from his armoury. 'A little wider, please, if you don't mind. . . .' What about a story of a dentist who falls in love with one of his patients? He shows her all the instruments, enthusiastically, wants her to like his favourites as much as he does. He pretends that there's more wrong with her teeth than there really is, in order to see her more often.

The dentist grew dim, he began the same gesture again

and again, very slowly, but could never finish it, having forgotten, half-way through the act, what he meant to do. At last he disappeared altogether. Miss Thriplow had fallen into a profound and tranquil sleep.

Chapter IV

It had been raining, stormily; but now the wind had fallen and between the heavy clouds the sun was brightly shining. The yellowing chestnut trees stood motionless in the still bright air, glittering with moisture. A noise of rapidly running water filled the ear. The grass of the steep meadows shone in the sunlight. Calamy stepped out from the dark and frowsty living-room of the cottage and walked up the steep path on to the road. He halted here and looked about him. The road at this point was terraced out of one of the sides of a deep valley. The ground rose steeply, in places almost precipitously, above it. Below it the green mountain meadows, brilliant in the sunshine and dotted here and there with clumps of chestnut trees, fell away into the depths of the valley, which the afternoon sun had left already in a vaporous smoky shadow. Profoundly shadowed, too, were the hills on the further side of the narrow cleft. Huge black masses, smoky with the same vapour as that which floated at the bottom of the valley, they rose up almost in silhouette against the bright light beyond. The sun looked down, over their clouded summits, across the intervening gulf, touching the green hillside, on the slope of which Calamy was standing, with a radiance that, in contrast to the dark hills opposite, seemed almost unearthly. To the right, at the head of the valley, a great pinnacle of naked rock, pale brown and streaked here and there with snow-white veins of marble, reached up into the clouds and above them, so that the summit shone like a precious stone in the sunlight, against the blue of the sky. A band of white vapour hung round the shoulders of the mountain. Beneath it appeared the lower buttresses of rock and the long slopes of hanging wood and meadowland falling away into the valley, all shadowy under the clouds, shadowy and dead, save where, here and there, a great golden beam broke through, touching some chosen tract of grass or woodland or rock with an intense and precarious life.

Calamy stood for a long time looking out at the scene. How beautiful it was, how beautiful! Glittering in the light, the withering trees seemed to have prepared themselves as though for a feast. For a feast—and yet it was winter and death that awaited them. Beautiful the mountains were, but menacing and terrible; terrible the deep gulf below him with its smoky vaporous shadows, far down, below the shining green. And the shadows mounted second after second as the sun declined. Beautiful, terrible and mysterious, pregnant with what enormous secret, symbolic of what formidable reality?

From the direction of the cottage below the road came a tinkle of bells and the shrill shouting of a child's voice. Half a dozen tall black and white goats, with long black beards, long twisted horns and yellow eyes, slitted with narrow pupils, came trotting up the slope, shaking their flat bells. A little boy scrambled after them, brandishing a stick and shouting words of command. To Calamy he touched his cap; they exchanged a few words in Italian, about the rain, the goats, the best pasture; then, waving his stick and peremptorily shouting at his little flock, the child moved on up the road. The goats trotted on in front, their hoofs clicking on the stones; every now and then they paused to pull a mouthful of grass from the bank at the side of the road; but the little boy would not let them pause. 'Via!' he shouted, and banged them with his stick. They bounded forward. Soon herdsman and flock were out of sight.

If he had been born that little boy, Calamy wondered, would he still be working, unquestioningly, among these hills: tending the beasts, cutting wood; every now and then carting his faggots and his cheeses down the long road to Vezza? Would he, still, unquestioningly? Would he see that the mountains were beautiful, beautiful and terrible? Or would he find them merely ungrateful land, demanding great labour, giving little in return? Would he believe in heaven and hell? And fitfully, when anything went wrong, would he still earnestly invoke the aid of the infant Jesus, of the Blessed Virgin and St. Joseph, that patriarchal family trinity—father, mother and baby—of the Italian peasant? Would he have married? By this time, very likely, his eldest children would be ten or twelve years old—driving the goats afield with shrill yellings and brandished sticks. Would he be living quietly and cheerfully the life of a young patriarch, happy in his children, his wife, his flocks and herds? Would he be happy to live thus, close to the earth, earthily, an ancient, instinctive, animally sagacious life? It seemed hardly imaginable. And yet, after all, it was likely enough. It needs a very strong, a passionately ardent spirit to disengage itself from childish tradition, from the life which circumstances impose upon it. Was his such a spirit?

He was startled out of his speculations by the sound of his own name, loudly called from a little distance. He turned round and saw Mr. Cardan and Chelifer striding up the road towards him. Calamy waved his hand and went to meet them. Was he pleased to see them or not? He hardly knew.

'Well,' said Mr. Cardan, twinkling jovially, as he approached, 'how goes life in the Thebaïd? Do you object to receiving a couple of impious visitors from Alexandria?'

Calamy laughed and shook their hands without answering.

'Did you get wet?' he asked, to change the conversation.

'We hid in a cave,' said Mr. Cardan. He looked round at the view. 'Pretty good,' he said encouragingly, as though it were Calamy who had made the landscape, 'pretty good, I must say.'

'Agreeably Wordsworthian,' said Chelifer in his precise voice.

'And where do you live?' asked Mr. Cardan.

Calamy pointed to the cottage. Mr. Cardan nodded comprehendingly.

'Hearts of gold, but a little niffy, eh?' he asked, lifting his raised white eyebrow still higher.

'Not to speak of,' said Calamy.

'Charming girls?' Mr. Cardan went on. 'Or goitres?'

'Neither,' said Calamy.

'And how long do you propose to stay?'

'I haven't the faintest idea.'

'Till you've got to the bottom of the cosmos, eh?'

Calamy smiled. 'That's about it.'

'Splendid,' said Mr. Cardan, patting him on the arm, 'splendid. I envy you. God, what wouldn't I give to be your age? What wouldn't I give?' He shook his head sadly. 'And, alas,' he added, 'what could I give, in point of actual fact? I put it at about twelve hundred quid at the present time. My total fortune. Shouldn't we sit down?' he added on another note.

Calamy led the way down the little path. Along the front of the cottage, under the windows, ran a long bench. The three men sat down. The sun shone full upon them; it was pleasantly warm. Beneath them was the narrow valley with its smoky shadows; opposite, the black hills, cloud-capped and silhouetted against the brightness of the sky about the sun.

'And the trip to Rome,' Calamy inquired, 'was that agreeable?'

'Tolerably,' said Chelifer, with precision.

'And Miss Elver?' he addressed himself politely to Mr. Cardan.

Mr. Cardan looked up at him. 'Hadn't you heard?' he asked.

'Heard what?'

'She's dead.' Mr. Cardan's face became all at once very hard and still.

'I'm sorry,' said Calamy. 'I didn't know.' He thought it more tactful to proffer no further condolences. There was a silence.

'That's something,' said Mr. Cardan at last, 'that you'll find it rather difficult to contemplate away, however long and mystically you stare at your navel.'

'What?' asked Calamy.

'Death,' Mr. Cardan answered. 'You can't get over the fact that, at the end of everything, the flesh gets hold of the spirit, and squeezes the life out of it, so that a man turns into something that's no better than a whining sick animal. And as the flesh sickens the spirit sickens, manifestly. Finally the flesh dies and putrefies; and the spirit presumably putrefies too. And there's an end of your omphaloskepsis, with all its by-products, God and justice and salvation and all the rest of them.'

'Perhaps it is,' said Calamy. 'Let's admit it as certain, even. I don't see that it makes the slightest difference. . . .'

'No difference?'

Calamy shook his head. 'Salvation's not in the next world; it's in this. One doesn't behave well here for the sake of a harp and wings after one is dead—or even for the sake of contemplating throughout eternity the good, the true and the beautiful. If one desires salvation, it's salvation here and now. The kingdom of God is within you—if you'll excuse the quotation,' he added, turning with a smile to Mr. Cardan. 'The conquest of that kingdom, now, in this life—that's your salvationist's ambition. There may be a life to come, or there may not; it's really quite irrelevant to the main issue. To be upset because the soul may decay with the body is really mediaeval. Your mediaeval theologian made up for his really frightful cynicism about this world by a childish optimism about the next. Future justice was to compensate for the disgusting horrors of the present. Take away the life to come and the horrors remain, untempered and unpalliated.'

'Quite so,' said Chelifer.

'Seen from the mediaeval point of view,' Calamy went on, 'the prospect is most disquieting. The Indians—and for that matter the founder of Christianity—supply the corrective with the doctrine of salvation in this life, irrespective of the life to come. Each man can achieve salvation in his own way.'

'I'm glad you admit that,' said Mr. Cardan. 'I was afraid you'd begin telling us that we all had to live on lettuces and look at our navels.'

'I have it from no less an authority than yourself,' Calamy answered, laughing, 'that there are—how many?—eighty-four thousand—isn't it?—different ways of achieving salvation.'

'Fully,' said Mr. Cardan, 'and a great many more for going to the devil. But all this, my young friend,' he pursued, shaking his head, 'doesn't in any way mitigate the disagreeableness of slowly becoming *gaga*, dying and being eaten by worms. One may have achieved salvation in this life, certainly; but that makes it none the less insufferable that, at the end of the account, one's soul should inevitably succumb to one's body. I, for example, am saved—I put the case quite hypothetically, mind you—I have been living in a state of moral integrity and this-worldly salvation for the last half-century, ever since I reached the age of puberty. Let this be granted. Have I, for this reason, any the less cause to be distressed by the prospect, in a few years' time, of becoming a senile imbecile, blind, deaf, toothless, witless, without interest in anything, partially paralysed, revolting to my fellows—and all the rest of the Burtonian catalogue? When my soul is at the mercy of my slowly rotting body, what will be the use of salvation then?'

'It will have profited during the fifty years of healthy life,' said Calamy.

'But I'm talking about the unhealthy years,' Mr. Cardan insisted, 'when the soul's at the mercy of the body.'

Calamy was silent for a moment. 'It's difficult,' he said pensively, 'it's horribly difficult. The fundamental question is this: Can you talk of the soul being at the mercy of the body, can you give any kind of an explanation of mind in terms of matter? When you reflect that it's the human mind that has invented space, time and matter, picking them out of reality in a quite arbitrary fashion—can you attempt to explain a thing in terms of something it has invented itself? That's the fundamental question.'

'It's like the question of the authorship of the *Iliad*,' said Mr. Cardan. 'The author of that poem is either Homer or, if not Homer, somebody else of the same name. Similarly, philosophically and even, according to the new physics, scientifically speaking, matter may not be matter, *really*. But the fact remains that something having all the properties we have always attributed to matter is perpetually getting in our way, and that our minds do, in point of fact, fall under the dominion of certain bits of this matter, known as our bodies, changing as they change and keeping pace with their decay.'

Calamy ran his fingers perplexedly through his hair. 'Yes, of course, it's devilishly difficult,' he said. 'You can't help behaving *as if* things really were as they seem to be. At the same time, there *is* a reality which is totally different and which a change in our physical environment, a removal of our bodily limitations, would enable us to get nearer to. Perhaps by thinking hard enough . . .' He paused, shaking his head. 'How many days did Gotama spend under the bo-tree? Perhaps if you spend long enough and your mind is the right sort of mind, perhaps you really do get, in some queer sort of way, beyond the limitations of ordinary existence. And you see that everything that seems real is in fact entirely illusory—*maya*, in fact, the cosmic illusion. Behind it you catch a glimpse of reality.'

'But what bosh your mystics talk about it,' said Mr. Cardan. 'Have you ever read Boehme, for example? Lights and darknesses, wheels and compunctions, sweets and bitters, mercury, salt and sulphur—it's a rigmarole.'

'It's only to be expected,' said Calamy. 'How is a man to give an account of something entirely unlike the phenomena of known existence in a language invented to describe these phenomena? You might give a deaf man a most detailed verbal description of the Fifth Symphony; but he wouldn't be much the wiser for it, and he'd think you were talking pure balderdash—which from his point of view you would be. . . .'

'True,' said Mr. Cardan; 'but I have my doubts whether any amount of sitting under bo-trees really makes it possible for any one to wriggle out of human limitations and get behind phenomena.'

'Well, I'm inclined to think that it does make it possible,' said Calamy. 'There we must agree to differ. But even if it is impossible to get at reality, the fact that reality exists and is manifestly very different from what we ordinarily suppose it to be, surely throws some light on this horrible death business. Certainly, as things seem to happen, it's as if the body did get hold of the soul and kill it. But the real facts of the case may be entirely different. The body as we know it is an invention of the mind. What is the reality on which the abstracting, symbolizing mind does its work of abstraction and symbolism? It is possible that, at death, we may find out. And in any case, what is death, *really*?'

'It's a pity,' put in Chelifer, in his dry, clear, accurate voice, 'it's a pity that the human mind didn't do its job of invention a little better while it was about it. We might, for example, have made our symbolic abstraction of reality in such a way that it would be unnecessary for a creative and possibly immortal soul to be troubled with the haemorrhoids.'

Calamy laughed. 'Incorrigible sentimentalist!'

'Sentimentalist?' echoed Chelifer, on a note of surprise.

'A sentimentalist inside out,' said Calamy, nodding affirmatively. 'Such wild romanticism as yours—I imagined it had been extinct since the deposition of Louis-Philippe.'

Chelifer laughed good-humouredly. 'Perhaps you're right,' he said. 'Though I must say I myself should have handed out the prize for sentimentality to those who regard what is commonly known as reality—the Harrow Road, for example, or the Café de la Rotonde in Paris—as a mere illusion, who run away from it and devote their time and energy to occupations which Mr. Cardan sums up and symbolizes in the word omphaloskepsis. Aren't they the soft-heads, the all-too-susceptible and sentimental imbeciles?'

'On the contrary,' Calamy replied, 'in point of historical fact they've generally been men of the highest intelligence. Buddha, Jesus, Lao-tsze, Boehme, in spite of his wheels and compunctions, his salt and sulphur, Swedenborg. And what about Sir Isaac Newton, who practically abandoned mathematics for mysticism after he was thirty? Not that he was a particularly good mystic; he wasn't. But he tried to be; and it can't be said that he was remarkable for the softness of his head. No, it's not fools who turn mystics. It takes a certain amount of intelligence and imagination to realize the extraordinary queerness and mysteriousness of the world in which we live. The fools, the innumerable fools, take it all for granted, skate about cheerfully on the surface and never think of inquiring what's underneath. They're content with appearances, such as your Harrow Road or Café de la Rotonde, call them realities and proceed to abuse any one who takes an interest in what lies underneath these superficial symbols, as a romantic imbecile.'

'But it's cowardice to run away,' Chelifer insisted. 'One has no right to ignore what for ninety-nine out of every hundred human beings is reality—even though it mayn't actually be the real thing. One has no right.'

'Why not?' asked Calamy. 'One has a right to be six foot nine inches high and to take sixteens in boots. One has a right, even though there are not more than three or four in every million like one. Why hasn't one the right to be born with an unusual sort of mind, a mind that can't be content with the surface-life of appearances?'

But such a mind is irrelevant, a freak,' said Chelifer. 'In real life—or if you prefer it, in the life that we treat as if it were real—it's the other minds that preponderate, that are the rule. The brutish minds. I repeat, you haven't the right to run away from that. If you want to know what human life is, you must be courageous and live as the majority of human beings actually do live. It's singularly revolting, I assure you.'

'There you are again with your sentimentality,' complained Calamy. 'You're just the common variety of sentimentalist reversed. The ordinary kind pretends that so-called real life is more rosy than it actually is. The reversed sentimentalist gloats over its horrors. The bad principle is the same in both cases—an excessive preoccupation with what is illusory. The man of sense sees the world of appearances neither too rosily nor too biliously and passes on. There is the ulterior reality to be looked for; it is more interesting. . . .'

'Then you'd condemn out of hand all the countless human beings whose life is passed on the surface?'

'Of course not,' Calamy replied. 'Who would be such a fool as to condemn a fact? These people exist; it's obvious. They have their choice of Mr. Cardan's eighty-four thousand paths to salvation. The path I choose will probably be different from others. That's all.'

'Very likely,' said Mr. Cardan, who had been engaged in lighting a cigar, 'very likely they'll find the road to their salvation more easily than you will find the road to yours. Being simpler, they'll have within them fewer causes for disharmony. Many of them are still practically in the tribal state, blindly obeying the social code that has been suggested into them from childhood. That's the pre-lapsarian state; they've not yet eaten of the tree of the knowledge of good and evil—or rather it's the whole tribe, not the individual, that has eaten. And the individual is so much a part of the tribe that it doesn't occur to him to act against its ordinances, any more than it occurs to my teeth to begin violently biting my tongue of their own accord. Those simple souls—and there are still a lot of them left, even among the motor buses—will find their way to salvation very easily. The difficulty begins when the individuals begin to get thoroughly conscious of themselves apart from the tribe. There's an immense number of people who ought to be tribal savages, but who have been made conscious of their individuality. They can't obey tribal morality blindly and they're too feeble to think for themselves. I should say that the majority of people in a modern educated democratic state are at that stage—too conscious of themselves to obey blindly, too inept to be able to behave in a reasonable manner on their own account. Hence that delightful contemporary state of affairs which so rejoices the heart of our friend Chelifer. We fall most horribly between two stools—the tribe and the society of conscious intelligent beings.'

'It's comforting to think,' said Chelifer, 'that modern civilization is doing its best to re-establish the tribal régime, but on an enormous, national and even international scale. Cheap printing, wireless telephones, trains, motor-cars, gramophones and all the rest are making it possible to consolidate tribes, not of a few thousands, but of millions. To judge from the Middle Western novelists, the process seems already to have gone a long way in America. In a few generations it may be that the whole planet will be covered by one vast American-speaking tribe, composed of innumerable individuals, all thinking and acting in exactly the same way, like the characters in a novel by Sinclair Lewis. It's a most pleasing speculation—though, of course,' Chelifer added guardedly, 'the future is no concern of ours.'

Mr. Cardan nodded and puffed at his cigar. 'That's certainly a possibility,' he said. 'A probability almost; for I don't see that it's in the least likely that we shall be able to breed a race of beings, at any rate within the next few thousand years, sufficiently intelligent to be able to form a stable non-tribal society. Education has made the old tribalism impossible and has done nothing—nor ever will do anything—to make the non-tribal society possible. It will be necessary, therefore, if we require social stability, to create a new kind of tribalism, on the basis of universal education for the stupid, using the press, wireless and all the rest as the instruments by which the new order is to be established. In a generation or two of steady conscious work it ought to be possible, as Chelifer says, to turn all but two or three hundred in every million of the inhabitants of the planet into Babbitts.'

'Perhaps a slightly lower standard would be necessary,' suggested Chelifer.

'It's a remarkable thing,' pursued Mr. Cardan meditatively, 'that the greatest and most influential reformer of modern times, Tolstoy, should also have proposed a reversion to tribalism as the sole remedy to civilized restlessness and uncertainty of purpose. But while we propose a tribalism based on the facts—or should I say the appearances?'—Mr. Cardan twinkled amicably at Calamy—'of modern life, Tolstoy proposed a return to the genuine, primordial, uneducated, dirty tribalism of the savage. That won't do, of course; because it's hardly probable, once they have tasted it, that men will allow *le confort moderne*, as they call it in hotels, to be taken from them. Our suggestion is the more practicable—the creation of a planet-wide tribe of Babbitts. They'd be much easier to propagate, now, than moujiks. But still the principle remains the same in both projects—a return to the tribal state. And when Tolstoy and Chelifer and myself agree about anything, believe me,' said Mr. Cardan, 'there's something in it. By the way,' he added, 'I hope we haven't been hurting your susceptibilities, Calamy. You're not moujiking up here, are you? Digging and killing pigs and so on. Are you? I trust not.'

Calamy shook his head, laughing. 'I cut wood in the mornings, for exercise,' he said. 'But not on principle, I assure you, not on principle.'

'Ah, that's all right,' said Mr. Cardan. 'I was afraid you might be doing it on principle.'

'It would be a stupidity,' said Calamy. 'What would be the point of doing badly something for which I have no aptitude; something, moreover, which would prevent me from doing the thing for which it seems to me just possible I may have some native capacity.'

'And what, might I ask,' said Mr. Cardan with an assumed diffidence and tactful courtesy, 'what may that thing be?'

'That's rather biting,' said Calamy, smiling. 'But you may well ask. For it has certainly been hard to see, until now, what my peculiar talent was. I've not even known myself. Was it making love? or riding? or shooting antelopes in Africa? or commanding a company of infantry? or desultory reading at lightning speeds? or drinking champagne? or a good memory? or my bass voice? Or what? I'm inclined to think it was the first: making love.'

'Not at all a bad talent,' said Mr. Cardan judicially.

'But not, I find, one that one can go on cultivating indefinitely,' said Calamy. 'And the same is true of the others—true at any rate for me. . . . No, if I had no aptitudes but those, I might certainly as well devote myself exclusively to digging the ground. But I begin to find in myself a certain aptitude for meditation which seems to me worth cultivating. And I doubt if one can cultivate meditation at the same time as the land. So I only cut wood for exercise.'

'That's good,' said Mr. Cardan. 'I should be sorry to think you were doing anything actively useful. You retain the instincts of a gentleman; that's excellent. . . .'

'Satan!' said Calamy, laughing. 'But do you suppose I don't know very well that you can make out the most damning case against the idle anchorite who sits looking at his navel while other people work? Do you suppose I haven't thought of that?'

'I'm sure you have,' Mr. Cardan answered, genially twinkling.

'The case looks damning enough, no doubt. But it's only really cogent when the anchorite doesn't do his job properly, when he's born to be active and not contemplative.

The imbeciles who rush about bawling that action is the end of life, and that thought has no value except in so far as it leads to action, are speaking only for themselves. There are eighty-four thousand paths. The pure contemplative has a right to one of them.'

'I should be the last to deny it,' said Mr. Cardan.

'And if I find that it's not my path,' pursued Calamy, 'I shall turn back and try what can be done in the way of practical life. Up till now, I must say I've not seen much hope for myself that way. But then, it must be admitted, I didn't look for the road in places where I was very likely to find it.'

'What has always seemed to me to be the chief objection to protracted omphaloskepsis,' said Mr. Cardan, after a little silence, 'is the fact that you're left too much to your personal resources; you have to live on your own mental fat, so to speak, instead of being able to nourish yourself from outside. And to know yourself becomes impossible; because you can't know yourself except in relation to other people.'

'That's true,' said Calamy. 'Part of yourself you can certainly get to know only in relation to what is outside. In the course of twelve or fifteen years of adult life I think I've got to know that part of me very thoroughly. I've met a lot of people, been in a great many curious situations, so that almost every potentiality latent in that part of my being has had a chance to unfold itself into actuality. Why should I go on? There's nothing more I really want to know about that part of myself; nothing more, of any significance, I imagine, that I could get to know by contact with what is external. On the other hand, there is a whole universe within me, unknown and waiting to be explored; a whole universe that can only be approached by way of introspection and patient uninterrupted thought. Merely to satisfy curiosity it would surely be worth exploring. But there are motives more impelling than curiosity to persuade me. What one may find there is so important that it's almost a matter of life and death to undertake the search.'

'Hm,' said Mr. Cardan. 'And what will happen at the end of three months' chaste meditation when some lovely young temptation comes toddling down this road, "balancing her haunches," as Zola would say, and rolling the large black eye? What will happen to your explorations of the inward universe then, may I ask?'

'Well,' said Calamy, 'I hope they'll proceed uninterrupted.'

'You hope? Piously?'

'And I shall certainly do my best to see that they do,' Calamy added.

'It won't be easy,' Mr. Cardan assured him.

'I know.'

'Perhaps you'll find that you can explore simultaneously both the temptation and the interior universe.'

Calamy shook his head. 'Alas, I'm afraid that's not practicable. It would be delightful if it were. But for some reason it isn't. Even in moderation it won't do. I know that, more or less, by experience. And the authorities are all agreed about it.'

'But after all,' said Chelifer, 'there have been religions that prescribed indulgence in these particular temptations as a discipline and ceremony at certain seasons and to celebrate certain feasts.'

'But they didn't pretend,' Calamy answered, 'that it was a discipline that made it easy for those who underwent it to explore the inward universe of mind.'

'Perhaps they did,' objected Chelifer. 'After all, there's no golden rule. At one time and in one place you honour your father and your mother when they grow old; elsewhere and at other periods you knock them on the head and put them into the *pot-au-feu*. Everything has been right at one time or another and everything has been wrong.'

'That's only true with reservations,' said Calamy, 'and the reservations are the most important part. There's a parallel, it seems to me, between the moral and the physical world. In the physical world you call the unknowable reality the Four-Dimensional Continuum. The Continuum is the same for all observers; but when they want to draw a picture of it for themselves, they select different axes for their graphs, according to their different motions—and according to their different minds and physical limitations. Human beings have selected three-dimensional space and time as their axes. Their minds, their bodies and the earth on which they live being what they are, human beings could not have done otherwise. Space and time are necessary and inevitable ideas for us. And when we want to draw a picture of that other reality in which we live—is it different, or is it somehow, incomprehensibly, the same?—we choose, unescapably—we cannot fail to choose, those axes of reference which we call good and evil; the laws of our being make it necessary for us to see things under the aspects of good and evil. The reality remains the same; but the axes vary with the mental position, so to speak, and the varying capacities of different observers. Some observers are clearer-sighted and in some way more advantageously placed than others. The incessantly changing social conventions and moral codes of history represent the shifting axes of reference chosen by the least curious, most myopic and worst-placed observers. But the axes chosen by the best observers have always been startlingly like one another. Gotama, Jesus and Lao-tsze, for example; they lived sufficiently far from one another in space, time and social position. But their pictures of reality resemble one another very closely. The nearer a man approaches these in penetration, the more nearly will his axes of moral reference correspond with theirs. And when all the most acute observers agree in saying that indulgence in these particular amusements interferes with the exploration of the spiritual world, then one can be pretty sure it's true. In itself, no doubt, the natural and moderate satisfaction of the sexual instincts is a matter quite indifferent to morality. It is only in relation to something else that the satisfaction of a natural instinct can be said to be good or bad. It might be bad, for example, if it involved deceit or cruelty. It is certainly bad when it enslaves a mind that feels, within itself, that it ought to be free—free to contemplate and recollect itself.'

'No doubt,' said Mr. Cardan. 'But as a practical man, I can only say that it's going to be most horribly difficult to preserve that freedom. That balancing of haunches . . .' He waved his cigar from side to side. 'I shall call again in six months and see how you feel about it all then. It's extraordinary what an effect the natural appetites do have on good resolutions. Satiated, one thinks regeneration will be so easy; but when one's hungry again, how hard it seems.'

They were silent. From the depths of the valley the smoky shadows had climbed higher and higher up the slope. The opposite hills were now profoundly black and the clouds in which their peaks were involved had become dark and menacing save where, on their upper surfaces, the sun touched them with, as it declined, an ever richer light. The shadow had climbed up to within a hundred feet of where they were sitting, soon it would envelop them. With a great jangling of bells and a clicking of small hard hoofs the six tall piebald goats came trotting down the steep path from the road. The little boy ran behind them, waving his stick. 'Eia-oo!' he shouted with a kind of Homeric fury; but at the sight of the three men sitting on the bench outside the house he suddenly became silent, blushed and slunk unheroically away, hardly daring to whisper to the goats while he drove them into their stable for the night.

'Dear me,' said Chelifer, who had followed the movements of the animals with a certain curiosity, 'I believe those are the first goats I have seen, or smelt, in the flesh since I took to writing about them in my paper. Most interesting. One tends to forget that the creatures really exist.'

'One tends to forget that anything or any one really exists, outside oneself,' said Mr. Cardan. 'It's always a bit of a shock to find that they do.'

'Three days hence,' said Chelifer meditatively, 'I shall be at my office again. Rabbits, goats, mice; Fetter Lane; the family *pension*. All the familiar horrors of reality.'

'Sentimentalist!' mocked Calamy.

'Meanwhile,' said Mr. Cardan, 'Lilian has suddenly decided to move on to Monte Carlo. I go with her, of course; one can't reject free meals when they're offered.' He threw away his cigar, got up and stretched himself. 'Well, we must be getting down before it gets dark.'

'I shan't see you again for some time, then?' said Calamy.

'I shall be here again at the end of six months, never fear,' said Mr. Cardan. 'Even if I have to come at my own expense.'

They climbed up the steep little path on to the road.

'Good-bye.'

'Good-bye.'

Calamy watched them go, watched them till they were out of sight round a bend in the road. A profound melancholy settled down upon him. With them, he felt, had gone all his old, familiar life. He was left quite alone with something new and strange. What was to come of this parting?

Or perhaps, he reflected, nothing would come of it. Perhaps he had been a fool.

The cottage was in the shadow now. Looking up the slope he could see a clump of trees still glittering as though prepared for a festival above the rising flood of darkness. And at the head of the valley, like an immense precious stone, glowing with its own inward fire, the limestone crags reached up through the clouds into the pale sky. Perhaps he had been a fool, thought Calamy. But looking at that shining peak, he was somehow reassured.

UNCLE SPENCER

SOME people I know can look back over the long series of their childish holidays and see in their memory always a different landscape—chalk downs or Swiss mountains; a blue and sunny sea or the grey, ever-troubled fringe of the ocean; heathery moors under the cloud with far away a patch of sunlight on the hills, golden as happiness and, like happiness, remote, precarious, impermanent, or the untroubled waters of Como, the cypresses and the Easter roses.

I envy them the variety of their impressions. For it is good to have seen something of the world with childish eyes, disinterestedly and uncritically, observing not what is useful or beautiful and interesting, but only such things as, to a being less than four feet high and having no knowledge of life or art, seem immediately significant. It is the beggars, it is the green umbrellas under which the cabmen sit when it rains, not Brunelleschi's dome, not the extortions of the hotel-keeper, not the tombs of the Medici that impress the childish traveller. Such impressions, it is true, are of no particular value to us when we are grown up. (The famous wisdom of babes, with those childish intimations of immortality and all the rest, never really amounted to very much; and the man who studies the souls of children in the hope of finding out something about the souls of men is about as likely to discover something important as the man who thinks he can explain Beethoven by referring him to the savage origins of music or religion by referring it to the sexual instincts.) None the less, it is good to have had such childish impressions, if only for the sake of comparing (so that we may draw the philosophic moral) what we saw of a place when we were six or seven with what we see again at thirty.

My holidays had no variety. From the time when I first went to my preparatory school to the time when my parents came back for good from India—I was sixteen or seventeen then, I suppose—they were all passed with my Uncle Spencer. For years the only places on the earth's surface of which I had any knowledge were Eastbourne, where I was at school; Dover (and that reduced itself to the harbour and station), where I embarked; Ostend, where Uncle Spencer met me; Brussels, where we changed trains; and finally Longres in Limburg, where my Uncle Spencer owned the sugar factory, which his mother, my grandmother, had inherited in her turn from her Belgian father, and had his home.

Hanging over the rail of the steamer as it moved slowly, stern foremost, through the narrow gullet of Ostend harbour, I used to strain my eyes, trying to pick out from among the crowd at the quay's edge the small, familiar figure. And always there he was, waving his coloured silk handkerchief, shouting inaudible greetings and advice, getting in the way of the porters and ticket-collectors, fidgeting with a hardly controllable impatience behind the barrier, until at last, squeezed and almost suffocated amongst the grown men and women—whom the process of disembarkation transformed as though by some malevolent Circean magic into brute beasts, reasonless and snarling—I struggled to shore, clutching in one hand my little bag and with the other holding to my head, if it was summer, a speckled straw, gaudy with the school colours; if winter, a preposterous bowler, whose eclipsing melon crammed over my ears made me look like a child in a comic paper pretending to be grown up.

'Well, here you are, here you are,' my Uncle Spencer

would say, snatching my bag from me. 'Eleven minutes late.' And we would dash for the custom-house as though our lives depended on getting there before the other trans-beasted passengers.

My Uncle Spencer was a man of about forty when first I came from my preparatory school to stay with him. Thin he was, rather short, very quick, agile, and impulsive in his movements, with small feet and small, delicate hands. His face was narrow, clear-cut, steep, and aquiline; his eyes dark and extraordinarily bright, deeply set under overhanging brows; his hair was black, and he wore it rather long, brushed back from his forehead. At the sides of his head it had already begun to go grey, and above his ears, as it were, two grey wings were folded against his head, so that, to look at him, one was reminded of Mercury in his winged cap.

'Hurry up!' he called. And I scampered after him. 'Hurry up!' But of course there was no use whatever in our hurrying; for even when we had had my little hand-bag examined, there was always the registered trunk to wait for; and that, for my Uncle Spencer, was agony. For though our places in the Brussels express were reserved, though he knew that the train would not in any circumstances start without us, this intellectual certainty was not enough to appease his passionate impatience, to allay his instinctive fears.

'Terribly slow,' he kept repeating. 'Terribly slow.' And for the hundredth time he looked at his watch. 'Dites-moi,' he would say, yet once more, to the sentry at the door of the customs-house, 'le grand bagage . . . ?' until in the end the fellow, exasperated by these questions which it was not his business to answer, would say something rude; upon which my Uncle Spencer, outraged, would call him *mal élevé* and a *grossier personnage*—to the fury of the sentry but correspondingly great relief of his own feelings ; for after such an outburst he could wait in patience for a good five minutes, so far forgetting his anxiety about the trunk that he actually began talking to me about other subjects, asking how I had got on this term at school, what was my batting average, whether I liked Latin, and whether Old Thunderguts, which was the name we gave to the headmaster on account of his noble baritone, was still as ill-tempered as ever.

But at the end of the five minutes, unless the trunk had previously appeared, my Uncle Spencer began looking at his watch again.

'Scandalously slow,' he said. And addressing himself to another official, 'Dites-moi, monsieur, le grand bagage . . . ?'

But when at last we were safely in the train and there was nothing to prevent him from deploying all the graces and amiabilities of his character, my Uncle Spencer, all charm and kindness now, devoted himself wholeheartedly to me.

'Look !' he said ; and from the pocket of his overcoat he pulled out a large and dampish parcel of whose existence my nose had long before made me aware. 'Guess what's in here.'

'Prawns,' I said, without an instant's hesitation.

And prawns it was, a whole kilo of them. And there we sat in opposite corners of our first-class carriage, with the little folding table opened out between us and the pink prawns on the table, eating with infinite relish and throwing the rosy carapaces, the tails, and the sucked heads out of the window. And the Flemish plain moved past us ; the long double files of poplars, planted along the banks of the canals, along the fringes of the high roads, moving as we moved, marched parallel with our course or presented, as we crossed them at right angles, for one significant flashing moment the entrance to Hobbema's avenue. And now the belfries of Bruges beckoned from far off across the plain; a dozen more shrimps and we were roaring through its station, all gloom and ogives in honour of Memling and the Gothic past. By the time we had eaten another hectogram of prawns, the modern quarter of Ghent was reminding us that art was only five years old and had been invented in Vienna. At Alost the factory chimneys smoked; and before we knew where we were, we were almost on the outskirts of Brussels, with two or three hundred grammes of sea-fruit still intact on the table before us.

'Hurry up!' cried my Uncle Spencer, threatened by another access of anxiety. 'We must finish them before we get to Brussels.'

And during the last five miles we ate furiously, shell and all; there was hardly time even to spit out the heads and tails.

'Nothing like prawns,' my Uncle Spencer never failed to say, as the express drew slowly into the station at Brussels, and the last tails and whiskers with the fishy paper were thrown out of the window. 'Nothing like prawns when the brain is tired. It's the phosphorus, you know. After all your end-of-term examinations you need them.' And then he patted me affectionately on the shoulder.

How often since then have I repeated in all earnestness my Uncle Spencer's words. 'It's the phosphorus,' I assure my fagged friends, as I insist that they shall make their lunch off shellfish. The words come gushing spontaneously out of me; the opinion that prawns and oysters are good for brain-fag is very nearly one of my fundamental and, so to say, instinctive beliefs. But sometimes, as I say the words, suddenly I think of my Uncle Spencer. I see him once more sitting opposite me in a corner of the Brussels express, his eyes flashing, his thin face expressively moving as he talks, while his quick, nervous fingers pick impatiently at the pink carapaces or with a disdainful gesture drop a whiskered head into the Flemish landscape outside the open window. And remembering my Uncle Spencer, I find myself somehow believing less firmly than I did in what I have been saying. And I wonder with a certain sense of disquietude how many other relics of my Uncle Spencer's spirit I still carry, all unconsciously, about with me

How many of our beliefs—more serious even than the belief that prawns revive the tired brain—come to us haphazardly from sources far less trustworthy than my Uncle Spencer! The most intelligent men will be found holding opinions about certain things, inculcated in them during their childhood by nurses or stable-boys. And up to the very end of our adolescence, and even after, there are for all of us certain admired beings, whose words sink irresistibly into our minds, generating there beliefs which reason does not presume to question, and which though they may be quite out of harmony with all our other opinions persist along with them without our ever becoming aware of the contradictions between the two sets of ideas. Thus an emancipated young man, whose father happens to have been a distinguished Indian civilian, is an ardent apostle of liberty and self-determination; but insists that the Indians are and for ever will be completely incapable of governing themselves. And an art critic, extremely sound on Vlaminck and Marie Laurencin, will praise as masterly and in the grand manner—and praise sincerely, for he genuinely finds them so—the works of an artist whose dim pretentious paintings of the Tuscan landscape used to delight, because they reminded her of her youth, an old lady, now dead, but whom as a very young man he greatly loved and admired.

My Uncle Spencer was for me, in my boyhood, one of these admired beings, whose opinions possess a more than earthly value for the admiring listener. For years my most passionately cherished beliefs were his. Those opinions which I formed myself, I held more diffidently, with less ardour; for they, after all, were only the fruits of my own judgment and observation, superficial rational growths; whereas the opinions I had taken from my Uncle Spencer—such as this belief in the curative properties of prawns—had nothing to do with my reason, but had been suggested directly into the sub-rational depths, where they seemed to attach themselves, like barnacles, to the very keel and bottom of my mind. Most of them, I hope, I have since contrived to scrape off; and a long, laborious, painful process it has been. But there are still, I dare say, a goodly number of them left, so deeply ingrained and grown in, that it is impossible for me to be aware of them. And I shall go down to my grave making certain judgments, holding certain opinions, regarding certain things and actions in a certain way—and the way, the opinions, the judgments will not be mine, but my Uncle Spencer's; and the obscure chambers of my mind will to the end be haunted by his bright, erratic, restless ghost.

There are some people whose habits of thought a boy or a young man might, with the greatest possible advantage to himself, make his own. But my Uncle Spencer was not one of them. His active mind darted hither and thither too wildly and erratically for it to be a safe guide for an inexperienced understanding. It was all too promptly logical to draw conclusions from false premises, too easily and enthusiastically accepted as true. Living as he did in solitude—in a mental solitude; for though he was no recluse and took his share in all social pleasures, the society of

Longres could not offer much in the way of high intellectual companionship—he was able to give free play to the native eccentricity of his mind. Having nobody to check or direct him, he would rush headlong down intellectual roads that led nowhere or into morasses of nonsense. When, much later, I used to amuse myself by listening on Sunday afternoons to the speakers at Marble Arch, I used often to be reminded of my Uncle Spencer. For they, like Uncle Spencer, lived in solitude, apart from the main contemporary world of ideas, unaware, or so dimly aware that it hardly counted, of the very existence of organized and systematic science, not knowing even where to look for the accumulated stores of human knowledge. I have talked in the Park to Bible students who boasted that during the day they cobbled or sold cheese, while at night they sat up learning Hebrew and studying the critics of the Holy Book. And I have been ashamed of my own idleness, ashamed of the poor use I have made of my opportunities. These humble scholars heroically pursuing enlightenment are touching and noble figures—but how often, alas, pathetically ludicrous too! For the critics my Bible students used to read and meditate upon were always at least three-quarters of a century out of date—exploded Tübingen scholars or literal inspirationalists; their authorities were always books written before the invention of modern historical research; their philology was the picturesque *lucus a non lucendo*, bloody from by-our-Lady type; their geology had irrefutable proofs of the existence of Atlantis; their physiology, if they happened to be atheists, was obsoletely mechanistic, if Christians, merely providential. All their dogged industry, all their years of heroic striving, had been completely wasted—wasted, at any rate, so far as the increase of human knowledge was concerned, but not for themselves, since the labour, the disinterested ambition, had brought them happiness.

My Uncle Spencer was spiritually a cousin of these Hyde Park orators and higher critics. He had all their passion for enlightenment and profound ideas, but not content with concentrating, like them, on a single subject such as the Bible, he allowed himself to be attracted by everything under the sun. The whole field of history, of science (or rather what my Uncle Spencer thought was science), of philosophy, religion, and art was his province. He had their industry too—an industry, in his case, rather erratic, fitful, and inconstant; for he would start passionately studying one subject, to turn after a little while to another whose aspect seemed to him at the moment more attractive. And like them he displayed—though to a less pronounced degree, since his education had been rather better than theirs (not much better, however, for he had never attended any seat of learning but one of our oldest and most hopeless public schools)—he displayed a vast unawareness of contemporary thought and an uncritical faith in authorities which to a more systematically educated man would have seemed quite obviously out of date; coupled with a profound ignorance of even the methods by which one could acquire a more accurate or at any rate a more 'modern' and fashionable knowledge of the universe.

My Uncle Spencer had views and information on almost every subject one cared to mention; but the information was almost invariably faulty and the judgments he based upon it fantastic. What things he used to tell me as we sat facing one another in the corners of our first-class carriage, with the prawns piled up in a little coralline mountain on the folding table between us! Fragments of his eager talk come back to me.

'There are cypresses in Lombardy that were planted by Julius Caesar. . . .'

'The human race is descended from African pygmies. Adam was black and only four feet high. . . .'

'*Similia similibus curantur.* Have you gone far enough with your Latin to know what that means?' (My Uncle Spencer was an enthusiastic homoeopathist, and the words of Hahnemann were to him as a mystic formula, a kind of *Om mani padme hum*, the repetition of which gave him an immense spiritual satisfaction.)

And once, I remember, as we were passing through the fabulous new station of Ghent—that station which fifteen or sixteen years later I was to see all smashed and gutted by the departing invaders—he began, apropos of a squad of soldiers standing on the platform, to tell me how a German professor had proved, mathematically, using the theories of ballistics and probabilities, that war was now impossible, modern quick-firing rifles and machine-guns being so efficient that it was, as my Uncle Spencer put it, 'sci-en-tif-ic-ally impossible' for any body of men to remain alive within a mile of a sufficient number of mitrailleuses, moving backwards and forwards through the arc of a circle and firing continuously all the time. I passed my boyhood in the serene certainty that war was now a thing of the past.

Sometimes he would talk to me earnestly across the prawns of the cosmogonies of Boehme or Swedenborg. But all this was so exceedingly obscure that I never took it in at all. In spite of my Uncle Spencer's ascendancy over my mind I was never infected by his mystical enthusiasms. These mental dissipations had been my Uncle Spencer's wild oats. Reacting from the rather stuffily orthodox respectability of his upbringing, he ran into, not vice, not atheism, but Swedenborg. He had preserved—a legacy from his prosperous nineteenth-century youth—an easy optimism, a great belief in progress and the superiority of modern over ancient times, together with a convenient ignorance of the things about which it would have been disquieting to think too much. This agreeable notion of the world I sucked in easily and copiously with my little crustaceans; my views about the universe and the destinies of man were as rosy in those days as the prawns themselves.

It was not till seven or eight o'clock in the evening that we finally got to our destination. My Uncle Spencer's carriage—victoria or brougham, according to the season and the state of the weather—would be waiting for us at the station door. In we climbed and away we rolled on our rubbered wheels in a silence that seemed almost magical, so deafeningly did common carts and the mere station cabs go rattling over the cobbles of the long and dismal Rue de la Gare. Even in the winter, when there was nothing to be seen of it but an occasional green gas-lamp, with a little universe of pavement, brick wall and shuttered window dependent upon it and created by it out of the surrounding darkness, the Rue de la Gare was signally depressing, if only because it was so straight and long. But in summer when the dismal brick houses by which it was flanked revealed themselves in the evening light, when the dust and the waste-paper came puffing along it in gusts of warm, stale-smelling wind, then the street seemed doubly long and disagreeable. But, on the other hand, the contrast between its sordidness and the cool, spacious Grand' Place into which, after what seemed a carefully studied preparatory twisting and turning among the narrow streets of the old town, it finally debouched, was all the more striking and refreshing. Like a ship floating out from between the jaws of a canyon into a wide and sunlit lake, our carriage emerged upon the Grand' Place. And the moment was solemn, breathlessly anticipated and theatrical, as though we were gliding in along the suspended calling of the oboes and bassoons, and the violins trembling with amorous anxiety all around us, rolling silently and with not a hitch in the stage carpentry on to some vast and limelit stage where, as soon as we had taken up our position well forward and in the centre, something tremendous, one imagined, would suddenly begin to happen —a huge orchestral tutti from contrabass trombone to piccolo, from bell instrument to triangle, and then the tenor and soprano in such a duet as had never in all the history of opera been heard before.

But when it came to the point, our entrance was never quite so dramatic as all that. One found, when one actually got there, that one had mistaken one's opera; it wasn't *Parsifal* or *Rigoletto*; it was *Pelléas* or perhaps the *Village Romeo and Juliet*. For there was nothing grandiosely Wagnerian, nothing Italian and showy about the Grand' Place at Longres. The last light was rosy on its towers, the shadows of the promenaders stretched half across the place, and in the vast square the evening had room to be cool and quiet. The Gothic Church had a sharp steeple and the seminary by its side a tower, and the little seventeenth-century Hôtel de Ville, with its slender belfry, standing in the middle of that open space as though not afraid to let itself be seen from every side, was a miracle of gay and sober architecture; and the houses that looked out upon it had faces simple indeed, burgess and ingenuous, but not without a certain nobility, not without a kind of unassuming provincial elegance. In, then, we glided, and the suspended oboeings of our entrance, instead of leading up to some grand and gaudy burst of harmony, fruitily protracted themselves in this evening beauty, exulted quietly in the rosy light, meditated among the lengthening shadows; and the violins, ceasing to tremble with anticipation, swelled and mounted, like light and leaping towers, into the serene sky.

And if the clock happened to strike at the moment that we entered, how charmingly the notes of the mechanical carillon harmonized with this imaginary music! At the hours, the bells in the high tower of the Hôtel de Ville played a minuet and trio, tinkly and formal like the first composition of an infant Boccherini, which lasted till fully three minutes past. At the half-hours it was a patriotic air of the same length. But at the quarters the bells no more than began a tune. Three or four bars and the music broke off, leaving the listener wondering what was to have followed, and attributing to this fragmentary stump of an air some rich outflowering in the pregnant and musical silence, some subtle development which should have made the whole otherwise enchanting than the completed pieces that followed and preceded, and whose charm, indeed, consisted precisely in their old-fashioned mediocrity, in the ancient, cracked, and quavering sweetness of the bells that played them, and the defects in the mechanism, which imparted to the rhythm that peculiar and unforeseeable irregularity which the child at the piano, tongue between teeth, eyes anxiously glancing from printed notes to fingers and back again, laboriously introduces into the flawless evenness of 'The Merry Peasant.'

This regular and repeated carillonage was and indeed still is—for the invaders spared the bells—an essential part of Longres, a feature like the silhouette of its three towers seen from far away between the poplars across the wide, flat land, characteristic and recognizable.

It is with a little laugh of amused delight that the stranger to Longres first hears the jigging airs and the clashes of thin, sweet harmony floating down upon him from the sky, note succeeding unmuted note, so that the vibrations mingle in the air, surrounding the clear outlines of the melody with a faint quivering halo of discord. After an hour or two the minuet and trio, the patriotic air, become all too familiar, while with every repetition the broken fragments at the quarters grow more and more enigmatic, pregnant, dubious, and irritating. The pink light fades from the three towers, the Gothic intricacies of the church sink into a flat black silhouette against the night sky; but still from high up in the topless darkness floats down, floats up and out over the housetops, across the flat fields, the minuet and trio. The patriotic air continues still, even after sunset, to commemorate the great events of 1830; and still the fragments between, like pencillings in the notebook of a genius, suggest to the mind in the scribble of twenty notes a splendid theme and the possibility of fifteen hundred variations. At midnight the bells are still playing; at half-past one the stranger starts yet again out of his sleep; re-evoked at a quarter to four his speculations about the possible conclusions of the unfinished symphony keep him awake long enough to hear the minuet and trio at the hour and to wonder how any one in Longres manages to sleep at all. But in a day or two he answers the question himself by sleeping unbrokenly through the hints from Beethoven's notebook, and the more deliberate evocations of Boccherini's childhood and the revolution of 1830. The disease creates its own antidote, and the habit of hearing the carillon induces gradually a state of special mental deafness in which the inhabitants of Longres permanently live.

Even as a small boy, to whom insomnia was a thing unknown, I found the bells, for the first night or two after my arrival in Longres, decidedly trying. My Uncle Spencer's house looked on to the Grand' Place itself, and my window on the third floor was within fifty yards of the belfry of the Hôtel de Ville and the source of the aerial music. Three-year-old Boccherini might have been in the room with me whenever the wind came from the south, banging his minuet in my ears. But after the second night he might bang and jangle as much as he liked; there was no bell in Longres could wake me.

What did wake me, however—every Saturday morning at about half-past four or five—was the pigs coming into market. One had to have spent a month of Saturdays in Longres before one could acquire the special mental deafness that could ignore the rumbling of cart-wheels over the cobbles and the squealing and grunting of two or three thousand pigs. And when one looked out what a sight it was! All the Grand' Place was divided up by rails into a multitude of pens and pounds, and every pound was seething with pink naked pigs that looked from above like so much Bergsonian *élan vital* in a state of incessant agitation. Men came and went between the enclosures, talking, bargaining, critically poking potential bacon or ham with the point of a stick. And when the bargain was struck, the owner would step into the pen, hunt down the victim, and, catching it up by one leather ear and its thin bootlace of a tail, carry it off amid grunts that ended in the piercing, long-drawn harmonics of a squeal to a netted cart or perhaps to some other pen a little farther down the line. Brought up in England to regard the infliction of discomfort upon an animal as being, if anything, rather more reprehensible than cruelty to my fellow-humans, I remember being horrified by this spectacle. So, too, apparently was the German army of occupation. For between 1914 and 1918 no pig in the Longres market might be lifted by tail or ear, the penalty for disobedience being a fine of twenty marks for the first offence, a hundred for the second, and after that a term of forced labour on the lines of communication. Of all the oppressive measures of the invader there was hardly one which more profoundly irritated the Limburgian peasantry. Nero was unpopular with the people of Rome, not because of his crimes and vices, not because he was a tyrant and a murderer, but for having built in the middle of the city a palace so large that it blocked the entrance to several of the main roads. If the Romans hated him, it was because his golden house compelled them to make a circuit of a quarter of a mile every time they wanted to go shopping. The little customary liberties, the right to do in small things what we have always done, are more highly valued than the greater, more abstract, and less immediate freedoms. And, similarly, most people will rather run the risk of catching typhus than take a few irksome sanitary precautions to which they are not accustomed. In this particular case, moreover, there was the further question: How *is* one to carry a pig except by its tail and ears? One must either throw the creature on its back and lift it up by its four cloven feet—a process hardly feasible, since a pig's centre of gravity is so near the ground that it is all but impossible to topple him over. Or else—and this is what the people of Longres found themselves disgustedly compelled to do—one must throw one's arms round the animal and carry it clasped to one's bosom as though it were a baby, at the risk of being bitten in the ear and with the certainty of stinking like a hog for the rest of the day.

The first Saturday after the departure of the German troops was a bad morning for the pigs. To carry a pig by the tail was an outward and visible symbol of recovered liberty; and the squeals of the porkers mingled with the cheers of the population and the trills and clashing harmonies of the bells awakened by the carilloneur from their four years' silence.

By ten o'clock the market was over. The railings of the pens had been cleared away, and but for the traces on the cobbles—and those too the municipal scavengers were beginning to sweep up—I could have believed that the scene upon which I had looked from my window in the bright early light had been a scene in some agitated morning dream.

But more dream-like and fantastical was the aspect of the Grand' Place when, every year during the latter part of August, Longres indulged in its traditional kermesse. For then the whole huge square was covered with booths, with merry-go-rounds turning and twinkling in the sun, with swings and switchbacks, with temporary pinnacles rivalling in height with the permanent and secular towers of the town, and from whose summits one slid, whooping uncontrollably with horrified delight, down a polished spiral track to the ground below. There was bunting everywhere, there were sleek balloons and flags, there were gaudily painted signs. Against the grey walls of the church, against the whitewashed house-fronts, against the dark brickwork of the seminary and the soft yellow stucco of the gabled Hôtel de Ville, a sea of many colours beat tumultuously. And an immense and featureless noise that was a mingling of the music of four or five steam organs, of the voices of thousands of people, of the blowing of trumpets and whistles, the clashing of cymbals, the beating of drums, of shouting, of the howling of children, of enormous rustic laughter, filled the space between the houses from brim to brim—a noise so continuous and so amorphous that hearkening from my high window it was almost, after a time, as though there were no noise at all, but a new kind of silence, in which the tinkling of the infant Boccherini's minuet, the patriotic air, and the fragmentary symphonies had become for some obscure reason utterly inaudible.

And after sunset the white flares of acetylene and the red flares of coal-gas scooped out of the heart of the night a little private day, in which the fun went on more noisily than ever. And the gaslight striking up on to the towers mingled half-way up their shafts with the moonlight from above, so that to me at my window the belfries seemed to belong half to the earth half to the pale silence overhead. But gradually, as the night wore on, earth abandoned its claims; the noise diminished; one after another the flares were put out, till at last the moon was left in absolute possession, with only a few dim greenish gas-lamps here and there, making no attempt to dispute her authority. The towers were hers down to the roots, the booths and the hooded roundabouts, the Russian mountains, the swings—all wore the moon's livery of silver and black; and audible once more the bells seemed in her honour to sound a sweeter, clearer, more melancholy note.

But it was not only from my window that I viewed the kermesse. From the moment that the roundabouts began to turn, which was as soon as the eleven o'clock Mass on the last Sunday but one in August was over, to the moment when they finally came to rest, which was at about ten or eleven on the night of the following Sunday, I moved almost unceasingly among the delights of the fair. And what a fair it was! I have never seen its like in England. Such splendour, such mechanical perfection in the swings, switchbacks, merry-go-rounds, towers, and the like! Such astonishing richness and variety in the side-shows! And withal such marvellous cheapness.

When one was tired of sliding and swinging, of being whirled and jogged, one could go and see for a penny the man who pulled out handfuls of his skin, to pin it up with safety-pins into ornamental folds and pleats. Or one could see the woman with no arms who opened a bottle of champagne with her toes and drank your health, lifting her glass to her lips with the same members. And then in another booth, over whose entry there waved—a concrete symbol of good faith—a pair of enormous female pantaloons, sat the Fat Woman—so fat that she could (and would, you were told, for four sous extra), in the words of the Flemish notice at the door, which I prefer to leave in their original dialectical obscurity, 'heur gezicht bet heur tiekes wassen.'

Next to the Fat Woman's hutch was a much larger tent, in which the celebrated Monsieur Figaro, with his wife and seven children, gave seven or eight times daily a dramatic version of the Passion of Our Saviour, at which even the priesthood was authorized to assist. The Figaro family was celebrated from one end of the country to another, and had been for I do not know how many years—forty or fifty at least. For there were several generations of Figaros; and if seven charming and entirely genuine children did indeed still tread the boards, it was not that the seven original sons and daughters of old M. Figaro had remained by some miracle perpetually young; but that marrying and becoming middle-aged they had produced little Figaros of their own, who in their turn gave rise to more, so that the aged and original M. Figaro could count among the seven members of his supposititious family more than one of his great-grandchildren. So celebrated was M. Figaro that there was even a song about him, of which unfortunately I can remember only two lines:

> 'Et le voilà, et le voilà, Fi-ga-ro,
> Le plus comique de la Belgique, Fi-ga-ro!'

But on what grounds and in what remote epoch of history he had been called ‘Le plus comique de la Belgique,’ I was never able to discover. For the only part I ever saw the venerable old gentleman play was that of Caiaphas in the *Passion of Our Saviour*, which was one of the most moving, or at any rate one of the most harrowingly realistic, performances I ever remember to have seen; so much so, that the voices of the actors were often drowned by sobs and sometimes by the piercing screams of a child who thought that they were really and genuinely driving nails into the graceful young Figaro of the third generation, who played the part of the Saviour.

Not a day of my first kermesses passed without my going at least once, and sometimes two or three times, to see the Figaros at their performance; partly, no doubt, because, between the ages of nine and thirteen, I was an extremely devout broad churchman, and partly because the rôle of the Magdalene was played by a little girl of twelve or thereabouts, with whom I fell in love, wildly, extravagantly, as one only can love when one is a child. I would have given fortunes and years of my life to have had the courage to go round to the back after the performance and talk to her. But I did not dare; and to give an intellectual justification for my cowardice, I assured myself that it would have been unseemly on my part to intrude upon a privacy which I invested with all the sacredness of the Magdalene's public life, an act of sacrilege like going into church with one's hat on. Moreover, I comforted myself, I should have profited little by meeting my inamorata face to face, since in all likelihood she spoke nothing but Flemish, and besides my own language I only spoke at that time a little French, with enough Latin to know what my Uncle Spencer meant when he said, ‘*Similia similibus curantur*.’ My passion for the Magdalene lasted through three kermesses, but waned, or rather suddenly came to an end, when, rushing to the first of the Figaros' performances at the fourth, I saw that the little Magdalene, who was now getting on for sixteen, had become, like so many young girls in their middle teens, plump and moony almost to the point of grossness. And my love after falling to zero in the theatre was turned to positive disgust when I saw her, a couple of mornings later before the performance began, walking about the Grand' Place in a dark blue blouse with a sailor collar, a little blue skirt down to her knees, and a pair of bright yellow boots lacing high up on her full-blown calves, which they compressed so tightly that the exuberant flesh overflowed on to the leather. The next year one of old M. Figaro's great-grandchildren, who could hardly have been more than seven or eight, took her place on the stage. My Magdalene had left it —to get married, no doubt. All the Figaros married early: it was important that there should be no failure in the supply of juvenile apostles and holy women. But by that time I had ceased to take the slightest interest either in her, her family, or their sacred performance; for it was about the time of my fifth kermesse, if I remember rightly, that my period of atheism began—an atheism, however, still combined with all my Uncle Spencer's cheerful optimism about the universe.

My Uncle Spencer, though it would have annoyed him to hear any one say so, enjoyed the kermesse almost as much as I did. In all the year, August was his best month; it contained within its thirty-one days less cause for anxiety, impatience, or irritation than any other month; so that my Uncle Spencer, left in peace by the malignant world, was free to be as high-spirited, as gay and kind-hearted as he possibly could be. And it was astonishing what a stock of these virtues he possessed. If he could have lived on one of those happy islands where nature provides bananas and cocoanuts enough for all and to spare, where the sun shines every day and a little tattooing is all the raiment one needs, where love is easy, commerce unknown, and neither sin nor progress ever heard of—if he could have lived on one of these carefree islands, how entirely happy and how uniformly a saint my Uncle Spencer would have been! But cares and worldly preoccupations too often overlaid his gaiety, stopped up the vents of his kindness; and his quick, nervous, and impulsive temperament—in the Augusts of his life a bubbling source of high spirits—boiled up in a wild impatience, in bilious fountains of irritation, whenever he found himself confronted by the passive malignity of matter, the stupidity or duplicity of man.

He was at his worst during the Christmas holidays; for the season of universal goodwill happened unfortunately to coincide with the season of sugar-making. With the first frosts the beetroots were taken out of the ground, and every day for three or four months three hundred thousand kilograms of roots went floating down the labyrinth of little canals that led to the washing-machines and the formidable slicers of my Uncle Spencer's factory. From every vent of the huge building issued a sickening smell of boiled beetroot, mingled with the more penetrating stink of the waste products of the manufacture—the vegetable fibre drained of its juice, which was converted on the upper floors of the building into cattle food and in the backyard into manure. The activity during those few months of the beetroot season was feverish, was delirious. A wild orgy of work, day and night, three shifts in the twenty-four hours. And then the factory was shut up, and for the rest of the year it stood there, alone, in the open fields beyond the fringes of the town, desolate as a ruined abbey, lifeless and dumb.

During the beetroot season my Uncle Spencer was almost out of his mind. Rimmed with livid circles of fatigue, his eyes glittered like the eyes of a madman; his thin face was no more than pale skin stretched over the starting bones. The slightest contrariety set him cursing and stamping with impatience; it was a torture for him to sit still. One Christmas holidays, I remember, something went wrong with the machinery at the factory, and for nearly five hours the slicers, the churning washers were still. My Uncle Spencer was almost a lost man when he got back to the Grand' Place for dinner that evening. It was as though a demon had possessed him, and had only been cast out as the result of a horrible labour. If the breakdown had lasted another hour, I really believe he would have gone mad.

No, Christmas at Uncle Spencer's was never very cheerful. But by the Easter holidays he was beginning to recover. The frenzied making of sugar had given place to the calmer selling of it. My Uncle Spencer's good nature began to have a chance of reasserting itself. By August, at the end of a long, calm summer, he was perfect; and the kermesse found him at his most exquisitely mellow. But with September a certain premonitory anxiety began to show itself; the machinery had to be overhauled, the state of the labour market examined, and when, about the twentieth of the month, I left again for school, it was a frowning, melancholy, and taciturn Uncle Spencer who travelled with me from Longres to Brussels, from Brussels to Ostend, and who, preoccupied with other thoughts, waved absent-mindedly from the quay, while the steamer slowly slid out through the false calm of the harbour mouth towards a menacing and equinoctial Channel.

But at the kermesse, as I have said, my Uncle Spencer was at his richest and ripest. Enjoying it all as much as

I did myself, he would spend long evenings with me, loitering among the attractions of the Grand' Place. He was sad, I think, that the dignity of his position as one of the leading citizens of Longres did not permit him to mount with me on the roundabouts, the swings, and the mountain railways. But a visit to the side-shows was not inconsistent with his gravity; we visited them all. While professing to find the exhibition of freaks and monsters a piece of deplorable bad taste, my Uncle Spencer never failed to take me to look at all of them. It was a cardinal point in his theory of education that the young should be brought as early as possible into contact with what he called the Realities of Life. And as nothing, it was obvious, could be more of a Reality than the armless woman or the man who pinned up his skin with safety-pins, it was important that I should make an early acquaintance with them in spite of the undoubtedly defective taste of the exhibition. It was in obedience to the same educational principle that my Uncle Spencer took me, one Easter holidays, to see the Lunatic Asylum. But the impression made upon me by the huge prison-like building and its queer occupants—one of whom, I remember, gambolled playfully around me wherever I went, patting my cheeks or affectionately pinching my legs—was so strong and disagreeable, that for several nights I could not sleep; or if I did, I was oppressed by hideous nightmares that woke me, screaming and sweating in the dark. My Uncle Spencer had to renounce his intention of taking me to see the anatomy room in the hospital.

Scattered among the monsters, the rifle-ranges, and the games of skill were little booths where one could buy drink and victuals. There was one vendor, for instance, who always did a roaring trade by selling, for two sous, as many raw mussels as any one could eat without coughing. Torn between his belief in the medicinal qualities of shellfish and his fear of typhoid fever, my Uncle Spencer hesitated whether he ought to allow me to spend my penny. In the end he gave his leave. ('It's the phosphorus, you know.') I put down my copper, took my mussel, bit, swallowed, and violently coughed. The fish were briny as though they had come out of the Dead Sea. The old vendor did an excellent business. Still, I have seen him sometimes looking anxious; for not all his customers were as susceptible as I. There were hardy young peasants who could put down half a pound of this Dead Sea fruit without turning a hair. In the end, however, the brine did its work on even the toughest gullet.

More satisfactory as food were the apple fritters, which were manufactured by thousands in a large temporary wooden structure that stood under the shade of the Hôtel de Ville. The Quality, like Uncle Spencer and myself, ate their fritters in the partial privacy of a number of little cubicles arranged like loose-boxes along one side of the building. My Uncle Spencer walked resolutely to our appointed box without looking to the left hand or to the right; and I was bidden to follow his example and not to show the least curiosity respecting the occupants of the other loose-boxes, whose entrances we might pass on the way to our own. There was a danger, my Uncle Spencer explained to me, that some of the families eating apple fritters in the loose-boxes might be Blacks—Blacks, I mean, politically, not ethnically—while we were Liberals or even, positively, Freemasons. Therefore—but as a mere stranger to Longres I was never, I confess, quite able to understand the force of this conclusion—therefore, though we might talk to male Blacks in a café, have business relations and even be on terms of friendship with them, it was impossible for us to be known by the female Blacks, even under a booth and over the ferial apple fritters; so that we must not look into the loose-boxes for fear that we might see there a dear old friend who would be in the embarrassing situation of not being able to introduce us to his wife and daughters. I accepted, without understanding, this law; and it seemed to be a perfectly good law until the day came when I found that it forbade me to make the acquaintance of even a single one of the eleven ravishing daughters of M. Moulle. It seemed to me then a stupid law.

In front of the booths where they sold sweets my Uncle Spencer never cared to linger. It was not that he was stingy; on the contrary, he was extremely generous. Nor that he thought it bad for me to eat sweets; he had a professional belief in the virtues of sugar. The fact was that the display in the booths embarrassed him. For already at the kermesse one began to see a sprinkling of those little objects in chocolate which, between the Feast of St. Nicholas and the New Year, fill the windows of every confectioner's shop in Belgium. My Uncle Spencer had passed a third of a lifetime at Longres, but even after all these years he was still quite unable to excuse or understand the innocent coprophily of its inhabitants. The spectacle, in a sweet-shop window, of a little *pot de chambre* made of chocolate brought the blush of embarrassment to his cheeks. And when at the kermesse I asked him to buy me some barley-sugar or a few *bêtises de Cambrai*, he pretended not to have heard what I asked, but walked hastily on; for his quick eyes had seen, on one of the higher shelves of the confectioner's booth, a long line of little brown pots, on whose equivocal aspect it would have been an agony to him if, standing there and waiting for the barley-sugar to be weighed out, I had naïvely commented. Not that I ever should have commented upon them; for I was as thoroughly English as my Uncle Spencer himself—more thoroughly, indeed, as being a generation further away from the Flemish mother, the admixture of whose blood, however, had availed nothing against my uncle's English upbringing. Me, too, the little brown pots astonished and appalled by their lack of reticence. If my companion had been another schoolboy of my own age, I should have pointed at the nameless things and sniggered. But since I was with my Uncle Spencer, I preserved with regard to them an eloquent and pregnant silence; I pretended not to have seen them, but so guiltily that my ignoring of them was in itself a comment that filled my poor Uncle Spencer with embarrassment. If we could have talked about them, if only we could have openly deplored them and denounced their makers, it would have been better. But obviously, somehow, we could not.

In the course of years, however, I learned, being young and still malleable, to be less astonished and appalled by the little chocolate pots and the other manifestations of the immemorial Flemish coprophily. In the end I took them almost for granted, like the natives themselves, till finally, when St. Nicholas had filled the shops with these scatological symbols, I could crunch a pot or two between meals as joyously and with as little self-consciousness as any Belgian child. But I had to eat my chocolate, when it was moulded in this particular form, out of my Uncle Spencer's sight. He, poor man, would have been horrified if he had seen me on these occasions.

On these occasions, then, I generally took refuge in the housekeeper's room—and in any case, at this Christmas season, when the sugar was being made, it was better to sit in the cheerful company of Mlle Leeauw than with my gloomy, irritable, demon-ridden Uncle Spencer. Mlle Leeauw was almost from the first one of my firmest and most trusted friends. She was a woman of, I suppose, about thirty-five when I first knew her, rather worn already by a life of active labour, but still preserving a measure of that blonde, decided, and regular beauty which had been hers in girlhood. She was the daughter of a small farmer near Longres, and had received the usual village education, supplemented, however, in recent years by what she had picked up from my Uncle Spencer, who occupied himself every now and then, in his erratic and enthusiastic way, with the improvement of her mind, lent her books from his library, and delivered lectures to her on the subjects that were at the moment nearest to his heart. Mlle Leeauw, unlike most women of her antecedents, felt an insatiable curiosity with regard to all that mysterious and fantastic knowledge which the rich and leisured keep shut up in their libraries; and not only in their books, as she had seen herself (for as a girl had she not served as nursery-maid in the house of that celebrated collector, the Comte de Zuitigny?) not only in their books, but in their pictures too—some of which, Mlle Leeauw assured me, a child could have painted, so badly drawn they were, so unlike life (and yet the count had given heaven only knew how much for them), in their Chinese pots, in the patterns of the very carpets on the floor. Whatever my Uncle Spencer gave her she read with eagerness, she listened attentively to what he said; and there emerged, speck-like in the boundless blank ocean of her ignorance, a few little islands of strange knowledge. One, for example, was called homoeopathy; another the Construction-of-Domes (a subject on which my Uncle Spencer was prepared to talk with a copious and perverse erudition for hours at a time; his thesis being that any mason who knew how to turn the vaulted roof of an oven could have built the cupolas of St. Peter's, St. Paul's, and Santa Maria del Fiore, and that therefore the praises lavished on Michelangelo, Wren, and Brunelleschi were entirely undeserved). A third was called Anti-Vivisection. A fourth Swedenborg. . . .

The result of my Uncle Spencer's teaching was to convince Mlle Leeauw that the knowledge of the rich was something even more fantastic than she had supposed—something unreal and utterly remote from life as it is actually lived, artificial and arbitrary, like the social activities of these same rich, who pass their time in one another's houses, eating at one another's expense, and being bored.

This conviction of the complete futility of knowledge did not make her any the less eager to learn what my Uncle Spencer, whom she regarded as a mine and walking compendium of all human learning, could offer her. And she enchanted him by her respectful attentiveness, by the quickness of her understanding—for she was a woman of very great natural intelligence—and her eagerness for every fresh enlightenment. She did not confide to him her real opinion of knowledge, which was that it was a kind of curious irrelevant joke on the margin of life, worth learning for precisely the same reasons as it is worth learning to handle the fork at table—because it is one of the secrets of the rich. Admiring my Uncle Spencer sincerely, she yet took nothing that he taught her seriously, and though, when with him, she believed in millionth-of-a-grain doses and high spiritual potencies, she continued, when she felt out of sorts or I had overeaten, to resort to the old tablespoonful of castor-oil; though with him she was a convinced Swedenborgian, in church she was entirely orthodox; though in his presence she thought vivisection monstrous, she would tell me with gusto of those happy childish days on the farm, when her father cut the pig's throat, her mother held the beast by the hind-legs, her sister danced on the body to make the blood flow, and she held the pail under the spouting artery.

If to my Uncle Spencer his housekeeper appeared as he liked to see her, and not as at ordinary times she really was, it was not that she practised with him a conscious insincerity. Hers was one of those quick, sensitive natures that adapt themselves almost automatically to the social atmosphere in which at the moment they happen to be. Thus with well-bred people she had beautiful manners; but the peasants from whose stock she had sprung found her as full of a hearty Flemish gusto, as grossly and innocently coarse as themselves. The core of her being remained solidly peasant; but the upper and conscious part of her mind was, so to speak, only loosely fastened to the foundation, so that it could turn freely this way and that, without strain or difficulty, according to changing circumstances. My Uncle Spencer valued her, not only as a competent, intelligent woman, which she always was in every company, but also because she was, considering her class and origins, so remarkably well-mannered and refined, which, except with him and his likes, she was not.

With me, however, Mlle Leeauw was thoroughly natural and Flemish. With her quick and, I might say, instinctive understanding of character, she saw that my abashed reaction to coprology, being of so much more recent date than that of my Uncle Spencer, was much less strong, less deeply rooted. At the same time, she perceived that I had no great natural taste for grossness, no leaning to what I may call Flemishism; so that in my presence she could be her natural Flemish self and thus correct an absurd acquired delicacy without running the risk of encouraging to any undue or distressing degree a congenital bias in the opposite direction. And I noticed that whenever Matthieu (or Tcheunke, as they called him), her cousin's boy, came into town and paid a call on her, Mlle Leeauw became almost as careful and refined as she was with my Uncle Spencer. Not that Tcheunke shared my uncle's susceptibilities. On the contrary, he took such an immoderate delight in everything that was excrementitious that she judged it best not in any way to indulge him in his taste, just as she judged it best not to indulge my national prejudice in favour of an excessive reticence about these and similar matters. She was right, I believe, in both cases.

Mlle Leeauw had an elder sister, Louise—Louiseke, in the language of Longres, where they put the symbol of the diminutive after almost every name. Louiseke, like her sister, had never married; and considering the ugliness of the woman—for she resembled Mlle Leeauw as a very mischievous caricature resembles its original, that is to say, very closely and at the same time hardly at all, the unlikeness being emphasized in this case by the fact that nature had, for the shaping of certain features, drawn on other ancestral sources, and worse ones, than those from which her sister's face had been made up—considering her ugliness, I repeat, it was not surprising. Though considering her dowry, perhaps it was. Louiseke was by no means rich; but she had the five hundred francs a year, or thereabouts, which her sister also had, after their father died and the farm was sold, together with another two hundred inherited from an old aunt of her mother's. This was a sufficient income to allow her to live without working in a leisure principally occupied by the performance of religious exercises.

On the outskirts of Longres there stands a small béguinage, long since abandoned by its Béguines, who are now all over Belgium a diminishing and nearly extinct community, and inhabited by a colony of ordinary poor folk. The little old gabled houses are built round the sides of a large grassy square, in the centre of which stands an abandoned church. Louiseke inhabited one of these houses, partly because the rent was very low, but also because she liked the religious associations of the place. There, in her peaked high house, looking out across the monastic quadrangle to the church, she could almost believe herself a genuine Béguine. Every morning she went out to hear early Mass, and on Sundays and days of festival she was assiduous in church almost to the point of supererogation.

At my Uncle Spencer's we saw a great deal of her; on her way to church, on her way home again, she never failed to drop in for a word with her sister Antonieke. Sometimes, I remember, she brought with her—hurrying on these occasions across the Grand' Place with the quick, anxious tread, the frightened, suspicious glances to left and right, of a traveller crossing a brigand-haunted moor—a large bag of green baize, full of strange treasures: the silver crown and sceptre of Our Lady, the gilded diadem of the Child, St. Joseph's halo, the jewelled silver book of I forget which Doctor of the Church, St. Dominick's lilies, and a mass of silver hearts with gilded flames coming out of them. Louiseke, whose zeal was noted and approved of by M. le Curé, had the rare privilege of being allowed to polish the jewellery belonging to the images in the church. A few days before each of the important feasts the painted plaster saints were stripped of their finery and the spoil handed over to Louiseke, who, not daring to walk with her precious burden under her arm as far as her own house in the béguinage, slipped across the Grand' Place to my Uncle Spencer's. There, on the table in Antonieke's room, the green baize bag was opened, and the treasures, horribly dirty and tarnished after their weeks or months of neglect, were spread out in the light. A kind of paste was then made out of French chalk mixed with gin, which the two sisters applied to the crowns and hearts with nail-brushes, or if the work was fine and intricate, with an old tooth-brush. The silver was then wiped dry with a cloth and polished with a piece of leather.

A feeling of manly pride forbade me to partake in what I felt to be a womanish labour; but I liked to stand by with my hands in my pockets, watching the sisters at work among these regal and sacred symbols, and trying to understand, so far as my limited knowledge of Flemish and my almost equally limited knowledge of life would admit, the gossip which Louiseke poured out incessantly in a tone of monotonous and unvarying censoriousness.

I myself always found Louiseke a little forbidding. She lacked the charm and the quality, which I can only call mellowness, of her sister; to me she seemed harsh, sour-tempered, and rather malevolent. But it is very possible that I judged her unfairly; for, I confess, I could never quite get over her ugliness. It was a sharp, hooky, witch-like type of ugliness, which at that time I found particularly repulsive.

How difficult it is, even with the best will in the world, even for a grown and reasonable man, to judge his fellow-beings without reference to their external appearance! Beauty is a letter of recommendation which it is almost impossible to ignore; and we attribute too often the ugliness of the face to the character. Or, to be more precise, we make no attempt to get beyond the opaque mask of the face to the realities behind it, but run away from the ugly at sight without even trying to find out what they are really like. That feeling of instinctive dislike which ugliness inspires in a grown man, but which he has reason and strength enough of will to suppress, or at least conceal, is uncontrollable in a child. At three or four years old a child will run screaming from the room at the aspect of a certain visitor whose face strikes him as disagreeable. Why? Because the ugly visitor is 'naughty,' is a 'bad man.' And up to a much later age, though we have succeeded in preventing ourselves from screaming when the ugly visitor makes his appearance, we do our best—at first, at any rate, or until his actions have strikingly proved that his face belies his character—to keep out of his way. So that if I always disliked Louiseke, it may be that she was not to blame, and that my own peculiar horror of ugliness made me attribute to her unpleasant characteristics which she did not in reality possess. She seemed to me, then, harsh and sour-tempered; perhaps she wasn't; but, in any case, I thought so. And that accounts for the fact that I never got to know her, never tried to know her, as I knew her sister. Even after the extraordinary event which, a year or two after my first visit to Longres, was to alter completely the whole aspect of her life, I still made no effort to understand Louiseke's character. How much I regret my remissness now! But, after all, one cannot blame a small boy for failing to have the same standards as a man. To-day, in retrospect, I find Louiseke's character and actions in the highest degree curious and worthy of study. But twenty years ago, when I knew her, her ugliness at first appalled me, and always, even after I had got over my disgust, surrounded her, for me, with a kind of unbreathable atmosphere, through which I could never summon the active interest to penetrate. Moreover, the event which now strikes me as so extraordinary, seemed to me then almost normal and of no particular interest. And since she died before my opinion about it had had time to change, I can only give a child's impression of her character and a bald recital of the facts so far as I knew them.

It was, then, at my second or third kermesse that a sideshow, novel not only for me (to whom indeed everything—fat women, fire-swallowers, elastic men, and down to the merest dwarfs and giants—was a novelty), but even to the oldest inhabitants of Longres, who might have been expected to have seen, in their time, almost everything that the world had ever parturated of marvels, rarities, monsters, and abortions, made its appearance on the Grand' Place. This was a troupe of devil dancers, self-styled Tibetan for the sake of the name's high-sounding and mysterious ring; but actually made up of two expatriated Hindus and a couple of swarthy meridional Frenchmen, who might pass at a pinch as the Aryan compatriots of these dark Dravidians. Not that it mattered much what the nationality or colour of the dancers might be; for on the stage they wore enormous masks—huge false heads, grinning, horned, and diabolic, which, it was claimed in the announcement, were those in which the ritual dances were performed before the Dalai Lama in the principal convent of Lhassa. Comparing my memories of them with such knowledge of oriental art as I now possess, I imagine that they came in reality from the shop of some theatrical property maker in Marseilles, from which place the devil dancers had originally started. But they were none the less startling and blood-curdling for that; just as the dances themselves were none the less salaciously symbolical, none the less typically and conventionally 'oriental' for having been in great measure invented by the Frenchmen, who provided all the plot and dramatic substance of the ballets, while the astonished and admiring Indians contributed only a few recollections of Siva worship and the cult of the beneficent *linga*. This co-operation between East and West was what ensured the performance its success; the western substance satisfied by its perfect familiarity, while the eastern detail gave to the old situations a specious air of novelty and almost a new significance.

Charmed by the prospect of seeing what he supposed would be a few characteristic specimens of the religious rites of the mysterious East, and ambitious to improve my education by initiating me into the secrets of this Reality, my Uncle Spencer took me to see the dancers. But the dramatic pantomime of the Frenchmen represented a brand of Reality that my uncle did not at all approve of. He got up abruptly in the middle of the first dance, saying that he thought the circus would be more amusing; which, for me, it certainly was. For I was not of an age to appreciate either the plastic beauty or the peculiar moral significance of the devil dancers' performance.

'Hinduism,' said my Uncle Spencer, as we threaded our way between the booths and the whirling machines, 'has sadly degenerated from its original Brahmanistic purity.' And he began to expound to me, raising his voice to make itself heard through the noise of the steam organs, the principles of Brahmanism. My Uncle Spencer had a great weakness for oriental religions.

'Well,' asked Mlle Leeauw, when we got back for dinner, 'and how did you enjoy the dancers?'

I told her that my Uncle Spencer had thought that I should find the circus more amusing. Antonieke nodded with a significant air of understanding. 'Poor man,' she said, and she went on to wonder how Louiseke, who was going to see the dancers that evening, would enjoy the show.

I never knew precisely what happened; for a mystery and, as it were, a zone of silence surrounded the event, and my curiosity about everything to do with Louiseke was too feeble to carry me through it. All I know is that, two or three days later, near the end of the kermesse, young Albert Snyders, the lawyer's son, came up to me in the street and asked, with the gleeful expression of one who says something which he is sure his interlocutor will find disagreeable: 'Well, and what do you think of your Louiseke and her carryings on with the black man?'

I answered truthfully that I had heard nothing about any such thing, and that in any case Louiseke wasn't our Louiseke, and that I didn't care in the least what she did or what might happen to her.

'Not heard about it?' said young Snyders incredulously. 'But the black man goes to her house every evening, and she gives him gin, and they sing together, and people see their shadows dancing on the curtains. Everybody's talking about it.'

I am afraid that I disappointed young Snyders. He had hoped to get a rise out of me, and he miserably failed. His errors were two: first, to have supposed that I regarded Louiseke as our Louiseke, merely because her sister happened to be my Uncle Spencer's housekeeper; and, secondly, to have attributed to me a knowledge of the world sufficient to allow me to realize the scandalousness of Louiseke's conduct. Whereas I disliked Louiseke, took no interest in her actions, and could, moreover, see nothing out of the ordinary in what she was supposed to have done.

Confronted by my unshakable calm, young Snyders retired, rather crestfallen. But he revenged himself before he went by telling me that I must be very stupid and, what I found more insulting, a great baby not to understand.

Antonieke, to whom I repeated young Snyders's words, merely said that the boy ought to be whipped, specifying with a wealth of precise detail and a gusto that were entirely Flemish how, with what instrument, and where the punishment ought to be applied. I thought no more about the incident. But I noticed after the kermesse was over and the Grand' Place had become once more the silent and empty Grand' Place of ordinary days, I noticed loitering aimlessly about the streets a stout, coffee-coloured man, whom the children of Longres, like those three rude boys in *Struwwelpeter*, pursued at a distance, contorting themselves with mirth. That year I went back to England earlier than usual; for I had been invited to spend the last three weeks of my holidays with a school friend (alas, at Hastings, so that my knowledge of the earth's surface was not materially widened by the visit). When I returned to Longres for the Christmas holidays I found that Louiseke was no longer mere Louiseke, but the bride of a coffee-coloured husband. Madame Alphonse they called her; for nobody could bother with the devil dancer's real name: it had an Al- in it somewhere—that was all that was known. Monsieur and Madame Alphonse. But the news when I heard it did not particularly impress me.

And even if I had been curious to know more, dense silence continued to envelop the episode. Antonieke never spoke to me of it; and lacking all interest in this kind of Reality, disapproving of it even, my Uncle Spencer seemed to take it silently for granted. That the subject was copiously discussed by the gossips of Longres I do not doubt; and remembering Louiseke's own censorious anecdotage, I can imagine how. But in my hearing it was never discussed; expressly, I imagine—for I lived under the protection of Antonieke, and people were afraid of Antonieke. So it came about that the story remained for me no more remarkable than that story recorded by Edward Lear of the

> '. . . old Man of Jamaica
> Who casually married a Quaker;
> But she cried out, " Alack,
> I have married a black ! "
> Which distressed that old Man of Jamaica.'

And perhaps, after all, that is the best way of regarding such incidents—unquestioningly, without inquisitiveness. For we are all much too curious about the affairs of our neighbours. Particularly about the affairs of an erotic nature. What an itch we have to know whether Mr. Smith makes love to his secretary, whether his wife consoles herself, whether a certain Cabinet Minister is really the satyr he is rumoured to be. And meanwhile the most incredible miracles are happening all round us: stones, when we lift them and let them go, fall to the ground; the sun shines; bees visit the flowers; seeds grow into plants, a cell in nine months multiplies its weight a few thousands of thousands of times, and is a child; and men think, creating the world they live in. These things leave us almost perfectly indifferent.

But concerning the ways in which different individuals satisfy the cravings of one particular instinct we have, in spite of the frightful monotony of the situation, in spite of the one well-known, inevitable consummation, an endless and ever-fresh curiosity. Some day, perhaps, we may become a little tired of books whose theme is always this particular instinct. Some day, it may be, the successful novelist will write about man's relation to God, to nature, to his own thoughts and the obscure reality on which they work, not about man's relation with woman. Meanwhile, however . .

By what stages the old maid passed from her devoutness and her censorious condemnation of love to her passion for the Dravidian, I can only guess. Most likely there were no stages at all, but the conversion was sudden and fulgurating, like that upon the road to Damascus—and like that, secretly and unconsciously prepared for, long before the event. It was the sheer wildness, no doubt, the triumphant bestiality and paganism of the dances that bowled her over, that irresistibly broke down the repressive barriers behind which, all too human, Louiseke's nature had so long chafed. As to Alphonse himself, there could be no question about his motives. Devil dancing, he had found, was an exhausting, precarious, and not very profitable profession. He was growing stout, his heart was not so strong as it had been, he was beginning to feel himself middle-aged. Louiseke and her little income came as a providence. What did her face matter? He did not hesitate.

Monsieur and Madame Alphonse took a little shop in the Rue Neuve. Before he left India and turned devil dancer, Alphonse had been a cobbler in Madras—and as such was capable of contaminating a Brahman at a distance of twenty-four feet; now, having become an eater of beef and an outcast, he was morally infectious at no less than sixty-four feet. But in Longres, luckily, there were no Brahmans.

He was a large, fat, snub-faced, and shiny man, constantly smiling, with a smile that reminded me of a distended accordion. Many a pair of boots I took to him to be soled—for Antonieke, though she was horrified at having what she called a negro for her brother-in-law, though she had quarrelled with her sister about her insane and monstrous folly, and would hardly be reconciled to her, Antonieke insisted that all our custom should go to the new cobbler. That, as she explained, 'owed itself.' The duty of members of one family to forward one another's affairs overrode, in her estimation, the mere personal quarrels that might arise between them.

My Uncle Spencer was a frequent caller at the cobbler's shop, where he would sit for hours, while M. Alphonse tapped away at his last, listening to mythological anecdotes out of the 'Ramayana' or 'Mahabharata,' and discussing the Brahmanistic philosophy, of which, of course, he knew far more than a poor Sudra like Alphonse. My Uncle Spencer would come back from these visits in the best of humours.

'A most interesting man, your brother-in-law,' he would say to Antonieke. 'We had a long talk about Siva this afternoon. Most interesting!'

But Antonieke only shrugged her shoulders. '*Mais c'est un nègre*,' she muttered. And my Uncle Spencer might assure her as much as he liked that Dravidians were not negroes and that Alphonse very likely had good Aryan blood in his veins. It was useless. Antonieke would not be persuaded, would not even listen. It was all very well for the rich to believe things like that, but a negro, after all, was a negro; and that was all about it.

M. Alphonse was a man of many accomplishments; for besides all the rest, he was an expert palmist and told fortunes from the hand with a gravity, a magisterial certainty, that were almost enough in themselves to make what he said come true. This magian and typically oriental accomplishment was learnt on the road between Marseilles and Longres from a charlatan in the travelling company of amusement makers with whom he had come. But he did the trick in the grand prophetic style, so that people credited his cheiromancy with all the magical authority of the mysterious East. But M. Alphonse could not be persuaded to prophesy for every comer. It was noticed that he selected his subjects almost exclusively from among his female customers, as though he were only interested in the fates of women. I could hint as much as I liked that I should like to have my fortune told, I could ask him outright to look at my hand; but in vain. On these occasions he was always too busy to look, or was not feeling in the prophetic mood. But if a young woman should now come into the shop, time immediately created itself, the prophetic mood came back. And without waiting for her to ask him, he would seize her hand, pore over it, pat and prod the palm with his thick brown fingers, every now and then turning up towards his subject those dark eyes, made the darker and more expressive by the brilliance of the bluish whites in which they were set, and expanding his accordion smile. And he would prophesy love—a great deal of it—love with superb dark men, and rows of children; benevolent dark strangers and blond villains; unexpected fortunes, long life—all, in fact, that the heart could desire. And all the time he squeezed and patted the hand—white between his dark Dravidian paws—from which he read these secrets; he rolled his eyes within their shiny blue enamel setting, and across all the breadth of his fat cheeks the accordion of his smile opened and shut.

My pride and my young sense of justice were horribly offended on these occasions. The inconsistency of a man who had no time to tell my fortune, but an infinite leisure for others, seemed to me abstractly reprehensible and personally insulting. I professed, even at that age, not to believe in palmistry; that is to say, I found the fortunes which M. Alphonse prophesied for others absurd. But my interest in my own personality and my own fate was so enormous that it seemed to me, somehow, that everything said about me must have a certain significance. And if M. Alphonse had taken my hand, looked at it, and said, 'You are generous; your head is as large as your heart; you will have a severe illness at thirty-eight, but your life after that will be healthy into extreme old age; you will make a large fortune early in your career, but you must beware of fair-haired strangers with blue eyes,' I should have made an exception and decided for the nonce that there must be something in it. But alas, M. Alphonse never did take my hand; he never told me anything. I felt most cruelly offended, and I felt astonished too. For it seemed to me a most extraordinary thing that a subject which was so obviously fascinating and so important as my character and future should not interest M. Alphonse as much as it did me. That he should prefer to dabble in the dull fates and silly insignificant characters of a lot of stupid young women seemed to me incredible and outrageous.

There was another who, it seemed, shared my opinion. That was Louiseke. If ever she came into the shop from the little back sitting-room—and she was perpetually popping out through the dark doorway like a cuckoo on the stroke of noon from its clock—and found her husband telling the fortune of a female customer, her witch-like face would take on an expression more than ordinarily malevolent.

'Alphonse!' she would say significantly.

And Alphonse dropped his subject's hand, looked round towards the door, and, rolling his enamelled eyes, creasing his fat cheeks in a charming smile, flashing his ivory teeth, would say something amiable.

But Louiseke did not cease to frown. 'If you must tell somebody's fortune,' she said, when the customer had left the shop, 'why don't you tell the little gentleman's?' pointing to me. 'I'm sure he would be only too delighted.'

But instead of being grateful to Louiseke, instead of saying, 'Oh, of course I'd like it,' and holding out my hand, I always perversely shook my head. 'No, no,' I said. 'I don't want to worry M. Alphonse.' But I longed for Alphonse to insist on telling me about my exquisite and marvellous self. In my pride, I did not like to owe my happiness to Louiseke, I did not want to feel that I was taking advantage of her irritation and Alphonse's desire to mollify her. And besides pride, I was actuated by that strange nameless perversity, which so often makes us insist on doing what we do not want to do—such as making love to a woman we do not like and whose intimacy, we know, will bring us nothing but vexation—or makes us stubbornly decline to do what we have been passionately desiring, merely because the opportunity of doing what we wanted has not presented itself in exactly the way we anticipated, or because the person who offered to fulfil our desires has not been sufficiently insistent with his offers. Alphonse, on these occasions, having no curiosity about my future and taking no pleasure in kneading my small and dirty hand, always took my refusals quite literally and finally, and began to work again with a redoubled ardour. And I would leave the shop, vexed with myself for having let slip the opportunity when it was within my grasp; furious with Louiseke for having presented it in such a way that the seizing of it would be humiliating, and with Alphonse for his obtuseness in failing to observe how much I desired that he should look at my hand, and his gross discourtesy for not insisting even in the teeth of my refusal.

Years passed; my holidays and the seasons succeeded one another with regularity. Summer and the green poplars and my Uncle Spencer's amiability gave place to the cold season of sugar-making, to scatological symbols in chocolate, to early darkness and the moral gloom of my Uncle Spencer's annual neurasthenia. And half-way between the two extremes came the Easter holidays, pale green and hopefully burgeoning, tepid with temperate warmth and a moderate amiability. There were terms, too, as well as holidays. Eastbourne knew me no more; my knowledge of the globe expanded; I became a public schoolboy.

At fifteen, I remember, I entered upon a period of

priggishness which made me solemn beyond my years. There are many boys who do not know how young they are till they have come of age, and a young man is often much less on his dignity than a growing schoolboy, who is afraid of being despised for his callowness. It was during this period that I wrote from Longres a letter to one of my school friends, which he fortunately preserved, so that we were able to re-read it, years later, and to laugh and marvel at those grave, academic old gentlemen we were in our youth. He had written me a letter describing his sister's marriage, to which I replied in these terms:

'How rapidly, my dear Henry, the saffron robe and Hymen's torches give place to the naenia, the funeral urn, and the cypress! While your days have been passed among the jocundities of a marriage feast, mine have been darkened by the circumambient horrors of death. Such, indeed, is life.'

And I underlined the philosophic reflection.

The horrors of death made more show in my sonorous antitheses than they did in my life. For though the event made a certain impression upon me—for it was the first thing of the kind that had happened within my own personal orbit—I cannot pretend that I was very seriously moved when Louiseke died, too old to have attempted the experiment, in giving birth to a half-Flemish, half-Dravidian daughter, who died with her. My Uncle Spencer, anxious to introduce me to the Realities of Life, took me to see the corpse. Death had a little tempered Louiseke's ugliness. In the presence of that absolute repose I suddenly felt ashamed of having always disliked Louiseke so much. I wanted to be able to explain to her that, if only I had known she was going to die, I would have been nicer to her, I would have tried to like her more. And all at once I found myself crying.

Downstairs in the back parlour M. Alphonse was crying too, noisily, lamentably, as was his duty. Three days later, when his duty had been sufficiently done and the conventions satisfied, he became all at once exceedingly philosophic about his loss. Louiseke's little income was now his; and adding to it what he made by his cobbling, he could live in almost princely style. A week or two after the funeral the kermesse began. His old companions, who had danced several times backwards and forwards across the face of Europe since they were last in Longres, reappeared unexpectedly on the Grand' Place. Alphonse treated himself to the pleasure of playing the generous host, and every evening when their show was over the devils unhorned themselves, and over the glasses in the little back parlour behind Alphonse's shop they talked convivially of old times, and congratulated their companion, a little enviously, on his prodigious good fortune.

In the years immediately preceding the war I was not often in Longres. My parents had come back from India; my holidays were passed with them. And when holidays transformed themselves into university vacations and I was old enough to look after myself, I spent most of my leisure in travelling in France, Italy, or Germany, and it was only rarely and fleetingly—on the way to Milan, on my way back from Cologne, or after a fortnight among the Dutch picture galleries—that I now revisited the house on the Grand' Place, where I had passed so many, and on the whole such happy, days. I liked my Uncle Spencer still, but he had ceased to be an admired being, and his opinions, instead of rooting themselves and proliferating within my mind, as once they did, seemed mostly, in the light of my own knowledge and experience, too fantastic even to be worth refuting. I listened to him now with all the young man's intolerance of the opinions of the old (and my Uncle Spencer, though only fifty, seemed to me utterly fossilized and antediluvian), acquiescing in all that he said with a smile in which a more suspicious and less single-hearted man would have seen the amused contempt. My Uncle Spencer was leaning during these years more and more towards the occult sciences. He talked less of the construction of domes and more of Hahnemann's mystic high potentials, more of Swedenborg, more of Brahmanistic philosophy, in which he had by this time thoroughly indoctrinated M. Alphonse; and he was enthusiastic now about a new topic—the calculating horses of Elberfeld, which, at that time, were making a great noise in the world by their startling ability to extract cube roots in their heads. Strong in the materialistic philosophy, the careless and unreflecting scepticism which were, in those days, the orthodoxy of every young man who thought himself intelligent, I found my Uncle Spencer's mystical and religious preoccupations marvellously ludicrous. I should think them less ridiculous now, when it is the easy creed of my boyhood that has come to look rather queer. Now it is possible—it is, indeed, almost necessary—for a man of science to be also a mystic. But there were excuses then for supposing that one could only combine mysticism with the faulty knowledge and the fantastic mental eccentricity of an Uncle Spencer. One lives and learns.

With Mlle Leeauw, on these later visits, I felt, I must confess, not entirely at my ease. Antonieke saw me as essentially the same little boy who had come so regularly all those years, holiday after holiday, to Longres. Her talk with me was always of the joyous events of the past—of which she had that extraordinarily accurate and detailed memory which men and women, whose minds are not exercised by intellectual preoccupations and who do not read much, always astonish their more studious fellows by possessing. Plunged as I then was in all the newly discovered delights of history, philosophy, and art, I was too busy to take more than a very feeble interest in my childish past. Had there been skating on the canals in 1905? Had I been bitten by a horse-fly, the summer before, so poisonously that my cheek swelled up like a balloon and I had to go to bed? Possibly, possibly; now that I was reminded of these things I did, dimly, remember. But of what earthly interest were facts such as these when I had Plato, the novels of Dostoievsky, the frescoes of Michelangelo to think of? How entirely irrelevant they were to, shall we say, David Hume! How insipid compared with the sayings of Zarathustra, the Coriolan overture, the poetry of Arthur Rimbaud! But for poor Antonieke they were all her life. I felt all the time that I was not being as sympathetic with her as I ought to have been. But was it my fault? Could I re-become what I had been, or make her suddenly different from what she was?

At the beginning of August, 1914, I was staying at Longres on my way to the Ardennes, where I meant to settle down quietly for a month or so with two or three friends, to do a little solid reading before going south to Italy in September. Strong in the faith of the German professor who had proved, by the theories of ballistics and probabilities, that war was now out of the question, my Uncle Spencer paid no attention to the premonitory rumbles. It was just another little Agadir crisis and would lead to nothing. I too—absorbed, I remember, in the reading of William James's *Varieties of Religious Experience*—paid no attention; I did not even look at the papers. At that time, still, my Uncle Spencer's convictions about the impossibility of war were also mine; I had had no experience to make me believe them unfounded, and, besides, they fitted in very well with my hopes, my aspirations, my political creed—for at that time I was an ardent syndicalist and internationalist.

And then, suddenly, it was all on top of us.

My Uncle Spencer, however, remained perfectly optimistic. After a week of fighting, he prophesied, the German professor would be proved right and they would have to stop. My own feeling, I remember, was one of a rather childish exhilaration; my excitement was much more powerful than my shock of horror. I felt rather as I had felt on the eve of the kermesse when, looking from my window, I gazed down at the mountebanks setting up their booths and engines in the square below. Something was really going to happen. That childish sense of excitement is, I suppose, the prevailing emotion at the beginning of a war. An intoxicating Bank Holiday air seems to blow through the streets. War is always popular, at the beginning.

I did not return immediately to England, but lingered for a few days at Longres, in the vague hope that I might 'see something,' or that perhaps my Uncle Spencer might really—as I still believed—be right, and that, perhaps, the whole thing would be over in a few days. My hope that I should 'see something' was fulfilled. But the something was not one of those brilliant and romantic spectacles I had imagined. It consisted of a few little troops of refugees from the villages round Liége—unshaven men, and haggard women with long tear-marks on their dusty cheeks, and little boys and girls tottering along as though in their sleep, dumb and stupid with fatigue. My Uncle Spencer took a family of them into his house. 'In a few days,' he said, 'when everything's over, they'll be able to go home again.' And when indignantly Antonieke repeated to him their stories of burnings and shootings, he wouldn't believe them.

'After all,' he said, 'this is the twentieth century. These things don't happen nowadays. These poor people are too tired and frightened to know exactly what they are saying.'

In the second week of August I went back to England. My Uncle Spencer was quite indignant when I suggested that he should come back with me. To begin with, he said, it would all be over so very soon. In the second place, this was the twentieth century—which was what the Cretans said, no doubt, when in 1500 B.C., after two thousand years of peace, prosperity, and progressive civilization, they were threatened by the wild men from the north. In the third place, he must stay at Longres to look after his interests. I did not press him any further; it would have been useless.

'Good-bye, dear boy,' he said, and there was an unaccustomed note of emotion in his voice, 'good-bye.'

The train slowly moved away. Looking out of the window, I could see him standing on the platform, waving his hat. His hair was white all over now, but his face was as young, his eyes as darkly bright, his small spare body as straight and agile as when I had known him first.

'Good-bye, good-bye.'

I was not to see him again for nearly five years.

Louvain was burnt on the 19th of August. The Germans entered Brussels on the 20th. Longres, though farther east than Louvain, was not occupied till two or three days later—for the town lay off the direct route to Brussels and the interior. One of the first acts of the German commandant was to put my Uncle Spencer and M. Alphonse under arrest. It was not that they had done anything;

it was merely to their existence that he objected. The fact that they were British subjects was in itself extremely incriminating.

'Aber wir sind,' my Uncle Spencer protested in his rather rudimentary German, 'im zwanzigsten jahrhunderd. Und der—or is it das?—krieg wird nicht lang . . .' he stammered, searched hopelessly for the word, 'well, in any case,' he concluded, relapsing into his own language and happy to be able to express his astonished protest with fluency, 'it won't last a week.'

'So we hope,' the commandant replied in excellent English, smiling. 'But meanwhile I regret . . .'

My Uncle Spencer and his fellow-Briton were locked up for the time being in the lunatic asylum. A few days later they were sent under escort to Brussels. Alphonse, my Uncle Spencer told me afterwards, bore his misfortune with exemplary and oriental patience. Mute, uncomplaining, obedient, he stayed where his captors put him, like a large brown bundle left by the traveller on the platform, while he goes to the buffet for a drink and a sandwich. And more docile than a mere bundle, mutely, obediently, he followed wherever he was led.

'I wish I could have imitated him,' said my Uncle Spencer. 'But I couldn't. My blood fairly boiled.'

And from what I remembered of him in the sugar-making season I could imagine the depth, the fury of my Uncle Spencer's impatience and irritation.

'But this is the twentieth century,' he kept repeating to the guards. 'And I have nothing to do with your beastly war. And where the devil are you taking us? And how much longer are we to wait in this damned station without our lunch?' He spoke as a rich man, accustomed to being able to buy every convenience and consideration. The soldiers, who had the patience of poor men and were well used to being ordered hither and thither, to waiting indefinitely in the place where they were told to wait, could not understand this wild irritation against what they regarded as the natural order of things. My Uncle Spencer first amused them; then, as his impatience grew greater instead of less, he began to annoy them.

In the end, one of his guards lost patience too, and gave him a great kick in the breech to make him hold his tongue. My Uncle Spencer turned round and rushed at the man; but another soldier tripped him up with his rifle, and he tumbled heavily to the ground. Slowly he picked himself up; the soldiers were roaring with laughter. Alphonse, like a brown package, stood where they had put him, motionless, expressionless, his eyes shut.

In the top floor of the Ministry of the Interior the German authorities had established a sort of temporary internment camp. All suspicious persons—dubious foreigners, recalcitrant natives, any one suspected by the invaders of possessing a dangerous influence over his neighbours—were sent to Brussels and shut up in the Ministry of the Interior, to remain there until the authorities should have time to go into their case. It was into this makeshift prison that my Uncle Spencer and his Dravidian compatriot were ushered, one sweltering afternoon towards the end of August. In an ordinary year, my Uncle Spencer reflected, the kermesse at Longres would now be in full swing. The fat woman would be washing her face with her bosom, the Figaros would be re-enacting amid sobs the Passion of Our Saviour, the armless lady would be drinking healths with her toes, the vendor of raw mussels would be listening anxiously for the first hoarse sound that might be taken for a cough. Where were they all this year, all these good people? And where was he himself? Incredulously he looked about him.

In the attics of the Ministry of the Interior the company was strange and mixed. There were Belgian noblemen whom the invaders considered it unsafe to leave in their châteaux among their peasantry. There were a Russian countess and an anarchist, incarcerated on account of their nationality. There was an opera singer, who might be an international spy. There was a little golden-haired male impersonator, who had been appearing at a music-hall in Liége, and whose offence, like that of my Uncle Spencer and the Dravidian, was to have been a British subject. There were a number of miscellaneous Frenchmen and Frenchwomen, caught on the wrong side of the border. There was an organ-grinder, who had gone on playing the 'Brabançonne' when told to stop, and a whole collection of other Belgians, of all classes and both sexes, from every part of the country, who had committed some crime or other, or perhaps had contrived merely to look suspicious, and who were now waiting to have their fate decided, as soon as the authorities should have time to pay attention to them.

Into this haphazardly assembled society my Uncle Spencer and the Dravidian were now casually dropped. The door closed behind them; they were left, like new arrivals in hell, to make the best of their situation.

The top floor of the Ministry of the Interior was divided up into one very large and a number of small rooms, the latter lined, for the most part, with pigeon-holes and filing cabinets in which were stored the paper products of years of bureaucratic activity.

In the smaller chambers the prisoners had placed the straw mattresses allotted to them by their gaolers; the men slept in the rooms at one end of the corridor, the women in those at the other end. The big room, which must once have housed the staff of the Ministry's registry, still contained a number of desks, tables, and chairs; it served now as the prisoners' drawing-room, dining-room, and recreation ground. There was no bathroom, and only one washing-basin and one *châlet de nécessité*, as my Uncle Spencer, with a characteristic euphemism, always called it. Life in the attics of the Ministry of the Interior was not particularly agreeable.

My Uncle Spencer noticed that those of the prisoners who were not sunk in gloom and a sickening anxiety for the future, preserved an almost too boisterous cheerfulness. You had, it seemed, either to take this sort of thing as a prodigious joke, or brood over it as the most horrible of nightmares. There seemed to be no alternative. In time, no doubt, the two extremes would level down to the same calm resignation. But confinement had still been too short for that; the situation was still too new, dream-like, and phantasmagorical, and fate too uncertain.

The cheerful ones abounded in japes, loud laughter, and practical jokes. They had created in the prison a kind of private-school atmosphere. Those whose confinement was oldest (and some had been in the Ministry for nearly a week now, almost from the day of the German entry into Brussels) assumed the inalienable right of seniors to make the new arrivals feel raw and uncomfortable. Each fresh man was subjected to a searching cross-examination, like that which awaits the new boy at his first school. Sometimes, if the latest victim seemed particularly ingenuous, they would play a little practical joke on him.

The leader of the cheerful party was a middle-aged Belgian journalist—a powerful, stout man, with carroty red moustaches and a high crimson complexion, a huge roaring voice and a boundless gift for laughter and genial Rabelaisian conversation. At the appearance of the meek Dravidian he had fairly whooped with delight. So great, indeed, was his interest in Alphonse that my Uncle Spencer escaped with the most perfunctory examination and the minimum of playful 'ragging.' It was perhaps for the best; my Uncle Spencer was in no mood to be trifled with, even by a fellow-sufferer.

Round poor Alphonse the journalist immediately improvised a farce. Sitting like a judge at one of the desks in the large room, he had the Dravidian brought before him, giving him to understand that he was the German commissary who had to deal with his case. Under cross-examination the Dravidian was made to tell his whole history. Born, Madras; profession, cobbler—a clerk took down all his answers as he delivered them. When he spoke of devil dancing, the judge made him give a specimen of his performance there and then in front of the desk. The question of his marriage with Louiseke was gone into in the most intimate detail. Convinced that his liberty and probably his life depended on his sincerity, Alphonse answered every question as truthfully as he possibly could.

In the end, the journalist, clearing his throat, gravely summed up and gave judgment. Innocent. The prisoner would forthwith be released. On a large sheet of official paper he wrote *laissez passer*, signed it Von der Golz, and, opening a drawer of the desk, selected from among the numerous official seals it contained that with which, in happier times, certain agricultural diplomas were stamped. On the thick red wax appeared the figure of a prize shorthorn cow with, round it, the words: 'Pour l'amélioration de la race bovine.'

'Here,' roared the journalist, handing him the sealed paper. 'You may go.'

Poor Alphonse took his *laissez passer* and, bowing at intervals almost to the ground, retreated backwards out of the room. Joyously he picked up his hat and his little bundle, ran to the door, knocked and called. The sentry outside opened to see what was the matter. Alphonse produced his passport.

'Aber wass ist das?' asked the sentry.

Alphonse pointed to the seal: for the amelioration of the bovine race; to the signature: Von der Golz. The sentry, thinking that it was he, not the Dravidian, who was the victim of the joke, became annoyed. He pushed Alphonse roughly back through the door; and when, protesting, propitiatively murmuring and smiling, the poor man advanced again to explain to the sentry his mistake, the soldier picked up his rifle and with the butt gave him a prod in the belly, which sent him back, doubled up and coughing, along the corridor. The door slammed to. Vainly, when he had recovered, Alphonse hammered and shouted. It did not open again. My Uncle Spencer found him standing there—knocking, listening, knocking again. The tears were streaming down his cheeks; it was a long time before my Uncle Spencer could make him understand that the whole affair had been nothing but a joke. At last, however, Alphonse permitted himself to be led off to his mattress. In silence he lay down and closed his eyes. In his right hand he still held the passport—firmly, preciously between his thick brown fingers. He would not throw it away; not yet. Perhaps if he went to sleep this incident at the door would prove, when he woke up, to have been a dream. The paper would have ceased to be a joke, and when, to-morrow, he showed it again, who knew? the sentry would present arms and he would walk downstairs; and all the soldiers in the courtyard would salute and he would walk out into the sunny streets, waving the signature, pointing to the thick red seal.

Quite still he lay there. His arm was crossed over his body. From between the fingers of his hand hung the paper. Bold, as only the signature of a conquering general could be, Von der Golz sprawled across the sheet. And in the bottom right-hand corner, stamped in the red wax, the image of the sacred cow was like a symbol of true salvation from across the separating ocean and the centuries. *Pour l'amélioration de la race bovine.* But might it not be more reasonable, in the circumstances, to begin with the human race?

My Uncle Spencer left him to go and expostulate with the journalist on the barbarity of his joke. He found the man sitting on the floor—for there were not enough chairs to go round—teaching the golden-haired male impersonator how to swear in French.

'And this,' he was saying, in his loud, jolly voice, 'this is what you must say to Von der Golz if ever you see him.' And he let off a string of abusive words, which the little male impersonator carefully repeated, distorted by her drawling English intonation, in her clear, shrill voice: 'Sarl esspayss de coshaw.' The journalist roared with delighted laughter and slapped his thighs. 'What comes after that?' she asked.

'Excuse me,' said my Uncle Spencer, breaking in on the lesson. He was blushing slightly. He never liked hearing this sort of language—and in the mouth of a young woman (a compatriot too, it seemed) it sounded doubly distressing. 'Excuse me.' And he begged the journalist not to play any more jokes on Alphonse. 'He takes it too much to heart,' he explained.

At his description of the Dravidian's despair, the little male impersonator was touched almost to tears. And the journalist who, like all the rest of us, had a heart of gold whenever he was reminded of its existence—and, like all the rest of us, he needed pretty frequent reminders; for his own pleasures and interests prevented him very often from remembering it—the journalist was extremely sorry at what he had done, declared that he had no idea that Alphonse would take the little farce so seriously, and promised for the future to leave him in peace.

The days passed; the nightmare became habitual, followed a routine. Three times a day the meagre supply of unappetizing food arrived and was consumed. Twice a day an officer with a little squad of soldiers behind him made a tour of inspection. In the morning one waited for one's turn to wash; but the afternoons were immense gulfs of hot time, which the prisoners tried to fill with games, with talk, with the reading of ancient dossiers from the files, with solitary brooding or with pacing up and down the corridor—twenty steps each way, up and down, up and down, till one had covered in one's imagination the distance between one loved and familiar place and another. Up and down, up and down. My Uncle Spencer sometimes walked along the poplar-lined high road between Longres and Waret; sometimes from Charing Cross along the Strand, under the railway bridge and up the hill to St. Paul's, and from St. Paul's to the Bank, and from the Bank tortuously to the Tower of London, the river, and the ships. Sometimes he walked with his brother from Chamonix to the Montanvert; from Grenoble over the pass to the Grande Chartreuse. Sometimes, less strenuously, he walked with his long-dead mother through the glades of Windsor Forest, where the grass is so green in early summer that it seems as though each blade were an emerald illumined from within; and here and there among the oak trees the dark-leaved rhododendrons light their innumerable rosy lamps.

In the evening the cheerful ones, with the journalist at their head, organized entertainments for the amusement of the company. The journalist himself recited poems of his own composition about the Kaiser. One of the Frenchmen did some amateur conjuring with packs of cards, handkerchiefs, and coins. The opera singer bawled out at the top of his prodigious tenor, 'La donna è mobile,' 'O sole mio,' and when something more serious was called for, César Franck's 'Dieu s'avance à travers la lande'; which last, however, he sang in so richly operatic a style that my Uncle Spencer, who was very fond of this particular song, could hardly recognize it. But the most popular turn was always that of 'the celebrated diva, Emmy Wendle,' as the journalist called her, when he introduced her to the company. The enthusiasm was tremendous when Emmy Wendle appeared—dressed in an Eton jacket, broad starched collar, striped trousers, and a top hat, and carrying in her hand a little cane—did two or three rattling clog dances and sang a song with the chorus:

> 'We are the nuts that get the girls
> Ev-ery time;
> We get the ones with the curly curls,
> We get the peaches, we get the pearls—
> Ev-ery time.'

And when, at the end of the turn, she took off her top hat, and, standing rigidly at attention, like a soldier, her childish snubby little face very grave, her blue eyes fixed on visions not of this world, sang in her tuneless street-urchin's voice an astonishingly English version of the 'Brabançonne,' then there was something more than enthusiasm. For men would suddenly feel the tears coming into their eyes, and women wept outright; and when it was over, everybody violently stamped and clapped and waved handkerchiefs, and laughed, and shouted imprecations against the Germans, and said, 'Vive la Belgique!' and ran to Emmy Wendle, and took her hand, or slapped her on the back as though she had really been a boy, or kissed her—but as though she were not a girl, and dressed in rather tight striped trousers at that—kissed her as though she were a symbol of the country, a visible and charming personification of their own patriotism and misfortunes.

When the evening's entertainment was over, the company began to disperse. Stretched on their hard mattresses along the floor, the prisoners uneasily slept or lay awake through the sultry nights, listening to the steps of the sentries in the court below and hearing every now and then, through the unnatural silence of the invaded town, the heavy beat, beat, beat of a regiment marching along the deserted street, the rumble and sharp, hoofy clatter of a battery on the move towards some distant front.

The days passed. My Uncle Spencer soon grew accustomed to the strange little hell into which he had been dropped. He knew it by heart. A huge, square room, low-ceilinged and stifling under the hot leads. Men in their shirt-sleeves standing, or sitting, some on chairs, some on the corner of a desk or a table, some on the floor. Some leaned their elbows on the window-sill and looked out, satisfying their eyes with the sight of the trees in the park across the street, breathing a purer air—for the air in the room was stale, twice-breathed, and smelt of sweat, tobacco, and cabbage soup.

From the first the prisoners had divided themselves, automatically almost, into little separate groups. Equal in their misery, they still retained their social distinctions. The organ-grinder and the artisans and peasants always sat together in one corner on the floor, playing games with a greasy pack of cards, smoking and, in spite of expostulations, in spite of sincere efforts to restrain themselves, spitting on the floor all round them.

'Mine!' the organ-grinder would say triumphantly, and

plank down his ace of hearts. 'Mine!' And profusely, to emphasize his satisfaction, he spat. 'Ah, pardon!' Remembering too late, he looked apologetically round the room. 'Excuse me.' And he would get up, rub the gob of spittle into the floor with his boot, and going to the window would lean out and spit again—not that he felt any need to, having spat only a moment before, but for the sake of showing that he had good manners and could spit out of the window and not on the floor when he thought of it.

Another separate group was that of the aristocracy. There was the little old count with a face like a teapot—such shiny round cheeks, such a thin, irrelevant nose; and the young count with the monocle—the one so exquisitely affable with every one and yet so remote and aloof under all his politeness; the other so arrogant in manner, but, one could see, so wistfully wishing that his social position would permit him to mingle with his spiritual equals. The old count politely laughed whenever the journalist or some other member of the cheerful party made a joke; the young count scowled, till the only smooth surface left in his corrugated face was the monocle. But he longed to be allowed to join in the horse-play and the jokes. With the two counts were associated two or three rich and important citizens, among them during the first days my Uncle Spencer. But other interests were to make him abandon their company almost completely after a while.

On the fringes of their circle hovered occasionally the Russian countess. This lady spent most of the day in her sleeping apartment, lying on her mattress and smoking cigarettes. She had decided views about the respect that was due to her rank, and expected the wash-house to be immediately evacuated whenever she expressed a desire to use it. On being told that she must wait her turn, she flew into a rage. When she was bored with being alone, she would come into the living-room to find somebody to talk to. On one occasion she took my Uncle Spencer aside and told him at great length and with a wealth of intimate detail about the ninth and greatest love affair of her life. In future, whenever my Uncle Spencer caught sight of her turning her large, dark, rather protruding eyes round the room, he took care to be absorbed in conversation with somebody else.

Her compatriot, the anarchist, was a Jewish-looking man with a black beard and a nose like the figure six. He associated himself with none of the little groups, was delighted by the war, which he gleefully prophesied would destroy so-called civilization, and made a point of being as disagreeable as he could to every one—particularly to the countess, whom he was able to insult confidentially in Russian. It was in obedience to the same democratic principles that he possessed himself of the only arm-chair in the prison—it must have been the throne of at least a *sous chef de division*—refusing to part with it even for a lady or an invalid. He sat in it immovably all day, put it between his mattress and the wall at night, and took it with him even into the wash-house and the *châlet de nécessité.*

The cheerful party grouped itself, planet fashion, round the radiant jollity of the journalist. His favourite amusement was hunting through the files for curious dossiers which he could read out, with appropriate comments and improvised emendations to the assembled group. But the most relished of all his jokes was played ritually every morning when he went through the papers of nobility of the whole Belgic aristocracy (discovered, neatly stowed away, in a cupboard in the corridor), selecting from among the noble names a few high-sounding titles which he would carry with him to the chalet of necessity. His disciples included a number of burgesses, French and Belgian; a rather odious and spotty young English bank clerk caught on his foreign holiday; the Russian countess in certain moods; the male impersonator, on and off; and the opera singer.

With this last my Uncle Spencer, who was a great lover of music and even a moderately accomplished pianist, made frequent attempts to talk about his favourite art. But the opera singer, he found, was only interested in music in so far as it affected the tenor voice. He had consequently never heard of Bach or Beethoven. On Leoncavallo, however, on Puccini, Saint-Saëns, and Gounod he was extremely knowledgeable. He was an imposing personage, with a large, handsome face and the gracious, condescending smile of a great man who does not object to talking even with you. With ladies, as he often gave it to be understood, he had a great success. But his fear of doing anything that might injure his voice was almost as powerful as his lasciviousness and his vanity; he passed his life, like a monk of the Thebaid, in a state of perpetual conflict. Outwardly and professedly a member of the cheerful party, the opera singer was secretly extremely concerned about his future. In private he discussed with my Uncle Spencer the horrors of the situation.

More obviously melancholy was the little grey-haired professor of Latin who spent most of the day walking up and down the corridor like a wolf in a cage, brooding and pining. Poor Alphonse, squatting with his back to the wall near the door, was another sad and solitary figure. Sometimes he looked thoughtfully about him, watching his fellow-prisoners at their various occupations with the air of an inhabitant of eternity watching the incomprehensible antics of those who live in time. Sometimes he would spend whole hours with closed eyes in a state of meditation. When some one spoke to him, he came back to the present as though from an immense distance.

But, for my Uncle Spencer, how remote, gradually, they all became! They receded, they seemed to lose light; and with their fading the figure of Emmy Wendle came closer, grew larger and brighter. From the first moment he set eyes on her, sitting there on the floor, taking her lesson in vituperation from the journalist, my Uncle Spencer had taken particular notice of her. Making his way towards the pair of them, he had been agreeably struck by the childishness and innocence of her appearance—by the little snub nose, the blue eyes, the yellow hair, so stubbornly curly that she had to wear it cut short like a boy's, for there was no oiling down or tying back a long mane of it; even in her private feminine life there was a hint—and it only made her seem the more childish—of male impersonation. And then, coming within earshot, it had been 'sarl esspayss de coshaw' and a string besides of less endearing locutions proceeding from these lips. Startling, shocking. But a moment later, when he was telling them how hardly poor Alphonse had taken the joke, she said the most charming things and with such real feeling in her cockney voice, such a genuine expression of sympathy and commiseration on her face, that my Uncle Spencer wondered whether he had heard aright, or if that 'sarl coshaw' and all the rest could really have been pronounced by so delicate and sensitive a creature.

The state of agitation in which my Uncle Spencer had lived ever since his arrest, the astonishing and horrible novelty of his situation, had doubtless in some measure predisposed him to falling in love. For it frequently happens that one emotion—providing that it is not so powerful as to make us unconscious of anything but itself—will stimulate us to feel another. Thus danger, if it is not acute enough to cause panic, tends to attach us to those with whom we risk it, the feelings of compassion, sympathy, and even love being stimulated and quickened by apprehension. Grief, in the same way, often brings with it a need of affection and even, though we do not like to admit it to ourselves, even obscurely a kind of desire; so that a passion of sorrow will convert itself by scarcely perceptible degrees, or sometimes suddenly, into a passion of love. My Uncle Spencer's habitual attitude towards women was one of extreme reserve. Once, as a young man, he had been in love and engaged to be married; but the object of his affections had jilted him for somebody else. Since then, partly from a fear of renewing his disappointment, partly out of a kind of romantic fidelity to the unfaithful one, he had avoided women, or at least taken pains not to fall in love any more, living always in a state of perfect celibacy, which would have done credit to the most virtuous of priests. But the agitations of the last few days had disturbed all his habits of life and thought. Apprehension of danger, an indignation that was a very different thing from the recurrent irritability of the sugar-making season, profound bewilderment, and a sense of mental disorientation had left him without his customary defences and in a state of more than ordinary susceptibility; so that when he saw, in the midst of his waking nightmare, that charming childish head, when he heard those gentle words of sympathy for the poor Dravidian, he was strangely moved; and he found himself aware of Emmy Wendle as he had not been aware of any woman since the first unfaithful one of his youth had left him.

Everything conspired to make my Uncle Spencer take an interest in Emmy Wendle—everything, not merely his own emotional state, but the place, the time, the outward circumstances. He might have gone to see her at the music-hall every night for a year; and though he might have enjoyed her turn—and as a matter of fact he would not, for he would have thought it essentially rather vulgar—though he might have found her pretty and charming, it would never have occurred to him to try to make her acquaintance or introduce himself into her history. But here, in this detestable makeshift prison, she took on a new significance, she became the personification of all that was gracious, sweet, sympathetic, of all that was not war. And at the end of her performance (still, it was true, in poorish taste, but more permissible, seeing that it was given for the comfort of the afflicted) how profoundly impressive was her singing of the 'Brabançonne'! She had become great with the greatness of the moment, with the grandeur of the emotions to which she was giving utterance in that harsh guttersnipe's voice of hers—singing of exultations, agonies, and man's unconquerable mind. We attribute to the symbol something of the sacredness of the thing or idea symbolized. Two bits of wood set cross-wise are not two ordinary bits of wood, and a divinity has hedged the weakest and worst of kings. Similarly, at any crisis in our lives, the most trivial object, or a person in himself insignificant, may become, for some reason, charged with all the greatness of the moment.

Even the 'sarl coshaw' incident had helped to raise my Uncle Spencer's interest in Emmy Wendle. For if she was gentle, innocent, and young, if she personified in her small, bright self all the unhappiness and all the courage of a country, of the whole afflicted world, she was also fallible, feminine, and weak; she was subject to bad influences, she might be led astray. And the recollection of those gross phrases, candidly, innocently, and openly uttered (as the most prudish can always utter them when they happen to be in an unfamiliar language, round whose words custom has not crystallized that wealth of associations which give to the native locutions their peculiar and, from age to age, varying significance), filled my Uncle Spencer with alarm and with a missionary zeal to rescue so potentially beautiful and even grand a nature from corruption.

For her part, Emmy Wendle was charmed, at any rate during the first days of their acquaintance, with my Uncle Spencer. He was English, to begin with, and spoke her language; he was also—which the equally English and intelligible bank clerk was not—a gentleman. More important for Emmy, in her present mood, he did not attempt to flirt with her. Emmy wanted no admirers, at the moment. In the present circumstances she felt that it would have been wrong, uncomely, and rather disreputable to think of flirtation. She sang the 'Brabançonne' with too much religious ardour for that; the moment was too solemn, too extraordinary. True, the solemnity of the moment and the ardour of her patriotic feelings might, if a suitable young man had happened to find himself with her in the attics of the Ministry of the Interior, have caused her to fall in love with a fervour having almost the religious quality of her other feelings. But no suitable young man, unfortunately, presented himself. The bank clerk had spots on his face and was not a gentleman, the journalist was middle-aged and too stout. Both tried to flirt with her. But their advances had, for Emmy, all the impropriety of a flirtation in a sacred place. With my Uncle Spencer, however, she felt entirely safe. It was not merely that he had white hair; Emmy had lived long enough to know that that symbol was no guarantee of decorous behaviour—on the contrary; but because he was, obviously, such a gentleman, because of the signs of unworldliness and mild idealism stamped all over his face.

At first, indeed, it was only to escape from the tiresome and indecorous attentions of the bank clerk and the journalist that she addressed herself to Uncle Spencer. But she soon came to like his company for its own sake; she began to take an interest in what he said, she listened seriously to my Uncle Spencer's invariably serious conversation—for he never talked except on profitable and intellectual themes, having no fund of ordinary small talk.

During the first days Emmy treated him with the respectful courtesy which, she felt, was due to a man of his age, postion, and character. But later, when he began to follow her with his abject adoration, she became more familiar. Inevitably; for one cannot expect to be treated as old and important by some one at whom one looks with the appealing eyes of a dog. She called him Uncle Spenny and ordered him about, made him carry and fetch as though he were a trained animal. My Uncle Spencer was only too delighted, of course, to obey her. He was charmed by the familiarities she took with him. The period of her pretty teasing familiarity (intermediate between her respectfulness and her later cruelty) was the happiest, so far as my Uncle Spencer was concerned, in their brief connection. He loved and felt himself, if not loved in return, at least playfully tolerated.

Another man would have permitted himself to take liberties in return, to be sportive, gallant, and importunate. But my Uncle Spencer remained gravely and tenderly himself. His only reprisal for 'Uncle Spenny' and the rest was to call her by her Christian name instead of 'Miss Wendle,' as he had always solemnly done before. Yes, Emmy felt herself safe with Uncle Spenny; almost too safe, perhaps.

My Uncle Spencer's conversations were always, as I have said, of a very serious cast. They were even more serious at this time than usual; for the catastrophe, and now his passion, had brought on in his mind a very severe fit of thinking. There was so much that, in the light of the happenings of the last few weeks, needed reconsidering. From the German professor's theory to the problem of good and evil; from the idea of progress (for, after all, was not this the twentieth century?) to the austere theory and the strange new fact of love; from internationalism to God—everything had to be considered afresh. And he considered them out loud with Emmy Wendle. Goodness, for example, was that no more than a relative thing, an affair of social conventions, gauged by merely local and accidental standards? Or was there something absolute, ultimate, and fundamental about the moral idea? And God—could God be absolutely good? And was there such a vast difference between the twentieth and other centuries? Could fact ever rhyme with ideal? All these disturbing questions had to be asked and answered to his own satisfaction once again.

It was characteristic of my Uncle Spencer that he answered them all—even after taking into consideration everything that had happened—on the hopeful side, just as he had done before the catastrophe; and what was more, with a deeper conviction. Before, he had accepted the cheerful idealistic view a little too easily. He had inherited it from the century in which he was born, had sucked it in from the respectable and ever-prospering elders among whom he had been brought up. Circumstances were now making that facile cheerfulness seem rather stupid. But it was precisely because he had to reconsider the objections to optimism, the arguments against hopefulness, not theoretically in the void, but practically and in the midst of personal and universal calamity (the latter very bearable if one is comfortably placed oneself, but real, but disturbing, if one is also suffering a little), that he now became convinced, more hardly but more profoundly, of the truth of what he had believed before, but lightly and, as he now saw, almost accidentally. Events were shortly to disturb this new-found conviction.

Emmy listened to him with rapture. The circumstances, the time, the place, inclined her to the serious and reflective mood. My Uncle Spencer's discourses were just what she needed at this particular moment. Naturally superstitious, she lived at all times under the protection of a small gold lucky pig and a coral cross which had once belonged to her mother. And when luck was bad, she went to church and consulted crystal gazers. That time she broke her leg and had to cancel that wonderful engagement to tour in Australia, she knew it was because she had been neglecting God in all the prosperous months before; she prayed and she promised amendment. When she got better, God sent her an offer from Cohen's Provincial Alhambras Ltd., in token that her repentance was accepted and she was forgiven. And now, though she had seemed to belong to the cheerful party in the attics of the Ministry of the Interior, her thoughts had secretly been very grave. At night, lying awake on her mattress, she wondered in the darkness what was the reason of all this—the war, her bad luck in getting caught by the Germans. Yes, what could the reason be? Why was God angry with her once again?

But of course she knew why. It was all that dreadful, dreadful business last June when she was working at Wimbledon. That young man who had waited for her at the stage door; and would she do him the honour of having supper with him? And she had said yes, though it was all against her rules. Yes: because he had such a beautiful voice, so refined, almost like a very high-class

West End actor's voice. 'I came to see the marionettes,' he told her. 'Marionettes never seem to get farther than the suburbs, do they? But I stayed for you.'

They drove in a taxi all the way from Wimbledon to Piccadilly. 'Some day,' she said, pointing to the Pavilion, 'you'll see my name there, in big electric letters: EMMY WENDLE.' A hundred pounds a week and the real West End. What a dream!

He had such beautiful manners and he looked so handsome when you saw him in the light. They had champagne for supper.

In the darkness, Emmy blushed with retrospective shame. She buried her face in the pillow as though she were trying to hide from some searching glance. No wonder God was angry. In an agony she kissed the coral cross. She pulled at the blue ribbon, at the end of which, between her two small breasts, hung the golden pig; she held the mascot in her hand, tightly, as though hoping to extract from it something of that power for happiness stored mysteriously within it, as the power to attract iron filings is stored within the magnet.

A few feet away the Russian countess heavily breathed. At the stertorous sound Emmy shuddered, remembering the wickedness that slumbered so near her. For if she herself had ceased to be, technically, a good girl, she was—now that her luck had turned—ashamed of it; she knew, from God's anger, that she had done wrong. But the countess, if sleep had not overtaken her, would have gone on boasting all night about her lovers. To middle-class Emmy the countess's frankness, her freedom from the ordinary prejudices, her aristocratic contempt for public opinion, and her assumption—the assumption of almost all idle women and of such idle men as have nothing better to do or think about—that the only end of life is to make love, complicatedly, at leisure and with a great many people, seemed profoundly shocking. It didn't so much matter that she wasn't a good girl—or rather a good ripe widow. What seemed to Emmy so dreadful was that she should talk about it as though not being good were natural, to be taken for granted, and even positively meritorious. No wonder God was angry.

To Emmy my Uncle Spencer—or shall I call him now her Uncle Spenny?—came as a comforter and sustainer in her remorseful misery. His wandering speculations were not, it was true, always particularly relevant to her own trouble; nor did she always understand what he was talking about. But there was a certain quality in all his discourses, whatever the subject, which she found uplifting and sustaining. Thus my Uncle Spencer quoting Swedenborg to prove that, in spite of all present appearances to the contrary, things were probably all right, was the greatest of comforts. There was something about him like a very high-class clergyman—a West End clergyman, so to say. When he talked she felt better and in some sort safer.

He inspired in her so much confidence that one day, while the journalist was playing some noisy joke that kept all the rest of the company occupied, she took him aside into the embrasure of one of the windows and told him all, or nearly all, about the episode on account of which God was now so angry. My Uncle Spencer assured her that God didn't see things in quite the way she imagined; and that if He had decided that there must be a European War, it was not, in all human probability, to provide an excuse for getting Emmy Wendle—however guilty—locked up in the attics of the Ministry of the Interior at Brussels. As for the sin itself, my Uncle Spencer tried to make her believe that it was not quite so grave as she thought. He did not know that she only thought it grave because she was in prison and, naturally, depressed.

'No, no,' he said comfortingly, 'you mustn't take it to heart like that.'

But the knowledge that this exquisite and innocent young creature had once—and if once, why not twice, why not (my Uncle Spencer left to his own midnight thoughts feverishly speculated), why not fifty times?—fallen from virtue distressed him. He had imagined her, it was true, surrounded by bad influences, like the journalist; but between being taught to say 'sarl coshaw' and an actual lapse from virtue, there was a considerable difference. It had never occurred to my Uncle Spencer that Emmy could have got beyond the 'coshaw' stage. And now he had it from her own lips that she had.

Celibate like a priest, my Uncle Spencer had not enjoyed the priest's vicarious experience in the confessional. He had not read those astonishing handbooks of practical psychology, fruit of the accumulated wisdom of centuries, from which the seminarist learns to understand his penitents, to classify and gauge their sins, and, incidentally—so crude, bald, and uncompromising are the descriptions of human vice that they contain—to loathe the temptations which, when rosily and delicately painted, can seem so damnably alluring. His ignorance of human beings was enormous. In his refinement he had preferred not to know; and circumstances, so far, had wonderfully conspired to spare him knowledge.

Years afterwards, I remember, when we met again, he asked me after a silence, and speaking with an effort, as though overcoming a repugnance, what I really thought about women and all 'that sort of thing.' It was a subject about which at that time I happened to feel with the bitterness and mirthful cynicism of one who has been only too amply successful in love with the many in whom he took no interest, and lamentably and persistently unsuccessful with the one being, in whose case success would have been in the least worth while.

'You really think, then,' said my Uncle Spencer, when I paused for breath, 'that a lot of that sort of thing actually does go on?'

I really did.

He sighed and shut his eyes, as though to conceal their expression from me. He was thinking of Emmy Wendle. How passionately he had hoped that I should prove her, necessarily and *a priori*, virtuous!

There are certain sensitive and idealistic people in whom the discovery that the world is what it is brings on a sudden and violent reaction towards cynicism. From soaring in spheres of ideal purity they rush down into the mud, rub their noses in it, eat it, bathe and wallow. They lacerate their own highest feelings and delight in the pain. They take pleasure in defiling the things which before they thought beautiful and noble; they pore with a disgusted attention over the foul entrails of the things whose smooth and lovely skin was what they had once worshipped.

Swift, surely, was one of these—the greatest of them. His type our islands still produce; and more copiously, perhaps, during the last two or three generations than ever before. For the nineteenth century specialized in that romantic, optimistic idealism which postulates that man is on the whole good and inevitably becoming better. The idealism of the men of the Middle Ages was more sensible; for it insisted, to begin with, that man was mostly and essentially bad, a sinner by instinct and heredity. Their ideals, their religion, were divine and unnatural antidotes to original sin. They saw the worst first and could be astonished by no horror—only by the occasional miracle of sweetness and light. But their descendants of the romantic, optimistic, humanitarian century, in which my Uncle Spencer was born and brought up, vented their idealism otherwise. They began by seeing the best; they insisted that men were naturally good, spiritual, and lovely. A sensitive youth brought up in this genial creed has only to come upon a characteristic specimen of original sin to be astonished, shocked, and disillusioned into despair. Circumstances and temperament had permitted my Uncle Spencer to retain his romantic optimism very much longer than most men.

The tardy recognition of the existence of original sin disturbed my Uncle Spencer's mind. But the effects of it were not immediate. At the moment, while he was in Emmy's pretty and intoxicating presence, and while she was still kind, he could not believe that she too had her share of original sin. And even when he forced himself to do so, her childish ingenuous face was in itself a complete excuse. It was later—and especially when he was separated from her—that the poison began slowly to work, embittering his whole spirit. At present Emmy's confession only served to increase his passion for her. For, to begin with, it made her seem more than ever in need of protection. And next, by painfully satisfying a little of his curiosity about her life, it quickened his desire to know all, to introduce himself completely into her history. And at the same time it provoked a retrospective jealousy, together with an intense present suspiciousness and an agonized anticipation of future dangers. His passion became like a painful disease. He pursued her with an incessant and abject devotion.

Relieved, partly by my Uncle Spencer's spiritual ministrations, partly by the medicating power of time, from her first access of remorse, depression, and self-reproach, Emmy began to recover her normal high spirits. My Uncle Spencer became less necessary to her as a comforter. His incomprehensible speculations began to bore her. Conversely, the jokes of the cheerful ones seemed more funny, while the gallantries of the journalist and the bank clerk appeared less repulsive, because—now that her mood had changed—they struck her as less incongruous and indecorous. She was no longer, spiritually speaking, in church. In church, my Uncle Spencer's undemonstrative and unimportunate devotion had seemed beautifully in place. But now that she was emerging again out of the dim religious into the brightly secular mood, she found it rather ridiculous and, since she did not return the adoration, tiresome.

'If you could just see yourself now, Uncle Spenny,' she said to him, 'the way you look.'

And she drew down the corners of her mouth, then opened her eyes in a fishy, reverential stare. Then the grimace in which my Uncle Spencer was supposed to see his adoration truly mirrored, disintegrated in laughter; the eyes screwed themselves up, a little horizontal wrinkle appeared near the tip of the snub nose, the mouth opened, waves of mirth seemed to ripple out from it across the face, and a shrill peal of laughter mocked him into an attempted smile.

'Do I really look like that?' he asked.

'You really do,' Emmy nodded. 'Not a very cheerful thing to have staring at one day and night, is it?'

Sometimes—and this to my Uncle Spencer was inexpressibly painful—she would even bring in some third person to share the sport at his expense; she would associate the bank clerk, the opera singer, or the journalist in her mocking laughter. The teasing which, in the first days, had been so light and affectionate, became cruel.

Emmy would have been distressed, no doubt, if she had

known how much she hurt him. But he did not complain. All she knew was that my Uncle Spencer was ridiculous. The temptation to say something smart and disagreeable about him was irresistible.

To my Uncle Spencer's company she now preferred that of the journalist, the bank clerk, and the opera singer. With the bank clerk she talked about West End actors and actresses, music-hall artists, and cinema stars. True, he was not much of a gentleman; but on this absorbing subject he was extremely knowledgeable. The singer revealed to her the gorgeous and almost unknown universe of the operatic stage—a world of art so awe-inspiringly high that it was above even the West End. The journalist told her spicy stories of the Brussels stage. My Uncle Spencer would sit at the fringes of the group, listening in silence and across a gulf of separation, while Emmy and the bank clerk agreed that Clarice Mayne was sweet, George Robey a scream, and Florence Smithson a really high-class artist. When asked for his opinion, my Uncle Spencer always had to admit that he had never seen the artist in question. Emmy and the bank clerk would set up a howl of derision; and the opera singer, with biting sarcasm, would ask my Uncle Spencer how a man who professed to be fond of music could have gone through life without even making an attempt to hear Caruso. My Uncle Spencer was too sadly depressed to try to explain.

The days passed. Sometimes a prisoner would be sent for and examined by the German authorities. The little old nobleman like a teapot was released a week after my Uncle Spencer's arrival; and a few days later the haughty and monocled one disappeared. Most of the peasants next vanished. Then the Russian anarchist was sent for, lengthily examined and sent back again, to find that his arm-chair was being occupied by the journalist.

In the fourth week of my Uncle Spencer's imprisonment Alphonse fell ill. The poor man had never recovered from the effects of the practical joke that had been played upon him on the day of his arrival. Melancholy, oppressed by fears, the more awful for being vague and without a definite object (for he could never grasp why and by whom he had been imprisoned; and as to his ultimate fate—no one could persuade him that it was to be anything but the most frightful and lingering of deaths), he sat brooding by himself in a corner. His free pardon, signed Von der Golz and sealed with the image of the Sacred Cow, he still preserved; for though he was now intellectually certain that the paper was valueless, he still hoped faintly in the depths of his being that it might turn out, one day, to be a talisman; and, in any case, the image of the Cow was very comforting. Every now and then he would take the paper out of his pocket, tenderly unfold it and gaze with large sad eyes at the sacred effigy: *Pour l'amélioration de la race bovine*—and tears would well up from under his eyelids, would hang suspended among the lashes and roll at last down his brown cheeks.

They were not so round now, those cheeks, as they had been. The skin sagged, the bright convex high-lights had lost their brilliance. Miserably he pined. My Uncle Spencer did his best to cheer him. Alphonse was grateful, but would take no comfort. He had lost all interest even in women; and when, learning from my Uncle Spencer that the Indian was something of a prophet, Emmy asked him to read her hand, he looked at her listlessly as though she had been a mere male and not a male impersonator, and shook his head.

One morning he complained that he was feeling too ill to get up. His head was hot, he coughed, breathed shortly. and with difficulty, felt a pain in his right lung. My Uncle

Spencer tried to think what Hahnemann would have prescribed in the circumstances, and came to the conclusion that the thousandth of a grain of aconite was the appropriate remedy. Unhappily, there was not so much as a millionth of a grain of aconite to be found in all the prison. Enquiry produced only a bottle of aspirin tablets and, from the Russian countess, a packet of cocaine snuff. It was thought best to give the Dravidian a dose of each and wait for the doctor.

At his midday visit the inspecting officer was informed of Alphonse's state, and promised to have the doctor sent at once. But it was not, in point of fact, till the next morning that the doctor came. My Uncle Spencer, meanwhile, constituted himself the Dravidian's nurse. The fact that Alphonse was the widower of his housekeeper's sister, and had lived in his city of adoption, made my Uncle Spencer feel somehow responsible for the poor Indian. Moreover, he was glad to have some definite occupation which would allow him to forget, if only partially and for an occasional moment, his unhappy passion.

From the first, Alphonse was certain that he was going to die. To my Uncle Spencer he foretold his impending extinction, not merely with equanimity, but almost with satisfaction. For by dying, he felt, he would be spiting and cheating his enemies, who desired so fiendishly to put an end to him at their own time and in their own horrible fashion. It was in vain that my Uncle Spencer assured him that he would not die, that there was nothing serious the matter with him. Alphonse stuck to his assertion.

'In eight days,' he said, 'I shall be dead.'

And shutting his eyes, he was silent.

The doctor, when he came next day, diagnosed acute lobar pneumonia. Through the oppression of his fever, Alphonse smiled at my Uncle Spencer with a look almost of triumph. That night he was delirious and began to rave in a language my Uncle Spencer could not understand.

My Uncle Spencer listened in the darkness to the Dravidian's incomprehensible chattering; and all at once, with a shudder, with a sense of terror he felt—in the presence of this man of another race, speaking in an unknown tongue words uttered out of obscure depths for no man's hearing and which even his own soul did not hear or understand—he felt unutterably alone. He was imprisoned within himself. He was an island surrounded on every side by wide and bottomless solitudes. And while the Indian chattered away, now softly, persuasively, cajolingly, now with bursts of anger, now loudly laughing, he thought of all the millions and millions of men and women in the world—all alone, all solitary and confined. He thought of friends, incomprehensible to one another and opaque after a lifetime of companionship; he thought of lovers remote in one another's arms. And the hopelessness of his passion revealed itself to him—the hopelessness of every passion, since every passion aims at attaining to what, in the nature of things, is unattainable: the fusion and interpenetration of two lives, two separate histories, two solitary and for ever sundered individualities.

The Indian roared with laughter.

But the unattainableness of a thing was never a reason for ceasing to desire it. On the contrary, it tends to increase and even to create desire. Thus our love for those we know, and our longing to be with them, are often increased by their death. And the impossibility of ever communicating with him again will actually create out of indifference an affection, a respect and esteem for some one whose company in life seemed rather tedious than desirable. So, for the lover, the realization that what he desires is unattainable, and that every possession will reveal yet vaster tracts of what is unpossessed and unpossessable, is not a deterrent, is not an antidote to his passion; but serves rather to exacerbate his desire, sharpening it to a kind of desperation, and at the same time making the object of his desire seem more than ever precious.

The Indian chattered on, a ghost among the ghosts of his imagination, remote as though he were speaking from another world. And Emmy—was she not as far away, as unattainable? And being remote, she was the more desirable; being mysterious, she was the more lovely. A more brutal and experienced man than my Uncle Spencer would have devoted all his energies to seducing the young woman, knowing that after a time the satisfaction of his physical desire would probably make him cease to take any interest in her soul or her history. But physical possession was the last thing my Uncle Spencer thought of, and his love had taken the form of an immense desire for the impossible union, not of bodies, but of minds and lives. True, what he had so far learned about her mind and history was not particularly encouraging. But for my Uncle Spencer her silliness, love of pleasure, and frivolity were strange and mysterious qualities—for he had known few women in his life and none, before, like Emmy Wendle—rather lovely still in their unfamiliarity, and if recognized as at all bad, excused as being the symptoms of a charming childishness and an unfortunate upbringing. Her solicitude, that first day, about poor Alphonse convinced him that she was fundamentally good-hearted; and if she had proved herself cruel since then towards himself, that was more by mistake and because of surrounding bad influences than from natural malignity. And, then, there was the way in which she sang the 'Brabançonne.' It was noble, it was moving. To be able to sing like that one must have a fine and beautiful character. In thinking like this, my Uncle Spencer was forgetting that no characteristic is incompatible with any other, that any deadly sin may be found in company with any cardinal virtue, even the apparently contradictory virtue. But unfortunately that is the kind of wisdom which one invariably forgets precisely at the moment when it might be of use to one. One learns it almost in the cradle; at any rate, I remember at my preparatory school reading, in Professor Oman's *Shorter History of England*, of 'the heroic though profligate Duke of Ormond,' and of a great English king who was none the less, 'a stuttering, lolling pedant with a tongue too big for his mouth.' But though one knows well enough in theory that a duke can be licentious as well as brave, that majestic wisdom may be combined with pedantry and defective speech, yet in practice one continues to believe that an attractive woman is kind because she is charming, and virtuous because she rejects your first advances; without reflecting that the grace of her manner may thinly conceal an unyielding ruthlessness and selfishness, while the coyness in face of insistence may be a mere device for still more completely ensnaring the victim. It is only in the presence of unsympathetic persons that we remember that the most odious actions are compatible with the most genuinely noble sentiments, and that a man or woman who does one thing, while professing another, is not necessarily a conscious liar or hypocrite. If only we could steadfastly bear this knowledge in mind when we are with persons whom we find sympathetic!

Desiring Emmy as passionately as he did, my Uncle Spencer would not have had much difficulty in persuading himself—even in spite of her recent cruelty towards him—that the spirit with which he longed to unite his own was on the whole a beautiful and interesting spirit; would indeed have had no difficulty at all, had it not been for that unfortunate confession of hers. This, though it flattered him as a token of her confidence in his discretion and wisdom, had sadly disturbed him and was continuing to disturb him more and more. For out of all her history—the history in which it was his longing to make himself entirely at home as though he had actually lived through it with her—this episode was almost the only chapter he knew. Like a thin ray of light her confession had picked it out for him, from the surrounding obscurity. And what an episode! The more my Uncle Spencer reflected on it, the more he found it distressing.

The brutal practical man my Uncle Spencer was not would have taken this incident from the past as being of good augury for his own future prospects. But since he did not desire, consciously at any rate, the sort of success it augured, the knowledge of this incident brought him an unadulterated distress. For however much my Uncle Spencer might insist in his own mind on the guiltiness of external circumstance and of the other party, he could not entirely exonerate Emmy. Nor could he pretend that she had not in some sort, if only physically, taken part in her own lapse. And perhaps she had participated willingly. And even if she had not, the thought that she had been defiled, however reluctantly, by the obscene contact was unspeakably painful to him. And while the Indian raved, and through the long, dark silences during which there was no sound but the unnaturally quick and shallow breathing, and sometimes a moan, and sometimes a dry cough, my Uncle Spencer painfully thought and thought; and his mind oscillated between a conviction of her purity and the fear that perhaps she was utterly corrupt. He saw in his imagination, now her childish face and the rapt expression upon it while she sang the 'Brabançonne,' now the sweet, solicitous look while she commiserated on poor

Alphonse's unhappiness, and then, a moment later, endless embracements, kisses brutal and innumerable. And always he loved her.

Next day the Dravidian's fever was still high. The doctor, when he came, announced that red hepatization of both lungs was already setting in. It was a grave case which ought to be at the hospital; but he had no authority to have the man sent there. He ordered tepid spongings to reduce the fever.

In the face of the very defective sanitary arrangements of the prison, my Uncle Spencer did his best. He had a crowd of willing assistants; everybody was anxious to do something helpful. Nobody was more anxious than Emmy Wendle. The forced inaction of prison life, even when it was relieved by the jokes of the cheerful ones, by theatrical discussions and the facetious gallantry of the bank clerk and the journalist, was disagreeable to her. And the prospect of being able to do something, and particularly (since it was war-time, after all) of doing something useful and charitable, was welcomed by her with a real satisfaction. She sat by the Dravidian's mattress, talked to him, gave him what he asked for, did the disagreeable jobs that have to be done in the sick-room, ordered my Uncle Spencer and the others about, and seemed completely happy.

For his part, my Uncle Spencer was delighted by what he regarded as a reversion to her true self. There could be no doubt about it now: Emmy was good, was kind, a ministering angel, and therefore (in spite of the professor's heroic though profligate duke), therefore pure, therefore interesting, therefore worthy of all the love he could give her. He forgot the confession, or at least he ceased to attach importance to it; he was no longer haunted by the odious images which too much brooding over it evoked in his mind. What convinced him, perhaps, better than everything of her essential goodness, was the fact that she was once more kind to him. Her young energy, fully occupied in practical work (which was not, however, sufficiently trying to overtax the strength or set the nerves on edge), did not have to vent itself in laughter and mockery, as it had done when she recovered from the mood of melancholy which had depressed it during the first days of her imprisonment. They were fellow-workers now.

The Dravidian, meanwhile, grew worse and worse, weaker and weaker every day. The doctor was positively irritated.

'The man has no business to be so ill as he is,' he grumbled. 'He's not old, he isn't an alcoholic or a syphilitic, his constitution is sound enough. He's just letting himself die. At this rate he'll never get past the crisis.'

At this piece of news Emmy became grave. She had never seen death at close quarters—a defect in her education which my Uncle Spencer, if he had had the bringing up of her, would have remedied. For death was one of those Realities of Life with which, he thought, every one ought to make the earliest possible acquaintance. Love, on the other hand, was not one of the desirable Realities. It never occurred to him to ask himself the reason for this invidious distinction. Indeed, there was no reason; it just was so.

'Tell me, Uncle Spenny,' she whispered, when the doctor had gone, 'what *does* really happen to people when they die?'

Charmed by this sign of Emmy's renewed interest in serious themes, my Uncle Spencer explained to her what Alphonse at any rate thought would happen to him.

At midday, over the repeated cabbage soup and the horrible boiled meat, the bank clerk, with characteristically tasteless facetiousness, asked, 'How's our one little nigger boy?"

Emmy looked at him with disgust and anger. 'I think you're perfectly horrible,' she said. And, lowering her voice reverently, she went on, 'The doctor says he's going to die.'

The bank clerk was unabashed. 'Oh, he's going to kick the bucket, is he? Poor old blacky!'

Emmy made no answer; there was a general silence. It was as though somebody had started to make an unseemly noise in a church.

Afterwards, in the privacy of the little room, where, among the filing cabinets and the dusty papers, the Dravidian lay contentedly dying, Emmy turned to my Uncle Spencer and said, 'You know, Uncle Spenny, I think you're a wonderfully decent sort. I do, really.'

My Uncle Spencer was too much overcome to say anything but 'Emmy, Emmy,' two or three times. He took her hand and, very gently, kissed it.

That afternoon they went on talking about all the things that might conceivably happen after one were dead. Emmy told my Uncle Spencer all that she had thought when she got the telegram—two years ago it was, and she was working in a hall at Glasgow, one of her first engagements, too—saying that her father had suddenly died. He drank too much, her father did; and he wasn't kind to mother when he wasn't himself. But she had been very fond of him, all the same; and when that telegram came she wondered and wondered. . . .

My Uncle Spencer listened attentively, happy in having this new glimpse of her past; he forgot the other incident, which the beam of her confession had illumined for him.

Late that evening, after having lain for a long time quite still, as though he were asleep, Alphonse suddenly stirred, opened his large black eyes, and began to talk, at first in the incomprehensible language which came from him in delirium, then, when he realized that his listeners did not understand him, more slowly and in his strange pidgin-French.

'I have seen everything just now,' he said—'everything.'

'But what?' they asked.

'All that is going to happen. I have seen that this war will last a long time—a long time. More than fifty months.' And he prophesied enormous calamities.

My Uncle Spencer, who knew for certain that the war couldn't possibly last more than three months, was incredulous. But Emmy, who had no preconceived ideas on war and a strong faith in oracles, stopped him impatiently when he wanted to bring the Dravidian to silence.

'Tell me,' she said, 'what's going to happen to us.' She had very little interest in the fate of civilization.

'I am going to die,' Alphonse began.

My Uncle Spencer made certain deprecating little noises. 'No, no,' he protested.

The Indian paid no attention to him. 'I am going to die,' he repeated. 'And you,' he said to my Uncle Spencer, 'you will be let go and then again be put into prison. But not here. Somewhere else. A long way off. For a long time—a very long time. You will be very unhappy.' He shook his head. 'I cannot help it; even though you have been so good to me. That is what I see. But the man who deceived me'—he meant the journalist—'he will very soon be set free and he will live in freedom, all the time. In such freedom as there will be here. And he who sits in the chair will at last go back to his own country. And he who sings will go free like the man who deceived me. And the small grey man will be sent to another prison in another country. And the fat woman with a red mouth will be sent to another country; but she will not be in prison. I think she will be married there—again.' The portraits were recognizably those of the Russian countess and the professor of Latin. 'And the man with carbuncles on his face' (this was the bank clerk, no doubt) 'will be sent to another prison in another country; and there he will die. And the woman in black who is so sad . . .'

But Emmy could bear to wait no longer. 'What about me?' she asked. 'Tell me what you see about me.'

The Dravidian closed his eyes and was silent for a moment. 'You will be set free,' he said. 'Soon. And some day,' he went on, 'you will be the wife of this good man.' He indicated my Uncle Spencer. 'But not yet; not for a long time; till all this strife is at an end. You will have children . . . good fortune. . . .' His words grew fainter; once more he closed his eyes. He sighed as though utterly exhausted. 'Beware of fair strangers,' he murmured, reverting to the old familiar formula. He said no more.

Emmy and my Uncle Spencer were left looking at one another in silence.

'What do you think, Uncle Spenny?' she whispered at last. 'Is it true?'

Two hours later the Indian was dead.

My Uncle Spencer slept that night, or rather did not sleep, in the living-room. The corpse lay alone among the archives. The words of the Indian continued to echo and re-echo in his mind: 'Some day you will be the wife of this kind man.' Perhaps, he thought, on the verge of death, the spirit already begins to try its wings in the new world. Perhaps already it has begun to know the fringes, as it were, of secrets that are to be revealed to it. To my Uncle Spencer there was nothing repugnant in the idea. There was room in his universe for what are commonly and perhaps wrongly known as miracles. Perhaps the words were a promise, a statement of future fact. Lying on his back, his eyes fixed on the dark blue starry sky beyond the open window, he meditated on that problem of fixed fate and free will, with which the devils in Milton's hell wasted their infernal leisure. And like a refrain the words repeated themselves: 'Some day you will be the wife of this good man.' The stars moved slowly across the opening of the window. He did not sleep.

In the morning an order came for the release of the journalist and the opera singer. Joyfully they said good-bye to their fellow-prisoners; the door closed behind them. Emmy turned to my Uncle Spencer with a look almost of terror in her eyes; the Indian's prophesies were already beginning to come true. But they said nothing to one another. Two days later the bank clerk left for an internment camp in Germany.

And then, one morning, my Uncle Spencer himself was sent for. The order came quite suddenly; they left him no time to take leave. He was examined by the competent authority, found harmless, and permitted to return to Longres, where, however, he was to live under supervision. They did not even allow him to go back to the prison and say good-bye; a soldier brought his effects from the Ministry; he was put on to the train, with orders to report to the commandant at Longres as soon as he arrived.

Antonieke received her master with tears of joy. But my Uncle Spencer took no pleasure in his recovered freedom. Emmy Wendle was still a prisoner. True, she would soon be set free; but then, he now realized to his horror, she did not know his address. He had been released at such startlingly short notice that he had had no time to arrange with her about the possibilities of future meetings; he had not even seen her on the morning of his liberation.

Two days after his return to Longres, he asked permission from the commandant, to whom he had to report himself, every day, whether he might go to Brussels. He was asked why; my Uncle Spencer answered truthfully that it was to visit a friend in the prison from which he himself had just been released. Permission was at once refused.

My Uncle Spencer went to Brussels all the same. The sentry at the door of the prison arrested him as a suspicious person. He was sent back to Longres; the commandant talked to him menacingly. The next week, my Uncle Spencer tried again. It was sheer insanity, he knew; but doing something idiotic was preferable to doing nothing. He was again arrested.

This time they condemned him to internment in a camp in Germany. The Indian's prophecies were being fulfilled with a remarkable accuracy. And the war did last for more than fifty months. And the carbuncular bank clerk, whom he found again in the internment camp, did, in fact, die. . . .

What made him confide in me—me, whom he had known as a child and almost fathered—I do not know. Or perhaps I do know. Perhaps it was because he felt that I should be more competent to advise him on this sort of subject than his brother—my father—or old Mr. Bullinger, the Dante scholar, or any other of his friends. He would have felt ashamed, perhaps, to talk to them about this sort of thing. And he would have felt, too, that perhaps it wouldn't be much good talking to them, and that I, in spite of my youth, or even because of it, might actually be more experienced in these matters than they. Neither my father nor Mr. Bullinger, I imagine, knew very much about male impersonators.

At any rate, whatever the cause, it was to me that he talked about the whole affair, that spring of 1919, when he was staying with us in Sussex, recuperating after those dreary months of confinement. We used to go for long walks together, across the open downs, or between the grey pillars of the beechwoods; and painfully overcoming reluctance after reluctance, proceeding from confidence to more intimate confidence, my Uncle Spencer told me the whole story.

The story involved interminable discussions by the way. For we had to decide, first of all, whether there was any possible scientific explanation of prophecy; whether there was such a thing as an absolute future waiting to be lived through. And at much greater length, even, we had to argue about women—whether they were really 'like that' (and into what depths of cynicism my poor Uncle Spencer had learned, during the long, embittered meditations of his prison days and nights, to plunge and wallow!), or whether they were like the angels he had desired them to be.

But more important than to speculate on Emmy's possible character was to discover where she now was. More urgent than to wonder if prophecy could conceivably be reliable, was to take steps to fulfil this particular prophecy. For weeks my Uncle Spencer and I played at detectives.

I have often fancied that we must have looked, when we made our enquiries together, uncommonly like the traditional pair in the stories—my Uncle Spencer, the bright-eyed, cadaverous, sharp-featured genius, the Holmes of the combination; and I, moon-faced and chubby, a very youthful Watson. But, as a matter of fact, it was I, if I may say so without fatuity, who was the real Holmes of the two. My Uncle Spencer was too innocent of the world to know how to set about looking for a vanished mistress; just as he was too innocent of science to know how or where to find out what there was to be discovered on any abstracter subject.

It was I who took him to the British Museum and made him look up all the back numbers of the theatrical papers to see when Emmy had last advertised her desire to be engaged. It was I, the apparent Watson, who thought of the theatrical agencies and the stage doors of all the suburban music-halls. Sleuth-like in aspect, innocent at heart, my Uncle Spencer followed, marvelling at my familiarity with the ways of the strange world.

But I must temper my boasting by the confession that we were always entirely unsuccessful. No agency had heard of Emmy Wendle since 1914. Her card had appeared in no paper. The porters of music-halls remembered her, but only as something antediluvian. 'Emmy Wendle? Oh yes, Emmy Wendle . . .' And scratching their heads, they strove by a mental effort to pass from the mere name to the person, like palaeontologists reconstructing the whole diplodocus from the single fossil bone.

Two or three times we were even given addresses. But the landladies of the lodging-houses where she had stayed did not even remember her; and the old aunt at Ealing, from whom we joyfully hoped so much, had washed her hands of Emmy two or three months before the war began. And the conviction she then had that Emmy was a bad girl was only intensified and confirmed by our impertinent enquiries. No, she knew nothing about Emmy Wendle, now, and didn't want to know. And she'd trouble us to leave respectable people like herself in peace. And, defeated, we climbed back into our taxi, while the inhabitants of the squalid little street peered out at us and our vehicle, as though we had been visitors from another planet, and the metropolitan hackney carriage a fairy chariot

'Perhaps she's dead,' said my Uncle Spencer softly, after a long silence.

'Perhaps,' I said brutally, 'she's found a husband and retired into private life.'

My Uncle Spencer shut his eyes, sighed, and drew his hand across his forehead. What dreadful images filled his mind? He would almost have preferred that she should be dead.

'And yet the Indian,' he murmured, 'he was always right . . .'

And perhaps he may still be right in this. Who knows?

LITTLE MEXICAN.

AFTER THE FIREWORKS

I

'LATE as usual. Late.' Judd's voice was censorious. The words fell sharp, like beak-blows. 'As though I were a nut,' Miles Fanning thought resentfully, 'and he were a woodpecker. And yet he's devotion itself, he'd do anything for me. Which is why, I suppose, he feels entitled to crack my shell each time he sees me.' And he came to the conclusion, as he had so often come before, that he really didn't like Colin Judd at all. 'My oldest friend, whom I quite definitely don't like. Still . . .' Still, Judd was an asset, Judd was worth it.

'Here are your letters,' the sharp voice continued.

Fanning groaned as he took them. 'Can't one ever escape from letters? Even here, in Rome? They seem to get through everything. Like filter-passing bacteria. Those blessed days before post offices!' Sipping, he examined, over the rim of his coffee cup, the addresses on the envelopes.

'You'd be the first to complain if people didn't write,' Judd rapped out. 'Here's your egg. Boiled for three minutes exactly. I saw to it myself.'

Taking his egg, 'On the contrary,' Fanning answered, 'I'd be the first to rejoice. If people write, it means they exist; and all I ask for is to be able to pretend that the world doesn't exist. The wicked flee when no man pursueth. How well I understand them! But letters don't allow you to be an ostrich. The Freudians say . . .' He broke off suddenly. After all he was talking to Colin—to *Colin*. The confessional, self-accusatory manner was wholly misplaced. Pointless to give Colin the excuse to say something disagreeable. But what he had been going to say about the Freudians was amusing. 'The Freudians,' he began again.

But taking advantage of forty years of intimacy, Judd had already started to be disagreeable. 'But you'd be miserable,' he was saying, 'if the post didn't bring you your regular dose of praise and admiration and sympathy and . . .'

'And humiliation,' added Fanning, who had opened one of the envelopes and was looking at the letter within. 'Listen to this. From my American publishers. Sales and Publicity Department. "My dear Mr. Fanning." *My* dear, mark you. Wilbur F. Schmalz's dear. "My dear Mr. Fanning,—Won't you take us into your confidence with regard to your plans for the Summer Vacation? What aspect of the Great Outdoors are you favouring this year? Ocean or Mountain, Woodland or purling Lake? I would esteem it a great privilege if you would inform me, as I am preparing a series of notes for the Literary Editors of our leading journals, who are, as I have often found in the past, exceedingly receptive to such personal material, particularly when accompanied by well-chosen snapshots. So won't you co-operate with us in providing this service? Very cordially yours, Wilbur F. Schmalz." Well, what do you think of that?'

'I think you'll answer him,' said Judd. 'Charmingly,' he added, envenoming his malice. Fanning gave a laugh, whose very ease and heartiness betrayed his discomfort. 'And you'll even send him a snapshot.'

Contemptuously—too contemptuously (he felt it at the time)—Fanning crumpled up the letter and threw it into the fireplace. The really humiliating thing, he reflected, was that Judd was quite right: he *would* write to Mr. Schmalz about the Great Outdoors, he *would* send the first snapshot anybody took of him. There was a silence. Fanning ate two or three spoonfuls of egg. Perfectly boiled, for once. But still, what a relief that Colin was going away! After all, he reflected, there's a great deal to be said for a friend who has a house in Rome and who invites you to stay, even when he isn't there. To such a man much must be forgiven—even his infernal habit of being a woodpecker. He opened another envelope and began to read.

Possessive and preoccupied, like an anxious mother, Judd watched him. With all his talents and intelligence, Miles wasn't fit to face the world alone. Judd had told him so (peck, peck!) again and again. 'You're a child!' He had said it a thousand times. 'You ought to have somebody to look after you.' But if any one other than himself offered to do it, how bitterly jealous and resentful he became! And the trouble was that there were always so many applicants for the post of Fanning's bear-leader. Foolish men or, worse and more frequently, foolish women, attracted to him by his reputation and then conquered by his charm. Judd hated and professed to be loftily contemptuous of them. And the more Fanning liked his admiring bear-leaders, the loftier Judd's contempt became. For that was the bitter and unforgivable thing: Fanning manifestly preferred their bear-leading to Judd's. They flattered the bear, they caressed and even worshipped him; and the bear, of course, was charming to them, until such time as he growled, or bit, or, more often, quietly slunk away. Then they were surprised, they were pained. Because, as Judd would say with a grim satisfaction, they didn't know what Fanning was *really* like. Whereas he did know and had known since they were schoolboys together, nearly forty years before. Therefore he had a right to like him—a right and, at the same time, a duty to tell him all the reasons why he ought not to like him. Fanning didn't much enjoy listening to these reasons; he preferred to go where the bear was a sacred animal. With that air, which seemed so natural on his grey sharp face, of being dispassionately impersonal, 'You're afraid of healthy criticism,' Judd would tell him. 'You always were, even as a boy.'

'He's Jehovah,' Fanning would complain. 'Life with Judd is one long Old Testament. Being one of the Chosen People must have been bad enough. But to be *the* Chosen Person, in the singular . . .' And he would shake his head. 'Terrible!'

And yet he had never seriously quarrelled with Colin Judd. Active unpleasantness was something which Fanning avoided as much as possible. He had never even made any determined attempt to fade out of Judd's existence as he had faded, at one time or another, out of the existence of so many once intimate bear-leaders. The habit of their intimacy was of too long standing and, besides, old Colin was so useful, so bottomlessly reliable. So Judd remained for him the Oldest Friend whom one definitely dislikes; while for Judd, he was the Oldest Friend whom one adores and at the same time hates for not adoring back, the Oldest Friend whom one never sees enough of, but whom, when he *is* there, one finds insufferably exasperating, the Oldest Friend whom, in spite of all one's efforts, one is always getting on the nerves of.

'If only,' Judd was thinking, 'he could have faith!' The Catholic Church was there to help him. (Judd himself was a convert of more than twenty years' standing.) But the trouble was that Fanning didn't want to be helped by the Church; he could only see the comic side of Judd's religion. Judd was reserving his missionary efforts till his friend should be old or ill. But if only, meanwhile, if only, by some miracle of grace . . . So thought the good Catholic; but it was the jealous friend who felt and who obscurely schemed. Converted, Miles Fanning would be separated from his other friends and brought, Judd realized, nearer to himself.

Watching him, as he read his letter, Judd noticed, all at once, that Fanning's lips were twitching involuntarily into a smile. They were full lips, well cut, sensitive and sensual; his smiles were a little crooked. A dark fury suddenly fell on Colin Judd.

'Telling *me* that you'd like to get no letters!' he said with an icy vehemence. 'When you sit there grinning to yourself over some silly woman's flatteries.'

Amazed, amused, 'But what an outburst!' said Fanning, looking up from his letter.

Judd swallowed his rage; he had made a fool of himself. It was in a tone of calm dispassionate flatness that he spoke. Only his eyes remained angry. 'Was I right?' he asked.

'So far as the woman was concerned,' Fanning answered. 'But wrong about the flattery. Women have no time nowadays to talk about anything except themselves.'

'Which is only another way of flattering,' said Judd obstinately. 'They confide in you, because they think you'll like being treated as a person who understands.'

'Which is what, after all, I am. By profession even.' Fanning spoke with an exasperating mildness. 'What *is* a novelist, unless he's a person who understands?' He paused; but Judd made no answer, for the only words he could have uttered would have been whirling words of rage and jealousy. He was jealous not only of the friends, the lovers, the admiring correspondents; he was jealous of a part of Fanning himself, of the artist, the public personage; for the artist, the public personage seemed so often to stand between his friend and himself. He hated, while he gloried in them.

Fanning looked at him for a moment, expectantly; but the other kept his mouth tight shut, his eyes averted. In the same exasperatingly gentle tone, 'And flattery or no flattery,' Fanning went on, 'this is a charming letter. And the girl's adorable.'

He was having his revenge. Nothing upset poor Colin Judd so much as having to listen to talk about women or love. He had a horror of anything connected with the act, the mere thought, of sex. Fanning called it his perversion. 'You're one of those unspeakable chastity-perverts,' he would say, when he wanted to get his own back after a bout of pecking. 'If I had children, I'd never allow them to frequent your company. Too dangerous.' When he spoke of the forbidden subject, Judd would either writhe, a martyr, or else unchristianly explode. On this occasion he writhed and was silent. 'Adorable,' Fanning repeated, provocatively. 'A ravishing little creature. Though of course she *may* be a huge great camel. That's the danger of unknown correspondents. The best letter-writers are often camels. It's a piece of natural history I've learned by the bitterest experience.' Looking back at the letter, 'All the same,' he went on, 'when a young girl writes to one that she's sure one's the only person in the world who can tell her exactly who and what (both heavily underlined) she is—well, one's rather tempted, I must confess, to try yet once more. Because even if she were a camel she'd be a very young one. Twenty-one—isn't that what she says?' He turned over a page of the letter. 'Yes; twenty-one. Also she writes in orange ink. And doesn't like the Botticelli's at the Uffizi. But I hadn't told you; she's at Florence. This letter has been to London and back. We're practically neighbours. And here's something that's really rather good. Listen. "What I like about the Italian women is that they don't seem to be rather ashamed of being women, like so many English girls are, because English girls seem to go about apologizing for their figures, as though they were punctured, the way they hold themselves—it's really rather abject. But here they're all pleased and proud and not a bit apologetic or punctured, but just the opposite, which I really like, don't you?" Yes, I do,' Fanning answered, looking up from the letter. 'I like it very much indeed. I've always been opposed to these modern *Ars est celare arsem* fashions. I like unpuncturedness and I'm charmed by the letter. Yes, charmed. Aren't you?'

In a voice that trembled with hardly restrained indignation, 'No, I'm not!' Judd answered; and without looking at Fanning, he got up and walked quickly out of the room.

II

Judd had gone to stay with his old Aunt Caroline at Montreux. It was an annual affair; for Judd lived chronometrically. Most of June and the first half of July were always devoted to Aunt Caroline and devoted, invariably, at Montreux. On the fifteenth of July, Aunt Caroline was rejoined by her friend Miss Gaskin and Judd was free to proceed to England. In England he stayed till September the thirteenth, when he returned to Rome—'for the praying season,' as Fanning irreverently put it. The beautiful regularity of poor Colin's existence was a source of endless amusement to his friend. Fanning never had any plans. 'I just accept what turns up,' he would explain. 'Heads or tails—it's the only rational way of living. Chance generally knows so much better than we do. The Greeks elected most of their officials by lot—how wisely! Why shouldn't we toss up for Prime Ministers? We'd be much better governed. Or a sort of Calcutta Sweep for all the responsible posts in Church and State. The only horror would be if one were to win the sweep oneself. Imagine drawing the Permanent Under-Secretaryship for Education! Or the Archbishopric of Canterbury! Or the Vice-royalty of India ! One would just have to drink weed-killer. But as things are, luckily . . .'

Luckily, he was at liberty, under the present dispensation, to stroll, very slowly, in a suit of cream-coloured silk, down the shady side of the Via Condotti towards the Spanish Steps. Slowly, slowly. The air was streaked with invisible bars of heat and cold. Coolness came flowing out of shadowed doorways, and at every transverse street the sun breathed fiercely. Like walking through the ghost of a zebra, he thought.

Three beautiful young women passed him, talking and laughing together. Like laughing flowers, like deer, like little horses. And of course absolutely unpunctured, unapologetic. He smiled to himself, thinking of the letter and also of his own reply to it.

A pair of pink and white monsters loomed up, as though from behind the glass of an aquarium. But not speechless. For '*Grossartig !*' fell enthusiastically on Fanning's ear as they passed, and '*Fabelhaft !*' These Nordics ! He shook his head. Time they were put a stop to.

In the looking-glasses of a milliner's window a tall man in creamy-white walked slowly to meet him, hat in hand. The face was aquiline and eager, brown with much exposure to the sun. The waved, rather wiry hair was dark almost to blackness. It grew thickly, and the height of the forehead owed nothing to the approach of baldness. But what pleased Fanning most was the slimness and straightness of the tall figure. Those sedentary men of letters, with their sagging tremulous paunches—they were enough to make one hate the very thought of literature. What had been Fanning's horror when, a year before, he had realized that his own paunch was showing the first preliminary signs of sagging ! But Mr. Hornibrooke's exercises had been wonderful. 'The Culture of the Abdomen.' So much more important, as he had remarked in the course of the last few months at so many dinner tables, than the culture of the mind ! For of course he had taken everybody into his confidence about the paunch. He took everybody into his confidence about almost everything. About his love-affairs and his literary projects; about his illnesses and his philosophy ; his vices and his bank balance. He lived a rich and variegated private life in public; it was one of the secrets of his charm. To the indignant protests of poor jealous Colin, who reproached him with being an exhibitionist, shameless, a self-exploiter, 'You take everything so moralistically,' he had answered. 'You seem to imagine people do everything on purpose. But people do hardly anything on purpose. They behave as they do because they can't help it; that's what they happen to be like. "I am that I am"; Jehovah's is the last word in realistic psychology. I am what *I* am—a sort of soft transparent jelly-fish. While you're what *you* are—very tightly shut, opaque, heavily armoured: in a word, a giant clam. Morality doesn't enter; it's a case for scientific classification. You should be more of a Linnaeus, Colin, and less the Samuel Smiles.' Judd had been reduced to a grumbling silence. What he really resented was the fact that Fanning's confidences were given to upstart friends, to strangers even, before they were given to him. It was only to be expected. The clam's shell keeps the outside things out as effectually as it keeps the inside things in. In Judd's case, moreover, the shell served as an instrument of reproachful pinching.

From his cool street Fanning emerged into the Piazza di Spagna. The sunlight was stinging hot and dazzling. The flower venders on the steps sat in the midst of great explosions of colour. He bought a gardenia from one of them and stuck it in his buttonhole. From the windows of the English bookshop '*The Return of Eurydice*, by Miles Fanning' stared at him again and again. They were making a regular display of his latest volume in Tauchnitz. Satisfactory, no doubt; but also, of course, rather ridiculous and even humiliating, when one reflected that the book would be read by people like that estimable upper middle-class couple there, with their noses at the next window—that Civil Servant, he guessed, with the sweet little artistic wife and the artistic little house on Campden Hill—would be read by them dutifully (for of course they worked hard to keep abreast of everything) and discussed at their charming little dinner parties and finally condemned as 'extraordinarily brilliant, but . . .' Yes, but, but, but. For they were obviously regular subscribers to *Punch*, were vertebrae in the backbone of England, were upholders of all that was depressingly finest, all that was lifelessly and genteelly best in the English upper-class tradition. And when they recognized him (as it was obvious to Fanning, in spite of their discreet politeness, that they did) his vanity, instead of being flattered, was hurt. Being recognized by people like that—such was fame! What a humiliation, what a personal insult!

At Cook's, where he now went to draw some money on his letter of credit, Fame still pursued him, trumpeting. From behind the brass bars of his cage the cashier smiled knowingly as he counted out the bank-notes.

'Of course your name's very familiar to me, Mr. Fanning,' he said; and his tone was at once ingratiating and self-satisfied; the compliment to Fanning was at the same time a compliment to himself. 'And if I may be permitted to say so,' he went on, pushing the money through the bars, as one might offer a piece of bread to an ape, 'gratters on your last book. Gratters,' he repeated, evidently delighted with his very public-schooly colloquialism.

'All gratitude for gratters,' Fanning answered and turned away. He was half amused, half annoyed. Amused by the absurdity of those more than Etonian congratulations, annoyed at the damned impertinence of the congratulator. So intolerably patronizing ! he grumbled to himself. But most admirers were like that ; they thought they were doing you an enormous favour by admiring you. And how much more they admired themselves for being capable of appreciating than they admired the object of their appreciation ! And then there were the earnest ones who thanked you for giving such a perfect expression to their ideas and sentiments. They were the worst of all. For, after all, what were they thanking you for ? For being *their* interpreter, *their* dragoman, for playing John the Baptist to *their* Messiah. Damn their impertinence ! Yes, damn their impertinence !

'Mr. Fanning.' A hand touched his elbow.

Still indignant with the thought of damned impertinences, Fanning turned round with an expression of such ferocity on his face, that the young woman who had addressed him involuntarily fell back.

'Oh . . . I'm so sorry,' she stammered ; and her face, which had been bright, deliberately, with just such an impertinence as Fanning was damning, was discomposed into a child-like embarrassment. The blood tingled painfully in her cheeks. Oh, what a fool, she thought, what a fool she was making of herself ! This idiotic blushing ! But the way he had turned round on her, as if he were going to bite . . . Still, even that was no excuse for blushing and saying she was sorry, as though she were still at school and he were Miss Huss. Idiot ! she inwardly shouted at herself. And making an enormous effort, she readjusted her still scarlet face, giving it as good an expression of smiling nonchalance as she could summon up. 'I'm sorry,' she repeated, in a voice that was meant to be light, easy, ironically polite, but which came out (oh, idiot, idiot !) nervously shaky and uneven. 'I'm afraid I disturbed you. But I just wanted to introduce . . . I mean, as you were passing . . .'

'But how charming of you!' said Fanning, who had had time to realize that this latest piece of impertinence was one to be blessed, not damned. 'Charming!' Yes, charming it was, that young face with the grey eyes and the little straight nose, like a cat's, and the rather short upper lip. And the heroic way she had tried, through all her blushes, to be the accomplished woman of the world—that too was charming. And touchingly charming even were those rather red, large-wristed English hands, which she wasn't yet old enough to have learnt the importance of tending into whiteness and softness. They were still the hands of a child, a tomboy. He gave her one of those quick, those brilliantly and yet mysteriously significant smiles of his; those smiles that were still so youthfully beautiful when they came spontaneously. But they could also be put on; he knew how to exploit their fabricated charm, deliberately. To a sensitive eye, the beauty of his expression was, on these occasions, subtly repulsive.

Reassured, 'I'm Pamela Tarn,' said the young girl, feeling warm with gratitude for the smile. He was handsomer, she was thinking, than in his photographs. And much more fascinating. It was a face that had to be seen in movement.

'Pamela Tarn?' he repeated questioningly.

'The one who wrote you a letter.' Her blush began to deepen again. 'You answered so nicely. I mean, it was so kind . . . I thought . . .'

'But of course!' he cried, so loudly, that people looked round, startled. 'Of course!' He took her hand and held it, shaking it from time to time, for what seemed to Pamela hours. 'The most enchanting letter. Only I'm so bad at names. So you're Pamela Tarn.' He looked at her appraisingly. She returned his look for a moment, then flinched away in confusion from his bright dark eyes.

'Excuse me,' said a chilly voice; and a very large suit of plus-fours edged past them to the door.

'I like you,' Fanning concluded, ignoring the plus-fours; she uttered an embarrassed little laugh. 'But then, I liked you before. You don't know how pleased I was with what you said about the difference between English and Italian women.' The colour rose once more into Pamela's cheeks. She had only written those sentences after long hesitation, and had written them then recklessly, dashing them down with a kind of anger, just because Miss Huss would have been horrified by their unwomanliness, just because Aunt Edith would have found them so distressing, just because they had, when she spoke them aloud one day in the streets of Florence, so shocked the two school-mistresses from Boston whom she had met at the pension and was doing the sights with. Fanning's mention of them pleased her and at the same time made her feel dreadfully guilty. She hoped he wouldn't be too specific about those differences; it seemed to her that every one was listening. 'So profound,' he went on in his musical ringing voice. 'But out of the mouths of babes, with all due respect.' He smiled again, 'And "punctured"—that was really the *mot juste*. I shall steal it and use it as my own.'

'*Permesso.*' This time it was a spotted muslin and brown arms and a whiff of synthetic carnations.

'I think we're rather in the way,' said Pamela, who was becoming more and more uncomfortably aware of being conspicuous. And the spirit presences of Miss Huss, of Aunt Edith, of the two American ladies at Florence seemed to hang about her, hauntingly. 'Perhaps we'd better . . . I mean . . .' And, turning, she almost ran to the door.

'Punctured, punctured,' repeated his pursuing voice behind her. 'Punctured with the shame of being warm-blooded mammals. Like those poor lank creatures that were standing at the counter in there,' he added, coming abreast with her, as they stepped over the threshold into the heat and glare. 'Did you see them? So pathetic. But, oh dear!' he shook his head. 'Oh dear, oh dear!'

She looked up at him, and Fanning saw in her face a new expression, an expression of mischief and laughing malice and youthful impertinence. Even her breasts, he now noticed with an amused appreciation, even her breasts were impertinent. Small, but beneath the pale blue stuff of her dress, pointed, firm, almost comically insistent. No ashamed deflation here.

'Pathetic,' she mockingly echoed, 'but, oh dear, how horrible, how disgusting! Because they *are* disgusting,' she added defiantly, in answer to his look of humorous protest. Here in the sunlight and with the noise of the town isolating her from every one except Fanning, she had lost her embarrassment and her sense of guilt. The spiritual presences had evaporated. Pamela was annoyed with herself for having felt so uncomfortable among those awful old English cats at Cook's. She thought of her mother; her mother had never been embarrassed, or at any rate she had always managed to turn her embarrassment into something else. Which was what Pamela was doing now. 'Really disgusting,' she almost truculently insisted. She was reasserting herself, she was taking a revenge.

'You're very ruthless to the poor old things,' said Fanning. 'So worthy in spite of their mangy dimness, so obviously good.'

'I hate goodness,' said Pamela with decision, speeding the

parting ghosts of Miss Huss and Aunt Edith and the two ladies from Boston.

Fanning laughed aloud. 'Ah, if only we all had the courage to say so, like you, my child!' And with a familiar affectionate gesture, as though she were indeed a child and he had known her from the cradle, he dropped a hand on her shoulder. 'To say so and to act up to our beliefs. As you do, I'm sure.' And he gave the slim hard little shoulder a pat. 'A world without goodness—it'd be Paradise.'

They walked some steps in silence. His hand lay heavy and strong on her shoulder, and a strange warmth that was somehow intenser than the warmth of mere flesh and blood seemed to radiate through her whole body. Her heart quickened its beating; an anxiety oppressed her lungs; her very mind was as though breathless.

'Putting his hand on my shoulder like that!' she was thinking. 'It would have been cheek if some one else . . . Perhaps I ought to have been angry, perhaps . . .' No, that would have been silly. 'It's silly to take things like that too seriously, as though one were Aunt Edith.' But meanwhile his hand lay heavy on her shoulder, broodingly hot, its weight, its warmth insistently present in her consciousness.

She remembered characters in his books. Her namesake Pamela in *Pastures New*. Pamela the cold, but for that very reason an experimenter with passion; cold and therefore dangerous, full of power, fatal. Was she like Pamela? She had often thought so. But more recently she had often thought she was like Joan in *The Return of Eurydice*—Joan, who had emerged from the wintry dark underworld of an unawakened life with her husband (that awful, good, disinterested husband—so like Aunt Edith) into the warmth and brilliance of that transfiguring passion for Walter, for the adorable Walter whom she had always imagined must be so like Miles Fanning himself. She was sure of it now. But what of her own identity? Was she Joan, or was she Pamela? And which of the two would it be nicer to be? Warm Joan, with her happiness—but at the price of surrender? Or the cold, the unhappy, but conquering, dangerous Pamela? Or wouldn't it perhaps be best to be a little of both at once? Or first one and then the other? And in any case there was to be no goodness in the Aunt Edith style; he had been sure she wasn't good.

In her memory the voice of Aunt Edith sounded, as it had actually sounded only a few weeks before, in disapproving comment on her reference to the passionless experimental Pamela of *Pastures New*. 'It's a book I don't like. A most unnecessary book.' And then, laying her hand on Pamela's, 'Dear child,' she had added, with that earnest, that dutifully willed affectionateness, which Pamela so bitterly resented, 'I'd rather you didn't read any of Miles Fanning's books.'

'Mother never objected to my reading them. So I don't see . . .' The triumphant consciousness of having at this very moment the hand that had written those unnecessary books upon her shoulder was promising to enrich her share of the remembered dialogue with a lofty impertinence which the original had hardly possessed. 'I don't see that you have the smallest right . . .'

Fanning's voice fell startlingly across the eloquent silence. 'A penny for your thoughts, Miss Pamela,' it said.

He had been for some obscure reason suddenly depressed by his own last words. 'A world without goodness—it'd be Paradise.' But it wouldn't, no more than now. The only paradises were fools' paradises, ostriches' paradises. It was as though he had suddenly lifted his head out of the sand and seen time bleeding away—like the stabbed bull at the end of a bull-fight, swaying on his legs and soundlessly spouting the red blood from his nostrils—bleeding, bleeding away stanchlessly into the darkness. And it was all, even the loveliness and the laughter and the sunlight, finally pointless. This young girl at his side, this beautiful pointless creature pointlessly walking down the Via del Babuino . . . The feelings crystallized themselves, as usual, into whole phrases in his mind, and suddenly the phrases were metrical.

> Pointless and arm in arm with pointlessness,
> I pace and pace the Street of the Baboon.

Imbecile ! Annoyed with himself, he tried to shake off his mood of maudlin depression, he tried to force his spirit back into the ridiculous and charming universe it had inhabited, on the whole so happily, all the morning.

'A penny for your thoughts,' he said, with a certain rather forced jocularity, giving her shoulder a little clap. 'Or forty centesimi, if you prefer them.' And, dropping his hand to his side, 'In Germany,' he went on, 'just after the War one could afford to be more munificent. There was a time when I regularly offered a hundred and ninety million marks for a thought—yes, and gained on the exchange. But now . . .'

'Well, if you really want to know,' said Pamela, deciding to be bold, 'I was thinking how much my Aunt Edith disapproved of your books.'

"Did she ? I suppose it was only to be expected. Seeing that I don't write for aunts—at any rate, not for aunts in their specifically auntly capacity. Though, of course, when they're off duty . . .'

'Aunt Edith's never off duty.'

'And I'm never on. So you see.' He shrugged his shoulders. 'But I'm sure,' he added, 'you never paid much attention to her disapproval.'

'None,' she answered, playing the un-good part for all it was worth. 'I read Freud this spring,' she boasted, 'and Gide's autobiography, and Krafft-Ebbing. . . .'

'Which is more than I've ever done,' he laughed.

The laugh encouraged her. 'Not to mention all *your* books, years ago. You see,' she added, suddenly fearful lest she might have said something to offend him, 'my mother never minded my reading your books. I mean, she really encouraged me, even when I was only seventeen or eighteen. My mother died last year,' she explained. There was a silence. 'I've lived with Aunt Edith ever since,' she went on. 'Aunt Edith's my father's sister. Older than he was. Father died in 1923.'

'So you're all alone now?' he questioned. 'Except, of course, for Aunt Edith.'

'Whom I've now left.' She was almost boasting again. 'Because when I was twenty-one . . .'

'You stuck out your tongue at her and ran away. Poor Aunt Edith!'

'I won't have you being sorry for her,' Pamela answered hotly. 'She's really awful, you know. Like poor Joan's husband in *The Return of Eurydice*.' How easy it was to talk to him!

'So you even know,' said Fanning, laughing, 'what it's like to be unhappily married. Already. Indissolubly wedded to a virtuous aunt.'

'No joke, I can tell you. *I'm* the one to be sorry for. Besides, she didn't mind my going away, whatever she might say.'

'She did say something, then?'

'Oh yes. She always says things. More in sorrow than in anger, you know. Like head-mistresses. So gentle and good, I mean. When all the time she really thought me too awful. I used to call her Hippo, because she was such a hypocrite—*and* so fat. Enormous. Don't you *hate* enormous people? No, she's really delighted to get rid of me,' Pamela concluded, 'simply delighted.' Her face was flushed and as though luminously alive; she spoke with a quick eagerness.

'What a tremendous hurry she's in,' he was thinking, 'to tell me all about herself. If she were older or uglier, what an intolerable egotism it would be! As intolerable as mine would be if I happened to be less intelligent. But as it is . . .' His face, as he listened to her, expressed a sympathetic attention.

'She always disliked me,' Pamela had gone on. 'Mother too. She couldn't abide my mother, though she was always sweetly hippo-ish with her.'

'And your mother—how did she respond?'

'Well, not hippo-ishly, of course. She couldn't be that. She treated Aunt Edith—well, how *did* she treat Aunt Edith?' Pamela hesitated, frowning. 'Well, I suppose you'd say she was just natural with the Hippo. I mean . . .' She bit her lip. 'Well, if she ever *was* really natural. *I* don't know. Is anybody natural?' She looked up questioningly at Fanning. 'Am I natural, for example?'

Smiling a little at her choice of an example, 'I should think almost certainly not,' Fanning answered, more or less at random.

'You're right, of course,' she said despairingly, and her face was suddenly tragic, almost there were tears in her eyes. 'But isn't it awful? I mean, isn't it simply hopeless?'

Pleased that his chance shot should have gone home, 'At your age,' he said consolingly, 'you can hardly expect to be natural. Naturalness is something you learn, painfully, by trial and error. Besides,' he added, 'there are some people who are unnatural by nature.'

'Unnatural by nature.' Pamela nodded, as she repeated

the words, as though she were inwardly marshalling evidence to confirm their truth. 'Yes, I believe that's us,' she concluded. 'Mother and me. Not hippos, I mean, not *poseuses*, but just unnatural by nature. You're quite right. As usual,' she added, with something that was almost resentment in her voice.

'I'm sorry,' he apologized.

'How is it you manage to know so much?' Pamela asked in the same resentful tone. By what right was he so easily omniscient, when she could only grope and guess in the dark?

Taking to himself a credit that belonged, in this case, to chance, 'Child's play, my dear Watson,' he answered banteringly. 'But I suppose you're too young to have heard of Sherlock Holmes. And anyhow,' he added, with an ironical seriousness, 'don't let's waste any more time talking about me.'

Pamela wasted no more time. 'I get so depressed with myself,' she said with a sigh. 'And after what you've told me I shall get still more depressed. Unnatural by nature. And by upbringing too. Because I see now that my mother was like that. I mean, she was unnatural by nature too.'

'Even with you?' he asked, thinking that this was becoming interesting. She nodded without speaking. He looked at her closely. 'Were you very fond of her?' was the question that now suggested itself.

After a moment of silence, 'I loved my father more,' she answered slowly. 'He was more . . . more reliable. I mean, you never quite knew where you were with my mother. Sometimes she almost forgot about me; or else she didn't forget me enough and spoiled me. And then sometimes she used to get into the most terrible rages with me. She really frightened me then. And said such terribly hurting things. But you mustn't think I didn't love her.

I did.' The words seemed to release a spring; she was suddenly moved. There was a little silence. Making an effort, 'But that's what she was like,' she concluded at last.

'But I don't see,' said Fanning gently, 'that there was anything specially unnatural in spoiling you and then getting cross with you.' They were crossing the Piazza del Popolo; the traffic of four thronged streets intricately merged and parted in the open space. 'You must have been a charming child. And also . . . Look out!' He laid a hand on her arm. An electric bus passed noiselessly, a whispering monster. 'Also maddeningly exasperating. So where the unnaturalness came in . . .'

'But if you'd known her,' Pamela interrupted, 'you'd have seen exactly where the unnaturalness . . .'

'Forward!' he called and, still holding her arm, he steered her on across the Piazza.

She suffered herself to be conducted blindly. 'It came out in the way she spoiled me,' she explained, raising her voice against the clatter of a passing lorry. 'It's so difficult to explain, though; because it's something I felt. I mean, I've never really tried to put it into words till now. But it was as if . . . as if she weren't just herself spoiling me, but the picture of a young mother—do you see what I mean?—spoiling the picture of a little girl. Even as a child I kind of felt it wasn't quite as it should be. Later on I began to *know* it too, here.' She tapped her forehead. 'Particularly after father's death, when I was beginning to grow up. There were times when it was almost like listening to recitations—dreadful. One feels so blushy and prickly; you know the feeling.'

He nodded. 'Yes, I know. Awful!'

'Awful,' she repeated. 'So you can understand what a beast I felt, when it took me that way. So disloyal, I mean. So ungrateful. Because she was being so wonderfully sweet to me. You've no idea. But it was just when she was being her sweetest that I got the feeling worst. I shall never forget when she made me call her Clare—that was her Christian name. "Because we're going to be companions," she said, and all that sort of thing. Which was simply too sweet and too nice of her. But if you'd heard the way she said it! So dreadfully unnatural. I mean, it was almost as bad as Aunt Edith reading *Prospice*. And yet I know she meant it, I know she wanted me to be her companion. But somehow something kind of went wrong on the way between the wanting and the saying. And then the doing seemed to go just as wrong as the saying. She always wanted to do things excitingly, romantically, like in a play. But you can't *make* things be exciting and romantic, can you?' Fanning shook his head. 'She wanted to kind of force things to be thrilling by thinking and wishing, like Christian Science. But it doesn't work. We had wonderful times together; but she always tried to make out that they were more wonderful than they really were. Which only made them less wonderful. Going to the Paris Opera on a gala night is wonderful; but it's never as wonderful as when Rastignac goes, is it?'

'I should think it wasn't!' he agreed. 'What an insult to Balzac to imagine that it could be!'

'And the real thing's less wonderful,' she went on, 'when you're being asked all the time to see it as Balzac, and to *be* Balzac yourself. When you aren't anything of the kind. Because, after all, what am I? Just good, ordinary, middle-class English.'

She pronounced the words with a kind of defiance. Fanning imagined that the defiance was for him and, laughing, prepared to pick up the ridiculous little glove. But the glove was not for him; Pamela had thrown it down to a memory, to a ghost, to one of her own sceptical and mocking selves. It had been on the last day of their last stay together in Paris—that exciting, exotic Paris of poor Clare's imagination, to which their tickets from London never seemed quite to take them. They had gone to lunch at La Pérouse. 'Such a marvellous, *fantastic* restaurant! It makes you feel as though you were back in the Second Empire.' (Or was it the First Empire? Pamela could not exactly remember.) The rooms were so crowded with Americans, that it was with some difficulty that they secured a table. 'We'll have a marvellous lunch,' Clare had said, as she unfolded her napkin. 'And some day, when you're in Paris with your lover, you'll come here and order just the same things as we're having to-day. And perhaps you'll think of me. Will you, darling?' And she had smiled at her daughter with that intense, expectant expression that was so often on her face, and the very memory of which made Pamela feel subtly uncomfortable. 'How should I ever forget?' she had answered, laying her hand on her mother's and smiling. But after a second her eyes had wavered away from that fixed look, in which the intensity had remained as desperately on the stretch, the expectancy as wholly unsatisfied, as hungrily insatiable as ever. The waiter, thank goodness, had created a timely diversion; smiling at him confidentially, almost amorously, Clare had ordered like a princess in a novel of high life. The bill, when it came, was enormous. Clare had had to scratch the bottom of her purse for the last stray piece of nickel. 'It looks as though we should have to carry our own bags at Calais and Dover. I didn't realize I'd run things so fine.' Pamela had looked at the bill. 'But, Clare,' she had protested, looking up again at her mother with an expression of genuine horror, 'it's wicked! Two hundred and sixty francs for a lunch! It wasn't worth it.' The blood had risen darkly into Clare's face. 'How can you be so disgustingly *bourgeoise*, Pamela? So crass, so crawling?' Incensed by the heaping up of this abuse, 'I think it's stupid to do things one can't afford,' the girl had answered; 'stupid and vulgar.' Trembling with rage, Clare had risen to her feet. 'I'll never take you out again. Never.' (How often since then Pamela had recalled that terribly prophetic word!) 'You'll never understand life, you'll never be anything but a sordid little middle-class Englishwoman. Never, never.' And she had swept out of the room, like an insulted queen. Overheard by Pamela, as she undignifiedly followed, 'Gee!' an American voice had remarked, 'it's a regular cat-fight.'

The sound of another, real voice overlaid the remembered Middle Western accents.

'But after all,' Fanning was saying, 'it's better to be a good ordinary bourgeois than a bad ordinary bohemian, or a sham aristocrat, or a second-rate intellectual. . . .'

'I'm not even third-rate,' said Pamela mournfully. There had been a time when, under the influence of the now abhorred Miss Huss, she had thought she would like to go up to Oxford and read Greats. But Greek grammar was so awful . . . 'Not even fourth-rate.'

'Thank goodness,' said Fanning. 'Do you know what third- and fourth-rate intellectuals are? They're professors of philology and organic chemistry at the minor universities, they're founders and honorary life presidents of the Nuneaton Poetry Society and the Baron's Court Debating Society; they're the people who organize and sedulously attend all those Conferences for promoting international goodwill and the spread of culture that are perpetually being held at Buda-Pesth and Prague and Stockholm. Admirable and indispensable creatures, of course! But impossibly dreary; one simply cannot have any relations with them. And how virtuously they disapprove of those of us who have something better to do than disseminate culture or foster goodwill—those of us who are concerned, for example, with creating beauty—like me; or, like you, my child, in deliciously *being* beauty.'

Pamela blushed with pleasure, and for that reason felt it necessary immediately to protest. 'All the same,' she said, 'it's rather humiliating not to be able to do anything but be. I mean, even a cow can be.'

'Damned well, too,' said Fanning. 'If I *were* as intensely as a cow *is*, I'd be uncommonly pleased with myself. But this is getting almost too metaphysical. And do you realize what the time is?' He held out his watch; it was ten past one. 'And where we are? At the Tiber. We've walked miles.' He waved his hand; a passing taxi swerved in to the pavement beside them. 'Let's go and eat some lunch. You're free?'

'Well . . .' She hesitated. It was marvellous, of course; so marvellous that she felt she ought to refuse. 'If I'm not a bore. I mean, I don't want to impose . . . I mean . . .'

'You mean you'll come and have lunch. Good. Do you like marble halls and bands? Or local colour?'

Pamela hesitated. She remembered her mother once saying that Valadier and the Ulpia were the *only* two restaurants in Rome.

'Personally,' Fanning went on, 'I'm slightly avaricious about marble halls. I rather resent spending four times as much as eating about two-thirds as well. But I'll overcome my avarice if you prefer them.'

Pamela duly voted for local colour; he gave an address to the driver and they climbed into the cab.

'It's a genuinely Roman place,' Fanning explained. 'I hope you'll like it.'

'Oh, I'm sure I shall.' All the same, she did rather wish they were going to Valadier's.

III

Fanning's old friend, Dodo del Grillo, was in Rome for that one night and had urgently summoned him to dine. His arrival was loud and exclamatory.

'Best of all possible Dodos!' he cried, as he advanced with outstretched hands across the enormous baroque saloon. 'What an age! But what a pleasure!'

'At last, Miles,' she said reproachfully; he was twenty minutes late.

'But I know you'll forgive me.' And laying his two hands on her shoulders he bent down and kissed her. He made a habit of kissing all his women friends.

'And even if I didn't forgive, you wouldn't care two pins.'

'Not one.' He smiled his most charming smile. 'But if it gives you the smallest pleasure, I'm ready to say I'd be inconsolable.' His hands still resting on her shoulders, he looked at her searchingly, at arm's length. 'Younger than ever,' he concluded.

'I couldn't look as young as you do,' she answered. 'You know, Miles, you're positively indecent. Like Dorian Gray. What's your horrible secret?'

'Simply Mr. Hornibrooke,' he explained. 'The culture of the abdomen. So much more important than the culture of the mind.' Dodo only faintly smiled; she had heard the joke before. Fanning was sensitive to smiles; he changed the subject. 'And where's the marquis?' he asked.

The marchesa shrugged her shoulders. Her husband was one of those dear old friends whom somehow one doesn't manage to see anything of nowadays. 'Filippo's in Tanganyika,' she explained. 'Hunting lions.'

'While you hunt them at home. And with what success! You've bagged what's probably the finest specimen in Europe this evening. Congratulations!'

'*Merci, cher maître !*' she laughed. 'Shall we go in to dinner?'

The words invited, irresistibly. 'If only I had the right to answer: *Oui, chère maîtresse !*' Though as a matter of fact, he reflected, he had never really found her at all interesting in that way. A woman without temperament. But very pretty once—that time (how many years ago?) when there had been that picnic on the river at Bray, and he had drunk a little too much champagne. 'If only!' he repeated; and then was suddenly struck by a grotesque thought. Suppose she were to say yes, now—now! 'If only I had the right!'

'But luckily,' said Dodo, turning back towards him, as she passed through the monumental door into the dining-room, 'luckily you haven't the right. You ought to congratulate me on my immense good sense. Will you sit there?'

'Oh, I'll congratulate. I'm always ready to congratulate people who have sense.' He unfolded his napkin. 'And to condole.' Now that he knew himself safe, he could condole as much as he liked. 'What you must have suffered, my poor sensible Dodo, what you must have missed!'

'Suffered less,' she answered, 'and missed more unpleasantnesses than the women who didn't have the sense to say no.'

'What a mouthful of negatives! But that's how sensible people always talk about love—in terms of negatives. Never of positives; they ignore those and go about sensibly avoiding the discomforts. Avoiding the pleasures and exultations too, poor sensible idiots! Avoiding all that's valuable and significant. But it's always like that. The human soul is a fried whiting. (What excellent red mullet this is, by the way! Really excellent.) Its tail is in its mouth. All progress finally leads back to the beginning again. The most sensible people—dearest Dodo, believe me—are the most foolish. The most intellectual are the stupidest. I've never met a really good metaphysician, for example, who wasn't in one way or another bottomlessly stupid. And as for the really spiritual people, look what they revert to. Not merely to silliness and stupidity, but finally to crass non-existence. The highest spiritual state is ecstasy, which is just not being there at all. No, no; we're all fried whitings. Heads are invariably tails.'

'In which case,' said Dodo, 'tails must also be heads. So that if you want to make intellectual or spiritual progress, you must behave like a beast—is that it?'

Fanning held up his hand. 'Not at all. If you rush too violently towards the tail, you run the risk of shooting down the whiting's open mouth into its stomach, and even further. The wise man . . .'

'So the whitings are fried without being cleaned?'

'In parables,' Fanning answered reprovingly, 'whitings are always fried that way. The wise man, as I was saying, oscillates lightly from head to tail and back again. His whole existence—or shall we be more frank and say "my" whole existence?—is one continual oscillation. I am never too consistently sensible, like you; or too consistently feather-headed like some of my other friends. In a word,' he wagged a finger, 'I oscillate.'

Tired of generalizations, 'And where exactly,' Dodo enquired, 'have you oscillated to at the moment? You've left me without your news so long. . . .'

'Well, at the moment,' he reflected aloud, 'I suppose you might say I was at a dead point between desire and renunciation, between sense and sensuality.'

'Again?' She shook her head. 'And who is she this time?'

Fanning helped himself to asparagus before replying.

'Who is she?' he echoed. 'Well, to begin with, she's the writer of admiring letters.'

Dodo made a grimace of disgust. 'What a horror!' For some reason she felt it necessary to be rather venomous about this new usurper of Fanning's heart. 'Vamping by correspondence—it's really the lowest . . .'

'Oh, I agree,' he said. 'On principle and in theory I entirely agree.'

'Then why . . .' she began, annoyed by his agreement; but he interrupted her.

'Spiritual adventuresses,' he said. 'That's what they generally are, the women who write you letters. Spiritual adventuresses. I've suffered a lot from them in my time.'

'I'm sure you have.'

'They're a curious type,' he went on, ignoring her sarcasms. 'Curious and rather horrible. I prefer the good old-fashioned vampire. At least one knew where one stood with her. There she was—out for money, for power, for a good time, occasionally, perhaps, for sensual satisfactions. It was all entirely above-board and obvious. But with the spiritual adventuress, on the contrary, everything's most horribly turbid and obscure and slimy. You see, she doesn't want money or the commonplace good time. She wants Higher Things—damn her neck! Not large pearls and a large motor-car, but a large soul—that's what she pines for: a large soul and a large intellect, and a huge philosophy, and enormous culture, and out sizes in great thoughts.'

Dodo laughed. 'You're fiendishly cruel, Miles.'

'Cruelty can be a sacred duty,' he answered. 'Besides, I'm getting a little of my own back. If you knew what these spiritual vamps had done to me! I've been one of their appointed victims. Yes, appointed; for, you see, they can't have their Higher Things without attaching themselves to a Higher Person.'

'And are you one of the Higher People, Miles?'

'Should I be dining here with you, my dear, if I weren't?' And without waiting for Dodo's answer, 'They attach themselves like lice,' he went on. 'The contact with the Higher Person makes them feel high themselves; it magnifies them, it gives them significance, it satisfies their parasitic will to power. In the past they could have gone to religion—fastened themselves on the nearest priest (that's what the priest was there for), or sucked the spiritual blood of some saint. Nowadays they've got no professional victims; only a few charlatans and swamis and higher-thought-mongers. Or alternatively the artists. Yes, the artists. They find our souls particularly juicy. What I've suffered! Shall I ever forget that American woman who got so excited by my book on Blake that she came specially to Tunis to see me? She had an awful way of opening her mouth very wide when she talked, like a fish. You were perpetually seeing her tongue; and, what made it worse, her tongue was generally white. Most distressing. And how the tongue wagged! In spite of its whiteness. Wagged like mad, and mostly about the Divine Mind.'

'The Divine Mind?'

He nodded. 'It was her speciality. In Rochester, N.Y., where she lived, she was never out of touch with it. You've no idea what a lot of Divine Mind there is floating about in Rochester, particularly in the neighbourhood of women with busy husbands and incomes of over fifteen thousand dollars. If only she could have stuck to the Divine Mind! But the Divine Mind has one grave defect: it won't make love to you. That was why she'd come all the way to Tunis in search of a merely human specimen.'

'And what did you do about it?'

'Stood it nine days and then took the boat to Sicily. Like a thief in the night. The wicked flee, you know. God, how they can flee!'

'And she?'

'Went back to Rochester, I suppose. But I never opened any more of her letters. Just dropped them into the fire whenever I saw the writing. Ostrichism—it's the only rational philosophy of conduct. According to the Freudians we're all unconsciously trying to get back to . . .'

'But poor woman!' Dodo burst out. 'She must have suffered.'

'Nothing like what I suffered. Besides, she had the Divine Mind to go back to; which was her version of the Freudians' pre-natal . . .'

'But I suppose you'd encouraged her to come to Tunis?'

Reluctantly, Fanning gave up his Freudians. 'She could write good letters,' he admitted. 'Inexplicably good, considering what she was at close range.'

'But then you treated her abominably.'

'But if you'd seen her, you'd realize how abominably she'd treated me.'

'You?'

'Yes, abominably—by merely existing. She taught me to be very shy of letters. That was why I was so pleasantly surprised this morning when my latest correspondent suddenly materialized at Cook's. Really ravishing. One could forgive her everything for the sake of her face and that charming body. Everything, even the vamping. For a vamp I suppose she is, even this one. That is, if a woman *can* be a spiritual adventuress when she's so young and pretty and well-made. Absolutely and *sub specie aeternitatis*, I suppose she can. But from the very sublunary point of view of the male victim, I doubt whether, at twenty-one . . .'

'Only twenty-one?' Dodo was disapproving. 'But Miles!'

Fanning ignored her interruption. 'And another thing you must remember,' he went on, 'is that the spiritual vamp who's come of age this year is not at all the same as the spiritual vamp who came of age fifteen, twenty, twenty-five years ago. She doesn't bother much about Mysticism, or the Lower Classes, or the Divine Mind, or any nonsense of that sort. No, she goes straight to the real point—the point which the older vamps approached in such a tiresomely circuitous fashion—she goes straight to herself. But straight!' He stabbed the air with his fruit-knife. 'A bee-line. Oh, it has a certain charm that directness. But whether it won't be rather frightful when they're older is another question. But then almost everything is rather frightful when people are older.'

'Thank you,' said Dodo. 'And what about you?'

'Oh, an old satyr,' he answered with that quick, brilliantly mysterious smile of his. 'A superannuated faun. I know it; only too well. But at the same time, most intolerably, a Higher Person. Which is what draws the spiritual vamps. Even the youngest ones. Not to talk to me about the Divine Mind, of course, or their views about Social Reform. But about themselves. Their Individualities, their Souls, their Inhibitions, their Unconsciouses, their Pasts, their Futures. For them, the Higher Things are all frankly and nakedly personal. And the function of the Higher Person is to act as a sort of psycho-analytical father confessor. He exists to tell them all about their strange and wonderful psyches. And meanwhile, of course, his friendship inflates their egotism. And if there should be any question of love, what a personal triumph!'

'Which is all very well,' objected Dodo. 'But what about the old satyr? Wouldn't it also be a bit of a triumph for him? You know, Miles,' she added gravely, 'it would really be scandalous if you were to take advantage . . .'

'But I haven't the slightest intention of taking any advantages. If only for my own sake. Besides, the child is too ingenuously absurd. The most hair-raising theoretical knowledge of life, out of books. You should hear her prattling away about inverts and perverts and birth control—but prattling from unplumbed depths of innocence and practical ignorance. Very queer. And touching too. Much more touching than the old-fashioned innocences of the young creatures who thought babies were brought by storks. Knowing all about love and lust, but in the same way as one knows all about quadratic equations. And her knowledge of the other aspects of life is really of the same kind. What she's seen of the world she's seen in her mother's company. The worst guide imaginable, to judge from the child's account. (Dead now, incidentally.) The sort of woman who could never live on top gear so to speak—only at one or two imaginative removes from the facts. So that, in her company, what was nominally real life became actually just literature—yet more literature. Bad, inadequate Balzac in flesh and blood instead of genuine, good Balzac out of a set of nice green volumes. The child realizes it herself. Obscurely, of course; but distressfully. It's one of the reasons why she's applied to me: she hopes I can explain what's wrong. And correct it in practice. Which I won't do in any drastic manner, I promise you. Only mildly, by precept—that is, if I'm not too bored to do it at all.'

'What's the child's name?' Dodo asked.

'Pamela Tarn.'

'Tarn? But was her mother by any chance Clare Tarn?'

He nodded. 'That was it. She even made her daughter call her by her Christian name. The companion stunt.'

'But I used to know Clare Tarn quite well,' said Dodo

in an astonished, feeling voice. 'These last years I'd hardly seen her. But when I was more in London just after the War . . .'

'But this begins to be interesting,' said Fanning. 'New light on my little friend. . . .'

'Whom I absolutely forbid you,' said Dodo emphatically, 'to . . .'

'Tamper with the honour of,' he suggested. 'Let's phrase it as nobly as possible.'

'No, seriously, Miles. I really won't have it. Poor Clare Tarn's daughter. If I didn't have to rush off to-morrow I'd ask her to come and see me, so as to warn her.'

Fanning laughed. 'She wouldn't thank you. And besides, if any one is to be warned, I'm the one who's in danger. But I shall be firm, Dodo—a rock. I won't allow her to seduce me.'

'You're incorrigible, Miles. But mind, if you dare . . .'

'But I won't. Definitely.' His tone was reassuring. 'Meanwhile I must hear something about the mother.'

The marchesa shrugged her shoulders. 'A woman who couldn't live on top gear. You've really said the last word.'

'But I want first words,' he answered. 'It's not the verdict that's interesting. It's the whole case, it's all the evidence. You're *sub-poenaed*, my dear. Speak up.'

'Poor Clare!'

'Oh, *nil nisi bonum*, of course, if that's what disturbs you.'

'She'd have so loved it to be not *bonum*, poor dear!' said the marchesa, tempering her look of vague condolence with a little smile. 'That was her great ambition—to be thought rather wicked. She'd have liked to have the reputation of a vampire. Not a spiritual one, mind you. The other sort. Lola Montes—that was her ideal.'

'It's an ideal,' said Fanning, 'that takes some realizing, I can tell you.'

Dodo nodded. 'And that's what she must have found out, pretty soon. She wasn't born to be a fatal woman; she lacked the gifts. No staggering beauty, no mysterious fascination or intoxicating vitality. She was just very charming, that was all; and at the same time rather impossible and absurd. So that there weren't any aspiring victims to be fatal to. And a vampire without victims is—well, *what*?'

'Certainly not a vampire,' he concluded.

'Except, of course, in her own imagination, if she chooses to think so. In her own imagination Clare certainly was a vampire.'

'Reduced, in fact, to being her own favourite character in fiction.'

'Precisely. You always find the phrase.'

'Only too fatally!' He made a little grimace. 'I often wish I didn't. The luxury of being inarticulate! To be able to wallow indefinitely long in every feeling and sensation, instead of having to clamber out at once on to a hard, dry, definite phrase. But what about your Clare?'

'Well, she started, of course, by being a riddle to me. Unanswerable, or rather answerable, answered, but so very strangely that I was still left wondering. I shall never forget the first time Filippo and I went to dine there. Poor Roger Tarn was still alive then. While the men were drinking their port, Clare and I were alone in the drawing-room. There was a little chit-chat, I remember, and then, with a kind of determined desperation, as though she'd that second screwed herself up to jumping off the Eiffel Tower, suddenly, out of the blue, she asked me if I'd ever had one of those *wonderful* Sicilian peasants—I can't possibly reproduce the tone, the expression—as a lover. I was a bit taken aback, I must confess. "But we don't live in Sicily," was the only thing I could think of answering—too idiotically!

" Our estates are all in Umbria and Tuscany." " But the Tuscans are *superb* creatures too," she insisted. Superb, I agreed. But, as it happens, I don't have affairs with even the superbest peasants. Nor with anybody else, for that matter. Clare was dreadfully disappointed. I think she'd expected the most romantic confidences—moonlight and mandolines and *stretti, stretti, nell'estasi d'amor*. She was really very ingenuous. " Do you mean to say you've really never . . . ? " she insisted. I ought to have got angry, I suppose; but it was all so ridiculous, that I never thought of it. I just said, " Never," and felt as though I were refusing her a favour. But she made up for my churlishness by being lavish to herself. But lavish! You can't imagine what a tirade she let fly at me. How *wonderful* it was to get away from self-conscious, complicated, sentimental love! How profoundly *satisfying* to feel oneself at the mercy of the dumb, dark forces of physical passion! How *intoxicating* to humiliate one's culture and one's class feeling before some *magnificent* primitive, some *earthily* beautiful satyr, some *divine* animal! And so on, *crescendo*. And it ended with her telling me the story of her *extraordinary* affair with—was it a gamekeeper? or a young farmer? I forget. But there was something about rabbit-shooting in it, I know.'

'It sounds like a chapter out of George Sand.'

'It was.'

'Or still more, I'm afraid,' he said, making a wry face, 'like a most deplorable parody of my *Endymion and the Moon*.'

'Which I've never read, I'm ashamed to say.'

'You should, if only to understand this Clare of yours.'

'I will. Perhaps I'd have solved her more quickly, if I'd read it at the time. As it was I could only be amazed—and a little horrified. That rabbit-shooter!' She shook her head. 'He ought to have been so romantic. But I could only think of that awful yellow kitchen soap he'd be sure to wash himself with, or perhaps carbolic, so that he'd smell like washed dogs—dreadful! And the flannel shirts, not changed quite often enough. And the hands, so horny, with very short nails, perhaps broken. No, I simply couldn't understand her.'

'Which is to your discredit, Dodo, if I may say so.'

'Perhaps. But you must admit, I never pretended to be anything but what I am—a perfectly frivolous and respectable member of the upper classes. With a taste, I must confess, for the scandalous. Which was one of the reasons, I suppose, why I became so intimate with poor Clare. I was really fascinated by her confidences.'

'Going on the tiles vicariously, eh?'

'Well, if you choose to put it grossly and vulgarly. . . .'

'Which I *do* choose,' he interposed. 'To be tactfully gross and appositely vulgar—that, my dear, is one of the ultimate artistic refinements. One day I shall write a monograph on the aesthetics of vulgarity. But meanwhile shall we say that you were inspired by an intense scientific curiosity to . . .'

Dodo laughed. 'One of the tiresome things about you, Miles, is that one can never go on being angry with you.'

'Yet another subject for a monograph!' he answered, and his smile was at once confidential and ironical, affectionate and full of mockery. 'But let's hear what the scientific curiosity elicited?'

'Well, to begin with, a lot of really rather embarrassingly intimate confidences and questions, which I needn't repeat.'

'No, don't. I know what those feminine conversations are. I have a native modesty. . . .'

'Oh, so have I. And, strangely enough, so had Clare. But somehow she wanted to outrage herself. You felt it all the time. She always had that desperate jumping-off-the-

Eiffel-Tower manner, when she began to talk like that. It was a kind of martyrdom. But enjoyable. Perversely.' Dodo shook her head. 'Very puzzling. I used to have to make quite an effort to change the conversation from gynaecology to romance. Oh, those lovers of hers! Such stories! The most fantastic adventures in East End opium dens, in aeroplanes, and even, I remember (it was that very hot summer of 'twenty-two), even in a refrigerator!'

'My dear!' protested Fanning.

'Honestly! I'm only repeating what she told me.'

'But do you mean to say you believed her?'

'Well, by that time, I must admit, I was beginning to be rather sceptical. You see, I could never elicit the names of these creatures. Nor any detail. It was as though they didn't exist outside the refrigerator and the aeroplane.'

'How many of them were there?'

'Only two at that particular moment. One was a Grand Passion, and the other a Caprice. A Caprrice,' she repeated, rolling the r. 'It was one of poor Clare's favourite words. I used to try and pump her. But she was mum. "I want them to be *mysterious*," she told me the last time I pressed her for details, "anonymous, without an *état civil*. Why should I show you their passports and identity cards?" "Perhaps they haven't got any," I suggested. Which was malicious. I could see she was annoyed. But a week later she showed me their photographs. There they were; the camera cannot lie; I had to be convinced. The Grand Passion, I must say, was a very striking-looking creature. Thin-faced, worn, a bit Roman and sinister. The Caprice was more ordinarily the nice young Englishman. Rather childish and simple, Clare explained; and she gave me to understand that she was initiating him. It was the other, the Grand P., who thought of such refinements as the refrigerator. Also, she now confided to me for the first time, he was mildly a sadist. Having seen his face, I could believe it. " Am I ever likely to meet him ? " I asked. She shook her head. He moved in a very different world from mine.'

'A rabbit-shooter ?' Fanning asked.

'No: an intellectual. That's what I gathered.'

'Golly!'

'So there was not the slightest probability, as you can see, that *I* should ever meet him,' Dodo laughed. 'And yet almost the first face I saw on leaving Clare that afternoon was the Grand P.'s.'

'Coming to pay his sadistic respects ?'

'Alas for poor Clare, no. He was behind glass in the show-case of a photographer in the Brompton Road, not a hundred yards from the Tarns' house in Ovington Square. The identical portrait. I marched straight in. " Can you tell me who that is ? " But it appears that photography is done under the seal of confession. They wouldn't say. Could I order a copy ? Well, yes, as a favour, they'd let me have one. Curiously enough, they told me, as they were taking down my name and address, another lady had come in only two or three days before and also ordered a copy. " Not by any chance a rather tall lady with light auburn hair and a rather amusing mole on the left cheek ? " That did sound rather like the lady. " And with a very confidential manner," I suggested, " as though you were her oldest friends ? " Exactly, exactly ; they were unanimous. That clinched it. Poor Clare, I thought, as I walked on towards the Park, poor, poor Clare !'

There was a silence.

'Which only shows,' said Fanning at last, 'how right the Church has always been to persecute literature. The harm we imaginative writers do ! Enormous ! We ought all to be on the Index, every one. Consider your Clare, for example. If it hadn't been for books, she'd never have known that such things as passion and sensuality and perversity even existed. Never.'

'Come, come,' she protested.

But, 'Never,' Fanning repeated. 'She was congenitally as cold as a fish; it's obvious. Never had a spontaneous, untutored desire in her life. But she'd read a lot of books. Out of which she'd fabricated a theory of passion and perversity. Which she then consciously put into practice.'

'Or rather didn't put into practice. Only day-dreamed that she did.'

He nodded. 'For the most part. But sometimes, I don't mind betting, she realized the day-dreams in actual life. Desperately, as you so well described it, with her teeth clenched and her eyes shut, as though she were jumping off the Eiffel Tower. That rabbit-shooter, for instance. . . .'

'But do you think the rabbit-shooter really existed?'

'Perhaps not that particular one. But *a* rabbit-shooter, perhaps several rabbit-shooters—at one time or another, I'm sure, they genuinely existed. Though never *genuinely*, of course, for her. For her, it's obvious, they were just phantoms, like the other inhabitants of her dreamery. Phantoms of flesh and blood, but still phantoms. I see her as a kind of Midas, turning everything she touched into imagination. Even in the embraces of a genuine, solid rabbit-shooter, she was still only indulging in her solitary sultry dream—a dream inspired by Shakespeare, or Mrs. Barclay, or the Chevalier de Nerciat, or D'Annunzio, or whoever her favourite author may have been.'

'Miles Fanning, perhaps,' Dodo mockingly suggested.

'Yes, I feared as much.'

'What a responsibility!'

'Which I absolutely refuse to accept. What have I ever written but solemn warnings against the vice of imagination? Sermons against mental licentiousness of every kind—intellectual licentiousness, mystical licentiousness, fantastic-amorous licentiousness. No, no. I'll accept no responsibility. Or at least no special responsibility—only the generic responsibility of being an imaginative author, the original sin of writing in such a way as to influence people. And when I say "influence," of course I don't really mean *influence*. Because a writer can't influence people, in the sense of making them think and feel and act as he does. He can only influence them to be more, or less, like one of their own selves. In other words, he's never understood. (Thank goodness ! because it would be very humiliating to be really understood by one's readers.) What readers get out of him is never, finally, *his* ideas, but theirs. And when they try to imitate him or his creations, all that they can ever do is to act one of their own potential rôles. Take this particular case. Clare read and, I take it, was impressed. She took my warnings against mental licentiousness to heart and proceeded to do—what ? Not to become a creature of spontaneous, unvitiated impulses—for the good reason that that wasn't in her power—but only to imagine that she was such a creature. She imagined herself a woman like the one I put into *Endymion and the Moon* and acted accordingly—or else didn't act, only dreamed ; it makes very little difference. In a word, she did exactly what all my books told her not to do. Inevitably ; it was her nature. I'd influenced her, yes. But she didn't become more like one of my heroines. She only became more intensely like herself. And then, you must remember, mine weren't the only books on her shelves. I think we can take it that she'd read *Les Liaisons Dangereuses* and Casanova and some biography, shall we say, of the Maréchal de Richelieu. So that those spontaneous unvitiated impulses—how ludicrous they are, anyhow, when you *talk* about them !—became identified in her mind with the most elegant forms of " caprice"—wasn't that the word? She was a child of nature —but with qualifications. The kind of child of nature that lived at Versailles or on the Grand Canal about 1760. Hence those rabbit-shooters and hence also those sadistic intellectuals, whether real or imaginary—and imaginary even when real. I may have been a favourite author. But I'm not responsible for the rabbit-shooters or the Grand P.'s. Not more responsible than any one else. She'd heard of the existence of love before she'd read me. We're all equally to blame, from Homer downwards. Plato wouldn't have any of us in his Republic. He was quite right, I believe. Quite right.'

'And what about the daughter?' Dodo asked, after a silence.

He shrugged his shoulders. 'In reaction against the mother, so far as I could judge. In reaction, but also influenced by her, unconsciously. And the influence is effective because, after all, she's her mother's daughter and probably resembles her mother, congenitally. But consciously, on the surface, she knows she doesn't want to live as though she were in a novel. And yet can't help it, because that's her nature, that's how she was brought up. But she's miserable, because she realizes that fiction-life *is* fiction. Miserable and very anxious to get out—out through the covers of the novel into the real world.'

'And are you her idea of the real world?' Dodo enquired.

He laughed. 'Yes, I'm the real world. Strange as it may seem. And also, of course, pure fiction. The Writer, the Great Man—the Official Biographer's fiction, in a word. Or, better still, the autobiographer's fiction. Chateaubriand, shall we say? And her breaking out—that's fiction too. A pure Miles Fanningism, if ever there was one. And, poor child, she knows it. Which makes her so cross with herself. Cross with me too, in a curious obscure way. But at the same time she's thrilled. What a thrilling situation! And herself walking about in the middle of it. She looks on and wonders and wonders what the next instalment of the feuilleton's going to contain.'

'Well, there's one thing we're quite certain it's not going to contain, aren't we? Remember your promise, Miles.'

'I think of nothing else,' he bantered.

'Seriously, Miles, seriously.'

'I think of nothing else,' he repeated in a voice that was the parody of a Shakespearean actor's.

Dodo shook her finger at him. 'Mind,' she said, 'mind!' Then, pushing back her chair, 'Let's move into the drawing room,' she went on. 'We shall be more comfortable there.'

IV

'And to think,' Pamela was writing in her diary, 'how nervous I'd been beforehand, and the trouble I'd taken to work out the whole of our first meeting, question and answer, like the Shorter Catechism, instead of which I was like a fish in water, really at home, for the first time in my life, I believe. No, perhaps not more at home than with Ruth and Phyllis, but then they're girls, so they hardly count. Besides, when you've once been at home in the sea, it doesn't seem much fun being at home in a little glass bowl, which is rather unfair to Ruth and Phyllis, but after all it's not their fault and they can't help being little bowls, just as M. F. can't help being a sea, and when you've swum about a bit in all that intelligence and knowledge and really *devilish* understanding, well, you find the bowls rather narrow, though of course they're sweet little bowls and I shall always be very fond of them, especially Ruth. Which makes me wonder if what he said about Clare and me—unnatural by nature—is always true, because hasn't every unnatural person got somebody she can be natural with, or even that she can't help being natural with, like oxygen and that other stuff making water? Of course it's not guaranteed that you find the other person who makes you natural, and I think perhaps Clare never did find her person, because I don't believe it was Daddy. But in my case there's Ruth and Phyllis and now to-day M. F.; and he really proves it, because I *was* natural with him more than with any one, even though he did say I was unnatural by nature. No, I feel that if I were with him always, I should always be my *real* self, just kind of easily spouting, like those lovely fountains we went to look at this afternoon, not all tied up in knots and squirting about vaguely in every kind of direction, and muddy at that, but beautifully clear in a big gushing spout, like what Joan in *The Return of Eurydice* finally became when she'd escaped from that awful, awful man and found Walter. But does that mean I'm in love with him?'

Pamela bit the end of her pen and stared, frowning, at the page before her. Scrawled large in orange ink, the question stared back. Disquietingly and insistently stared. She remembered a phrase of her mother's. 'But if you knew,' Clare had cried (Pamela could *see* her, wearing the black afternoon dress from Patou, and there were yellow roses in the bowl on the table under the window), 'if you knew what certain writers were to me! *Shrines*—there's no other word. I could worship the Tolstoy of Anna Karenina.' But Harry Braddon, to whom the words were addressed, had laughed at her. And, though she hated Harry Braddon, so had Pamela, mockingly. For it was absurd; nobody was a shrine, nobody. And anyhow, what *was* a shrine? Nothing. Not nowadays, not when one had stopped being a child. She told herself these things with a rather unnecessary emphasis, almost truculently, in the style of the professional atheists in Hyde Park. One didn't worship—for the good reason that she herself once had worshipped. Miss Figgis, the classical mistress, had been her pash for more than a year. Which was why she had gone to Early Service so frequently in those days and been so keen to go up to Oxford and take Greats. (Besides, she had even, at that time, rather liked and admired Miss Huss. Ghastly old Hussy! It seemed incredible now.) But oh, that grammar! And Caesar was such a bore, and Livy still worse, and as for Greek . . . She had tried very hard for a time. But when Miss Figgis so obviously preferred that priggish little beast Kathleen, Pamela had just let things slide. The bad marks had come in torrents and old Hussy had begun being more sorrowful than angry, and finally more angry than sorrowful. But she hadn't cared. What made not caring easier was that she had her mother behind her. 'I'm so delighted,' was what Clare had said when she heard that Pamela had given up wanting to go to Oxford. 'I'd have felt so terribly inferior if you'd turned out a blue-stocking. Having my frivolity rebuked by my own daughter!' Clare had always boasted of her frivolity. Once, under the influence of old Hussy and for the love of Miss Figgis, an earnest disapprover, Pamela had become an apostle of her mother's gospel. 'After all,' she had pointed out to Miss Figgis, 'Cleopatra didn't learn Greek.' And though Miss Figgis was able to point out, snubbingly, that the last of the Ptolemies had probably spoken nothing but Greek, Pamela could still insist that in principle she was quite right: Cleopatra hadn't learnt Greek, or what, if you were a Greek, corresponded to Greek. So why should she? She began to parade a violent and childish cynicism, a cynicism which was still (though she had learnt, since leaving school, to temper the ridiculous expression of it) her official creed. There were no shrines—though she sometimes wistfully and rather shamefacedly wished there were. One didn't, determinedly didn't worship. She herself might admire Fanning's books, *did* admire them, enormously. But as for worshipping—no, she absolutely declined. Clare had overdone it all somehow—as usual. Pamela was resolved that there should be no nonsense about *her* feelings.

'But does that mean I'm in love with him?' insisted the orange scrawl.

As though in search of an answer, Pamela turned back the pages of her diary (she had already covered nearly eight of them with her account of this memorable twelfth of June). 'His face,' she read, 'is very brown, almost like an Arab's, except that he has blue eyes, as he lives mostly in the South, because he says that if you don't live in the sun, you go slightly mad, which is why people in the North, like us and the Germans and the Americans, are so tiresome, though of course you go still madder where there's too much sun, like in India, where they're even more hopeless. He's very good-looking and you don't think of him as being either old or young, but as just being there, like that, and the way he smiles is really very extraordinary, and so are his eyes, and I simply *adored* his white silk suit.' But the question was not yet answered. His silk suit wasn't him, nor was his voice, even though he had 'an awfully nice one, rather like that man who talks about books on the wireless, only nicer.' She turned over a page. 'But M. F. is different from most clever people,' the orange scrawl proclaimed, 'because he doesn't make you feel a fool even when he does laugh at you, and never, which is so *ghastly* with men like Professor Cobley, talks down to you in that awful patient, gentle way, which makes you feel a million times more of a worm than being snubbed or ignored, because, if you have any pride, that sort of intelligence without tears is just loathsome, as though you were being given milk pudding out of charity. No, M. F. talks to you on the level, and the extraordinary thing is that, while he's talking to you and you're talking to him, you *are* on a level with him, or at any rate you feel as though you were, which comes to the same thing. He's like influenza, you catch his intelligence.' Pamela let the leaves of the notebook flick past, one by one, under her thumb. The final words on the half-blank page once more stared at her, questioningly. 'But does that mean I'm in love with him?' Taking her pen from between her teeth, 'Certainly,' she wrote, 'I do find him terribly attractive physically.' She paused for a moment to reflect, then added, frowning as though with the effort of raising an elusive fact from the depths of memory, of solving a difficult problem in algebra: 'Because really, when he put his hand on my shoulder, which would have been simply intolerable if any one else had done it, but somehow with him I didn't mind, I felt all thrilled with an absolute frisson.' She ran her pen through the last word and substituted 'thrill,' which she underlined to make it seem less lamely a repetition. 'Frisson' had been one of Clare's favourite words; hearing it pronounced in her mother's remembered voice, Pamela had felt a sudden mistrust of it; it seemed to cast a kind of doubt on the feelings it stood for, a doubt of which she was ashamed—it seemed so disloyal and the voice had sounded so startlingly, so heart-rendingly clear and near—but which she still couldn't help experiencing. She defended herself; 'frisson' had simply had to go, because the thrill was genuine, absolutely genuine, she insisted. 'For a moment,' she went on, writing very fast, as though she were trying to run away from the sad, disagreeable thoughts that had intruded upon her, 'I thought I was going to faint when he touched me, like when one's coming to after chloroform, which I've certainly never felt like with any one else.' As a protest against the doubts inspired by that unfortunate frisson she underlined 'never,' heavily. Never; it was quite true. When Harry Braddon had tried to kiss her, she had been furious and disgusted—disgusting beast! Saddening and reproachful, Clare's presence hovered round her once more; Clare had liked Harry Braddon. Still, he was a beast. Pamela had never told her mother about that kiss. She shut her eyes excludingly and thought instead of Cecil Rudge, poor, timid, unhappy little Cecil, whom she liked so much, was so genuinely sorry for. But when, that afternoon at Aunt Edith's, when at last, after an hour's visibly laborious screwing to the sticking point, he had had the courage to take her hand and say 'Pamela' and kiss it, she had just laughed, oh! unforgivably, but she simply couldn't help it; he was so ridiculous. Poor lamb, he had been terribly upset. 'But I'm so sorry,' she had gasped between the bursts of her laughter, 'so dreadfully sorry. Please don't be hurt.' But his face, she could see, was agonized. 'Please! Oh, I feel so miserable.' And she had gone off into another explosion of laughter which almost choked her. But when she could breathe again, she had run to him where he stood, averted and utterly unhappy, by the window, she had taken his hand and, when he still refused to look at her, had put her arm round his neck and kissed him. But the emotion that had filled her eyes with tears was nothing like passion. As for Hugh Davies—why, it certainly had been rather thrilling when Hugh kissed her. It had been thrilling, but certainly not to fainting point. But then had she *really* felt like fainting to-day? a small voice questioned. She drowned the small voice with the scratching of her pen. 'Consult the oracles of passion,' she wrote and, laying down her pen, got up and crossed the room. A copy of *The Return of Eurydice* was lying on the bed; she picked it up and turned over the pages. Here it was! 'Consult the oracles of passion,' she read aloud, and her own voice sounded, she thought, strangely oracular in the solitude. 'A god speaks in them, or else a devil, one can never tell which beforehand, nor even, in most cases, afterwards. And, when all is said, does it very much matter? God and devil are equally supernatural, that is the important thing; equally supernatural and therefore, in this all too flatly natural world of sense and science and society, equally desirable, equally significant.' She shut the book and walked back to the table. 'Which is what he said this afternoon,' she went on writing, 'but in that laughing way, when I said I could never see why one shouldn't do what one liked, instead of all this Hussy and Hippo rigmarole about service and duty, and he said yes, that was what Rabelais had said' (there seemed to be an awful lot of 'saids' in this sentence, but it couldn't be helped; she scrawled on); 'which I pretended I'd read—why can't one tell the truth? particularly as I'd just been saying at the same time that one ought to say what one thinks as well as do what one likes; but it seems to be hopeless—and he said he entirely agreed, it was perfect, so long as you had the luck to like the sort of things that kept you on the right side of the prison bars and think the sort of things that don't get you murdered when you say them. And I said I'd rather say what I thought and do what I liked and be murdered and put in gaol than be a Hippo, and he said I was an idealist, which annoyed me and I said I certainly wasn't, all I was was some one who didn't want to go mad with inhibitions. And he laughed, and I wanted to quote him his own words about the oracles, but somehow it was so shy-making that I didn't. All the same, it's what I intensely feel, that one *ought* to consult the oracles of passion. And I shall consult them.' She leaned back in her chair and shut her eyes. The orange question floated across the darkness: 'But does that mean I'm in love with him?' The oracle seemed to be saying yes. But oracles, she resolutely refused to remember, can be rigged to suit the interests of the questioner. Didn't the admirer of *The*

Return of Eurydice secretly *want* the oracle to say yes? Didn't she think she'd almost fainted, because she'd wished she'd almost fainted, because she'd come desiring to faint? Pamela sighed; then, with a gesture of decision, she slapped her notebook to and put away her pen. It was time to get ready for dinner; she bustled about efficiently and distractingly among her trunks. But the question returned to her as she lay soaking in the warm other-world of her bath. By the time she got out she had boiled herself to such a pitch of giddiness that she could hardly stand.

For Pamela, dinner in solitude, especially the public solitude of hotels, was a punishment. Companionlessness and compulsory silence depressed her. Besides, she never felt quite eye-proof; she could never escape from the obsession that every one was looking at her, judging, criticizing. Under a carapace of rather impertinent uncaringness she writhed distressfully. At Florence her loneliness had driven her to make friends with two not very young American women who were staying in her hotel. They were a bit earnest and good and dreary. But Pamela preferred even dreariness to solitude. She attached herself to them inseparably. They were touched. When she left for Rome, they promised to write to her, they made her promise to write to them. She was so young; they felt responsible; a steadying hand, the counsel of older friends. . . . Pamela had already received two steadying letters. But she hadn't answered them, never would answer them. The horrors of lonely dining cannot be alleviated by correspondence.

Walking down to her ordeal in the restaurant, she positively yearned for her dreary friends. But the hall was a desert of alien eyes and faces; and the waiter who led her through the hostile dining-room, had bowed, it seemed to her, with an ironical politeness, had mockingly smiled. She sat down haughtily at her table and almost wished she were under it. When the *sommelier* appeared with his list, she ordered half a bottle of something absurdly expensive, for fear he might think she didn't know anything about wine.

She had got as far as the fruit, when a presence loomed over her; she looked up. 'You?' Her delight was an illumination; the young man was dazzled. 'What marvellous luck!' Yet it was only Guy Browne, Guy whom she had met a few times at dances and found quite pleasant—that was all. 'Think of your being in Rome!' She made him sit down at her table. When she had finished her coffee, Guy suggested that they should go out and dance somewhere. They went. It was nearly three when Pamela got to bed. She had had a most enjoyable evening.

V

But how ungratefully she treated poor Guy when, next day at lunch, Fanning asked her how she had spent the evening! True, there were extenuating circumstances, chief among which was the fact that Fanning had kissed her when they met. By force of habit he himself would have explained, if any one had asked him why, because he kissed every presentable face. Kissing was in the great English tradition. 'It's the only way I can be like Chaucer,' he liked to affirm. 'Just as knowing a little Latin and less Greek is my only claim to resembling Shakespeare and as lying in bed till ten's the nearest I get to Descartes.' In this particular case, as perhaps in every other particular case, the force of habit had been seconded by a deliberate intention; he was accustomed to women being rather in love with him, he liked the amorous atmosphere and could use the simplest as well as the most complicated methods to create it. Moreover he was an experimentalist, he genuinely wanted to see what would happen. What happened was that Pamela was astonished, embarrassed, thrilled, delighted, bewildered. And what with her confused excitement and the enormous effort she had made to take it all as naturally and easily as he had done, she was betrayed into what, in other circumstances, would have been a scandalous ingratitude. But when one has just been kissed, for the first time and at one's second meeting with him, kissed offhandedly and yet (she felt it) significantly, by Miles Fanning—actually Miles Fanning!—little men like Guy Browne do seem rather negligible, even though one did have a very good time with them the evening before.

'I'm afraid you must have been rather lonely last night,' said Fanning, as they sat down to lunch. His sympathy hypocritically covered a certain satisfaction that it should be his absence that had condemned her to dreariness.

'No, I met a friend,' Pamela answered with a smile which the inward comparison of Guy with the author of *The Return of Eurydice* had tinged with a certain amused condescendingness.

'A friend?' He raised his eyebrows. '*Amico* or *amica*? Our English is so discreetly equivocal. With this key Bowdler locked up his heart. But I apologize. *Co* or *ca*?'

'*Co.* He's called Guy Browne and he's here learning Italian to get into the Foreign Office. He's a nice boy.' Pamela might have been talking about a favourite, or even not quite favourite, retriever. 'Nice; but nothing very special. I mean, not in the way of intelligence.' She shook her head patronizingly over Guy's very creditable First in History as a guttersnipe capriciously favoured by an archduke might learn in his protector's company to shake his head and patronizingly smile at the name of a marquis of only four or five centuries' standing. 'He can dance, though,' she admitted.

'So I suppose you danced with him?' said Fanning in a tone which, in spite of his amusement at the child's assumption of an aged superiority, he couldn't help making rather disobligingly sarcastic. It annoyed him to think that Pamela should have spent an evening, which he had pictured as dismally lonely, dancing with a young man.

'Yes, we danced,' said Pamela, nodding.

'Where?'

'Don't ask me. We went to about six different places in the course of the evening.'

'Of course you did,' said Fanning almost bitterly. 'Moving rapidly from one place to another and doing exactly the same thing in each—that seems to be the young's ideal of bliss.'

Speaking as a young who had risen above such things, but who still had to suffer from the folly of her unregenerate contemporaries, 'It's quite true,' Pamela gravely confirmed.

'They go to Pekin to listen to the wireless and to Benares to dance the fox-trot. I've seen them at it. It's incomprehensible. And then the tooting up and down in automobiles, and the roaring up and down in aeroplanes, and the stinking up and down in motor-boats. Up and down, up and down, just for the sake of not sitting still, of having never time to think or feel. No, I give them up, these young of yours.' He shook his head. 'But I'm becoming a minor prophet,' he added; his good humour was beginning to return.

'But after all,' said Pamela, 'we're not *all* like that.'

Her gravity made him laugh. 'There's at least one who's ready to let herself be bored by a tiresome survivor from another civilization. Thank you, Pamela.' Leaning across the table, he took her hand and kissed it. 'I've been horribly ungrateful,' he went on, and his face as he looked at her was suddenly transfigured by the bright enigmatic beauty of his smile. 'If you knew how charming you looked!' he said; and it was true. That ingenuous face, those impertinent little breasts—charming. 'And how charming you *were*! But of course you *do* know,' a little demon prompted him to add: 'no doubt Mr. Browne told you last night.'

Pamela had blushed—a blush of pleasure, and embarrassed shyness, and excitement. What he had just said and done was more significant, she felt, even than the kiss he had given her when they met. Her cheeks burned; but she managed, with an effort, to keep her eyes unwaveringly on his. His last words made her frown. 'He certainly didn't,' she answered. 'He'd have got his face smacked.'

'Is that a delicate hint?' he asked. 'If so,' and he leaned forward, 'here's the other cheek.'

Her face went redder than ever. She felt suddenly miserable; he was only laughing at her. 'Why do you laugh at me?' she said aloud, unhappily.

'But I wasn't,' he protested. 'I really did think you were annoyed.'

'But why should I have been?'

'I can't imagine.' He smiled. 'But if you would have smacked Mr. Browne's face . . .'

'But Guy's quite different.'

It was Fanning's turn to wince. 'You mean he's young, while I'm only a poor old imbecile who needn't be taken seriously?'

'Why are you so stupid?' Pamela asked almost fiercely. 'No, but I mean,' she added in quick apology, 'I mean . . . well, I don't care two pins about Guy. So you see, it would annoy me if he tried to push in, like that. Whereas with somebody who does mean something to me . . .' Pamela hesitated. 'With *you*,' she specified in a rather harsh, strained voice and with just that look of despairing determination, Fanning imagined, just that jumping-off-the-

Eiffel-Tower expression, which her mother's face must have assumed in moments such as this, 'it's quite different. I mean, with you of course I'm not annoyed. I'm pleased. Or at least I *was* pleased, till I saw you were just making a fool of me.'

Touched and flattered, 'But, my dear child,' Fanning protested, 'I wasn't doing anything of the kind. I meant what I said. And much more than I said,' he added, in the teeth of the warning and reproachful outcry raised by his common sense. It was amusing to experiment, it was pleasant to be adored, exciting to be tempted (and how young she was, how perversely fresh!). There was even something quite agreeable in resisting temptation; it had the charms of a strenuous and difficult sport. Like mountain climbing. He smiled once more, consciously brilliant.

This time Pamela dropped her eyes. There was a silence which might have protracted itself uncomfortably, if the waiter had not broken it by bringing the *tagliatelle.* They began to eat. Pamela was all at once exuberantly gay.

After coffee they took a taxi and drove to the Villa Giulia. 'For we mustn't,' Fanning explained, 'neglect your education.'

'Mustn't we?' she asked. 'I often wonder why we mustn't. Truthfully now, I mean without any hippoing and all that—why shouldn't I neglect it? Why should I go to this beastly museum?' She was preparing to play the cynical, boastfully unintellectual part which she had made her own. 'Why?' she repeated truculently. Behind the rather vulgar low-brow mask she cultivated wistful yearnings and concealed the uneasy consciousness of inferiority. 'A lot of beastly old Roman odds and ends!' she grumbled; that was one for Miss Figgis.

'Roman?' said Fanning. 'God forbid! Etruscan.'

'Well, Etruscan, then; it's all the same, anyhow. Why

shouldn't I neglect the Etruscans? I mean, what have they got to do with me—*me*?' And she gave her chest two or three little taps with the tip of a crooked forefinger.

'Nothing, my child,' he answered. 'Thank goodness, they've got absolutely nothing to do with you, or me, or anybody else.'

'Then why . . .?'

'Precisely for that reason. That's the definition of culture—knowing and thinking about things that have absolutely nothing to do with us. About Etruscans, for example; or the mountains on the moon; or cat's-cradle among the Chinese; or the Universe at large.'

'All the same,' she insisted, 'I still don't see.'

'Because you've never known people who weren't cultured. But make the acquaintance of a few practical business-men—the kind who have no time to be anything but alternately efficient and tired. Or of a few workmen from the big towns. (Country people are different; they still have the remains of the old substitutes for culture—religion, folk-lore, tradition. The town fellows have lost the substitutes without acquiring the genuine article.) Get to know those people; *they'll* make you see the point of culture. Just as the Sahara'll make you see the point of water. And for the same reason: they're arid.'

'That's all very well; but what about people like Professor Cobley?'

'Whom I've happily never met,' he said, 'but can reconstruct from the expression on your face. Well, all that can be said about those people is: just try to imagine them if they'd never been irrigated. Gobi or Shamo.'

'Well, perhaps.' She was dubious.

'And anyhow the biggest testimony to culture isn't the soulless philistines—it's the soulful ones. My sweet Pamela,' he implored, laying a hand on her bare brown arm, 'for heaven's sake don't run the risk of becoming a soulful philistine.'

'But as I don't know what that is,' she answered, trying to persuade herself, as she spoke, that the touch of his hand was giving her a tremendous frisson—but it really wasn't.

'It's what the name implies,' he said. 'A person without culture who goes in for having a soul. An illiterate idealist. A Higher Thinker with nothing to think about but his—or more often, I'm afraid, *her*—beastly little personal feelings and sensations. They spend their lives staring at their own navels and in the intervals trying to find other people who'll take an interest and come and stare too. Oh, figuratively,' he added, noticing the expression of astonishment which had passed across her face. '*En tout bien, tout honneur.* At least, sometimes and to begin with. Though I've known cases . . .' But he decided it would be better not to speak about the lady from Rochester, N.Y. Pamela might be made to feel that the cap fitted. Which it did, except that her little head was such a charming one. 'In the end,' he said, 'they go mad, these soulful philistines. Mad with self-consciousness and vanity and egotism and a kind of hopeless bewilderment; for when you're utterly without culture, every fact's an isolated, unconnected fact, every experience is unique and unprecedented. Your world's made up of a few bright points floating about inexplicably in the midst of an unfathomable darkness. Terrifying! It's enough to drive any one mad. I've seen them, lots of them, gone utterly crazy. In the past they had organized religion, which meant that somebody had once been cultured for them, vicariously. But what with protestantism and the modernists, their philistinism's absolute now. They're alone with their own souls. Which is the worst companionship a human being can have. So bad that it sends you dotty. So beware, Pamela, beware! You'll go mad if you think only of what has something to do with you. The Etruscans will keep you sane.'

'Let's hope so.' She laughed. 'But aren't we there?'

The cab drew up at the door of the villa; they got out.

'And remember that the things that start with having nothing to do with you,' said Fanning, as he counted out the money for the entrance tickets, 'turn out in the long run to have a great deal to do with you. Because they become a part of you and you of them. A soul can't know or fully become itself without knowing and therefore to some extent becoming what isn't itself. Which it does in various ways. By loving, for example.'

'You mean . . .?' The flame of interest brightened in her eyes.

But he went on remorselessly. 'And by thinking of things that have nothing to do with you.'

'Yes, I see.' The flame had dimmed again.

'Hence my concern about your education.' He beckoned her through the turnstile into the museum. 'A purely selfish concern,' he added, smiling down at her. 'Because I don't want the most charming of my young friends to grow into a monster, whom I shall be compelled to flee from. So resign yourself to the Etruscans.'

'I resign myself,' said Pamela, laughing. His words had made her feel happy and excited. 'You can begin.' And in a theatrical voice, like that which used to make Ruth go off into such fits of laughter, 'I am all ears,' she added, 'as they say in the Best Books.' She pulled off her hat and shook out the imprisoned hair.

To Fanning, as he watched her, the gesture brought a sudden shock of pleasure. The impatient, exuberant youthfulness of it! And the little head, so beautifully shaped, so gracefully and proudly poised on its long neck! And her hair was drawn back smoothly from the face to explode in a thick tangle of curls on the nape of the neck. Ravishing !

'All ears,' she repeated, delightedly conscious of the admiration she was receiving.

'All ears.' And almost meditatively, 'But do you know,' he went on, 'I've never even seen your ears. May I ?' And without waiting for her permission, he lifted up the soft, goldy-brown hair that lay in a curve, drooping, along the side of her head.

Pamela's face violently reddened ; but she managed none the less to laugh. 'Are they as long and furry as you expected ?' she asked.

He allowed the lifted hair to fall back into its place and, without answering her question, 'I've always,' he said, looking at her with a smile which she found disquietingly enigmatic and remote, 'I've always had a certain fellow-feeling for those savages who collect ears and thread them on strings as necklaces.'

'But what a horror !' she cried out.

'You think so ?' He raised his eyebrows.

But perhaps, Pamela was thinking, he was a sadist. In that book of Krafft-Ebbing's there had been a lot about sadists. It would be queer if he were . . .

'But what's certain,' Fanning went on in another, business-like voice, 'what's only too certain is that ears aren't culture. They've got too much to do with us. With me, at any rate. Much too much.' He smiled at her again. Pamela smiled back at him, fascinated and obscurely a little frightened ; but the fright was an element in the fascination. She dropped her eyes. 'So don't let's waste any more time,' his voice went on. 'Culture to right of us, culture to left of us. Let's begin with this culture on the left. With the vases. They really have absolutely nothing to do with us.'

He began and Pamela listened. Not very attentively,

however. She lifted her hand and, under the hair, touched her ear. 'A fellow-feeling for those savages.' She remembered his words with a little shudder. He'd almost meant them. And 'ears aren't culture. Too much to do with us. With me. Much too much.' He'd meant that too, genuinely and whole-heartedly. And his smile had been a confirmation of the words; yes, and a comment, full of mysterious significance. What *had* he meant? But surely it was obvious what he had meant. Or wasn't it obvious?

The face she turned towards him wore an expression of grave attention. And when he pointed to a vase and said, 'Look,' she looked, with what an air of concentrated intelligence! But as for knowing what he was talking about! She went on confusedly thinking that he had a fellow-feeling for those savages, and that her ears had too much to do with him, much too much, and that perhaps he was in love with her, perhaps also that he was like those people in Krafft-Ebbing, perhaps . . .; and it seemed to her that her blood must have turned into a kind of hot, red soda-water, all fizzy with little bubbles of fear and excitement.

She emerged, partially at least, out of this bubbly and agitated trance to hear him say, 'Look at that now.' A tall statue towered over her. 'The Apollo of Veii,' he explained. 'And really, you know, it *is* the most beautiful statue in the world. Each time I see it, I'm more firmly convinced of that.'

Dutifully, Pamela stared. The God stood there on his pedestal, one foot advanced, erect in his draperies. He had lost his arms, but the head was intact and the strange Etruscan face was smiling, enigmatically smiling. Rather like *him*, it suddenly occurred to her.

'What's it made of?' she asked; for it was time to be intelligent.

'Terracotta. Originally coloured.'

'And what date?'

'Late sixth century.'

'B.C.?' she queried, a little dubiously, and was relieved when he nodded. It really would have been rather awful if it had been A.D. 'Who by?'

'By Vulca, they say. But as that's the only Etruscan sculptor they know the name of . . .' He shrugged his shoulders, and the gesture expressed a double doubt—doubt whether the archaeologists were right and doubt whether it was really much good talking about Etruscan art to some one who didn't feel quite certain whether the Apollo of Veii was made in the sixth century before or after Christ.

There was a long silence. Fanning looked at the statue. So did Pamela, who also, from time to time, looked at Fanning. She was on the point, more than once, of saying something; but his face was so meditatively glum that, on each occasion, she changed her mind. In the end, however, the silence became intolerable.

'I think it's extraordinarily fine,' she announced in the rather religious voice that seemed appropriate. He only nodded. The silence prolonged itself, more oppressive and embarrassing than ever. She made another and despairing effort. 'Do you know, I think he's really rather like you. I mean, the way he smiles. . . .'

Fanning's petrified immobility broke once more into life. He turned towards her, laughing. 'You're irresistible, Pamela.'

'Am I?' Her tone was cold; she was offended. To be told you were irresistible always meant that you'd behaved like an imbecile child. But her conscience was clear; it was a gratuitous insult—the more intolerable since it had been offered by the man who, a moment before, had been saying that he had a fellow-feeling for those savages and that her ears had altogether *too* much to do with him.

Fanning noticed her sudden change of humour and obscurely divined the cause. 'You've paid me the most irresistible compliment you could have invented,' he said, doing his best to undo the effect of his words. For after all what did it matter, with little breasts like that and thin brown arms, if she did mix up the millenniums a bit? 'You could hardly have pleased me more if you'd said I was another Rudolph Valentino.'

Pamela had to laugh.

'But seriously,' he said, 'if you knew what this lovely God means to me, how much . . .'

Mollified by being once more spoken to seriously, 'I think I can understand,' she said in her most understanding voice.

'No, I doubt if you can.' He shook his head. 'It's a question of age, of the experience of a particular time that's not your time. I shall never forget when I came back to Rome for the first time after the War and found this marvellous creature standing here. They only dug him up in 'sixteen, you see. So there it was, a brand new experience, a new and apocalyptic voice out of the past. Some day I shall try to get it on to paper, all that this God has taught me.' He gave a little sigh; she could see that he wasn't thinking about her any more; he was talking for himself. 'Some day,' he repeated. 'But it's not ripe yet. You can't write a thing before it's ripe, before it wants to be written. But you can talk about it, you can take your mind for walks all round it and through it.' He paused and, stretching out a hand, touched a fold of the God's sculptured garment, as though he were trying to establish a more intimate, more real connection with the beauty before him. 'Not that what he taught me was fundamentally new,' he went on slowly. 'It's all in

Homer, of course. It's even partially expressed in the archaic Greek sculpture. Partially. But Apollo here expresses it wholly. He's *all* Homer, *all* the ancient world, concentrated in a single lump of terracotta. That's his novelty. And then the circumstances gave him a special point. It was just after the War that I first saw him—just after the apotheosis and the logical conclusion of all the things Apollo *didn't* stand for. You can imagine how marvellously new he seemed by contrast. After that horrible enormity, he was a lovely symbol of the small, the local, the kindly. After all that extravagance of beastliness—yes, and all that extravagance of heroism and self-sacrifice—he seemed so beautifully sane. A God who doesn't admit the separate existence of either heroics or diabolics, but somehow includes them in his own nature and turns them into something else—like two gases combining to make a liquid. Look at him,' Fanning insisted. 'Look at his face, look at his body, see how he stands. It's obvious. He's neither the God of heroics, nor the God of diabolics. And yet it's equally obvious that he knows all about both, that he includes them, that he combines them into a third essence. It's the same with Homer. There's no tragedy in Homer. He's pessimistic, yes; but never tragic. His heroes aren't heroic in our sense of the word; they're men.' (Pamela took a very deep breath; if she had opened her mouth, it would have been a yawn.) 'In fact, you can say there aren't any heroes in Homer. Nor devils, nor sins. And none of our aspiring spiritualities, and, of course, none of our horrible, nauseating disgusts—because they're the complement of being spiritual, they're the tails to its heads. You couldn't have had Homer writing "the expense spirit in a waste of shame." Though, of course, with Shakespeare, it may have been physiological; the passion violent and brief, and then the most terrible reaction. It's the sort of thing that colours a whole life, a whole work. Only of course one's never allowed to say so. All that one isn't allowed to say!' He laughed. Pamela also laughed. 'But physiology or no physiology,' Fanning went on, 'he couldn't have written like that if he'd lived before the great split—the great split that broke life into spirit and matter, heroics and diabolics, virtue and sin and all the other accursed antitheses. Homer lived before the split; life hadn't been broken when he wrote. They're complete, his men and women, complete and real; for he leaves nothing out, he shirks no issue, even though there is no tragedy. He knows all about it—*all*.' He laid his hand again on the statue. 'And this God's his portrait. He's Homer, but with the Etruscan smile. Homer smiling at the sad, mysterious, beautiful absurdity of the world. The Greeks didn't see that divine absurdity as clearly as the Etruscans. Not even in Homer's day; and by the time you get to any sculptor who was anything like as accomplished as the man who made this, you'll find that they've lost it altogether. True, the earliest Greeks' God used to smile all right—or rather grin; for subtlety wasn't their strong point. But by the end of the sixth century they were already becoming a bit too heroic; they were developing those athlete's muscles and those tiresomely noble poses and damned superior faces. But our God here refused to be a prize-fighter or an actor-manager. There's no *terribiltà* about him, no priggishness, no sentimentality. And yet without being in the least pretentious, he's beautiful, he's grand, he's authentically divine. The Greeks took the road that led to Michelangelo and Bernini and Thorwaldsen and Rodin. A rake's progress. These Etruscans were on a better track. If only people had had the sense to follow it! Or at least get back to it. But nobody has, except perhaps old Maillol. They've all allowed themselves to be lured away. Plato was the arch-seducer. It was he who first sent us whoring after spirituality and heroics, whoring after the complementary demons of disgust and sin. We needs must love—well, not the highest, except sometimes by accident—but always the most extravagant and exciting. Tragedy was much more exciting than Homer's luminous pessimism, than this God's smiling awareness of the divine absurdity. Being alternately a hero and a sinner is much more sensational than being an integrated man. So as men seem to have the Yellow Press in the blood, like syphilis, they went back on Homer and Apollo; they followed Plato and Euripides. And Plato and Euripides handed them over to the Stoics and the Neo-Platonists. And these in turn handed humanity over to the Christians. And the Christians have handed us over to Henry Ford and the machines. So here we are.'

Pamela nodded intelligently. But what she was chiefly conscious of was the ache in her feet. If only she could sit down!

But, 'How poetical and appropriate,' Fanning began again, 'that the God should have risen from the grave exactly when he did, in 1916! Rising up in the midst of the insanity, like a beautiful, smiling reproach from another world. It was dramatic. At least I felt it so, when I saw him for the first time just after the War. The resurrection of Apollo, the Etruscan Apollo. I've been his worshipper and self-appointed priest ever since. Or at any rate I've tried to be. But it's difficult.' He shook his head. 'Perhaps it's even impossible for us to recapture . . .' He left the sentence unfinished and, taking her arm, led her out into the great courtyard of the Villa. Under the arcades was a bench. Thank goodness, said Pamela inwardly. They sat down.

'You see,' he went on, leaning forward, his elbows on his knees, his hands clasped, 'you can't get away from the things that the God protests against. Because they've become a part of you. Tradition and education have driven them into your very bones. It's a case of what I was speaking about just now—of the things that have nothing to do with you coming by force of habit to have everything to do with you. Which is why I'd like you to get Apollo and his Etruscans into your system while you're still young. It may save you trouble. Or on the other hand,' he added with a rueful little laugh, 'it may not. Because I really don't know if he's everybody's God. He may do for me—and do, only because I've got Plato and Jesus in my bones. But does he do for you? *Chi lo sa?* The older one grows, the more often one asks that question. Until, of course, one's arteries begin to harden, and then one's opinions begin to harden too, harden till they fossilize into certainty. But meanwhile, *chi lo sa? chi lo sa?* And after all it's quite agreeable, not knowing. And knowing, and at the same time knowing that it's no practical use knowing—that's not disagreeable either. Knowing, for example, that it would be good to live according to this God's commandments, but knowing at the same time that one couldn't do it even if one tried, because one's very guts and skeleton are already pledged to other Gods.'

'I should have thought that was awful,' said Pamela.

'For you, perhaps. But I happen to have a certain natural affection for the accomplished fact. I like and respect it, even when it is a bit depressing. Thus, it's a fact that I'd like to think and live in the unsplit, Apollonian way. But it's also a fact—and the fact as such is lovable—that I can't help indulging in aspirations and disgusts; I can't help thinking in terms of heroics and diabolics. Because the division, the splitness, has been worked right into my bones. So has the microbe of sensationalism; I can't help wallowing in the excitements of mysticism and the tragic sense. Can't help it.' He shook his head. 'Though perhaps I've wallowed in them rather more than I was justified in wallowing—justified by my upbringing, I mean. There was a time when I was really quite perversely preoccupied with mystical experiences and ecstasies and private universes.'

'Private universes?' she questioned.

'Yes, private, not shared. You create one, you live in it, each time you're in love, for example.' (Brightly serious, Pamela nodded her understanding and agreement; yes, yes, she knew all about *that.*) 'Each time you're spiritually exalted,' he went on, 'each time you're drunk, even. Everybody has his own favourite short cuts to the other world. Mine, in those days, was opium.'

'Opium?' She opened her eyes very wide. 'Do you mean to say you smoked opium?' She was thrilled. Opium was a vice of the first order.

'It's as good a way of becoming supernatural,' he answered, 'as looking at one's nose or one's navel, or not eating, or repeating a word over and over again, till it loses its sense and you forget how to think. All roads lead to Rome. The only bother about opium is that it's rather an unwholesome road. I had to go to a nursing home in Cannes to get disintoxicated.'

'All the same,' said Pamela, doing her best to imitate the quiet casualness of his manner, 'it must be rather delicious, isn't it? Awfully exciting, I mean,' she added, forgetting not to be thrilled.

'*Too* exciting.' He shook his head. 'That's the trouble. We needs must love the excitingest when we see it. The supernatural *is* exciting. But I don't want to love the supernatural, I want to love the natural. Not that a little supernaturalness isn't, of course, perfectly natural and necessary. But you can overdo it. I overdid it then. I was all the time in t'other world, never here. I stopped smoking because I was ill. But even if I hadn't been, I'd have stopped sooner or later for aesthetic reasons. The supernatural world is so terribly baroque—altogether too Counter-Reformation and Bernini. At its best it can be Greco. But you can have too much even of Greco. A big dose of him makes you begin to pine for Vulca and his Apollo.'

'But doesn't it work the other way too?' she asked. 'I mean, don't you sometimes *long* to start smoking again?' She was secretly hoping that he'd let her try a pipe or two.

Fanning shook his head. 'One doesn't get tired of very good bread,' he answered. 'Apollo's like that. I don't pine for supernatural excitements. Which doesn't mean,' he added, 'that I don't in practice run after them. You can't disintoxicate yourself of your culture. That sticks deeper than a mere taste for opium. I'd like to be able to think and live in the spirit of the God. But the fact remains that I can't.'

'Can't you?' said Pamela with a polite sympathy. She was more interested in the opium.

'No, no, you can't entirely disintoxicate yourself of mysticism and the tragic sense. You can't take a Turvey treatment for spirituality and disgust. You can't. Not nowadays. Acceptance is impossible in a split world like ours. You've got to recoil. In the circumstances it's right and proper. But absolutely it's wrong. If only one could accept as this God accepts, smiling like that . . .'

'But you *do* smile like that,' she insisted.

He laughed and, unclasping his hands, straightened himself up in his seat. 'But unhappily,' he said, 'a man can smile and smile and not be Apollo. Meanwhile, what's becoming of your education? Shouldn't we . . .?'

'Well, if you like,' she assented dubiously. 'Only my feet are rather tired. I mean, there's something about sight-seeing . . .'

'There is indeed,' said Fanning. 'But I was prepared to

be a martyr to culture. Still, I'm thankful you're not.' He smiled at her, and Pamela was pleased to find herself once more at the focus of his attention. It had been very interesting to hear him talk about his philosophy and all that. But all the same . . .

'Twenty to four,' said Fanning, looking at his watch. 'I've an idea; shouldn't we drive out to Monte Cavo and spend the evening up there in the cool? There's a view. And a really very eatable dinner.'

'I'd love to. But . . .' Pamela hesitated. 'Well, you see I did tell Guy I'd go out with him this evening.'

He was annoyed. 'Well, if you prefer . . .'

'But I don't prefer,' she answered hastily. 'I mean, I'd much rather go with you. Only I wondered how I'd let Guy know I wasn't . . .'

'Don't let him know,' Fanning answered, abusing his victory. 'After all, what are young men there for, except to wait when young women don't keep their appointments? It's their function in life.'

Pamela laughed. His words had given her a pleasing sense of importance and power. 'Poor Guy!' she said through her laughter, and her eyes were insolently bright.

'You little hypocrite.'

'I'm not,' she protested. 'I really *am* sorry for him.'

'A little hypocrite *and* a little devil,' was his verdict. He rose to his feet. 'If you could see your own eyes now! But *andiamo*.' He held out his hand to help her up. 'I'm beginning to be rather afraid of you.'

'What nonsense!' She was delighted. They walked together towards the door.

Fanning made the driver go out by the Appian Way. 'For the sake of your education,' he explained, pointing at the ruined tombs, 'which we can continue, thank heaven, in comfort, and at twenty miles an hour.'

Leaning back luxuriously in her corner, Pamela laughed. 'But I must say,' she had to admit, 'it is really rather lovely.'

From Albano the road mounted through the chestnut woods towards Rocca di Papa. A few miles brought them to a turning on the right; the car came to a halt.

'It's barred,' said Pamela, looking out of the window. Fanning had taken out his pocket-book and was hunting among the bank-notes and the old letters. 'The road's private,' he explained. 'They ask for your card—heaven knows why. The only trouble being, of course, that I've never possessed such a thing as a visiting-card in my life. Still, I generally have one or two belonging to other people. Ah, here we are! Good!' He produced two pieces of pasteboard. A gatekeeper had appeared and was waiting by the door of the car. 'Shall we say we're Count Keyserling?' said Fanning, handing her the count's card. 'Or alternatively,' he read from the other, 'that we're Herbert Watson, Funeral Furnisher, Funerals conducted with Efficiency and Reverence, Motor Hearses for use in every part of the Country.' He shook his head. 'The last relic of my poor old friend Tom Hatchard. Died last year. I had to bury him. Poor Tom! On the whole I think we'd better be Herbert Watson. *Ecco!*' He handed out the card; the man saluted and went to open the gate. 'But give me back Count Keyserling.' Fanning stretched out his hand. 'He'll come in useful another time.'

The car started and went roaring up the zig-zag ascent. Lying back in her corner, Pamela laughed and laughed, inextinguishably.

'But what *is* the joke?' he asked.

She didn't know herself. Mr. Watson and the Count had only been a pretext; this enormous laughter, which they had released, sprang from some other, deeper source. And perhaps it was a mere accident that it should be laughter at all. Another pretext, a different finger on the trigger, and it might have been tears, or anger, or singing 'Constantinople' at the top of her voice—anything.

She was limp when they reached the top. Fanning made her sit down where she could see the view and himself went off to order cold drinks at the bar of the little inn that had once been the monastery of Monte Cavo.

Pamela sat where he had left her. The wooded slopes fell steeply away beneath her, down, down to the blue shining of the Alban Lake; and that toy palace perched on the hill beyond was the Pope's, that tiny city in a picture-book, Marino. Beyond a dark ridge on the left the round eye of Nemi looked up from its crater. Far off, behind Albano an expanse of blue steel, burnished beneath the sun, was the Tyrrhenian, and flat like the sea, but golden with ripening corn and powdered goldenly with a haze of dust, the Campagna stretched away from the feet of the subsiding hills, away and up towards a fading horizon, on which the blue ghosts of mountains floated on a level with her eyes. In the midst of the expanse a half-seen golden chaos was Rome. Through the haze the dome of St. Peter's shone faintly in the sun with a glitter as of muted glass. There was an enormous silence, sad, sad but somehow consoling. A sacred silence. And yet when, coming up from behind her Fanning broke it, his voice, for Pamela, committed no iconoclasm; for it seemed, in the world of her feelings, to belong to the silence, it was made, as it were, of the same intimate and friendly substance. He squatted down on his heels beside her, laying a hand on her shoulder to steady himself.

'What a panorama of space and time!' he said. 'So many miles, such an expanse of centuries! You can still walk on the paved road that led to the temple here. The generals used to march up sometimes in triumph. With elephants.'

The silence enveloped them again, bringing them together; and they were alone and as though conspiratorially isolated in an atmosphere of solemn amorousness.

'*I signori son serviti*,' said a slightly ironic voice behind them.

'That's our drinks,' said Fanning. 'Perhaps we'd better . . .' He got up and, as he unbent them, his knees cracked stiffly. He stooped to rub them, for they ached; his joints were old. 'Fool!' he said to himself, and decided that to-morrow he'd go to Venice. She was too young, too dangerously and perversely fresh.

They drank their lemonade in silence. Pamela's face wore an expression of grave serenity which it touched and flattered and moved him to see. Still, he was a fool to be touched and flattered and moved.

'Let's go for a bit of a stroll,' he said, when they had slaked their thirst. She got up without a word, obediently, as though she had become his slave.

It was breathless under the trees and there was a smell of damp, hot greenness, a hum and flicker of insects in the probing slants of sunlight. But in the open spaces the air of the heights was quick and nimble, in spite of the sun; the broom-flower blazed among the rocks; and round the bushes where the honeysuckle had clambered, there hung invisible islands of perfume, cool and fresh in the midst of the hot sea of bracken smell. Pamela moved here and there with little exclamations of delight, pulling at the tough sprays of honeysuckle. 'Oh, look!' she called to him in her rapturous voice. 'Come and look!'

'I'm looking,' he shouted back across the intervening space. 'With a telescope. With the eye of faith,' he corrected; for she had moved out of sight. He sat down on a smooth rock and lighted a cigarette. Venice, he reflected, would be rather boring at this particular season. In a few minutes Pamela came back to him, flushed, with a great bunch of honeysuckle between her hands.

'You know, you ought to have come,' she said reproachfully. 'There were such *lovely* pieces I couldn't reach.'

Fanning shook his head. 'He also serves who only sits and smokes,' he said, and made room for her on the stone beside him. 'And what's more,' he went on, '"let Austin have his swink to him reserved." Yes, let him. How wholeheartedly I've always agreed with Chaucer's Monk! Besides, you seem to forget, my child, that I'm an old, old gentleman.' He was playing the safe, the prudent part. Perhaps if he played it hard enough, it wouldn't be necessary to go to Venice.

Pamela paid no attention to what he was saying. 'Would you like this one for your buttonhole, Miles?' she asked, holding up a many-trumpeted flower. It was the first time she had called him by his Christian name, and the accomplishment of this much-meditated act of daring made her blush. 'I'll stick it in,' she added, leaning forward, so that he shouldn't see her reddened cheeks, till her face was almost touching his coat.

Near and thus offered (for it was an offer, he had no doubt of that, a deliberate offer) why shouldn't he take this lovely, this terribly and desperately tempting freshness? It was a matter of stretching out one's hands. But no; it would be too insane. She was near, this warm young flesh, this scent of her hair, near and offered—with what an innocent perversity, what a touchingly ingenuous and uncomprehending shamelessness! But he sat woodenly still, feeling all of a sudden as he had felt when, a lanky boy, he had been too shy, too utterly terrified, in spite of his longings, to kiss that Jenny—what on earth was her name?—that Jenny Something-or-Other he had danced the polka with at Uncle

Fred's one Christmas, how many centuries ago !—and yet only yesterday, only this instant.

'There !' said Pamela, and drew back. Her cheeks had had time to cool a little.

'Thank you.' There was a silence.

'Do you know,' she said at last, efficiently, 'you've got a button loose on your coat.'

He fingered the hanging button. 'What a damning proof of celibacy !'

'If only I had a needle and thread . . .'

'Don't make your offer too lightly. If you knew what a quantity of unmended stuff I've got at home . . .'

'I'll come and do it all to-morrow,' she promised, feeling delightfully protective and important.

'Beware,' he said. 'I'll take you at your word. It's sweated labour.'

'I don't mind. I'll come.'

'Punctually at ten-thirty, then.' He had forgotten about Venice. 'I shall be a ruthless taskmaster.'

Nemi was already in shadow when they walked back; but the higher slopes were transfigured with the setting sunlight. Pamela halted at a twist of the path and turned back towards the western sky. Looking up, Fanning saw her standing there, goldenly flushed, the colours of her skin, her hair, her dress, the flowers in her hands, supernaturally heightened and intensified in the almost level light.

'I think this is the most lovely place I've ever seen.' Her voice was solemn with a natural piety. 'But you're not looking,' she added in a different tone, reproachfully.

'I'm looking at you,' he answered. After all, if he stopped in time, it didn't matter his behaving like a fool—it didn't finally matter and, meanwhile, was very agreeable.

An expression of impertinent mischief chased away the solemnity from her face. 'Trying to see my ears again ?' she asked ; and, breaking off a honeysuckle blossom, she threw it down in his face, then turned and ran up the steep path.

'Don't imagine I'm going to pursue,' he called after her. 'The Pan and Syrinx business is a winter pastime. Like football.'

Her laughter came down to him from among the trees ; he followed the retreating sound. Pamela waited for him at the top of the hill and they walked back together towards the inn.

'Aren't there any ruins here ?' she asked. 'I mean, for my education.'

He shook his head. 'The Young Pretender's brother pulled them all down and built a monastery with them. For the Passionist Fathers,' he added after a little pause. 'I feel rather like a Passionist Father myself at the moment.' They walked on without speaking, enveloped by the huge, the amorously significant silence.

But a few minutes later, at the dinner table, they were exuberantly gay. The food was well cooked, the wine an admirable Falernian. Fanning began to talk about his early loves. Vaguely at first, but later, under Pamela's questioning, with an ever-increasing wealth of specific detail. They were indiscreet, impudent questions, which at ordinary times she couldn't have uttered, or at least have only despairingly forced out, with a suicide's determination. But she was a little tipsy now, tipsy with the wine and her own laughing exultation ; she rapped them out easily, without a tremor. 'As though you were the immortal Sigmund himself,' he assured her, laughing. Her impudence and that knowledgeable, scientific ingenuousness amused him, rather perversely ; he told her everything she asked.

When she had finished with his early loves, she questioned him about the opium. Fanning described his private universes and that charming nurse who had looked after him while he was being disintoxicated. He went on to talk about the black poverty he'd been reduced to by the drug. 'Because you can't do journalism or write novels in the other world,' he explained. 'At least I never could.' And he told her of the debts he still owed and of his present arrangements with his publishers.

Almost suddenly the night was cold and Fanning became aware that the bottle had been empty for a long time. He threw away the stump of his cigar. 'Let's go.' They took their seats and the car set off, carrying with it the narrow world of form and colour created by its head-lamps. They were alone in the darkness of their padded box. An hour before Fanning had decided that he would take this opportunity to kiss her. But he was haunted suddenly by the memory of an Australian who had once complained to him of the sufferings of a young colonial in England. 'In Sydney,' he had said, 'when I get into a taxi with a nice girl, I know exactly what to do. And I know exactly what to do when I'm in an American taxi. But when I apply my knowledge in London—God, isn't there a row!' How vulgar and stupid it all was! Not merely a fool, but a vulgar, stupid fool. He sat unmoving in his corner. When the lights of Rome were round them, he took her hand and kissed it.

'Good-night.'

She thanked him. 'I've had the loveliest day.' But her eyes were puzzled and unhappy. Meeting them, Fanning suddenly regretted his self-restraint, wished that he had been stupid and vulgar. And, after all, would it have been so stupid and vulgar? You could make any action seem anything you liked, from saintly to disgusting, by describing it in the appropriate words. But his regrets had come too late. Here was her hotel. He drove home to his solitude feeling exceedingly depressed.

VI

June 14th. Spent the morning with M., who lives in a house belonging to a friend of his who is a Catholic and lives in Rome, M. says, because he likes to get his popery straight from the horse's mouth. A nice house, old, standing just back from the Forum, which I said I thought was like a rubbish heap and he agreed with me, in spite of my education, and said he always preferred live dogs to dead lions and thinks it's awful the way the Fascists are pulling down nice ordinary houses and making holes to find more of these beastly pillars and things. I sewed on a lot of buttons, etc., as he's living in only two rooms on the ground floor and the servants are on their holiday, so he eats out and an old woman comes to clean up in the afternoons, but doesn't do any mending, which meant a lot for me, but I liked doing it, in spite of the darning, because he sat with me all the time, sometimes talking, sometimes just working. When he's writing or sitting with his pen in his hand thinking, his face is quite still and *terribly* serious and far, far away, as though he were a picture, or more like some sort of not human person, a sort of angel, if one can imagine them without nightdresses and long hair, really rather frightening, so that one longed to shout or throw a reel of cotton at him so as to change him back again into a man. He has very beautiful hands, rather long and bony, but strong. Sometimes, after he'd sat thinking for a long time, he'd get up and walk about the room, frowning and looking kind of angry, which was still more terrifying—sitting there while he walked up and down quite close to me, as though he were absolutely alone. But one time he suddenly stopped his walking up and down and said how profusely he apologized for his toes, because I was darning, and it was really very wonderful to see him suddenly changed back from that picture-angel sort of creature into a human being. Then he sat down by me and said he'd been spending the morning wrestling with the problem of speaking the truth in books; so I said, but haven't you always spoken it? because that always seemed to me the chief point of M.'s books. But he said, not much, because most of it was quite unspeakable in our world, as we found it too shocking and humiliating. So I said, all the same I didn't see why it shouldn't be spoken, and he said, nor did he in theory, but in practice he didn't want to be lynched. And he said, look for example at those advertisements in American magazines with the photos and life stories of people with unpleasant breath. So I said, yes, aren't they simply *too* awful. Because they really do make one shudder. And he said, precisely, there you are, and they're so successful because every one thinks them so perfectly awful. They're outraged by them, he said, just as you're outraged, and they rush off and buy the stuff in sheer terror, because they're so terrified of being an outrage physically to other people. And he said, that's only one small sample of all the class of truths, pleasant and unpleasant, that you can't speak, except in scientific books, but that doesn't count, because you deliberately leave your feelings outside in the cloak-room when you're being scientific. And just because they're unspeakable, we pretend they're unimportant, but they aren't, on the contrary, they're terribly important, and he said, you've only got to examine your memory quite sincerely for five minutes to realize it, and of course he's quite right. When I think of Miss Poole giving me piano lessons—but no, really, one *can't* write these things, and yet one obviously ought to, because they *are* so important, the humiliating physical facts, both pleasant and unpleasant (though I must say, most of the ones I can think of seem to be unpleasant), so important in all human relationships, he says, even in love, which is really rather awful, but of course one must admit it. And M. said it would take a whole generation of being shocked and humiliated and lynching the shockers and humiliators before people could settle down to listening to that sort of truth calmly, which they did do, he says, at certain times in the past, at any rate much more so than now. And he says that when they can listen to it completely calmly, the world will be quite different from what it is now, so I asked, in what way? but he said he couldn't clearly imagine, only he knew it would be different. After that he went back to his table and wrote very quickly for about half an hour without stopping, and I longed to ask him if he'd been writing the truth, and if so, what about, but I didn't have the nerve, which was stupid.

We lunched at our usual place, which I really don't much like, as who wants to look at fat business-men and farmers from the country simply *drinking* spaghetti? even if the spaghetti *is* good, but M. prefers it to the big places, because he says that in Rome one must do as the Romans do, not as the Americans. Still, I must say I do like looking at people who dress well and have good manners and nice jewels and things, which I told him, so he said all right, we'd go to Valadier to-morrow to see how the rich ate macaroni, which made me wretched, as it looked as though I'd been cadging, and of course that's the last thing in the world I meant to do, to make him waste a lot of money on me, particularly after what he told me yesterday about his debts and what he made on the average, which still seems to me shockingly little, considering who he is, so I said no, wouldn't he lunch with *me* at Valadier's, and he laughed and said it was the first time he'd heard of a gigolo of fifty being taken out by a woman of twenty. That rather upset me—the way it seemed to bring what we are to each other on to the wrong level, making it all a sort of joke and sniggery, like something in *Punch*. Which is hateful, I can't bear it. And I have the feeling that he does it on purpose, as a kind of protection, because he doesn't want to care too much, and that's why he's always saying he's so old, which is all nonsense, because you're only as old as you feel, and sometimes I even feel older than he does, like when he gets so amused and interested with little boys in the street playing that game of sticking out your fingers and calling a number, or when he talks about that awful old Dickens. Which I told him, but he only laughed and said age is a circle and you grow into a lot of the things you grew out of, because the whole world is a fried whiting with its tail in its mouth, which only confirms what I said about his saying he was old being all nonsense. Which I told him and he said, quite right, he only *said* he felt old when he *wished* that he felt old. Which made me see still more clearly that it was just a defence. A defence of *me*, I suppose, and all that sort of nonsense. What I'd have liked to say, only I didn't, was that I don't want to be defended, particularly if being defended means his defending himself against me and making stupid jokes about gigolos and old gentlemen. Because I think he really does rather care underneath—from the way he looks at me sometimes—and he'd like to say so and act so, but he won't on principle, which is really against all *his* principles, and some time I *shall* tell him so. I insisted he should lunch with me and in the end he said he would, and then he was suddenly very silent and, I thought, glum and unhappy, and after coffee he said he'd have to go home and write all the rest of the day. So I came back to the hotel and had a rest and wrote this, and now it's nearly seven and I feel terribly sad, almost like crying. *Next day.* Rang up Guy and had less difficulty than I expected getting him to forgive me for yesterday, in fact he almost apologized himself. Danced till 2.15.

June 15th. M. still sad and didn't kiss me when we met,

on purpose, which made me angry, it's so humiliating to be defended. He was wearing an open shirt, like Byron, which suited him; but I told him, you look like the devil when you're sad (which is true, because his face ought to move, not be still), and he said that was what came of feeling and behaving like an angel; so of course I asked why he didn't behave like a devil, because in that case he'd look like an angel, and I preferred his looks to his morals, and then I blushed, like an idiot. But really it is too stupid that women aren't supposed to say what they think. Why can't we say, I like you, or whatever it is, without being thought a kind of monster, if we say it first, and even thinking ourselves monsters? Because one ought to say what one thinks and do what one likes or else one becomes like Aunt Edith, hippo-ish and dead inside. Which is after all what M.'s constantly saying in his books, so he oughtn't to humiliate me with his beastly defendings. Lunch at Valadier's was really rather a bore. Afterwards we went and sat in a church, because it was so hot, a huge affair full of pink marble and frescoes and marble babies and gold. M. says that the modern equivalent is Lyons' Corner House, and that the Jesuits were so successful because they gave the poor a chance of feeling what it was like to live in a palace, or something better than a palace, because he says the chief difference between a Corner House and the state rooms at Buckingham Palace is that the Corner House is so much more sumptuous, almost as sumptuous as these Jesuit churches. I asked him if he believed in God and he said he believed in a great many gods, it depended on what he was doing, or being, or feeling at the moment. He said he believed in Apollo when he was working, and in Bacchus when he was drinking, and in Buddha when he felt depressed, and in Venus when he was making love, and in the Devil when he was afraid or angry, and in the Categorical Imperative when he had to do his duty. I asked him which he believed in now and he said he didn't quite know, but he thought it was the Categorical Imperative, which really made me furious, so I answered that I only believed in the Devil and Venus, which made him laugh, and he said I looked as though I were going to jump off the Eiffel Tower, and I was just going to say what I thought of his hippo-ishness, I mean I'd really made up my mind, when a most horrible old verger rushed up and said we must leave the church, because it seems the Pope doesn't allow you to be in a church with bare arms, which is really *too* indecent. But M. said that after all it wasn't surprising, because every god has to protect himself against hostile gods, and the gods of bare skin *are* hostile to the gods of souls and clothes, and he made me stop in front of a shop window where there were some mirrors and said, you can see for yourself, and I must say I really did look very nice in that pale green linen which goes so awfully well with the skin, when one's a bit sunburnt. But he said, it's not merely a question of seeing, you must touch too, so I stroked my arms and said yes, they were nice and smooth, and he said, precisely, and then he stroked my arm very lightly, like a moth crawling, agonizingly creepy but delicious, once or twice, looking very serious and attentive, as though he were tuning a piano, which made me laugh, and I said I supposed he was experimenting to see if the Pope was in the right, and then he gave me the most horrible pinch and said, yes, the Pope was quite right and I ought to be muffled in Jaeger from top to toe. But I was so angry with the pain, because he pinched me really terribly, that I just rushed off without saying anything and jumped into a cab that was passing and drove straight to the hotel. But I was so wretched by the time I got there that I started crying in the lift and the lift man said he hoped I hadn't had any *dispiacere di famiglia*, which made me laugh and that made the crying much worse, and then I suddenly thought of Clare and felt such a horrible beast, so I lay on my bed and simply howled for about an hour, and then I got up and wrote a letter and sent one of the hotel boys with it to M.'s address, saying I was so sorry and would he come at once. But he didn't come, not for hours and hours, and it was simply too awful, because I thought he was offended, or despising, because I'd been such a fool, and I wondered whether he really did like me at all and whether this defending theory wasn't just my imagination. But at last, when I'd quite given him up and was so miserable I didn't know what I should do, he suddenly appeared—because he'd only that moment gone back to the house and found my note—and was too wonderfully sweet to me, and said he was so sorry, but he'd been on edge (though he didn't say why, but I know now that the defending theory wasn't just imagination) and I said I was so sorry and I cried, but I was happy, and then we laughed because it had all been so stupid and then M. quoted a bit of Homer which meant that after they'd eaten and drunk they wept for their friends and after they'd wept a little they went to sleep, so we went out and had dinner and after dinner we went and danced, and he dances really very well, but we stopped before midnight, because he said the noise of the jazz would drive him crazy. He was perfectly sweet, but though he didn't say anything sniggery, I could feel he was on the defensive all the time, sweetly and friendlily on the defensive, and when he said good-night he only kissed my hand.

June 18th. Stayed in bed till lunch re-reading *The Return of Eurydice*. I understand Joan so well now, better and better, she's *so* like me in all she feels and thinks. M. went to Tivoli for the day to see some Italian friends who have a house there. What is he like with other people, I wonder? Got two tickets for the fireworks to-morrow night, the hotel porter says they'll be good, because it's the first Girandola since the War. Went to the Villa Borghese in the afternoon for my education, to give M. a surprise when he comes back, and I must say some of the pictures and statues were very lovely, but the most awful looking fat man would follow me round all the time, and finally the old beast even had the impertinence to speak to me, so I just said, *Lei è un porco*, which I must say was very effective. But it's extraordinary how things do just depend on looks and being sympathique, because if he hadn't looked such a pig, I shouldn't have thought him so piggish, which shows again what rot hippo-ism is. Went to bed early and finished *Eurydice*. This is the fifth time I've read it.

VII

'Oh, it was marvellous before the War, the Girandola. Really marvellous.'

'But then what wasn't *marvellous* before the War?' said Pamela sarcastically. These references to a Golden Age in which she had had no part always annoyed her.

Fanning laughed. 'Another one in the eye for the aged gentleman!'

There, he had slipped back again behind his defences! She did not answer for fear of giving him some excuse to dig himself in, impregnably. This hateful bantering with feelings! They walked on in silence. The night was breathlessly warm; the sounds of brassy music came to them faintly through the dim enormous noise of a crowd that thickened with every step they took towards the Piazza del Popolo. In the end they had to shove their way by main force.

Sunk head over ears in this vast sea of animal contacts, animal smells and noise, Pamela was afraid. 'Isn't it awful ?' she said, looking up at him over her shoulder; and she shuddered. But at the same time she rather liked her fear, because it seemed in some way to break down the barriers that separated them, to bring him closer to her—close with a physical closeness of protective contact that was also, increasingly, a closeness of thought and feeling.

'You're all right,' he reassured her through the tumult. He was standing behind her, encircling her with his arms. 'I won't let you be squashed'; and as he spoke he fended off the menacing lurch of a large back. '*Ignorante!*' he shouted at it.

A terrific explosion interrupted the distant selections from *Rigoletto* and the sky was suddenly full of coloured lights; the Girandola had begun. A wave of impatience ran through the advancing crowd; they were violently pushed and jostled. But, 'It's all right,' Fanning kept repeating, 'it's all right.' They were squeezed together in a staggering embrace. Pamela was terrified, but it was with a kind of swooning pleasure that she shut her eyes and abandoned herself limply in his arms.

'*Ma piano!*' shouted Fanning at the nearest jostlers. '*Piano!*' and ''Sblood!' he said in English, for he had the affectation of using literary oaths. 'Hell and Death!' But in the tumult his words were as though unspoken. He was silent; and suddenly, in the midst of that heaving chaos of noise and rough contacts, of movement and heat and smell, suddenly he became aware that his lips were almost touching her hair, and that under his right hand was the firm resilience of her breast. He hesitated for a moment on the threshold of his sensuality, then averted his face, shifted the position of his hand.

'At last!'

The haven to which their tickets admitted them was a little garden on the western side of the Piazza, opposite the

Pincio and the source of the fireworks. The place was crowded, but not oppressively. Fanning was tall enough to overlook the interposed heads, and when Pamela had climbed on to a little parapet that separated one terrace of the garden from another, she too could see perfectly.

'But you'll let me lean on you,' she said, laying a hand on his shoulder, 'because there's a fat woman next me who's steadily squeezing me off. I think she's expanding with the heat.'

'And she almost certainly understands English. So for heaven's sake . . .'

A fresh volley of explosions from the other side of the great square interrupted him and drowned the answering mockery of her laughter. 'Ooh! ooh!' the crowd was moaning in a kind of amorous agony. Magical flowers in a delirium of growth, the rockets mounted on their slender stalks and, ah! high up above the Pincian hill, dazzlingly, deafeningly, in a bunch of stars and a thunder-clap, they blossomed.

'Isn't it marvellous?' said Pamela, looking down at him with shining eyes. 'Oh God!' she added, in another voice. 'She's expanding again. Help!' And for a moment she was on the verge of falling. She leaned on him so heavily that he had to make an effort not to be pushed sideways. She managed to straighten herself up again into equilibrium.

'I've got you in case . . .' He put his arm round her knees to steady her.

'Shall I see if I can puncture the old beast with a pin?' And Fanning knew, by the tone of her voice, that she was genuinely prepared to make the experiment.

'If you do,' he said, 'I shall leave you to be lynched alone.'

Pamela felt his arm tighten a little about her thighs. 'Coward!' she mocked and pulled his hair.

'Martyrdom's not in my line,' he laughed back. 'Not

even martyrdom for your sake.' But her youth was a perversity, her freshness a kind of provocative vice. He had taken a step across that supernatural threshold. He had given—after all, why not?—a certain licence to his desires. Amid their multitudinous uncoiling, his body seemed to be coming to a new and obscure life of its own. When the time came he would revoke the licence, step back again into the daily world.

There was another bang, another, and the obelisk at the centre of the Piazza leapt out sharp and black against apocalypse after apocalypse of jewelled light. And through the now flushed, now pearly-brilliant, now emerald-shining smoke-clouds, a pine tree, a palm, a stretch of grass emerged, like strange unearthly visions of pine and palm and grass, from the darkness of the else invisible gardens.

There was an interval of mere lamplight—like sobriety, said Fanning, between two pipes of opium, like daily life after an ecstasy. And perhaps, he was thinking, the time to step back again had already come. 'If only one could live without any lucid intervals,' he concluded.

'I don't see why not.' She spoke with a kind of provocative defiance, as though challenging him to contradict her. Her heart beat very fast, exultantly. 'I mean, why shouldn't it be fireworks all the time?'

'Because it just isn't, that's all. Unhappily.' It was time to step back again; but he didn't step back.

'Well, then, it's a case of damn the intervals and enjoy . . . Oh!' She started. That prodigious bang had sent a large red moon sailing almost slowly into the sky. It burst into a shower of meteors that whistled as they fell, expiringly.

Fanning imitated their plaintive noise. 'Sad, sad,' he commented. 'Even the fireworks can be sad.'

She turned on him fiercely. 'Only because you want

them to be sad. Yes, you want them to be. Why do you want them to be sad?'

Yes, why? It was a pertinent question. She felt his arm tighten again round her knees and was triumphant. He was defending himself no more, he was listening to those oracles. But at the root of his deliberate recklessness, its contradiction and its cause, his sadness obscurely persisted. 'But I *don't* want them to be sad,' he protested.

Another garden of rockets began to blossom. Laughing, triumphant, Pamela laid her hand on his head.

'I feel so superior up here,' she said.

'On a pedestal, what?' He laughed. '"*Guardami ben; ben son, ben son Beatrice!*"'

'Such a comfort you're not bald,' she said, her fingers in his hair. 'That must be a great disadvantage of pedestals—I mean, seeing the baldness of the men down below.'

'But the great advantage of pedestals, as I now suddenly see for the first time . . .' Another explosion covered his voice. '. . . make it possible . . .' Bang!

'Oh, look!' A bluish light was brightening, brightening.

'. . . possible for even the baldest . . .' There was a continuous uninterrupted rattle of detonations. Fanning gave it up. What he had meant to say was that pedestals gave even the baldest men unrivalled opportunities for pinching the idol's legs.

'What were you saying?' she shouted through the battle.

'Nothing,' he yelled back. He had meant, of course, to suit the action to the word, playfully. But the fates had decided otherwise and he wasn't really sorry. For he was tired; he had realized it almost suddenly. All this standing. He was no good at standing nowadays.

A cataract of silver fire was pouring down the slopes of the Pincian Hill, and the shining smoke-clouds rolled away from it like the spray from a tumbling river. And suddenly, above it, the eagle of Savoy emerged from the darkness, enormous, perched on the lictor's axe and rods. There was applause and patriotic music. Then, gradually, the brightness of the cataract grew dim; the sources of its silver streaming were one by one dried up. The eagle moulted its shining plumage, the axe and rods faded, faded and at last were gone. Lit faintly by only the common lamplight, the smoke drifted slowly away towards the north. A spasm of motion ran through the huge crowd in the square below them. The show was over.

'But I feel,' said Pamela, as they shoved their way back towards the open streets, 'I feel as though the rockets were still popping off inside me.' And she began to sing to herself as she walked.

Fanning made no comment. He was thinking of that Girandola he'd seen with Alice and Tony and Laurina Frescobaldi—was it in 1907 or 1908? Tony was an ambassador now, and Alice was dead, and one of Laurina's sons (he recalled the expression of despair on that worn, but still handsome face, when she had told him yesterday, at Tivoli) was already old enough to be getting housemaids into trouble.

'Not only rockets,' Pamela went on, interrupting her singing, 'but even catherine-wheels. I feel all catherine-wheely. You know, like when one's a little drunk.' And she went on again with 'Old Man River,' tipsily happy and excited.

The crowd grew thinner around them and at last they were almost alone. Pamela's singing abruptly ceased. Here, in the open, in the cool of the dark night it had suddenly become inappropriate, a little shameful. She glanced anxiously at her companion; had he too remarked that inappropriateness, been shocked by it? But Fanning had noticed nothing; she wished he had. Head bent, his hands behind his back, he was walking at her side, but in another universe. When had his spirit gone away from her, and why? She didn't know, hadn't noticed. Those inward fireworks, that private festival of exultation had occupied her whole attention. She had been too excitedly happy with being in love to be able to think of the object of that love. But now, abruptly sobered, she had become aware of him again, repentantly at first, and then, as she realized his new remoteness, with a sinking of the heart. What had happened in these few moments? She was on the point of addressing him, then checked herself. Her apprehension grew and grew till it became a kind of terrified certainty that he'd never loved her at all, that he'd suddenly begun to hate her. But why, but why? They walked on.

'How lovely it is here!' she said at last. Her voice was timid and unnatural. 'And so deliciously cool.' They had emerged on to the embankment of the Tiber. Above the river, a second invisible river of air flowed softly through the hot night. 'Shall we stop for a moment?' He nodded without speaking. 'I mean, only if you want to,' she added. He nodded again.

They stood, leaning on the parapet, looking down at the black water. There was a long, long silence. Pamela waited for him to say something, to make a gesture; but he did not stir, the word never came. It was as though he were at the other end of the world. She felt almost sick with unhappiness. Heart-beat after heart-beat, the silence prolonged itself.

Fanning was thinking of to-morrow's journey. How he hated the train! And in this heat. . . . But it was necessary. The wicked flee, and in this case the fleeing would be an act of virtue—painful. Was it love? Or just an itch of desire, of the rather crazy, dirty desire of an ageing man? '*A cinquant' anni si diventa un po' pazzo.*' He heard his own voice speaking laughingly, mournfully, to Laurina. '*Pazzo e porco. Si, anch' io divento un porco. Le minorenni—a cinquant' anni, sa, sono un ossessione. Proprio un' ossessione.*' Was that all—just an obsession of crazy desire? Or was it love? Or wasn't there any difference, was it just a question of names and approving or disapproving tones of voice? What was certain was that you could be as desperately unhappy when you were robbed of your crazy desire as when you were robbed of your love. A *porco* suffers as much as Dante. And perhaps Beatrice too was lovely, in Dante's memory, with the perversity of youth, the shamelessness of innocence, the vice of freshness. Still, the wicked flee, the wicked flee. If only he'd had the strength of mind to flee before! A touch made him start. Pamela had taken his hand.

'Miles!' Her voice was strained and abnormal. Fanning turned towards her and was almost frightened by the look of determined despair he saw on her face. The Eiffel Tower . . . 'Miles!'

'What is it?'

'Why don't you speak to me?'

He shrugged his shoulders. 'I didn't happen to be feeling very loquacious. For a change,' he added, self-mockingly, in the hope (he knew it for a vain one) of being able to turn away her desperate attack with a counter-attack of laughter.

She ignored his counter-attack. 'Why do you shut yourself away from me like this?' she asked. 'Why do you hate me.'

'But, my sweet child . . .'

'Yes, you hate me. You shut me away. Why are you so cruel, Miles?' Her voice broke; she was crying. Lifting his hand, she kissed it, passionately, despairingly. 'I love you so much, Miles. I love you.' His hand was wet with her tears when almost by force, he managed to draw it away from her.

He put his arm round her, comfortingly. But he was annoyed as well as touched, annoyed by her despairing determination, by the way she had made up her mind to jump off the Eiffel Tower, screwed up her courage turn by turn. And now she was jumping—but how gracelessly ! The way he had positively had to struggle for his hand ! There was something forced and unnatural about the whole scene. She was being a character in fiction. But characters in fiction suffer. He patted her shoulder, he made consolatory murmurs. Consoling her for being in love with him ! But the idea of explaining and protesting and being lucidly reasonable was appalling to him at the moment, absolutely appalling. He hoped that she'd just permit herself to be consoled and ask no further questions, just leave the whole situation comfortably inarticulate. But his hope was again disappointed.

'Why do you hate me, Miles ?' she insisted.

'But, Pamela . . .'

'Because you did care a little, you did. I mean, I could see you cared. And now, suddenly . . . What have I done, Miles ?'

'But nothing, my child, nothing.' He could not keep a note of exasperation out of his voice. If only she'd allow him to be silent !

'Nothing ? But I can hear from the way you speak that there's something.' She returned to her old refrain. 'Because you did care, Miles ; a little, you did.' She looked up at him, but he had moved away from her, he had averted his eyes towards the street. 'You did, Miles.'

Oh God ! he was groaning to himself, God ! And aloud (for she had made his silence untenable, she had driven him out into articulateness), 'I cared too much,' he said. 'It would be so easy to do something stupid and irreparable, something mad, yes and bad, bad. I like you too much in other ways to want to run that risk. Perhaps, if I were twenty years younger . . . But I'm too old. It wouldn't do. And you're too young, you can't really understand, you . . . Oh, thank God, there's a taxi.' And he darted forward, waving and shouting. Saved! But when they had shut themselves into the cab, he found that the new situation was even more perilous than the old.

'Miles!' A flash of lamplight through the window of the cab revealed her face to him. His words had consoled her; she was smiling, was trying to look happy; but under the attempted happiness her expression was more desperately determined than ever. She was not yet at the bottom of her Tower. 'Miles!' And sliding across the seat towards him, she threw her arms round his neck and kissed him. 'Take me, Miles,' she said, speaking in quick abrupt little spurts, as though she were forcing the words out with violence against a resistance. He recognized the suicide's voice, despairing, strained, and at the same time, flat, lifeless. 'Take me. If you want me . . .'

Fanning tried to protest, to disengage himself, gently, from her embrace.

'But I want you to take me, Miles,' she insisted. 'I want you . . .' She kissed him again, she pressed herself against his hard body. 'I want you, Miles. Even if it is stupid and mad,' she added in another little spurt of desperation, making answer to the expression on his face, to the words she wouldn't permit him to utter. 'And it isn't. I mean, love isn't stupid or mad. And even if it were, I don't care. Yes, I want to be stupid and mad. Even if it were to kill me. So take me, Miles.' She kissed him again. 'Take me.'

He turned away his mouth from those soft lips. She was

forcing him back across the threshold. His body was uneasy with awakenings and supernatural dawn.

Held up by a tram at the corner of a narrow street, the cab was at a standstill. With quick strong gestures Fanning unclasped her arms from round his neck and, taking her two hands in his, he kissed first one and then the other. 'Good-bye, Pamela,' he whispered, and, throwing open the door, he was half out of the cab before she realized what he was doing.

'But what are you doing, Miles? Where . . .' The door slammed. He thrust some money into the driver's hand and almost ran. Pamela rose to her feet to follow him, but the cab started with a sudden jerk that threw her off her balance, and she fell back on to the seat.

'Miles!' she called, and then, 'Stop!'

But the driver either didn't hear, or else paid no attention. She did not call again, but sat, covering her face with her hands, crying and feeling so agonizingly unhappy that she thought she would die of it.

VIII

'By the time you receive this letter, I shall be—no, not dead, Pamela, though I know how thrilled and proud you'd be, through your temporary inconsolability, if I were to blow my brains out—not dead, but (what will be almost worse in these dog-days) in the train, bound for some anonymous refuge. Yes, a refuge, as though you were my worst enemy. Which in fact you almost are at the moment, for the good reason that you're acting as your own enemy. If I were less fond of you, I'd stay and join forces with you against yourself. And, frankly, I wish I were less fond of you. Do you know how desirable you are? Not yet, I suppose, not consciously, in spite of Prof. Krafft-Ebbing and the novels of Miles F. You can't yet know what a terrible army with banners you are, you and your eyes and your laughter and your impertinent breasts, like La Maja's, and those anti-educational ears in ambush under the hair. You can't know. But I know. Only too well. Just *how* well you'll realize, perhaps, fifteen or twenty years from now. For a time will come when the freshness of young bodies, the ingenuousness of young minds will begin to strike you as a scandal of shining beauty and attractiveness, and then finally as a kind of maddeningly alluring perversity, as the exhibition of a kind of irresistibly dangerous vice. The madness of the desirer—for middle-aged desires are mostly more or less mad desires—comes off on the desired object, staining it, degrading it. Which isn't agreeable if you happen to be fond of the object, as well as desiring. Dear object, let's be a little reasonable—oh, entirely against all my principles; I accept all the reproaches you made me the other day. But what are principles for but to be gone against in moments of crisis? And this *is* a moment of crisis. Consider: I'm thirty years older than you are; and even if one doesn't look one's age, one is one's age, somehow, somewhere; and even if one doesn't feel it, fifty's always fifty and twenty-one's twenty-one. And when you've considered that, let me put a few questions. First: are you prepared to be a disreputable woman? To which, of course, you answer yes, because you don't care two pins about what the old cats say. But I put another question: Do you know, by experience, what it's like to be a disreputable woman? And you must answer, no. Whereupon I retort: If you can't answer yes to the second, you've got no right to answer yes to the first. And I don't intend to give you the opportunity of answering yes to the second question. Which is all pure Podsnapism. But there are certain circumstances in which Podsnap is quite right.

Sweet Pamela, believe me when I say it would be fatal. For when you say you love me, what do you mean? Who and what is it you love? I'll tell you. You love the author of *Eurydice* and of all those portraits of yourself he's filled his books with. You love the celebrated man, who was not only unsnubbing and attentive, but obviously admiring. Even before you saw him, you vaguely loved his reputation, and now you love his odd confidences. You love a kind of conversation you haven't heard before. You love a weakness in him which you think you can dominate and protect. You love—as I, of course, intended you to love—a certain fascinating manner. You even love a rather romantic and still youthful appearance. And when I say (which as yet, you know, I haven't said) that I love you, what do *I* mean? That I'm amused, and charmed, and flattered, and touched, and puzzled, and affectionate, in a word, a Passionist Father. But chiefly that I find you terribly desirable—an army with banners. Bring these two loves together and what's the result? A manifold disaster. To begin with, the nearer you come to me and the longer you remain with me, the more alien you'll find me, the more fundamentally remote. Inevitably. For you and I are foreigners to one another, foreigners in time. Which is a greater foreignness than the foreignness of space and language. You don't realize it now, because you don't know me—you're only in love, at first sight (like Joan in *Eurydice*!) and, what's more, not really with me, with your imagination of me. When you come to know me better—well, you'll find that you know me much worse. And then one day you'll be attracted by a temporal compatriot. Perhaps, indeed, you're attracted already, only your imagination won't allow you to admit it. What about that long-suffering Guy of yours? Of whom I was, and am, so horribly jealous—jealous with the malignity of a weaker for a stronger rival; for though I seem to hold all the cards at the moment, the ace of trumps is his: he's young. And one day, when you're tired of living at cross-purposes with me, you'll suddenly realize it; you'll perceive that he speaks your language, that he inhabits your world of thought and feeling, that he belongs, in a word, to your nation—that great and terrible nation, which I love and fear and hate, the nation of Youth. In the end, of course, you'll leave the foreigner for the compatriot. But not before you've inflicted a good deal of suffering on every one concerned, including yourself. And meanwhile, what about me? Shall I be still there for you to leave? Who knows? Not I, at any rate. I can no more answer for my future desires than for the Shah of Persia. For my future affection, yes. But it may last (how often, alas, affections do last that way!) only on condition of its object being absent. There are so many friends whom one's fond of when they're not there. Will you be one of them? It's the more possible since, after all, you're just as alien to me as I am to you. My country's called Middle-Ageia and every one who was out of the egg of childhood before 1914 is my compatriot. Through all my desires, shouldn't I also pine to hear my own language, to speak with those who share the national traditions? Of course. But the tragedy of middle-aged life is that its army with banners is hardly ever captained by a compatriot. Passion is divorced from understanding, and the ageing man's desire attaches itself with an almost insane violence to precisely those outrageously fresh young bodies that house the most alien souls. Conversely, for the body of an understood and understanding soul, he seldom feels desire. And now, Pamela, suppose that my sentiment of your alienness should come to be stronger (as some time it must) than my desire for the lovely scandal of your young body. What then? This time I can answer; for I am answering for a self that changes very little through every change of circumstances—the self that doesn't intend to put up with more discomfort than it can possibly avoid; the self that, as the Freudians tell us, is homesick for that earthly paradise from which we've all been banished, our mother's womb, the only place on earth where man is genuinely omnipotent, where his every desire is satisfied, where he is perfectly at home and adapted to his surroundings, and therefore perfectly happy. Out of the womb we're in an unfriendly world, in which our wishes aren't anticipated, where we're no longer magically omnipotent, where we don't fit, where we're not snugly at home. What's to be done in this world? Either face out the reality, fight with it, resignedly or heroically accept to suffer or struggle. Or else flee. In practice even the strongest heroes do a bit of fleeing—away from responsibility into deliberate ignorance, away from uncomfortable fact into imagination. Even the strongest. And conversely even the weakest fleers can make themselves strong. No, not the weakest; that's a mistake. The weakest become day-dreamers, masturbators, paranoiacs. The strong fleer is one who starts with considerable advantages. Take my case. I'm so endowed by nature that I can have a great many of the prizes of life for the asking—success, money in reasonable quantities, love. In other words I'm not entirely out of the womb; I can still, even in the extra-uterine world, have at least some of my desires magically satisfied. To have my wishes fulfilled I don't have to rush off every time to some imaginary womb-substitute. I have the power to construct a womb for myself out of the materials of the real world. But of course it's not a completely perfect and water-tight womb; no post-natal uterus can ever in the nature of things be that. It lets in a lot of unpleasantness and alienness and obstruction to wishes. Which I deal with by flight, systematic flight into unawareness, into deliberate ignorance, into irresponsibility. It's a weakness which is a source of strength. For when you can flee at will and with success (which is only possible if nature has granted you, as she has to me, the possibility of anarchic independence of society), what quantities of energy you save, what an enormous amount of emotional and mental wear and tear is spared you? I flee from business by leaving all my affairs in the hands of lawyers and agents, I flee from criticism (both from the humiliations of misplaced and wrongly motived praise and from the pain of even the most contemptible vermin's blame) by simply not reading what anybody writes of me. I flee from time by living as far as possible only in and for the present. I flee from cold weather by taking the train or ship to places where it's warm. And from women I don't love any more, I flee by just silently vanishing. For, like Palmerston, I never explain and never apologize. I just fade out. I decline to admit their existence. I consign their letters to the waste-paper basket, along with the press cuttings. Simple, crude even, but incredibly effective, if one's ready to be ruthless in one's weakness, as I am. Yes, quite ruthless, Pamela. If my desire grew weary or I felt homesick for the company of my compatriots, I'd just run away, determinedly, however painfully much you might still be in love with me, or your imagination, or your own hurt pride and humiliated self-love. And you, I fancy, would have as little mercy on my desires if they should happen to outlive what you imagine to be your passion for me. So that our love-affair, if we were fools enough to embark on it, would be a race towards a series of successive goals—a race through boredom, misunderstanding, disillusion, towards the final winning-post of cruelty and betrayal. Which of us is likely to win the race? The betting, I should say, is about even, with a slight tendency in favour of myself. But there's not going to be a winner or a loser, for the good reason that there's not going to be any race. I'm too fond of you, Pamela, to . . .'

'Miles!'

Fanning started so violently that a drop of ink was jerked from his pen on to the paper. He felt as though his heart had fallen into an awful gulf of emptiness.

'Miles!'

He looked round. Two hands were clutching the bars of the unshuttered window and, as though desperately essaying to emerge from a subterranean captivity, the upper part of a face was peering in, over the high sill, with wide unhappy eyes.

'But Pamela!' There was reproach in his astonishment.

It was to the implied rebuke that she penitently answered. 'I couldn't help it, Miles,' she said; and, behind the bars, he saw her reddened eyes suddenly brighten and overflow with tears. 'I simply had to come.' Her voice trembled on the verge of breaking. '*Had* to.'

The tears, her words and that unhappy voice were moving. But he didn't want to be moved, he was angry with himself for feeling the emotion, with her for inspiring it. 'But, my dear child!' he began, and the reproach in his voice had shrilled to a kind of exasperation—the exasperation of one who feels himself hemmed in and helpless, increasingly helpless, against circumstances. 'But I thought we'd settled,' he began and broke off. He rose, and walked agitatedly towards the fireplace, agitatedly back again, like a beast in a cage; he was caught, hemmed in between those tearful eyes behind the bars and his own pity, with all those dangerous feelings that have their root in pity. 'I thought,' he began once more.

But, 'Oh!' came her sharp cry, and looking again towards the window he saw that only the two small hands and a pair of straining wrists were visible. The tragical face had vanished.

'Pamela?'

'It's all right.' Her voice came rather muffled and remote. 'I slipped. I was standing on a little kind of ledge affair. The window's so high from the ground,' she added plaintively.

'My poor child!' he said on a little laugh of amused commiseration. The reproach, the exasperation had gone out of his voice. He was conquered by the comic patheticness of her. Hanging on to the bars with those small, those rather red and childishly untended hands! And tumbling off the perch she had had to climb on, because the window was so high from the ground! A wave of sentimentality submerged him. 'I'll come and open the door.' He ran into the hall.

Waiting outside in the darkness, she heard the bolts being shot back, one by one. Clank, clank! and then 'Damn!' came his voice from the other side of the door. 'These things are so stiff. . . . I'm barricaded up as though I were in a safe.' She stood there waiting. The door shook as he tugged at the recalcitrant bolt. The waiting seemed interminable. And all at once a huge, black weariness settled on her. The energy of wrought-up despair deserted her and she was left empty of everything but a tired misery. What was the good, what was the good of coming like this to be turned away again? For he *would* turn her away; he didn't want her. What was the good of renewing suffering, of once more dying?

'Hell and Death!' On the other side of the door Fanning was cursing like an Elizabethan.

Hell and Death. The words reverberated in Pamela's mind. The pains of Hell, the darkness and dissolution of Death. What was the good?

Clank! Another bolt had gone back. 'Thank goodness. We're almost . . .' A chain rattled. At the sound Pamela turned and ran in a blind terror down the dimly lighted street.

'At last!' The door swung back and Fanning stepped out. But the sentimental tenderness of his outstretched hands wasted itself on empty night. Twenty yards away a pair of pale legs twinkled in the darkness. 'Pamela!' he called in astonishment. 'What the devil . . .?' The wasting on emptiness of his feelings had startled him into annoyance. He felt like one who has put forth all his strength to strike something and, missing his aim, swipes the unresisting air, grotesquely. 'Pamela!' he called again, yet louder.

She did not turn at the sound of his voice, but ran on. These wretched high-heeled shoes! 'Pamela!' And then came the sound of his pursuing footsteps. She tried to run faster. But the pursuing footsteps came nearer and nearer. It was no good. Nothing was any good. She slackened her speed to a walk.

'But what on earth?' he asked from just behind her, almost angrily. Pursuing, he had called up within him the soul of a pursuer, angry and desirous. 'What on earth?' And suddenly his hand was on her shoulder. She trembled a little at the touch. 'But why?' he insisted. 'Why do you suddenly run away?'

But Pamela only shook her averted head. She wouldn't speak, wouldn't meet his eyes. Fanning looked down at her intently, questioningly. Why? And as he looked at that weary hopeless face, he began to divine the reason. The anger of the pursuit subsided in him. Respecting her dumb, averted misery, he too was silent. He drew her comfortingly towards him. His arm round her shoulders, Pamela suffered herself to be led back towards the house.

Which would be best, he was wondering with the surface of his mind: to telephone for a taxi to take her back to the hotel, or to see if he could make up a bed for her in one of the upstairs rooms? But in the depths of his being he knew quite well that he would do neither of these things. He knew that he would be her lover. And yet, in spite of this deep knowledge, the surface mind still continued to discuss its little problem of cabs and bed-linen. Discussed it sensibly, discussed it dutifully. Because it would be a madness, he told himself, a criminal madness if he didn't send for the taxi or prepare that upstairs room. But the dark certainty of the depths rose suddenly and exploded at the surface in a bubble of ironic laughter, in a brutal and cynical word. 'Comedian!' he said to himself, to the self that agitatedly thought of telephones and taxis and pillow-slips. 'Seeing that it's obvious I'm going to have her.' And, rising from the depths, her nakedness presented itself to him palpably in an integral and immediate contact with his whole being. But this was shameful, shameful. He pushed the naked Anadyomene back into the depths. Very well, then, (his surface mind resumed its busy efficient rattle), seeing that it was perhaps rather late to start telephoning for taxis, he'd rig up one of the rooms on the first floor. But if he couldn't find any sheets . . . ? But here was the house, the open door.

Pamela stepped across the threshold. The hall was almost dark. Through a curtained doorway on the left issued a thin blade of yellow light. Passive in her tired misery, she waited. Behind her the chain rattled, as it had rattled only a few moments before, when she had fled from the ominous sound, and clank, clank! the bolts were thrust back into place.

'There,' said Fanning's voice. 'And now . . .' With a click, the darkness yielded suddenly to brilliant light.

Pamela uttered a little cry and covered her face with her hands. 'Oh, please,' she begged, 'please.' The light hurt her, was a sort of outrage. She didn't want to see, couldn't bear to be seen.

'I'm sorry,' he said, and the comforting darkness returned. 'This way.' Taking her arm he led her towards the lighted doorway on the left. 'Shut your eyes,' he commanded, as they approached the curtain. 'We've got to go into the light again; but I'll turn it out the moment I can get to the switch. Now!' She shut her eyes and suddenly, as the curtain rings rattled, she saw, through her closed eyelids, the red shining of transparent blood. Still holding her arm, he led her forward into the room.

Pamela lifted her free hand to her face. 'Please don't look at me,' she whispered. 'I don't want you to see me like this. I mean, I couldn't bear . . .' Her voice faded to silence.

'I won't look,' he assured her. 'And anyhow,' he added, when they had taken two or three more steps across the room, 'now I can't.' And he turned the switch.

The pale translucent red went black again before her eyes. Pamela sighed. 'I'm so tired,' she whispered. Her eyes were still shut; she was too tired to open them.

'Take off your coat.' A hand pulled at her sleeve. First one bare arm, then the other slipped out into the coolness.

Fanning threw the coat over a chair. Turning back, he could see her, by the tempered darkness that entered through the window, standing motionless before him, passive, wearily waiting, her face, her limp arms pale against the shadowy blackness.

'Poor Pamela,' she heard him say, and then suddenly light finger-tips were sliding in a moth-winged caress along her arm. 'You'd better lie down and rest.' The hand closed round her arm, she was pushed gently forward. That taxi, he was still thinking, the upstairs room . . . But his fingers preserved the silky memory of her skin, the flesh of her arm was warm and firm against his palm. In the darkness, the supernatural world was coming mysteriously, thrillingly into existence; he was once more standing upon its threshold.

'There, sit down,' came his voice. She obeyed; a low divan received her. 'Lean back.' She let herself fall on to pillows. Her feet were lifted on to the couch. She lay quite still. 'As though I were dead,' she thought, 'as though I were dead.' She was aware, through the darkness of her closed eyes, of his warm breathing presence, impending and very near. 'As though I were dead,' she inwardly repeated with a kind of pleasure. For the pain of her misery had ebbed away into the warm darkness, and to be tired, she found, to be utterly tired and to lie there utterly still were pleasures. 'As though I were dead.' And the light reiterated touch of his finger-tips along her arm—what were those caresses but another mode, a soothing and delicious mode, of gently dying?

In the morning, on his way to the kitchen to prepare their coffee, Fanning caught sight of his littered writing-table. He halted to collect the scattered sheets. Waiting for the water to boil, he read. 'By the time you receive this letter, I shall be—no, not dead, Pamela . . .' He crumpled up each page as he had finished reading it and threw it into the dust-bin.

IX

The architectural background was like something out of Alma Tadema. But the figures that moved across the sunlit atrium, that lingered beneath the colonnades and in the coloured shadow of the awnings, the figures were Hogarthian and Rowlandsonian, were the ferocious satires of Daumier and Rouveyre. Huge jellied females overflowed the chairs on which they sat. Sagging and with the gait of gorged bears, old men went slowly shambling down the porticoes. Like princes preceded by their outriders, the rich fat burgesses strutted with dignity behind their bellies. There was a hungry prowling of gaunt emaciated men and women, yellow-skinned and with tragical, bile-injected eyes. And, conspicuous by their trailing blackness, these bloated or cadaverous pencillings from an anti-clerical notebook were priests.

In the midst of so many monsters Pamela was a lovely miracle of health and beauty. These three months had subtly transformed her. The rather wavering and intermittent *savoir-vivre*, the child's forced easiness of manner, had given place to a woman's certainty, to that repose even in action, that decision even in repose, which are the ordinary fruits of the intimate knowledge, the physical understanding of love.

'For it isn't only murder that will out,' as Fanning had remarked some few days after the evening of the fireworks. 'It isn't only murder. If you could see yourself, my child! It's almost indecent. Any one could tell that you'd been in bed with your lover. Could tell in the dark, even; you're luminous, positively luminous. All shining and smooth and pearly with love-making. It's really an embarrassment to walk about with you. I've a good mind to make you wear a veil.'

She had laughed, delightedly. 'But I don't mind them seeing. I *want* them to see. I mean, why should one be ashamed of being happy?'

That had been three months since. At present she had no happiness to be ashamed of. It was by no shining of eyes, no luminous soft pearliness of smoothed and rounded contour that she now betrayed herself. All that her manner, her pose, her gestures proclaimed was the fact that there *had* been such shinings and pearly smoothings, once. As for the present, her shut and sullen face announced only that she was discontented with it and with the man who, sitting beside her, was the symbol and the embodiment of that unsatisfactory present. A rather sickly embodiment at the moment, a thin and jaundiced symbol. For Fanning was hollow-cheeked, his eyes darkly ringed, his skin pale and sallow under the yellowed tan. He was on his way to becoming one of those pump-room monsters at whom they were now looking, almost incredulously. For, 'Incredible!' was Fanning's comment. 'Didn't I tell you that they simply weren't to be believed?'

Pamela shrugged her shoulders, almost imperceptibly, and did not answer. She did not feel like answering, she wanted to be uninterested, sullen, bored.

'How right old Butler was!' he went on, rousing himself by the stimulus of his own talk from the depression into which his liver and Pamela had plunged him. 'Making the Erewhonians punish illness as a crime—how right! Because they *are* criminals, all these people. Criminally ugly and deformed, criminally incapable of enjoyment. Look at them. It's a caution. And when I think that I'm one of them . . .' He shook his head. 'But let's hope this will make me a reformed character.' And he emptied, with a grimace of disgust, his glass of tepid salt water. 'Revolting! But I suppose it's right that Montecatini should be a place of punishment as well as cure. One can't be allowed to commit jaundice with impunity. I must go and get another glass of my punishment—my purgatory, in every sense of the word,' he added, smiling at his own joke. He rose to his feet painfully (every movement was now a painful effort for him) and left her, threading his way through the crowd to where, behind their marble counters, the pump-room barmaids dispensed warm laxatives from rows of polished brass taps.

The animation had died out of Fanning's face as he turned away. No longer distracted and self-stimulated by talk, he relapsed at once into melancholy. Waiting his turn behind two bulging monsignori at the pump, he looked so gloomily wretched that a passing connoisseur of the waters pointed him out to his companion as a typical example of the hepatic pessimist. But bile, as a matter of fact, was not the only cause of Fanning's depression. There was also Pamela. And Pamela—he admitted it, though the fact belonged to that great class of humiliating phenomena whose existence we are always trying to ignore—Pamela, after all, was the cause of the bile. For if he had not been so extenuated by that crazy love-making in the narrow cells of the Passionist Fathers at Monte Cavo, he would never have taken chill and the chill would never have settled on his liver and turned to jaundice. As it was, however, that night of the full moon had finished him. They had gone out, groping their way through the terrors of the nocturnal woods, to a little grassy terrace among the bushes, from which there was a view of Nemi. Deep sunk in its socket of impenetrable darkness and more than half eclipsed by shadow, the eye of water gleamed up at them secretly, as though through eyelids almost closed. Under the brightness of the moon, the hills, the woods seemed to be struggling out of ghostly greyness towards colour, towards the warmth of life. They had sat there for a while, in silence, looking. Then, taking her in his arms, '"*Ceda al tatto la vista, al labro il lume*"' he had quoted with a kind of mockery—mocking her for the surrender to which he knew he could bring her, even against her will, even though, as he could see, she had made up her mind to sulk at him, mocking himself at the same time for the folly which drove him, weary and undesiring, to make the gesture. ' "*Al labro il lume*," ' he repeated with that undercurrent of derision in his voice, and leaned towards her. Desire returned to him as he touched her, and with it a kind of exultation, a renewal (temporary, he knew, and illusory) of all his energies.

'No, Miles. Don't. I don't want . . .' And she had averted her face, for she was angry, resentful, she wanted to sulk. Fanning knew it, mockingly, and mockingly he had turned back her face towards him—'*al labro il lume*'—and found her lips. She struggled a little in his arms, protested, and then was silent, lay still. His kisses had had the power to transform her. She was another person, different from the one who had sulked and been resentful. Or rather she was two people—the sulky and resentful one, with another person superimposed, a person who quiveringly sank and melted under his kisses, melted and sank down, down towards that mystical death, that apocalypse, that almost terrible transfiguration. But beneath, to one side, stood always the angry sulker, unappeased, unreconciled, ready to emerge again (full of a new resentment for the way she had been undignifiedly hustled off the stage) the moment the other should have retired. His realization of this made Fanning all the more perversely ardent, quickened the folly of his passion with a kind of derisive hostility. He drew his lips across her cheek and suddenly their soft electrical touch on her ear made her shudder. 'Don't!' she implored, dreading and yet desiring what was to come. Gently, inexorably his teeth closed, and the petal of cartilage was a firm elastic resistance between them. She shuddered yet more violently. Fanning relaxed the muscles of his jaws, then tightened them once more, gently, against that exquisite resistance. The felt beauty of rounded warmth and resilience was under his hand. In the darkness they were inhabitants of the supernatural world.

But at midnight they had found themselves, almost suddenly, on earth again, shiveringly cold under the moon. Cold, cold to the quick, Fanning had picked himself up. They stumbled homewards through the woods, in silence. It was in a kind of trance of chilled and sickened exhaustion that he had at last dropped down on his bed in the convent cell. Next morning he was ill. The liver was always his weak point. That had been nearly three weeks ago.

The second of the two monsignori moved away; Fanning stepped into his place. The barmaid handed him his hot dilute sulphate of soda. He deposited fifty centesimi as a largesse and walked off, meditatively sipping. But returning to the place from which he had come, he found their chairs occupied by a pair of obese Milanese business-men. Pamela had gone. He explored the Alma Tadema background; but there was no sign of her. She had evidently gone back to the hotel. Fanning, who still had five more glasses of water to get through, took his place among the monsters round the band-stand.

In her room at the hotel Pamela was writing up her diary. 'September 20th. Montecatini seems a beastly sort of hole, particularly if you come to a wretched little hotel like this, which M. insisted on doing, because he knows the proprietor, who is an old drunkard and also cooks the meals, and M. has long talks with him and says he's like a character in Shakespeare, which is all very well, but I'd prefer better food and a room with a bath, not to mention the awfulness of the other people in the hotel, one of whom is the chief undertaker in Florence, who's always boasting to the other people at meal times about his business and what a fine motor hearse with gilded angels he's got and the number of counts and dukes he's buried. M. had a long conversation with him and the old drunkard after dinner yesterday evening about how you preserve corpses on ice and the way to make money by buying up the best sites at the cemetery and holding them till you could ask five times as much as you paid, and it was the first time I'd seen him looking cheerful and amused since his illness and even for some time before, but I was so horrified that I went off to bed. This morning at eight to the pump-room, where M. has to drink eight glasses of different kinds of water before breakfast and there are hundreds of hideous people all carrying mugs, and huge fountains of purgatives, and a band playing the 'Geisha,' so I came away after half an hour, leaving M. to his waters, because I really can't be expected to watch him drinking, and it appears there are six hundred W.C.s.'

She laid down her pen and, turning round in her chair, sat for some time pensively staring at her own reflection in the wardrobe mirror. 'If you look long enough,' (she heard Clare's voice, she saw Clare, inwardly, sitting at her dressing-table), 'you begin to wonder if it isn't somebody else. And perhaps, after all, one *is* somebody else, all the time.' Somebody else, Pamela repeated to herself, somebody else. But was that a spot on her cheek, or a mosquito bite? A mosquito, thank goodness. 'Oh God,' she said aloud, and in the looking-glass somebody else moved her lips, 'if only I knew what to do! If only I were dead!' She touched wood hastily. Stupid to say such things. But if only one knew, one were certain! All at once she gave a little stiff sharp shudder of disgust, she grimaced as though she had bitten on something sour. Oh, oh! she groaned; for she had suddenly seen herself in the act of dressing, there, in that moon-flecked darkness, among the bushes, that hateful night just before Miles fell ill. Furious because he'd humiliated her, hating him; she hadn't wanted to and he'd made her. Somebody else had enjoyed beyond the limits of enjoyment, had suffered a pleasure transmuted into its opposite. Or rather *she* had done the suffering. And then that further humiliation of having to ask him to help her look for her suspender belt! And there were leaves in her hair. And when she got back to the hotel, she found a spider squashed against her skin under the chemise. Yes, *she* had found the spider, not somebody else.

. . . .

Between the brackish sips Fanning was reading in his pocket edition of the *Paradiso*. '*L'acqua che prendo giammai non si corse*,' he murmured;

'*Minerva spira e conducemi Apollo,*
e nove Muse mi dimostran l'Orse.'

He closed his eyes. '*E nove Muse mi dimostran l'Orse.*' What a marvel! 'And the nine Muses point me to the Bears.' Even translated the spell did not entirely lose its potency. 'How glad I shall be,' he thought, 'to be able to do a little work again.'

'*Il caffè?*' said a voice at his elbow. '*Non lo bevo mai, mai. Per il fegato, sa, è pessimo. Si dice anche che per gl'intestini . . .*' The voice receded out of hearing.

Fanning took another gulp of salt water and resumed his reading.

Voi altri pochi che drizzante il collo
per tempo al pan degli angeli, del quale
vivesi qui ma non sen vien satollo . . .

The voice had returned. '*Pesce bollito, carne ai ferri o arrostita, patate lesse . . .*'

He shut his ears and continued. But when he came to

La concreata e perpetua sete
del deiforme regno,

he had to stop again. This craning for angels' bread, this thirsting for the god-like kingdom . . . The words reverberated questioningly in his mind. After all, why not? Particularly when man's bread made you sick (he thought with horror of that dreadful vomiting of bile), when it was a case of *pesce bollito* and you weren't allowed to thirst for anything more palatable than this stuff. (He swigged again.) These were the circumstances when Christianity became appropriate. Christians, according to Pascal, ought to live like sick men; conversely, sick men can hardly escape being Christians. How pleased Colin Judd would be! But the thought of Colin was depressing, if only all Christians were like Dante! But in that case, what a frightful world it would be! Frightful.

La concreata e perpetua sete
del deiforme regno cen portava
Veloci, quasi come il ciel vedete.
Beatrice in suso ed io in lei guardava. . . .

He thought of Pamela at the fireworks. On that pedestal. *Ben son, ben son Beatrice* on that pedestal. He remembered what he had said beneath the blossoming of the rockets; and also what he had meant to say about those legs which the pedestal made it so easy for the worshipper to pinch. Those legs, how remote now, how utterly irrelevant! He finished off his third glass of Torretta and, rising, made his way to the bar for his first of Regina. Yes, how utterly irrelevant! he thought. A complete solution of continuity. You were on the leg level, then you vomited bile, and as soon as you were able to think of anything but vomiting, you found yourself on the Dante level. He handed his mug to the barmaid. She rolled black eyes at him as she filled it. Some liverish gentlemen, it seemed, could still feel amorous. Or perhaps it was only the obese ones. Fanning deposited his offering and retired. Irrelevant, irrelevant. It seemed, now, the unlikeliest story. And yet there it was, a fact. And Pamela was solid, too, too solid.

Phrases floated up, neat and ready-made, to the surface of his mind.

'What does he see in her? What on earth can she see in him?'

'But it's not a question of sight, it's a question of touch.'

And he remembered—*sentiments-centimètres*—that French pun about love, so appallingly cynical, so humiliatingly true. 'But only humiliating,' he assured himself, 'because we choose to think it so, arbitrarily, only cynical because *Beatrice in suso ed io in lei guardava*; only appalling because we're creatures who sometimes vomit bile and because, even without vomiting, we sometimes feel ourselves naturally Christians.' But in any case, *nove Muse mi dimostran l'Orse.* Meanwhile, however . . . He tilted another gill of water down his throat. And when he was well enough to work, wouldn't he also be well enough to thirst again for that other god-like kingdom, with its different ecstasies, its other peace beyond all understanding? But *tant mieux*, *tant mieux*, so long as the Bears remained unmoved and the Muses went on pointing.

. . . .

Pamela was looking through her diary. 'June 24th,' she read. 'Spent the evening with M. and afterwards he said how lucky it was for me that I'd been seduced by him, which hurt my feelings (that word, I mean) and also rather annoyed me, so I said he certainly hadn't seduced me, and he said, all right, if I liked to say that I'd seduced him, he didn't mind, but anyhow it was lucky because almost anybody else wouldn't have been such a good psychologist as he, not to mention physiologist, and I should have hated it. But I said, how could he say such things? because it wasn't that at all and I was happy because I loved him, but M. laughed and said, you don't, and I said, I do, and he said, you don't, but if it gives you any pleasure to imagine you do, imagine, which upset me still more, his not believing, which is due to his not wanting to love himself, because I *do* love . . .'

Pamela quickly turned the page. She couldn't read that sort of thing now.

'June 25th. Went to the Vatican where M. . . .' She skipped nearly a page of Miles's remarks on classical art and the significance of orgies in the ancient religions; on the duty of being happy and having the sun inside you, like a bunch of ripe grapes; on making the world appear infinite and holy by an improvement of sensual enjoyment; on taking things untragically, unponderously.

'M. dined out and I spent the evening with Guy, the first time since the night of the fireworks, and he asked me what I'd been doing all this time, so I said, nothing in particular, but I felt myself blushing, and he said, anyhow you look extraordinarily well and happy and pretty, which also made me rather uncomfortable, because of what M. said the other day about murder will out, but then I laughed, because it was the only thing to do, and Guy asked what I was laughing about, so I said, nothing, but I could see by the way he looked at me that he was rather thrilled, which pleased me, and we had a very nice dinner and he told me about a girl he'd been in love with in Ireland and it seems they went camping together for a week, but he was never her lover because she had a kind of terror of being touched, but afterwards she went to America and got married. Later on, in the taxi, he took my hand and even tried to kiss me, but I laughed, because it was somehow very funny, I don't know why, but afterwards, when he persisted, I got angry with him.

'June 27th. Went to look at mosaics to-day, rather fine, but what a pity they're all in churches and always pictures of Jesus and sheep and apostles and so forth. On the way home we passed a wine shop and M. went in and ordered a dozen bottles of champagne, because he said that love can exist without passion, or understanding, or respect, but not without champagne. So I asked him if he really loved me, and he said, *Je t'adore*, in French, but I said, no, do you really *love* me? But he said, silence is golden and it's better to use one's mouth for kissing and drinking champagne and eating caviar, because he'd also bought some caviar; and if you start talking about love and thinking about love, you get everything wrong, because it's not *meant* to be talked about, but acted, and if people want to talk and think they'd better talk about mosaics and that sort of thing. But I still went on asking him if he loved me. . . .'

'Fool, fool!' said Pamela aloud. She was ashamed of herself. Dithering on like that! At any rate Miles had been honest; she had to admit that. He'd taken care to keep the thing on the champagne level. And he'd always told her that she was imagining it all. Which had been intolerable, of course; he'd been wrong to be so right. She remembered how she had cried when he refused to answer her insistent question; had cried and afterwards allowed herself to be consoled. They went back to his house for supper; he opened a bottle of champagne, they ate the caviar. Next day he sent her that poem. It had arrived at the same time as some flowers from Guy. She reopened her notebook. Here it was.

> At the red fountain's core the thud of drums
> Quickens; for hairy-footed moths explore
> This aviary of nerves; the woken birds
> Flutter and cry in the branched blood; a bee

Hums with his million-times-repeated stroke
On lips your breast promotes geometers
To measure curves, to take the height of mountains,
The depth and silken slant of dells unseen.
I read your youth, as the blind student spells
With finger-tips the song from *Cymbeline*.
Caressing and caressed, my hands perceive
(In lieu of eyes) old Titian's paradise
With Eve unaproned; and the Maja dressed
Whisks off her muslins, that my skin may know
The blind night's beauty of brooding heat and cool,
Of silk and fibre, of molten-moist and dry,
Resistance and resilience.
But the drum
Throbs with yet faster beat, the wild birds go
Through their red liquid sky with wings yet more
Frantic and yet more desperate crying. Come!
The magical door its soft and breathing valves
Has set ajar. Beyond the threshold lie
Worlds after worlds receding into light,
As rare old wines on the ravished tongue renew
A miracle that deepens, that expands,
Blossoms, and changes hue, and chimes, and shines.
Birds in the blood and doubled drums incite
Us to the conquest of these new, strange lands
Beyond the threshold, where all common times,
Things, places, thoughts, events expire, and life
Enters eternity.

The darkness stirs, the trees are wet with rain;
Knock and it shall be opened, oh, again,
Again! The child is eager for its dam
And I the mother am of thirsty lips,
Oh, knock again!
Wild darkness wets this sound of strings.
How smooth it slides among the clarinets,
How easily slips through the trumpetings!

Sound glides through sound, and lo ! the apocalypse,
The burst of wings above a sunlit sea.
Must this eternal music make an end ?
Prolong, prolong these all but final chords !
Oh, wounded sevenths, breathlessly suspend
Our fear of dying, our desire to know
The song's last words !
Almost Bethesda sleeps, uneasily.
A bubble domes the flatness ; gyre on gyre,
The waves expand, expire, as in the deeps
The woken spring subsides.
Play, music, play !
Reckless of death, a singing giant rides
His storm of music, rides ; and suddenly
The tremulous mirror of the moon is broken ;
On the farthest beaches of our soul, our flesh,
The tides of pleasure foaming into pain
Mount, hugely mount ; break ; and retire again.
The final word is sung, the last word spoken.

'Do I like it, or do I rather hate it ? I don't know.'

'June 28th. When I saw M. at lunch to-day, I told him I didn't really know if I liked his poem, I mean apart from literature, and he said, yes, perhaps the young *are* more romantic than they think, which rather annoyed me, because I believe he imagined I was shocked, which is too ridiculous. All the same, I *don't* like it.'

Pamela sighed and shut her eyes, so as to be able to think more privately, without distractions. From this distance of time she could see all that had happened in perspective, as it were, and as a whole. It was her pride, she could see, her fear of looking ridiculously romantic that had changed the quality of her feelings towards Miles—a pride and a fear on which he had played, deliberately. She had given herself with passion and desperately, tragically, as she imagined that

Joan would have desperately given herself, at first sight, to a reluctant Walter. But the love he had offered her in return was a thing of laughter and frank, admitted sensuality, was a gay and easy companionship enriched, but uncomplicated, by pleasure. From the first he had refused to come up to her emotional level. From the first he had taken it for granted—and his taking it for granted was in itself an act of moral compulsion—that she should descend to his. And she had descended—reluctantly at first, but afterwards without a struggle. For she came to realize, almost suddenly, that after all she didn't really love him in the tragically passionate way she had supposed she loved him. In a propitious emotional climate her belief that she was a despairing Joan might perhaps have survived, at any rate for a time. But it was a hot-house growth of the imagination; in the cool dry air of his laughter and cheerfully cynical frankness it had withered. And all at once she had found herself, not satisfied, indeed, with what he offered, but superficially content. She returned him what he gave. Less even than he gave. For soon it became apparent to her that their rôles were being reversed, that the desperate one was no longer herself, but Miles. For 'desperate'—that was the only word to describe the quality of his desires. From light and gay—and perhaps, she thought, the lightness had been forced, the gaiety fabricated for the occasion as a defence against the tragical vehemence of her attack and of his own desires—his sensuality had become heavy, serious, intense. She had found herself the object of a kind of focused rage. It had been frightening sometimes, frightening and rather humiliating; for she had often felt that, so far as he was concerned, she wasn't there at all; that the body between those strong, those ruthless and yet delicate, erudite, subtly intelligent hands of his, that were like a surgeon's or a sculptor's hands, was not her body, was no one's body, indeed, but a kind of abstraction, tangible, yes, desperately tangible, but still an abstraction. She would have liked to rebel; but the surgeon was a master of his craft, the sculptor's fingers were delicately learned and intelligent. He had the art to overcome her reluctances, to infect her with some of his strange, concentrated seriousness. Against her will. In the intervals he resumed his old manner; but the laughter was apt to be bitter and spiteful, there was a mocking brutality in the frankness.

Pamela squeezed her eyes more tightly shut and shook her head, frowning at her memories. For distraction she turned back to her diary.

'June 30th. Lunched with Guy, who was really rather tiresome, because what is more boring than somebody being in love with you, when you're not in love with them? Which I told him quite frankly, and I could see he was dreadfully upset, but what was I to do?'

Poor Guy! she thought, and she was indignant, not with herself, but with Fanning. She turned over several pages. It was July now and they were at Ostia for the bathing. It was at Ostia that that desperate seriousness had come into his desire. The long hot hours of the siesta were propitious to his earnest madness. Propitious also to his talents, for he worked well in the heat. Behind her lowered eyelids Pamela had a vision of him sitting at his table, stripped to a pair of shorts, sitting there, pen in hand, in the next room and with an open door between them, but somehow at an infinite distance. Terrifyingly remote, a stranger more foreign for being known so well, the inhabitant of other worlds to which she had no access. They were worlds which she was already beginning to hate. His books were splendid, of course; still, it wasn't much fun being with a man who, for half the time, wasn't there at all. She saw him sitting there, a beautiful naked stranger, brown and wiry, with a face like brown marble, stonily focused on his paper. And then suddenly this stranger rose and came towards her through the door, across the room. 'Well?' she heard herself saying. But the stranger did not answer. Sitting down on the edge of her bed, he took the sewing out of her hands and threw it aside on to the dressing-table. She tried to protest, but he laid a hand on her mouth. Wordlessly he shook his head. Then, uncovering her mouth, he kissed her. Under his surgeon's, his sculptor's hands, her body was moulded to a symbol of pleasure. His face was focused and intent, but not on her, on something else, and serious, serious, like a martyr's, like a mathematician's, like a criminal's. An hour later he was back at his table in the next room, in the next world, remote, a stranger once again—but he had never ceased to be a stranger.

Pamela turned over two or three more pages. On July 12th they went sailing and she had felt sick; Miles had been provokingly well all the time. The whole of the sixteenth had been spent in Rome. On the nineteenth they drove to Cerveteri to see the Etruscan tombs. She had been furious with him, because he had put out the lamp and made horrible noises in the cold sepulchral darkness, underground—furious with terror, for she hated the dark.

Impatiently Pamela went on turning the pages. There was no point in reading; none of the really important things were recorded. Of the earnest madness of his love-making, of those hands, that reluctantly suffered pleasure she hadn't been able to bring herself to write. And yet those were the things that mattered. She remembered how she had tried to imagine that she was like her namesake of *Pastures New*—the fatal woman whose cool detachment gives her such power over her lovers. But the facts had proved too stubborn; it was simply impossible for her to pretend that this handsome fancy-picture was her portrait. The days flicked past under her thumb.

'July 30th. On the beach this morning we met some friends of M.'s, a journalist called Pedder, who has just come to Rome as correspondent for some paper or other, and his wife, rather awful, I thought, both of them, but M. seemed to be extraordinarily pleased to see them, and they bathed with us and afterwards came and had lunch at our hotel, which was rather boring so far as I was concerned, because they talked a lot about people I didn't know, and then there was a long discussion about politics and history and so forth, *too* highbrow, but what was intolerable was that the woman thought she ought to be kind and talk to me meanwhile about something I could understand, so she talked about shops in Rome and the best places for getting clothes, which was rather ridiculous, as she's obviously one of those absurd arty women, who appeared in M.'s novels as young girls just before and during the War, so advanced in those days, with extraordinary coloured stockings and frocks like pictures by Augustus John. Anyhow, what she was wearing at lunch was really too fancy-dress, and really at her age one ought to have a little more sense of the decencies, because she must have been quite thirty-five. So that the idea of talking about smart shops in Rome was quite ludicrous to start with, and anyhow it was so insulting to me, because it implied that I was too young and half-witted to be able to take an interest in their beastly conversation. But afterwards, apropos of some philosophical theory or other, M. began talking about his opium smoking, and he told them all the things he'd told me and a lot more besides, and it made me feel very uncomfortable and then miserable and rather angry, because I thought it was only me he talked to like that, so confidentially, but now I see he makes confidences to everybody and it's not a sign of his being particularly fond of a person, or in love with them, or anything like that. Which made me realize that I'm even less important to him than I thought, and I found I minded much more than I expected I should mind, because I thought I'd got past minding. But I *do* mind.'

Pamela shut her eyes again. 'I ought to have gone away then,' she said to herself. 'Gone straight away.' But instead of retiring, she had tried to come closer. Her resentment—for oh, how bitterly she resented those Pedders and his confidential manner towards them !—had quickened her love. She wanted to insist on being more specially favoured than a mere Pedder ; and, loving him, she had the right to insist. By a process of imaginative incubation, she managed to revive some of the emotions she had felt before the night of the fireworks. Tragically, with a suicide's determination, she tried to force herself upon him. Fanning fought a retreating battle, ruthlessly. Oh, how cruel he could be, Pamela was thinking, how pitilessly cruel ! The way he could shut himself up as though in an iron box of indifference ! The way he could just fade out into absent silence, into another world ! The way he could flutter out of an embarrassing emotional situation on the wings of some brilliant irrelevance ! And the way he could flutter back again, the way he could compel you, with his charm, with the touch of his hands, to reopen the gates of your life to him, when you'd made up your mind to shut them against him for ever ! And not content with forcing you to yield, he would mock you for your surrender, mock himself too for having attacked—jeering, but without seeming to jeer, indirectly, in some terrible little generalization about the weakness of the human soul, the follies and insanities of the body. Yes, how cruel he could be ! She reopened her eyes.

'August 10th. M. still very glum and depressed and silent, like a wall when I come near. I think he sometimes hates me for loving him. At lunch he said he'd got to go into Rome this afternoon, and he went and didn't come back till late, almost midnight. Waiting for him, I couldn't help crying.

'August 11th. Those Pedders came to lunch again to-day and all M.'s glumness vanished the moment he saw them and he was charming all through lunch and so amusing, that I couldn't help laughing, though I felt more like crying, because why should he be so much nicer and more *friendly* with them than with me? After lunch, when we went to rest, he came into my room and wanted to kiss me, but I wouldn't let him, because I said, I don't want to owe your fits of niceness to somebody else, and I asked him, why? why was he so much nicer to them than to me? And he said they were his people, they belonged to the same time as he did and meeting them was like meeting another Englishman in the middle of a crowd of Kaffirs in Africa. So I said, I suppose I'm the Kaffirs, and he laughed and said, no, not quite Kaffirs, not more than a Rotary Club dinner in Kansas City, with the Pedders playing the part of a man one had known at Balliol in 'ninety-nine. Which made me cry, and he sat on the edge of the bed and took my hand and said he was very sorry, but that's what life was like, and it couldn't be helped, because time was always time, but people weren't always the same people, but sometimes one person and sometimes another, sometimes Pedder-fanciers and sometimes Pamela-fanciers, and it wasn't my fault that I hadn't heard the first performance of *Pelléas* in 1902 and it wasn't Pedder's fault that he had, and therefore Pedder was his compatriot and I wasn't. But I said, after all, Miles, you're my lover, doesn't that make any difference? But he said, it's a question of speech, and bodies don't speak, only minds, and when two minds are of different ages it's hard for them to understand each other when they speak, but bodies can understand each other, because they don't talk, thank God, he said, because it's such a comfort to stop talking sometimes, to stop thinking and just *be*, for a change. But I said that might be all right for him, but just *being* was my ordinary life and the change for me was talking, was being friends with somebody who knew how to talk and do all the other things talking implies, and I'd imagined I was that, besides just being somebody he went to bed with, and that was why I was so miserable, because I found I wasn't, and those beastly Pedders were. But he said, damn the Pedders, damn the Pedders for making you cry ! and he was so *divinely* sweet and gentle that it was like gradually sinking, sinking and being drowned. But afterwards he began laughing again in that rather hurting way, and he said, your body's so much more beautiful than their minds—that is, so long as one's a Pamela-fancier ; which I am, he said, or rather was and shall be, but now I must go and work, and he got up and went to his room, and I was wretched again.'

The entries of a few days later were dated from Monte Cavo. A superstitious belief in the genius of place had made Pamela insist on the change of quarters. They had been happy on Monte Cavo ; perhaps they would be happy there again. And so, suddenly, the sea didn't suit her, she needed mountain air. But the genius of place is an unreliable deity. She had been as unhappy on the hill-top as by the sea. No, not quite so unhappy, perhaps. In the absence of the Pedders, the passion which their coming had renewed declined again. Perhaps it would have declined even if they had still been there. For the tissue of her imagination was, at the best of times, but a ragged curtain. Every now and then she came to a hole and through the hole she could see a fragment of reality, such as the bald and obvious fact that she didn't love Miles Fanning. True, after a peep through one of these indiscreet holes she felt it necessary to repent for having seen the facts, she would work herself up again into believing her fancies. But her faith was never entirely whole-hearted. Under the superficial layer of imaginative suffering lay a fundamental and real indifference. Looking back now, from the further shore of his illness, Pamela felt astonished that she could have gone on obstinately imagining, in spite of those loop-holes on reality, that she loved him. 'Because I didn't,' she said to herself, clear-sighted, weeks too late. 'I didn't' But the belief that she did had continued, even on Monte Cavo, to envenom those genuinely painful wounds inflicted by him on her pride, her self-respect, inflicted with a strange malice that seemed to grow on him with the passage of the days.

'August 23rd.' She had turned again to the note-book. 'M. gave me this at lunch to-day.

> Sensual heat and sorrow cold
>   Are undivided twins;
> For there where sorrow ends, consoled,
>   Lubricity begins.

I told him I didn't exactly see what the point of it was, but I supposed it was meant to be hurting, because he's always trying to be hurting now, but he said, no, it was just a Great Thought for putting into Christmas crackers. But he did mean to hurt, and yet in one way he's crazy about me, he's . . .'

Yes, crazy was the right word. The more and the more crazily he had desired her, the more he had seemed to want to hurt her, to hurt himself too—for every wound he inflicted on her was inflicted at the same time on himself. 'Why on earth didn't I leave him?' she wondered as she allowed a few more days to flick past.

'August 29th. A letter this morning from Guy in Scotland, so no wonder he took such an endless time to answer mine, which is a relief in one way, because I was beginning to wonder if he wasn't answering on purpose, but also rather depressing, as he says he isn't coming back to Rome till after the middle of September and goodness knows what will have happened by that time. So I felt very melancholy all the morning, sitting under the big tree in front of the monastery, such a marvellous huge old tree with very bright bits of sky between the leaves and bits of sun on the ground and moving across my frock, so that the sadness somehow got mixed up with the loveliness, which it often does do in a queer way, I find. M. came out unexpectedly and suggested going for a little walk before lunch, and he was very sweet for a change, but I dare say it was because he'd worked well. And I said, do you remember the first time we came up to Monte Cavo? and we talked about that afternoon and what fun it had been, even the museum, I said, even my education, because the Apollo was lovely. But he shook his head and said, *Apollo, Apollo, lama sabachthani*, and when I asked why he thought his Apollo had abandoned him he said it was because of Jesus and the Devil, and you're the Devil, I'm afraid, and he laughed and kissed my hand, but I ought to wring your neck, he said. For something that's *your* fault, I said, because it's you who make me a Devil for yourself. But he said it was me who made him make me into a Devil. So I asked how? And he said just by existing, just by having my particular shape, size, colour, and consistency, because if I'd looked like a beetle and felt like wood, I'd have never made him make me into a Devil. So I asked him why he didn't just go away seeing that what was wrong with me was that I was there at all. But that's easier said than done, he said, because a Devil's one of the very few things you can't run away from. And I asked why not? And he said because you can't run away from yourself and a Devil is at least half you. Besides, he said, the essence of a vice is that it *is* a vice—it holds you. Unless it unscrews itself, I said, because I'd made up my mind that minute that I'd go away, and it was such a relief having made up my mind, that I wasn't furious or miserable any more, and when M. smiled and said, if it *can* unscrew itself, I just laughed.'

A little too early, she reflected, as she read the words; she had laughed too early. That night had been the night of the full moon (oh, the humiliation of that lost suspender belt, the horror of that spider squashed against her skin!) and the next day he had begun to be ill. It had been impossible, morally impossible to leave him while he was ill. But how ghastly illness was! She shuddered with horror. Ghastly! 'I'm sorry to be so repulsive,' he had said to her one day, and from her place at his bedside she had protested, but hypocritically, hypocritically. As Aunt Edith might have protested. Still, one's *got* to be hippo-ish, she excused herself, simply *got* to be sometimes. 'But, thank goodness,' she thought, 'he's better now.' In a day or two he'd be quite fit to look after himself. These waters were supposed to be miraculous.

She took a sheet of writing-paper from the box on the table and uncorked the bottle of ink.

'Dear Guy,' she began, 'I wonder if you're back in Rome yet?'

HALF-HOLIDAY

I

It was Saturday afternoon and fine. In the hazy spring sunlight London was beautiful, like a city of the imagination. The lights were golden, the shadows blue and violet. Incorrigibly hopeful, the sooty trees in the Park were breaking into leaf; and the new green was unbelievably fresh and light and aerial, as though the tiny leaves had been cut out of the central emerald stripe of a rainbow. The miracle, to all who walked in the Park that afternoon, was manifest. What had been dead now lived; soot was budding into rainbow green. Yes, it was manifest. And, moreover, those who perceived this thaumaturgical change from death to life were themselves changed. There was something contagious about the vernal miracle. Loving more, the loitering couples under the trees were happier—or much more acutely miserable. Stout men took off their hats, and while the sun kissed their bald heads, made good resolutions—about whisky, about the pretty typist at the office, about early rising. Accosted by spring-intoxicated boys, young girls consented, in the teeth of all their upbringing and their alarm, to go for walks. Middle-aged gentlemen, strolling homewards through the Park, suddenly felt their crusted, business-grimy hearts burgeoning, like these trees, with kindness and generosity. They thought of their wives, thought of them with a sudden gush of affection, in spite of twenty years of marriage. 'Must stop on the way back,' they said to themselves, 'and buy the missus a little present.' What should it be? A box of candied fruits? She liked candied fruits. Or a pot of azaleas? Or . . . And then they remembered that it was Saturday afternoon. The shops would all be shut. And probably, they thought, sighing, the missus's heart would also be shut; for the missus had not walked under the budding trees. Such is life, they reflected, looking sadly at the boats on the glittering Serpentine, at the playing children, at the lovers sitting, hand in hand, on the green grass. Such is life; when the heart is open, the shops are generally shut. But they resolved nevertheless to try, in future, to control their tempers.

On Peter Brett, as on every one else who came within their range of influence, this bright spring sunlight and the new-budded trees profoundly worked. They made him feel, all at once, more lonely, more heartbroken than he had ever felt before. By contrast with the brightness around him, his soul seemed darker. The trees had broken into leaf; but he remained dead. The lovers walked in couples; he walked alone. In spite of the spring, in spite of the sunshine, in spite of the fact that to-day was Saturday and that to-morrow would be Sunday—or rather because of all these things which should have made him happy and which did make other people happy—he loitered through the miracle of Hyde Park feeling deeply miserable.

As usual, he turned for comfort to his imagination. For example, a lovely young creature would slip on a loose stone just in front of him and twist her ankle. Grown larger than life and handsomer, Peter would rush forward to administer first aid. He would take her in a taxi (for which he had money to pay) to her home—in Grosvenor Square. She turned out to be a peer's daughter. They loved each other. . . .

Or else he rescued a child that had fallen into the Round Pond and so earned the eternal gratitude, and more than the gratitude, of its rich young widowed mother. Yes, widowed; Peter always definitely specified her widowhood.

His intentions were strictly honourable. He was still very young and had been well brought up.

Or else there was no preliminary accident. He just saw a young girl sitting on a bench by herself, looking very lonely and sad. Boldly, yet courteously, he approached, he took off his hat, he smiled. 'I can see that you're lonely,' he said; and he spoke elegantly and with ease, without a trace of his Lancashire accent, without so much as a hint of that dreadful stammer which, in real life, made speech such a torment to him. 'I can see that you're lonely. So am I. May I sit down beside you?' She smiled, and he sat down. And then he told her that he was an orphan and that all he had was a married sister who lived in Rochdale. And she said, 'I'm an orphan too.' And that was a great bond between them. And they told one another how miserable they were. And she began to cry. And then he said, 'Don't cry. You've got me.' And at that she cheered up a little. And then they went to the pictures together. And finally, he supposed, they got married. But that part of the story was a little dim.

But of course, as a matter of fact, no accidents ever did happen and he never had the courage to tell any one how lonely he was; and his stammer was something awful; and he was small, he wore spectacles, and nearly always had pimples on his face; and his dark grey suit was growing very shabby and rather short in the sleeves; and his boots, though carefully blacked, looked just as cheap as they really were.

It was the boots which killed his imaginings this afternoon. Walking with downcast eyes, pensively, he was trying to decide what he should say to the peer's lovely young daughter in the taxi on the way to Grosvenor Square, when he suddenly became aware of his alternately striding boots, blackly obtruding themselves through the transparent phantoms of his inner life. How ugly they were! And how sadly unlike those elegant and sumptuously shining boots which encase the feet of the rich! They had been ugly enough when they were new; age had rendered them positively repulsive. No boot trees had corrected the effects of walking, and the uppers, just above the toe-caps, were deeply and hideously wrinkled. Through the polish he could see a network of innumerable little cracks in the parched and shoddy leather. On the outer side of the left boot the toe-cap had come unstitched and had been coarsely sewn up again; the scar was only too visible. Worn by much lacing and unlacing, the eyeholes had lost their black enamel and revealed themselves obtrusively in their brassy nakedness.

Oh, they were horrible, his boots; they were disgusting! But they'd have to last him a long time yet. Peter began to re-make the calculations he had so often and often made before. If he spent three-halfpence less every day on his lunch; if, during the fine weather, he were to walk to the office every morning instead of taking the bus. . . . But however carefully and however often he made his calculations, twenty-seven and sixpence a week always remained twenty-seven and six. Boots were dear; and when he had saved up enough to buy a new pair, there was still the question of his suit. And, to make matters worse, it was spring; the leaves were coming out, the sun shone, and among the amorous couples he walked alone. Reality was too much for him to-day; he could not escape. The boots pursued him whenever he tried to flee, and dragged him back to the contemplation of his misery.

II

The two young women turned out of the crowded walk along the edge of the Serpentine, and struck uphill by a smaller path in the direction of Watts's statue. Peter followed them. An exquisite perfume lingered in the air behind them. He breathed it greedily and his heart began to beat with unaccustomed violence. They seemed to him marvellous and hardly human beings. They were all that was lovely and unattainable. He had met them walking down there, by the Serpentine, had been overwhelmed by that glimpse of a luxurious and arrogant beauty, had turned immediately and followed them. Why? He hardly knew himself. Merely in order that he might be near them; and perhaps with the fantastic, irrepressible hope that something might happen, some miracle, that should project him into their lives.

Greedily he sniffed their delicate perfume; with a kind of desperation, as though his life depended on it, he looked at them, he studied them. Both were tall. One of them wore a grey cloth coat, trimmed with dark grey fur. The other's coat was all of fur; a dozen or two of ruddily golden foxes had been killed in order that she might be warm among the chilly shadows of this spring afternoon. One of them wore grey and the other buff-coloured stockings. One walked on grey kid, the other on serpent's leather. Their hats were small and close-fitting. A small black French bulldog accompanied them, running now at their heels, now in front of them. The dog's collar was trimmed with brindled wolf's fur that stuck out like a ruff round its black head.

Peter walked so close behind them that, when they were out of the crowd, he could hear snatches of their talk. One had a cooing voice; the other spoke rather huskily.

'Such a divine man,' the husky voice was saying, 'such a really divine man!'

'So Elizabeth told me,' said the cooing one.

'Such a perfect party, too,' Husky went on. 'He kept us laughing the whole evening. Everybody got rather buffy, too. When it was time to go, I said I'd walk and trust to luck to find a taxi on the way. Whereupon he invited me to come and look for a taxi in his heart. He said there were so many there, and all of them disengaged.'

They both laughed. The chatter of a party of children who had come up from behind and were passing at this moment prevented Peter from hearing what was said next. Inwardly he cursed the children. Beastly little devils—they were making him lose his revelation. And what a revelation! Of how strange, unfamiliar and gaudy a life! Peter's dreams had always been idyllic and pastoral. Even with the peer's daughter he meant to live in the country, quietly and domestically. The world in which there are perfect parties where everybody gets rather buffy and divine men invite young goddesses to look for taxis in their hearts was utterly unknown to him. He had had a glimpse of it now; it fascinated him by its exotic and tropical strangeness. His whole ambition was now to enter this gorgeous world, to involve himself, somehow and at all costs, in the lives of these young goddesses. Suppose, now, they were both simultaneously to trip over that projecting root and twist their ankles. Suppose . . . But they both stepped over it in safety. And then, all at once, he saw a hope—in the bulldog.

The dog had left the path to sniff at the base of an elm tree growing a few yards away on the right. It had sniffed, it had growled, it had left a challenging souvenir of its visit and was now indignantly kicking up earth and twigs with its hinder paws against the tree, when a yellow Irish terrier trotted up and began in its turn to sniff, first at the tree, then at the bulldog. The bulldog stopped its scrabbling in the dirt and sniffed at the terrier. Cautiously, the two beasts walked round one another, sniffing and growling as they went. Peter watched them for a moment with a vague and languid curiosity. His mind was elsewhere; he hardly saw the two dogs. Then, in an illuminating flash, it occurred to him that they might begin to fight. If they fought, he was a made man. He would rush in and separate them, heroically. He might even be bitten. But that didn't matter. Indeed, it would be all the better. A bite would be another claim on the goddesses' gratitude. Ardently, he hoped that the dogs would fight. The awful thing would be if the goddesses or the owners of the yellow terrier were to notice and interfere before the fight could begin. 'Oh God,' he fervently prayed, 'don't let them call the dogs away from each other now. But let the dogs fight. For Jesus Christ's sake. Amen.' Peter had been piously brought up.

The children had passed. The voices of the goddesses once more became audible.

'. . . Such a fearful bore,' the cooing one was saying. 'I can never move a step without finding him there. And nothing penetrates his hide. I've told him that I hate Jews, that I think he's ugly and stupid and tactless and impertinent and boring. But it doesn't seem to make the slightest difference.'

'You should make him useful, at any rate,' said Husky.

'Oh, I do,' affirmed Coo.

'Well, that's something.'

'Something,' Coo admitted. 'But not much.'

There was a pause. 'Oh, God,' prayed Peter, 'don't let them see.'

'If only,' began Coo meditatively, 'if only men would

understand that . . .' A fearful noise of growling and barking violently interrupted her. The two young women turned in the direction from which the sound came.

'Pongo!' they shouted in chorus, anxiously and commandingly. And again, more urgently, 'Pongo!'

But their cries were unavailing. Pongo and the yellow terrier were already fighting too furiously to pay any attention.

'Pongo! Pongo!'

And, 'Benny!' the little girl and her stout nurse to whom the yellow terrier belonged as unavailingly shouted. 'Benny, come here!'

The moment had come, the passionately anticipated, the richly pregnant moment. Exultantly, Peter threw himself on the dogs. 'Get away, you brute,' he shouted, kicking the Irish terrier. For the terrier was the enemy, the French bulldog—*their* French bulldog—the friend whom he had come, like one of the Olympian gods in the Iliad, to assist. 'Get away!' In his excitement, he forgot that he had a stammer. The letter G was always a difficult one for him; but he managed on this occasion to shout 'Get away' without a trace of hesitation. He grabbed at the dogs by their stumpy tails, by the scruffs of their necks, and tried to drag them apart. From time to time he kicked the yellow terrier. But it was the bulldog which bit him. Stupider even than Ajax, the bulldog had failed to understand that the immortal was fighting on his side. But Peter felt no resentment and, in the heat of the moment, hardly any pain. The blood came oozing out of a row of jagged holes in his left hand.

'Ooh!' cried Coo, as though it were her hand that had been bitten.

'Be careful,' anxiously admonished Husky. 'Be careful.'

The sound of their voices nerved him to further efforts.

He kicked and he tugged still harder; and at last, for a fraction of a second, he managed to part the angry beasts. For a fraction of a second neither dog had any portion of the other's anatomy in his mouth. Peter seized the opportunity, and catching the French bulldog by the loose skin at the back of his neck, he lifted him, still furiously snapping, growling and struggling, into the air. The yellow terrier stood in front of him, barking and every now and then leaping up in a frantic effort to snap the dangling black paws of his enemy. But Peter, with the gesture of Perseus raising on high the severed head of the Gorgon, lifted the writhing Pongo out of danger to the highest stretch of his arm. The yellow dog he kept off with his foot; and the nurse and the little girl, who had by this time somewhat recovered their presence of mind, approached the furious animal from behind and succeeded at last in hooking the leash to his collar. His four rigidly planted paws skidding over the grass, the yellow terrier was dragged away by main force, still barking, though feebly—for he was being half strangled by his efforts to escape. Suspended six feet above the ground by the leathery black scruff of his neck, Pongo vainly writhed.

Peter turned and approached the goddesses. Husky had narrow eyes and a sad mouth; it was a thin, tragic-looking face. Coo was rounder, pinker and whiter, bluer-eyed. Peter looked from one to the other and could not decide which was the more beautiful.

He lowered the writhing Pongo. 'Here's your dog,' was what he wanted to say. But the loveliness of these radiant creatures suddenly brought back all his self-consciousness and with his self-consciousness his stammer. 'Here's your . . .' he began; but could not bring out the dog. D, for Peter, was always a difficult letter.

For all common words beginning with a difficult letter

Peter had a number of easier synonyms in readiness. Thus, he always called cats 'pussies,' not out of any affectation of childishness, but because p was more pronounceable than the impossible c. Coal he had to render in the vaguer form of 'fuel.' Dirt, with him, was always 'muck.' In the discovery of synonyms he had become almost as ingenious as those Anglo-Saxon poets who, using alliteration instead of rhyme, were compelled, in their efforts to make (shall we say) the sea begin with the same letter as its waves or its billows, to call it the 'whale-road' or the 'bath of the swans.' But Peter, who could not permit himself the full poetic licence of his Saxon ancestors, was reduced sometimes to spelling the most difficult words to which there happened to be no convenient and prosaic equivalent. Thus, he was never quite sure whether he should call a cup a mug or a c, u, p. And since 'ovum' seemed to be the only synonym for egg, he was always reduced to talking of e, g, g's.

At the present moment, it was the miserable little word 'dog' that was holding him up. Peter had several synonyms for dog. P being a slightly easier letter than d, he could, when not too nervous, say 'pup.' Or if the p's weren't coming easily, he could call the animal, rather facetiously and mock-heroically, a 'hound.' But the presence of the two goddesses was so unnerving, that Peter found it as hopelessly impossible to pronounce a p or an h as a d. He hesitated painfully, trying to bring out in turn, first dog, then pup, then hound. His face became very red. He was in an agony.

'Here's your whelp,' he managed to say at last. The word, he was conscious, was a little too Shakespearean for ordinary conversation. But it was the only one which came.

'Thank you most awfully,' said Coo.

'You were splendid, really splendid,' said Husky. 'But I'm afraid you're hurt.'

'Oh, it's n-nothing,' Peter declared. And twisting his handkerchief round the bitten hand, he thrust it into his pocket.

Coo, meanwhile, had fastened the end of her leash to Pongo's collar. 'You can put him down now,' she said.

Peter did as he was told. The little black dog immediately bounded forward in the direction of his reluctantly retreating enemy. He came to the end of his tether with a jerk that brought him up on to his hind legs and kept him, barking, in the position of a rampant lion on a coat of arms.

'But are you sure it's nothing?' Husky insisted. 'Let me look at it.'

Obediently, Peter pulled off the handkerchief and held out his hand. It seemed to him that all was happening as he had hoped. Then he noticed with horror that the nails were dirty. If only, if only he had thought of washing before he went out! What would they think of him? Blushing, he tried to withdraw his hand. But Husky held it.

'Wait,' she said. And then added: 'It's a nasty bite.'

'Horrid,' affirmed Coo, who had also bent over it. 'I'm so awfully sorry that my stupid dog should have . . .'

'You ought to go straight to a chemist,' said Husky, interrupting her, 'and get him to disinfect it and tie it up.'

She lifted her eyes from his hand and looked into his face.

'A chemist,' echoed Coo, and also looked up.

Peter looked from one to the other, dazzled equally by the wide-open blue eyes and the narrowed, secret eyes of green. He smiled at them vaguely and vaguely shook his head. Unobtrusively he wrapped up his hand in his handkerchief and thrust it away, out of sight.

'It's n-nothing,' he said.

'But you must,' insisted Husky.

'You must,' cried Coo.

'N-nothing,' he repeated. He didn't want to go to a chemist. He wanted to stay with the goddesses.

Coo turned to Husky. 'Qu'est-ce qu'on donne à ce petit bonhomme?' she asked, speaking very quickly and in a low voice.

Husky shrugged her shoulders and made a little grimace suggestive of uncertainty. 'Il serait offensé, peut-être,' she suggested.

'Tu crois?'

Husky stole a rapid glance at the subject of their discussion, taking him in critically from his cheap felt hat to his cheap boots, from his pale spotty face to his rather dirty hands, from his steel-framed spectacles to his leather watch-guard. Peter saw that she was looking at him and smiled at her with shy, vague rapture. How beautiful she was! He wondered what they had been whispering about together. Perhaps they were debating whether they should ask him to tea. And no sooner had the idea occurred to him than he was sure of it. Miraculously, things were happening just as they happened in his dreams. He wondered if he would have the face to tell them—this first time—that they could look for taxis in his heart.

Husky turned back to her companion. Once more she shrugged her shoulders. 'Vraiment, je ne sais pas,' she whispered.

'Si on lui donnait une livre?' suggested Coo.

Husky nodded. 'Comme tu voudras.' And while the other turned away to fumble unobtrusively in her purse, she addressed herself to Peter.

'You were awfully brave,' she said, smiling.

Peter could only shake his head, blush and lower his eyes from before that steady, self-assured, cool gaze. He longed to look at her; but when it came to the point, he simply could not keep his eyes steadily fixed on those unwavering eyes of hers.

'Perhaps you're used to dogs,' she went on. 'Have you got one of your own?'

'N-no,' Peter managed to say.

'Ah, well, that makes it all the braver,' said Husky. Then, noticing that Coo had found the money she had been looking for, she took the boy's hand and shook it, heartily. 'Well, good-bye,' she said, smiling more exquisitely than ever. 'We're so awfully grateful to you. Most awfully,' she repeated. And as she did so, she wondered why she used that word 'awfully' so often. Ordinarily she hardly ever used it. It had seemed suitable somehow, when she was talking with this creature. She was always very hearty and emphatic and schoolboyishly slangy when she was with the lower classes.

'G-g-g . . .' began Peter. Could they be going, he wondered in an agony, suddenly waking out of his comfortable and rosy dream. Really going, without asking him to tea or giving him their addresses? He wanted to implore them to stop a little longer, to let him see them again. But he knew that he wouldn't be able to utter the necessary words. In the face of Husky's good-bye he felt like a man who sees some fearful catastrophe impending and can do nothing to arrest it. 'G-g . . .' he feebly stuttered. But he found himself shaking hands with the other one before he had got to the end of that fatal good-bye.

'You were really splendid,' said Coo, as she shook his hand. 'Really splendid. And you simply must go to a chemist and have the bite disinfected at once. Good-bye, and thank you very, very much.' As she spoke these last words she slipped a neatly folded one-pound note into his palm and with her two hands shut his fingers over it. 'Thank you *so* much,' she repeated.

Violently blushing, Peter shook his head. 'N-n . . .' he began, and tried to make her take the note back.

But she only smiled more sweetly. 'Yes, yes,' she insisted. 'Please.' And without waiting to hear any more, she turned and ran lightly after Husky, who had walked on, up the path, leading the reluctant Pongo, who still barked and strained heraldically at his leash.

'Well, that's all right,' she said, as she came up with her companion.

'He accepted it?' asked Husky.

'Yes, yes.' She nodded. Then changing her tone, 'Let me see,' she went on, 'what were we saying when this wretched dog interrupted us?'

'N-no,' Peter managed to say at last. But she had already turned and was hurrying away. He took a couple of strides in pursuit; then checked himself. It was no good. It would only lead to further humiliation if he tried to explain. Why, they might even think, while he was standing there, straining to bring out his words, that he had run after them to ask for more. They might slip another pound into his hand and hurry away still faster. He watched them till they were out of sight, over the brow of the hill; then turned back towards the Serpentine.

In his imagination he re-acted the scene, not as it had really happened, but as it ought to have happened. When Coo slipped the note into his hand he smiled and courteously returned it, saying: 'I'm afraid you've made a mistake. A quite justifiable mistake, I admit. For I look poor, and indeed I am poor. But I am a gentleman, you know. My father was a doctor in Rochdale. My mother was a doctor's daughter. I went to a good school till my people died. They died when I was sixteen, within a few months of one another. So I had to go to work before I'd finished my schooling. But you see that I can't take your money.' And then, becoming more gallant, personal and confidential, he went on: 'I separated those beastly dogs because I wanted to do something for you and your friend. Because I thought you so beautiful and wonderful. So that even if I weren't a gentleman, I wouldn't take your money.' Coo was deeply touched by this little speech. She shook him by the hand and told him how sorry she was. And he put her at her ease by assuring her that her mistake had been perfectly comprehensible. And then she asked if he'd care to come along with them and take a cup of tea. And from this point onwards Peter's imaginings became vaguer and rosier, till he was dreaming the old familiar dream of the peer's daughter, the grateful widow and the lonely orphan; only there happened to be two goddesses this time, and their faces, instead of being dim creations of fancy, were real and definite.

But he knew, even in the midst of his dreaming, that things hadn't happened like this. He knew that she had gone before he could say anything; and that even if he had run after them and tried to make his speech of explanation, he could never have done it. For example, he would have had to say that his father was a 'medico,' not a doctor (m being an easier letter than d). And when it came to telling them that his people had died, he would have had to say that they had 'perished'—which would sound facetious, as though he were trying to make a joke of it. No, no, the truth must be faced. He had taken the money and they had gone away thinking that he was just some sort of a street loafer, who had risked a bite for the sake of a good tip. They hadn't even dreamed of treating him as an equal. As for asking him to tea and making him their friend . . .

But his fancy was still busy. It struck him that it had been quite unnecessary to make any explanation. He might simply have forced the note back into her hand, without saying a word. Why hadn't he done it? He had to excuse himself for his remissness. She had slipped away too quickly; that was the reason.

Or what if he had walked on ahead of them and ostentatiously given the money to the first street-boy he happened to meet? A good idea, that. Unfortunately it had not occurred to him at the time.

All that afternoon Peter walked and walked, thinking of what had happened, imagining creditable and satisfying alternatives. But all the time he knew that these alternatives were only fanciful. Sometimes the recollection of his humiliation was so vivid that it made him physically wince and shudder.

The light began to fail. In the grey and violet twilight the lovers pressed closer together as they walked, more frankly clasped one another beneath the trees. Strings of yellow lamps blossomed in the increasing darkness. High up in the pale sky overhead, a quarter of the moon made itself visible. He felt unhappier and lonelier than ever.

His bitten hand was by this time extremely painful. He left the Park and walked along Oxford Street till he found a chemist. When his hand had been disinfected and bandaged he went into a tea-shop and ordered a poached e, g, g, a roll, and a mug of mocha, which he had to translate for the benefit of the uncomprehending waitress as a c, u, p of c, o, f, f, e, e.

'You seem to think I'm a loafer or a tout.' That's what he ought to have said to her, indignantly and proudly.

'You've insulted me. If you were a man, I'd knock you down. Take your dirty money.' But then, he reflected, he could hardly have expected them to become his friends, after that. On second thoughts, he decided that indignation would have been no good.

'Hurt your hand?' asked the waitress sympathetically, as she set down his egg and his mug of mocha.

Peter nodded. 'B-bitten by a d-d . . . by a h-h-hound.' The word burst out at last, explosively.

Remembered shame made him blush as he spoke. Yes, they had taken him for a tout, they had treated him as though he didn't really exist, as though he were just an instrument whose services you hired and to which, when the bill had been paid, you gave no further thought. The remembrance of humiliation was so vivid, the realization of it so profound and complete, that it affected not only his mind but his body too. His heart beat with unusual rapidity and violence; he felt sick. It was with the greatest difficulty that he managed to eat his egg and drink his mug of mocha.

Still remembering the painful reality, still feverishly constructing his fanciful alternatives to it, Peter left the tea-shop and, though he was very tired, resumed his aimless walking. He walked along Oxford Street as far as the Circus, turned down Regent Street, halted in Piccadilly to look at the epileptically twitching sky-signs, walked up Shaftesbury Avenue, and turning southwards made his way through by-streets towards the Strand.

In a street near Covent Garden a woman brushed against him. 'Cheer up, dearie,' she said. 'Don't look so glum.'

Peter looked at her in astonishment. Was it possible that she should have been speaking to him? A woman—was it possible? He knew, of course, that she was what people called a bad woman. But the fact that she should have spoken to him seemed none the less extraordinary; and he did not connect it, somehow, with her 'badness.'

'Come along with me,' she wheedled.

Peter nodded. He could not believe it was true. She took his arm.

'You got money?' she asked anxiously.

He nodded again.

'You look as though you'd been to a funeral,' said the woman.

'I'm l-lonely,' he explained. He felt ready to weep. He even longed to weep—to weep and to be comforted. His voice trembled as he spoke.

'Lonely? That's funny. A nice-looking boy like you's got no call to be lonely.' She laughed significantly and without mirth.

Her bedroom was dimly and pinkly lighted. A smell of cheap scent and unwashed underlinen haunted the air.

'Wait a tick,' she said, and disappeared through a door into an inner room.

He sat there, waiting. A minute later she returned, wearing a kimono and bedroom slippers. She sat on his knees, threw her arms round his neck and began to kiss him. 'Lovey,' she said in her cracked voice, 'lovey.' Her eyes were hard and cold. Her breath smelt of spirits. Seen at close range she was indescribably horrible.

Peter saw her, it seemed to him, for the first time—saw and completely realized her. He averted his face. Remembering the peer's daughter who had sprained her ankle, the lonely orphan, the widow whose child had tumbled into the Round Pond; remembering Coo and Husky, he untwined her arms, he pushed her away from him, he sprang to his feet.

'S-sorry,' he said. 'I must g-g . . . I'd forg-gotten

something. I . . .' He picked up his hat and moved towards the door.

The woman ran after him and caught him by the arm. 'You young devil, you,' she screamed. Her abuse was horrible and filthy. 'Asking a girl and then trying to sneak away without paying. Oh, no you don't, no you don't. You . . .'

And the abuse began again.

Peter dipped his hand into his pocket, and pulled out Coo's neatly folded note. 'L-let me g-go,' he said as he gave it her.

While she was suspiciously unfolding it, he hurried away, slamming the door behind him, and ran down the dark stairs, into the street.

TWO OR THREE GRACES

THE TILLOTSON BANQUET

I

YOUNG Spode was not a snob; he was too intelligent for that, too fundamentally decent. Not a snob; but all the same he could not help feeling very well pleased at the thought that he was dining, alone and intimately, with Lord Badgery. It was a definite event in his life, a step forward, he felt, towards that final success, social, material, and literary, which he had come to London with the fixed intention of making. The conquest and capture of Badgery was an almost essential strategical move in the campaign.

Edmund, forty-seventh Baron Badgery, was a lineal descendant of that Edmund, surnamed Le Blayreau, who landed on English soil in the train of William the Conqueror. Ennobled by William Rufus, the Badgerys had been one of the very few baronial families to survive the Wars of the Roses and all the other changes and chances of English history. They were a sensible and philoprogenitive race. No Badgery had ever fought in any war, no Badgery had ever engaged in any kind of politics. They had been content to live and quietly to propagate their species in a huge machicolated Norman castle, surrounded by a triple moat, only sallying forth to cultivate their property and to collect their rents. In the eighteenth century, when life had become relatively secure, the Badgerys began to venture forth into civilized society. From boorish squires they blossomed into *grands seigneurs*, patrons of the arts, virtuosi. Their property was large, they were rich; and with the growth of industrialism their riches also grew. Villages on their estate turned into manufacturing towns, unsuspected coal was discovered beneath the surface of their barren moorlands. By the middle of the nineteenth century the Badgerys were among the richest of English noble families. The forty-seventh baron disposed of an income of at least two hundred thousand pounds a year. Following the great Badgery tradition, he had refused to have anything to do with politics or war. He occupied himself by collecting pictures; he took an interest in theatrical productions; he was the friend and patron of men of letters, of painters, and musicians. A personage, in a word, of considerable consequence in that particular world in which young Spode had elected to make his success.

Spode had only recently left the university. Simon Gollamy, the editor of the *World's Review* (the 'Best of all possible Worlds'), had got to know him—he was always on the look out for youthful talent—had seen possibilities in the young man, and appointed him art critic of his paper. Gollamy liked to have young and teachable people about him. The possession of disciples flattered his vanity, and he found it easier, moreover, to run his paper with docile collaborators than with men grown obstinate and case-hardened with age. Spode had not done badly at his new job. At any rate, his articles had been intelligent enough to arouse the interest of Lord Badgery. It was, ultimately, to them that he owed the honour of sitting to-night in the dining-room of Badgery House.

Fortified by several varieties of wine and a glass of aged brandy, Spode felt more confident and at ease than he had done the whole evening. Badgery was rather a disquieting host. He had an alarming habit of changing the subject of any conversation that had lasted for more than two minutes. Spode had found it, for example, horribly mortifying when his host, cutting across what was, he prided himself, a particularly subtle and illuminating disquisition on baroque art, had turned a wandering eye about the room and asked him abruptly whether he liked parrots. He had flushed and glanced suspiciously towards him, fancying that the man was trying to be offensive. But no; Badgery's white, fleshy, Hanoverian face wore an expression of perfect good faith. There was no malice in his small greenish eyes. He evidently did genuinely want to know if Spode liked parrots. The young man swallowed his irritation and replied that he did. Badgery then told a good story about parrots. Spode was on the point of capping it with a better story, when his host began to talk about Beethoven. And so the game went on. Spode cut his conversation to suit his host's requirements. In the course of ten minutes he had made a more or less witty epigram on Benvenuto Cellini, Queen Victoria, sport, God, Stephen Phillips, and Moorish architecture. Lord Badgery thought him the most charming young man, and so intelligent.

'If you've quite finished your coffee,' he said, rising to his feet as he spoke, 'we'll go and look at the pictures.'

Spode jumped up with alacrity, and only then realized that he had drunk just ever so little too much. He would have to be careful, talk deliberately, plant his feet consciously, one after the other.

'This house is quite cluttered up with pictures,' Lord Badgery complained. 'I had a whole wagon-load taken away to the country last week; but there are still far too many. My ancestors would have their portraits painted by Romney. Such a shocking artist, don't you think? Why couldn't they have chosen Gainsborough, or even Reynolds? I've had all the Romneys hung in the servants' hall now. It's such a comfort to know that one can never possibly see them again. I suppose you know all about the ancient Hittites?'

'Well . . .' the young man replied, with befitting modesty.

'Look at that, then.' He indicated a large stone head which stood in a case near the dining-room door. 'It's not Greek, or Egyptian, or Persian, or anything else; so if it isn't ancient Hittite, I don't know what it is. And that reminds me of that story about Lord George Sanger, the Circus King . . .' and, without giving Spode time to examine the Hittite relic, he led the way up the huge staircase, pausing every now and then in his anecdote to point out some new object of curiosity or beauty.

'I suppose you know Deburau's pantomimes?' Spode rapped out as soon as the story was over. He was in an itch to let out his information about Deburau. Badgery had given him a perfect opening with his ridiculous Sanger. 'What a perfect man, isn't he? He used to . . .'

'This is my main gallery,' said Lord Badgery, throwing open one leaf of a tall folding door. 'I must apologize for it. It looks like a roller-skating rink.' He fumbled with the electric switches and there was suddenly light—light that revealed an enormous gallery, duly receding into distance according to all the laws of perspective. 'I dare say you've heard of my poor father,' Lord Badgery continued. 'A little insane, you know; sort of mechanical genius with a screw loose. He used to have a toy railway in this room. No end of fun he had, crawling about the floor after his trains. And all the pictures were stacked in the cellars. I can't tell you what they were like when I found them: mushrooms growing out of the Botticellis. Now I'm rather proud of this Poussin; he painted it for Scarron.'

'Exquisite!' Spode exclaimed, making with his hand a gesture as though he were modelling a pure form in the air. 'How splendid the onrush of those trees and leaning figures is! And the way they're caught up, as it were, and stemmed by that single godlike form opposing them with his contrary movement! And the draperies . . .'

But Lord Badgery had moved on, and was standing in front of a little fifteenth-century Virgin of carved wood.

'School of Rheims,' he explained.

They 'did' the gallery at high speed. Badgery never permitted his guest to halt for more than forty seconds before any work of art. Spode would have liked to spend a few moments of recollection and tranquillity in front of some of these lovely things. But it was not permitted.

The gallery done, they passed into a little room leading out of it. At the sight of what the lights revealed, Spode gasped.

'It's like something out of Balzac,' he exclaimed. 'Un de ces salons dorés où se déploie un luxe insolent. You know.'

'My nineteenth-century chamber,' Badgery explained. 'The best thing of its kind, I flatter myself, outside the State Apartments at Windsor.'

Spode tiptoed round the room, peering with astonishment at all the objects in glass, in gilded bronze, in china, in feathers, in embroidered and painted silk, in beads, in wax, objects of the most fantastic shapes and colours, all the queer products of a decadent tradition, with which the room was crowded. There were paintings on the walls —a Martin, a Wilkie, an early Landseer, several Ettys, a big Haydon, a slight pretty water-colour of a girl by Wainewright, the pupil of Blake and arsenic poisoner, and a score of others. But the picture which arrested Spode's attention was a medium-sized canvas representing Troilus riding into Troy among the flowers and plaudits of an admiring crowd, and oblivious (you could see from his expression) of everything but the eyes of Cressida, who looked down at him from a window, with Pandarus smiling over her shoulder.

'What an absurd and enchanting picture!' Spode exclaimed.

'Ah, you've spotted my Troilus.' Lord Badgery was pleased.

'What bright harmonious colours! Like Etty's, only stronger, not so obviously pretty. And there's an energy about it that reminds one of Haydon. Only Haydon could never have done anything so impeccable in taste. Who is it by?' Spode turned to his host enquiringly.

'You were right in detecting Haydon,' Lord Badgery answered. 'It's by his pupil, Tillotson. I wish I could get hold of more of his work. But nobody seems to know anything about him. And he seems to have done so little.'

This time it was the younger man who interrupted.

'Tillotson, Tillotson . . .' He put his hand to his forehead. A frown incongruously distorted his round, floridly curved face. 'No . . . yes, I have it.' He looked up triumphantly with serene and childish brows. 'Tillotson, Walter Tillotson—the man's still alive.'

Badgery smiled. 'This picture was painted in 1846, you know.'

'Well, that's all right. Say he was born in 1820, painted his masterpiece when he was twenty-six, and it's 1913 now; that's to say he's only ninety-three. Not as old as Titian yet.'

'But he's not been heard of since 1860,' Lord Badgery protested.

'Precisely. Your mention of his name reminded me of the discovery I made the other day when I was looking through the obituary notices in the archives of the *World's*

Review. (One has to bring them up to date every year or so for fear of being caught napping if one of these old birds chooses to shuffle off suddenly.) Well there, among them—I remember my astonishment at the time—there I found Walter Tillotson's biography. Pretty full to 1860, and then a blank, except for a pencil note in the early nineteen hundreds to the effect that he had returned from the East. The obituary has never been used or added to. I draw the obvious conclusion: the old chap isn't dead yet. He's just been overlooked somehow.'

'But this is extraordinary,' Lord Badgery exclaimed. 'You must find him, Spode—you must find him. I'll commission him to paint frescoes round this room. It's just what I've always vainly longed for—a real nineteenth-century artist to decorate this place for me. Oh, we must find him at once—at once.'

Lord Badgery strode up and down in a state of great excitement.

'I can see how this room could be made quite perfect,' he went on. 'We'd clear away all these cases and have the whole of that wall filled by a heroic fresco of Hector and Andromache, or "Distraining for Rent," or Fanny Kemble as Belvidera in "Venice Preserved"—anything like that, provided it's in the grand manner of the 'thirties and 'forties. And here I'd have a landscape with lovely receding perspectives, or else something architectural and grand in the style of Belshazzar's feast. Then we'll have this Adam fireplace taken down and replaced by something Mauro-Gothic. And on these walls I'll have mirrors, or no! let me see . . .'

He sank into meditative silence, from which he finally roused himself to shout:

'The old man, the old man! Spode, we must find this astonishing old creature. And don't breathe a word to anybody. Tillotson shall be our secret. Oh, it's too perfect, it's incredible! Think of the frescoes.'

Lord Badgery's face had become positively animated. He had talked of a single subject for nearly a quarter of an hour.

II

Three weeks later Lord Badgery was aroused from his usual after-luncheon somnolence by the arrival of a telegram. The message was a short one. 'Found.—SPODE.' A look of pleasure and intelligence made human Lord Badgery's clayey face of surfeit. 'No answer,' he said. The footman padded away on noiseless feet.

Lord Badgery closed his eyes and began to contemplate. Found! What a room he would have! There would be nothing like it in the world. The frescoes, the fireplace, the mirrors, the ceiling. . . . And a small, shrivelled old man clambering about the scaffolding, agile and quick like one of those whiskered little monkeys at the Zoo, painting away, painting away. . . . Fanny Kemble as Belvidera, Hector and Andromache, or why not the Duke of Clarence in the Butt, the Duke of Malmsey, the Butt of Clarence. . . . Lord Badgery was asleep.

Spode did not lag long behind his telegram. He was at Badgery House by six o'clock. His lordship was in the nineteenth-century chamber, engaged in clearing away with his own hands the bric-à-brac. Spode found him looking hot and out of breath.

'Ah, there you are,' said Lord Badgery. 'You see me already preparing for the great man's coming. Now you must tell me all about him.'

'He's older even than I thought,' said Spode. 'He's ninety-seven this year. Born in 1816. Incredible, isn't it! There, I'm beginning at the wrong end.'

'Begin where you like,' said Badgery genially.

'I won't tell you all the incidents of the hunt. You've no idea what a job I had to run him to earth. It was like a Sherlock Holmes story, immensely elaborate, too elaborate. I shall write a book about it some day. At any rate, I found him at last.'

'Where?'

'In a sort of respectable slum in Holloway, older and poorer and lonelier than you could have believed possible. I found out how it was he came to be forgotten, how he came to drop out of life in the way he did. He took it into his head, somewhere about the 'sixties, to go to Palestine to get local colour for his religious pictures—scapegoats and things, you know. Well, he went to Jerusalem and then on to Mount Lebanon and on and on, and then, somewhere in the middle of Asia Minor, he got stuck. He got stuck for about forty years.'

'But what did he do all that time?'

'Oh, he painted, and started a mission, and converted three Turks, and taught the local Pashas the rudiments of English, Latin, and perspective, and God knows what else. Then, in about 1904, it seems to have occurred to him that he was getting rather old and had been away from home for rather a long time. So he made his way back to England, only to find that every one he had known was dead, that the dealers had never heard of him and wouldn't buy his pictures, that he was simply a ridiculous old figure of fun. So he got a job as a drawing-master in a girls' school in Holloway, and there he's been ever since, growing older and older, and feebler and feebler, and blinder and deafer, and generally more gaga, until finally the school has given him the sack. He had about ten pounds in the world when I found him. He lives in a kind of black hole in a basement full of beetles. When his ten pounds are spent, I suppose he'll just quietly die there.'

Badgery held up a white hand. 'No more, no more. I find literature quite depressing enough. I insist that life at least shall be a little gayer. Did you tell him I wanted him to paint my room?'

'But he can't paint. He's too blind and palsied.'

'Can't paint?' Badgery exclaimed in horror. 'Then what's the good of the old creature?'

'Well, if you put it like that . . .' Spode began.

'I shall never have my frescoes. Ring the bell, will you?'

Spode rang.

'What right has Tillotson to go on existing if he can't paint?' went on Lord Badgery petulantly. 'After all, that was his only justification for occupying a place in the sun.'

'He doesn't have much sun in his basement.'

The footman appeared at the door.

'Get someone to put all these things back in their places,' Lord Badgery commanded, indicating with a wave of the hand the ravaged cases, the confusion of glass and china with which he had littered the floor, the pictures unhooked. 'We'll go to the library, Spode; it's more comfortable there.'

He led the way through the long gallery and down the stairs.

'I'm sorry old Tillotson has been such a disappointment,' said Spode sympathetically.

'Let us talk about something else; he ceases to interest me.'

'But don't you think we ought to do something about him? He's only got ten pounds between him and the workhouse. And if you'd seen the blackbeetles in his basement!'

'Enough—enough. I'll do everything you think fitting.'

'I thought we might get up a subscription amongst lovers of the arts.'

'There aren't any,' said Badgery.

'No; but there are plenty of people who will subscribe out of snobbism.'

'Not unless you give them something for their money.'

'That's true. I hadn't thought of that.' Spode was silent for a moment. 'We might have a dinner in his honour. The Great Tillotson Banquet. Doyen of British Art. A Link with the Past. Can't you see it in the papers? I'd make a stunt of it in the *World's Review*—That ought to bring in the snobs.'

'And we'll invite a lot of artists and critics—all the ones who can't stand one another. It will be fun to see them squabbling.' Badgery laughed. Then his face darkened once again. 'Still,' he added, 'it'll be a very poor second best to my frescoes. You'll stay to dinner, of course.'

'Well, since you suggest it. Thanks very much.'

III

The Tillotson Banquet was fixed to take place about three weeks later. Spode, who had charge of the arrangements, proved himself an excellent organizer. He secured the big banqueting-room at the Café Bomba, and was successful in bullying and cajoling the manager into giving fifty persons dinner at twelve shillings a head, including wine. He sent out invitations and collected subscriptions. He wrote an article on Tillotson in the *World's Review*—one of those charming, witty articles, couched in the tone of amused patronage and contempt with which one speaks of the great men of 1840. Nor did he neglect Tillotson himself. He used to go to Holloway almost every day to listen to the old man's endless stories about Asia Minor and the Great Exhibition of '51 and Benjamin Robert Haydon. He was sincerely sorry for this relic of another age.

Mr. Tillotson's room was about ten feet below the level of the soil of South Holloway. A little grey light percolated through the area bars, forced a difficult passage through panes opaque with dirt, and spent itself, like a drop of milk that falls into an inkpot, among the inveterate shadows of the dungeon. The place was haunted by the sour smell of damp plaster and of woodwork that has begun to moulder secretly at the heart. A little miscellaneous furniture, including a bed, a washstand and chest of drawers, a table and one or two chairs, lurked in the obscure corners of the den or ventured furtively out into the open. Hither Spode now came almost every day, bringing the old man news of the progress of the banquet scheme. Every day he found Mr. Tillotson sitting in the same place under the window, bathing, as it were, in his tiny puddle of light. 'The oldest man that ever wore grey hairs,' Spode reflected as he looked at him. Only there were very few hairs left on that bald, unpolished head. At the sound of the visitor's knock Mr. Tillotson would turn in his chair, stare in the direction of the door with blinking, uncertain eyes. He was always full of apologies for being so slow in recognizing who was there.

'No discourtesy meant,' he would say, after asking. 'It's not as if I had forgotten who you were. Only it's so dark and my sight isn't what it was.'

After that he never failed to give a little laugh, and, pointing out of the window at the area railings, would say:

'Ah, this is the place for somebody with good sight. It's the place for looking at ankles. It's the grand stand.'

It was the day before the great event. Spode came as usual, and Mr. Tillotson punctually made his little joke about the ankles and Spode as punctually laughed.

'Well, Mr. Tillotson,' he said, after the reverberation of the joke had died away, 'to-morrow you make your re-entry into the world of art and fashion. You'll find some changes.'

'I've always had such extraordinary luck,' said Mr. Tillotson, and Spode could see by his expression that he genuinely believed it, that he had forgotten the black hole and the blackbeetles and the almost exhausted ten pounds that stood between him and the workhouse. 'What an amazing piece of good fortune, for instance, that you should have found me just when you did. Now, this dinner will bring me back to my place in the world. I shall have money, and in a little while—who knows?—I shall be able to see well enough to paint again. I believe my eyes are getting better, you know. Ah, the future is very rosy.'

Mr. Tillotson looked up, his face puckered into a smile, and nodded his head in affirmation of his words.

'You believe in the life to come?' said Spode, and immediately flushed for shame at the cruelty of the words.

But Mr. Tillotson was in far too cheerful a mood to have caught their significance.

'Life to come,' he repeated. 'No, I don't believe in any of that stuff—not since 1859. The "Origin of Species" changed my views, you know. No life to come for me, thank you! You don't remember the excitement, of course. You're very young, Mr. Spode.'

'Well, I'm not so old as I was,' Spode replied. 'You know how middle-aged one is as a schoolboy and undergraduate. Now I'm old enough to know I'm young.'

Spode was about to develop this little paradox further, but he noticed that Mr. Tillotson had not been listening.

He made a note of the gambit for use in companies that were more appreciative of the subtleties.

'You were talking about the "Origin of Species,"' he said.

'Was I?' said Mr. Tillotson, waking from reverie.

'About its effect on your faith, Mr. Tillotson.'

'To be sure, yes. It shattered my faith. But I remember a fine thing by the Poet Laureate, something about there being more faith in honest doubt, believe me, than in all the . . . all the . . . I forget exactly what; but you see the train of thought. Oh, it was a bad time for religion. I am glad my master Haydon never lived to see it. He was a man of fervour. I remember him pacing up and down his studio in Lisson Grove, singing and shouting and praying all at once. It used almost to frighten me. Oh, but he was a wonderful man, a great man. Take him for all in all, we shall not look upon his like again. As usual, the Bard is right. But it was all very long ago, before your time, Mr. Spode.'

'Well, I'm not as old as I was,' said Spode, in the hope of having his paradox appreciated this time. But Mr. Tillotson went on without noticing the interruption.

'It's a very, very long time. And yet, when I look back on it, it all seems but a day or two ago. Strange that each day should seem so long and that many days added together should be less than an hour. How clearly I can see old Haydon pacing up and down! Much more clearly, indeed, than I see you, Mr. Spode. The eyes of memory don't grow dim. But my sight is improving, I assure you; it's improving daily. I shall soon be able to see those ankles.' He laughed, like a cracked bell—one of those little old bells, Spode fancied, that ring, with much rattling of wires, in the far-off servants' quarters of ancient houses. 'And very soon,' Mr. Tillotson went on,

'I shall be painting again. Ah, Mr. Spode, my luck is extraordinary. I believe in it, I trust it. And after all, what is luck? Simply another name for Providence, in spite of the "Origin of Species" and the rest of it. How right the Laureate was when he said that there was more faith in honest doubt, believe me, than in all the . . . er, the . . . er . . . well, you know. I regard you, Mr. Spode, as the emissary of Providence. Your coming marked a turning-point in my life, and the beginning, for me, of happier days. Do you know, one of the first things I shall do when my fortunes are restored will be to buy a hedgehog.'

'A hedgehog, Mr. Tillotson?'

'For the blackbeetles. There's nothing like a hedgehog for beetles. It will eat blackbeetles till it's sick, till it dies of surfeit. That reminds me of the time when I told my poor great master Haydon—in joke, of course—that he ought to send in a cartoon of King John dying of a surfeit of lampreys for the frescoes in the new Houses of Parliament. As I told him, it's a most notable event in the annals of British liberty—the providential and exemplary removal of a tyrant.'

Mr. Tillotson laughed again—the little bell in the deserted house; a ghostly hand pulling the cord in the drawing-room, and phantom footmen responding to the thin, flawed note.

'I remember he laughed, laughed like a bull in his old grand manner. But oh, it was a terrible blow when they rejected his designs, a terrible blow! It was the first and fundamental cause of his suicide.'

Mr. Tillotson paused. There was a long silence. Spode felt strangely moved, he hardly knew why, in the presence of this man, so frail, so ancient, in body three parts dead, in the spirit so full of life and hopeful patience. He felt ashamed. What was the use of his own youth and cleverness? He saw himself suddenly as a boy with a rattle, scaring birds—rattling his noisy cleverness, waving his arms in ceaseless and futile activity, never resting in his efforts to scare away the birds that were always trying to settle in his mind. And what birds! wide-winged and beautiful, all those serene thoughts and faiths and emotions that only visit minds that have humbled themselves to quiet. Those gracious visitants he was for ever using all his energies to drive away. But this old man, with his hedgehogs and his honest doubts and all the rest of it—his mind was like a field made beautiful by the free coming and going, the unafraid alightings of a multitude of white, bright-winged creatures. He felt ashamed. But then, was it possible to alter one's life? Wasn't it a little absurd to risk a conversion? Spode shrugged his shoulders.

'I'll get you a hedgehog at once,' he said. 'They're sure to have some at Whiteley's.'

Before he left that evening Spode made an alarming discovery. Mr. Tillotson did not possess a dress-suit. It was hopeless to think of getting one made at this short notice, and, besides, what an unnecessary expense!

'We shall have to borrow a suit, Mr. Tillotson. I ought to have thought of that before.'

'Dear me, dear me.' Mr. Tillotson was a little chagrined by this unlucky discovery. 'Borrow a suit?'

Spode hurried away for counsel to Badgery House. Lord Badgery surprisingly rose to the occasion. 'Ask Boreham to come and see me,' he told the footman who answered his ring.

Boreham was one of those immemorial butlers who linger on, generation after generation, in the houses of the great. He was over eighty now, bent, dried up, shrivelled with age.

'All old men are about the same size,' said Lord Badgery. It was a comforting theory. 'Ah, here he is. Have you got a spare suit of evening clothes, Boreham?'

'I have an old suit, my lord, that I stopped wearing in—let me see—was it nineteen seven or eight?'

'That's the very thing. I should be most grateful, Boreham, if you could lend it to me for Mr. Spode here for a day.'

The old man went out, and soon reappeared carrying over his arm a very old black suit. He held up the coat and trousers for inspection. In the light of day they were deplorable.

'You've no idea, sir,' said Boreham deprecatingly to Spode—'you've no idea how easy things get stained with grease and gravy and what not. However careful you are, sir—however careful.'

'I should imagine so.' Spode was sympathetic.

'However careful, sir.'

'But in artificial light they'll look all right.'

'Perfectly all right,' Lord Badgery repeated. 'Thank you, Boreham; you shall have them back on Thursday.'

'You're welcome, my lord, I'm sure.' And the old man bowed and disappeared.

On the afternoon of the great day Spode carried up to Holloway a parcel containing Boreham's retired evening-suit and all the necessary appurtenances in the way of shirts and collars. Owing to the darkness and his own feeble sight Mr. Tillotson was happily unaware of the defects in the suit. He was in a state of extreme nervous agitation. It was with some difficulty that Spode could prevent him, although it was only three o'clock, from starting his toilet on the spot.

'Take it easy, Mr. Tillotson, take it easy. We needn't start till half-past seven, you know.'

Spode left an hour later, and as soon as he was safely out of the room Mr. Tillotson began to prepare himself for the banquet. He lighted the gas and a couple of candles, and, blinking myopically at the image that fronted him in the tiny looking-glass that stood on his chest of drawers, he set to work, with all the ardour of a young girl preparing for her first ball. At six o'clock, when the last touches had been given, he was not unsatisfied.

He marched up and down his cellar, humming to himself the gay song which had been so popular in his middle years:

'Oh, oh, Anna Maria Jones!
Queen of the tambourine, the cymbals, and the bones!'

Spode arrived an hour later in Lord Badgery's second Rolls-Royce. Opening the door of the old man's dungeon, he stood for a moment, wide-eyed with astonishment, on the threshold. Mr. Tillotson was standing by the empty grate, one elbow resting on the mantelpiece, one leg crossed over the other in a jaunty and gentlemanly attitude. The effect of the candlelight shining on his face was to deepen every line and wrinkle with intense black shadow; he looked immeasurably old. It was a noble and pathetic head. On the other hand, Boreham's outworn evening-suit was simply buffoonish. The coat was too long in the sleeves and the tail; the trousers bagged in elephantine creases about his ankles. Some of the grease-spots were visible even in candlelight. The white tie, over which Mr. Tillotson had taken infinite pains and which he believed in his purblindness to be perfect, was fantastically lop-sided. He had buttoned up his waistcoat in such a fashion that one button was widowed of its hole and one hole of its button. Across his shirt front lay the broad green ribbon of some unknown Order.

'Queen of the tambourine, the cymbals, and the bones,'

Mr. Tillotson concluded in a gnat-like voice before welcoming his visitor.

'Well, Spode, here you are. I'm dressed already, you see. The suit, I flatter myself, fits very well, almost as though it had been made for me. I am all gratitude to the gentleman who was kind enough to lend it to me; I shall take the greatest care of it. It's a dangerous thing to lend clothes. For loan oft loseth both itself and friend. The Bard is always right.'

'Just one thing,' said Spode. 'A touch to your waistcoat.' He unbuttoned the dissipated garment and did it up again more symmetrically.

Mr. Tillotson was a little piqued at being found so absurdly in the wrong. 'Thanks, thanks,' he said protestingly, trying to edge away from his valet. 'It's all right, you know; I can do it myself. Foolish oversight. I flatter myself the suit fits very well.'

'And perhaps the tie might . . .' Spode began tentatively. But the old man would not hear of it.

'No, no. The tie's all right. I can tie a tie, Mr. Spode. The tie's all right. Leave it as it is, I beg.'

'I like your Order.'

Mr. Tillotson looked down complacently at his shirt front. 'Ah, you've noticed my Order. It's a long time since I wore that. It was given me by the Grand Porte, you know, for services rendered in the Russo-Turkish War. It's the Order of Chastity, the second class. They only give the first class to crowned heads, you know—crowned heads and ambassadors. And only Pashas of the highest rank get the second. Mine's the second. They only give the first class to crowned heads . . .'

'Of course, of course,' said Spode.

'Do you think I look all right, Mr. Spode?' Mr. Tillotson asked, a little anxiously.

'Splendid, Mr. Tillotson—splendid. The Order's magnificent.'

The old man's face brightened once more. 'I flatter myself,' he said, 'that this borrowed suit fits me very well. But I don't like borrowing clothes. For loan oft loseth both itself and friend, you know. And the Bard is always right.'

'Ugh, there's one of those horrible beetles!' Spode exclaimed.

Mr. Tillotson bent down and stared at the floor. 'I see it,' he said, and stamped on a small piece of coal, which crunched to powder under his foot. 'I shall certainly buy a hedgehog.'

It was time for them to start. A crowd of little boys and girls had collected round Lord Badgery's enormous car. The chauffeur, who felt that honour and dignity were at stake, pretended not to notice the children, but sat gazing, like a statue, into eternity. At the sight of Spode and Mr. Tillotson emerging from the house a yell of mingled awe and derision went up. It subsided to an astonished silence as they climbed into the car. 'Bomba's,' Spode directed. The Rolls-Royce gave a faintly stertorous sigh and began to move. The children yelled again, and ran along beside the car, waving their arms in a frenzy of excitement. It was then that Mr. Tillotson, with an incomparably noble gesture, leaned forward and tossed among the seething crowd of urchins his three last coppers.

IV

In Bomba's big room the company was assembling. The long gilt-edged mirrors reflected a singular collection of people. Middle-aged Academicians shot suspicious glances at youths whom they suspected, only too correctly, of being iconoclasts, organizers of Post-Impressionist Exhibitions. Rival art critics, brought suddenly face to face, quivered with restrained hatred. Mrs. Nobes, Mrs. Cayman, and Mrs. Mandragore, those indefatigable hunters of artistic big game, came on one another all unawares in this well-stored menagerie, where each had expected to hunt alone and were filled with rage. Through this crowd of mutually repellent vanities Lord Badgery moved with a suavity that seemed unconscious of all the feuds and hatreds. He was enjoying himself immensely. Behind the heavy waxen mask of his face, ambushed behind the Hanoverian nose, the little lustreless pig's eyes, the pale thick lips, there lurked a small devil of happy malice that rocked with laughter.

'So nice of you to have come, Mrs. Mandragore, to do honour to England's artistic past. And I'm so glad to see you've brought dear Mrs. Cayman. And is that Mrs. Nobes, too? So it is! I hadn't noticed her before. How delightful! I knew we could depend on your love of art.'

And he hurried away to seize the opportunity of introducing that eminent sculptor, Sir Herbert Herne, to the bright young critic who had called him, in the public prints, a monumental mason.

A moment later the Maître d'Hôtel came to the door of the gilded saloon and announced, loudly and impressively, 'Mr. Walter Tillotson.' Guided from behind by young Spode, Mr. Tillotson came into the room slowly and hesitatingly. In the glare of the lights his eyelids beat heavily, painfully, like the wings of an imprisoned moth, over his filmy eyes. Once inside the door he halted and drew himself up with a conscious assumption of dignity. Lord Badgery hurried forward and seized his hand.

'Welcome, Mr. Tillotson—welcome in the name of English art!'

Mr. Tillotson inclined his head in silence. He was too full of emotion to be able to reply.

'I should like to introduce you to a few of your younger colleagues, who have assembled here to do you honour.'

Lord Badgery presented every one in the room to the old painter, who bowed, shook hands, made little noises in his throat, but still found himself unable to speak. Mrs. Nobes, Mrs. Cayman, and Mrs. Mandragore all said charming things.

Dinner was served; the party took their places. Lord Badgery sat at the head of the table, with Mr. Tillotson on his right hand and Sir Herbert Herne on his left. Confronted with Bomba's succulent cooking and Bomba's wines, Mr. Tillotson ate and drank a good deal. He had the appetite of one who has lived on greens and potatoes for ten years among the blackbeetles. After the second glass of wine he began to talk, suddenly and in a flood, as though a sluice had been pulled up.

'In Asia Minor,' he began, 'it is the custom, when one goes to dinner, to hiccough as a sign of appreciative fullness. *Eructavit cor meum*, as the Psalmist has it; he was an Oriental himself.'

Spode had arranged to sit next to Mrs. Cayman; he had designs upon her. She was an impossible woman, of course, but rich and useful; he wanted to bamboozle her into buying some of his young friends' pictures.

'In a cellar?' Mrs. Cayman was saying, 'with blackbeetles? Oh, how dreadful! Poor old man! And he's ninety-seven, didn't you say? Isn't that shocking! I only hope the subscription will be a large one. Of course, one wishes one could have given more oneself. But then, you know, one has so many expenses, and things are so difficult now.'

'I know, I know,' said Spode, with feeling.

'It's all because of Labour,' Mrs. Cayman explained. 'Of course, I should simply love to have him in to dinner sometimes. But, then, I feel he's really too old, too *farouche* and *gâteux*; it would not be doing a kindness to him, would it? And so you are working with Mr. Gollamy now? What a charming man, so talented, such conversation . . .'

'*Eructavit cor meum*,' said Mr. Tillotson for the third time. Lord Badgery tried to head him off the subject of Turkish etiquette, but in vain.

By half-past nine a kinder vinolent atmosphere had put to sleep the hatreds and suspicions of before dinner. Sir Herbert Herne had discovered that the young Cubist sitting next him was not insane and actually knew a surprising amount about the Old Masters. For their part these young men had realized that their elders were not at all malignant; they were just very stupid and pathetic. It was only in the bosoms of Mrs. Nobes, Mrs. Cayman, and Mrs. Mandragore that hatred still reigned undiminished. Being ladies and old-fashioned, they had drunk almost no wine.

The moment for speech-making arrived. Lord Badgery rose to his feet, said what was expected of him, and called upon Sir Herbert to propose the toast of the evening. Sir Herbert coughed, smiled, and began. In the course of a speech that lasted twenty minutes he told anecdotes of Mr. Gladstone, Lord Leighton, Sir Alma Tadema, and the late Bishop of Bombay; he made three puns, he quoted Shakespeare and Whittier, he was playful, he was eloquent, he was grave. . . . At the end of his harangue Sir Herbert handed to Mr. Tillotson a silk purse containing fifty-eight pounds ten shillings, the total amount of the subscription. The old man's health was drunk with acclamation.

Mr. Tillotson rose with difficulty to his feet. The dry,

snakelike skin of his face was flushed; his tie was more crooked than ever; the green ribbon of the Order of Chastity of the second class had somehow climbed up his crumpled and maculate shirt-front.

'My lords, ladies, and gentlemen,' he began in a choking voice, and then broke down completely. It was a very painful and pathetic spectacle. A feeling of intense discomfort afflicted the minds of all who looked upon that trembling relic of a man, as he stood there weeping and stammering. It was as though a breath of the wind of death had blown suddenly through the room, lifting the vapours of wine and tobacco-smoke, quenching the laughter and the candle flames. Eyes floated uneasily, not knowing where to look. Lord Badgery, with great presence of mind, offered the old man a glass of wine. Mr. Tillotson began to recover. The guests heard him murmur a few disconnected words.

'This great honour . . . overwhelmed with kindness . . . this magnificent banquet . . . not used to it . . . in Asia Minor . . . *eructavit cor meum*.'

At this point Lord Badgery plucked sharply at one of his long coat tails. Mr. Tillotson paused, took another sip of wine, and then went on with a newly won coherence and energy.

'The life of the artist is a hard one. His work is unlike other men's work, which may be done mechanically, by rote and almost, as it were, in sleep. It demands from him a constant expense of spirit. He gives continually of his best life, and in return he receives much joy, it is true—much fame, it may be—but of material blessings, very few. It is eighty years since first I devoted my life to the service of art; eighty years, and almost every one of those years has brought me fresh and painful proof of what I have been saying: the artist's life is a hard one.'

This unexpected deviation into sense increased the general feeling of discomfort. It became necessary to take the old man seriously, to regard him as a human being. Up till then he had been no more than an object of curiosity, a mummy in an absurd suit of evening-clothes with a green ribbon across the shirt front. People could not help wishing that they had subscribed a little more. Fifty-eight pounds ten—it wasn't enormous. But happily for the peace of mind of the company, Mr. Tillotson paused again, took another sip of wine, and began to live up to his proper character by talking absurdly.

'When I consider the life of that great man, Benjamin Robert Haydon, one of the greatest men England has ever produced . . .' The audience heaved a sigh of relief; this was all as it should be. There was a burst of loud bravoing and clapping. Mr. Tillotson turned his dim eyes round the room, and smiled gratefully at the misty figures he beheld. 'That great man, Benjamin Robert Haydon,' he continued, 'whom I am proud to call my master and who, it rejoices my heart to see, still lives in your memory and esteem—that great man, one of the greatest that England has ever produced, led a life so deplorable that I cannot think of it without a tear.'

And with infinite repetitions and divagations, Mr. Tillotson related the history of B. R. Haydon, his imprisonments for debt, his battle with the Academy, his triumphs, his failures, his despair, his suicide. Half-past ten struck. Mr. Tillotson was declaiming against the stupid and prejudiced judges who had rejected Haydon's designs for the decoration of the new Houses of Parliament in favour of the paltriest German scribblings.

'That great man, one of the greatest England has ever produced, that great Benjamin Robert Haydon, whom I am proud to call my master and who, it rejoices me to see, still lives on in your memory and esteem—at that affront his great heart burst; it was the unkindest cut of all. He who had worked all his life for the recognition of the artist by the State, he who had petitioned every Prime Minister, including the Duke of Wellington, for thirty years, begging them to employ artists to decorate public buildings, he to whom the scheme for decorating the Houses of Parliament was undeniably due . . .' Mr. Tillotson lost a grip on his syntax and began a new sentence. 'It was the unkindest cut of all, it was the last straw. The artist's life is a hard one.'

At eleven Mr. Tillotson was talking about the pre-Raphaelites. At a quarter-past he had begun to tell the story of B. R. Haydon all over again. At twenty-five minutes to twelve he collapsed quite speechless into his chair. Most of the guests had already gone away; the few who remained made haste to depart. Lord Badgery led the old man to the door and packed him into the second Rolls-Royce. The Tillotson Banquet was over; it had been a pleasant evening, but a little too long.

Spode walked back to his rooms in Bloomsbury, whistling as he went. The arc lamps of Oxford Street reflected in the polished surface of the road: canals of dark bronze. He would have to bring that into an article some time. The Cayman woman had been very successfully nobbled. 'Voi che sapete,' he whistled—somewhat out of tune, but he could not hear that.

When Mr. Tillotson's landlady came in to call him on the following morning, she found the old man lying fully dressed on his bed. He looked very ill and very, very old; Boreham's dress-suit was in a terrible state, and the green ribbon of the Order of Chastity was ruined. Mr. Tillotson lay very still, but he was not asleep. Hearing the sound of footsteps, he opened his eyes a little and faintly groaned. His landlady looked down at him menacingly.

'Disgusting!' she said; 'disgusting, I call it. At your age.'

Mr. Tillotson groaned again. Making a great effort, he drew out of his trousers pocket a large silk purse, opened it, and extracted a sovereign.

'The artist's life is a hard one, Mrs. Green,' he said, handing her the coin. 'Would you mind sending for the doctor? I don't feel very well. And oh, what shall I do about these clothes? What shall I say to the gentleman who was kind enough to lend them to me? Loan oft loseth both itself and friend. The Bard is always right.'

MORTAL COILS

FAIRY GODMOTHER

I

At 17 Purlieu Villas it was a fairy godmother's arrival. The enormous Daimler—it looked larger than the house itself—rolled whispering up the street, dark blue and discreetly lustrous. ('Like stars on the sea'—the darkly glittering Daimler always reminded Susan of the Hebrew Melodies—'when the blue wave rolls nightly on deep Galilee.') Between lace curtains eyes followed its passage; it was rarely that forty horses passed these suburban windows. At the gate of Number Seventeen the portent came to a halt. The chauffeur jumped down and opened the door. The fairy godmother emerged.

Mrs. Escobar was tall and slender, so abnormally so, that, fashionably dressed, she looked like a fashion-plate—fabulously elegant, beyond all reality.

She was wearing black to-day—a black suit very thinly piped at the cuffs and collar, at the pockets and along the seams of the skirt, with red. A high muslin stock encased her neck and from it depended an elaborate frill, which projected from between the lapels of her coat like the idly waving fin of a tropical fish. Her shoes were red; there was a touch of red in the garnishing of her gloves, another in her hat.

She stepped out of the car and, turning back towards the open door, 'Well, Susan,' she said, 'you don't seem to be in any hurry to get out.'

Susan, who was bending down to pick up the parcels scattered on the floor of the car, looked up.

'I'm just coming,' she said.

She reached hurriedly for the bunch of white roses and

the terrine of *foie gras*. Reaching, she dropped the box containing the chocolate cake.

Mrs. Escobar laughed. 'You old goose,' she said, and a charming mockery set her voice deeply vibrating. 'Come out and let Robbins take the things. You'll take them, Robbins,' she added in a different tone, turning to the chauffeur, 'you'll take them, won't you?'

She looked at him intimately; her smile was appealing, almost languishing.

'Won't you, Robbins?' she repeated, as though she were asking the most immense of personal favours.

That was Mrs. Escobar's way. She liked to endow every relationship, the most casual, the most business-like or formal, with a certain intimate, heart-to-heart quality. She talked to shop assistants about their sweethearts, smiled at servants as though she wanted to make them her confidants or even her lovers, discussed philosophy with the plumber, gave chocolates to district messenger boys and even, when they were particularly cherubic, maternally kissed them. She wanted to 'get into touch with people,' as she called it, to finger and tweak their souls and squeeze the secrets out of their hearts. She wanted everybody to be aware of her, to like and adore her at first sight. Which did not prevent her from flying into rages with the shop assistants who could not provide her immediately with precisely the thing she wanted, from violently abusing the servants when they failed to answer the bell with a sufficient promptitude, from calling the dilatory plumber a thief and a liar, from dismissing the messenger boy who brought a present from the wrong admirer, not only chocolateless and unkissed, but without even a tip.

'Won't you?' And her look seemed to add, 'for *my* sake.' Her eyes were long and narrow. The lower lid described an almost straight horizontal line, the upper a gradual curve. Between the lids, a pair of pale blue irises rolled their lights expressively this way and that.

The chauffeur was young and new to his post. He blushed, he averted his eyes. 'Oh yes, m'm, of course,' he said, and touched his cap.

Susan abandoned the chocolate cake and the *foie gras* and stepped out. Her arms were full of parcels and flowers.

'You look like a little Mother Christmas,' said Mrs. Escobar, playfully affectionate. 'Let me take something.' She selected the bunch of white roses, leaving to Susan the bag of oranges, the cold roast chicken, the tongue and the teddy bear.

Robbins opened the gate; they stepped into the little garden.

'Where's Ruth?' said Mrs. Escobar. 'Isn't she expecting us?' Her voice expressed disappointment and implied reproof. Evidently, she had expected to be met at the gate and escorted across the garden.

'I suppose she couldn't leave Baby,' said Susan, looking anxiously at Mrs. Escobar over the top of her heaped-up parcels. 'One can never be certain of being able to do what one wants when one's got children, can one?' Still, she wished that Ruth had turned up at the gate. It would be dreadful if Mrs. Escobar were to think her negligent or ungrateful. 'Oh, Ruth, do come!' she said to herself, and she wished so hard that she found herself clenching her fists and contracting the muscles of her stomach.

The fists and the abdominal muscles did their work, for the door of the house suddenly burst open and Ruth came running down the steps, carrying Baby on her arm.

'I'm so sorry, Mrs. Escobar,' she began. 'But, you see, Baby was just . . .'

Mrs. Escobar did not allow her to finish her sentence. Momentarily clouded, her face lit up again. She smiled, ravishingly. Her eyelids came still closer together; little lines radiated out from them, a halo of charming humour. 'Here's little Mother Christmas,' she said, pointing at Susan. 'Loaded with goodness knows what! And a few poor flowers from me.' She raised the roses to her lips, kissed them and touched Ruth's cheek with the half-opened flowers. 'And how's this delicious person?' She took the child's little hand and kissed it. The child looked at her with large, grave eyes—candid and, by reason of their candour, profoundly critical, like the eyes of an angel on the day of judgment.

'How do you do?' he said in his solemn, childish voice.

'Sweet pet!' said Mrs. Escobar and paid no further attention to him. She was not much interested in children. 'And you, my dear?' she asked, addressing herself to Ruth. She kissed her. She kissed her on the lips.

'Very well, thanks, Mrs. Escobar.'

Mrs. Escobar scrutinized her at arms'-length, one hand on Ruth's shoulder. 'You certainly look well, my dear child,' she said. 'And prettier than ever.' She thrust the great sheaf of roses into the crook of the young mother's unoccupied arm. 'What a sweet little Madonna!' she exclaimed, and, turning to Susan, 'Did you ever see anything more charming?' she asked. Susan smiled and nodded, rather awkwardly; after all, Ruth was her elder sister. 'And so absurdly, *absurdly* young!' Mrs. Escobar went on. 'Why, it's positively a *détournement de mineur*, your being married and having a baby. Do you know, my dear, you really look younger than Susan. It's a scandal.'

Embarrassed by Mrs. Escobar's point-blank praises, Ruth blushed. And it was not modesty alone that brought the blood to her cheeks. This insistence on the youthfulness of her appearance humiliated her. For it was mostly due, this air of childishness, to her clothes. She made her own frocks—rather 'artistic' little affairs in brightly coloured linens or large checks—made them in the only way she knew how or had time to make them: straight up and down, with a yoke and no sleeves, to be worn over a shirt. Monotonously schoolgirlish! But what can you do, if you can't afford to buy decent clothes? And her bobbed hair was dreadfully schoolgirlish too. She knew it. But again, what could she do about that? Let it grow? It would be such a trouble to keep tidy, and she had so little time. Have it shingled? But she would need to get it waved as well, and it would always have to be kept trimmed by a good hairdresser. All that meant money. Money, money, money!

No, if she looked so preposterously young, that was simply because she was poor. Susan was a baby, five years her junior. But she looked more grown-up. She looked grown-up, because she was properly dressed in frocks from a real dressmaker. Grown-up clothes, though she was only seventeen. And her cropped brown hair was beautifully waved. Mrs. Escobar gave Susan everything she wanted. Every blessed thing.

Suddenly she found herself hating and despising this enviably happy sister of hers. After all, what was she? Just a little pet lapdog in Mrs. Escobar's house. Just a doll; Mrs. Escobar amused herself by dressing her up, playing with her, making her say 'Mama.' It was a despicable position, despicable. But even as she thought of Susan's contemptibleness, she was complaining to the fates which had not permitted her to share Susan's beatitude. Why should Susan have everything, when she . . . ?

But then, all at once, she remembered Baby. She turned

her head impulsively and kissed the child's round, peach-pink cheek. The skin was smooth, soft and cool, like the petal of a flower. Thinking of Baby made her think of Jim. She imagined how he would kiss her when he came back from work. And this evening, while she sewed, he would read aloud from Gibbon's *Decline and Fall.* How she adored him, when he sat there in his spectacles, reading! And the curious way he pronounced the word 'Persians'—not 'Pershuns,' but 'Perzyans.' The thought of the Perzyans made her violently wish that he were there beside her, so that she could throw her arms round his neck and kiss him. Perzyans, Perzyans—she repeated the word to herself. Oh, *how* she adored him!

With a sudden outburst of affection, intensified at once by repentance for her odious thoughts and the recollection of Jim, she turned to her sister.

'Well, Sue,' she said. They kissed over the cold roast chicken and the tongue.

Mrs. Escobar looked at the two sisters and, looking, was filled with pleasure. How charming they were, she thought; how fresh and young and pretty! She felt proud of them. For after all, were they not in some sort her own invention? A couple of young girls, nicely brought up, luxuriously even; then suddenly orphaned and left without a penny. They might simply have sunk, disappeared and never been heard of again. But Mrs. Escobar, who had known their mother, came to the rescue. They were to come and live with her, poor children! and she would be their mother. A little ungratefully, as it always seemed to her, Ruth had preferred to accept young Jim Waterton's offer of a premature and hazardous marriage. Waterton had no money, of course; he was only a boy, with all his career to make. But Ruth had made her choice, deliberately. They had been married nearly five years now. Mrs.

Escobar had been a little hurt. Still, she had periodically paid her fairy godmother's visits to Purlieu Villas; she had stood plain human godmother to the baby. Susan, meanwhile, who was only thirteen when her father died, had grown up under Mrs. Escobar's care. She was rising eighteen now, and charming.

'The greatest pleasure in the world,' Mrs. Escobar was fond of saying, 'is being kind to other people.' Particularly, she might have added, when the other people are young and ravishing little creatures who worship you.

'Dear children,' she said, and, coming between them, she put an arm round either's waist. She felt all at once deeply and beautifully moved—much as she felt when she heard the Sermon on the Mount or the story of the woman taken in adultery read out in church. 'Dear children.' Her rich voice trembled a little, the tears came into her eyes. She pressed the two girls more closely to her. Interlaced, they walked along the path towards the door of the house. Robbins followed at a respectful distance, carrying the *foie gras* and the chocolate cake.

II

'But why isn't it a train?' asked Baby.

'But it's such a lovely bear.'

'Such a beautiful . . .' Susan insisted.

The faces of the sisters expressed an embarrassed anxiety. Who could have foreseen it? Baby hated the teddy bear. He wanted a train, and nothing but a train. And Mrs. Escobar had chosen the bear herself. It was a most special bear, comic in a rather artistic way, don't you know; made of black plush, with very large eyes of white leather and boot-buttons.

'And see how it rolls,' wheedled Ruth. She gave the

animal a push; it rolled across the floor. 'On wheels,' she added. Baby had a weakness for wheels.

Susan reached out and drew the bear back again. 'And when you pull this string,' she explained, 'it roars.' She pulled the string. The bear squeaked hoarsely.

'But I want a train,' insisted the child. 'With rails and tunnels and signals.' He called them siggernals.

'Another time, my darling,' said Ruth. 'Now go and give your bear a big kiss. Poor Teddy! He's so sad.'

The child's lips trembled, his face became distorted with grief, he began to cry. 'I want siggernals,' he said. 'Why doesn't she bring me siggernals?' He pointed accusingly at Mrs. Escobar.

'Poor pet,' said Mrs. Escobar. 'He shall have his siggernals.'

'No, no,' implored Ruth. 'He really adores his bear, you know. It's just a foolish idea he's got into his head.'

'Poor *little* pet,' Mrs. Escobar repeated. But how badly brought up the child was, she thought. So spoiled, and *blasé* already. She had taken such trouble about the bear. A real work of art. Ruth ought to be told, for her own good and the child's. But she was so touchy. How silly it was of people to be touchy about this sort of thing! Perhaps the best thing would be to talk to Susan about it and let her talk to Ruth quietly, when they were alone together.

Ruth tried to make a diversion. 'Look at this lovely book Mrs. Escobar has brought you.' She held up a brand new copy of Lear's *Book of Nonsense*. 'Look.' She turned over the pages invitingly before the child's eyes.

'Don't want to look,' Baby replied, determined to be a martyr. In the end, however, he could not resist the pictures. 'What's that?' he asked, sulkily, still trying to pretend that he wasn't interested.

'Would you like me to read you one of these lovely poems?' asked Mrs. Escobar, heaping coals of fire on the despiser of the bear.

'Oh yes,' cried Ruth with an anxious eagerness. 'Yes, please.'

'Please,' repeated Susan.

Baby said nothing, but when his mother wanted to hand the book to Mrs. Escobar, he tried to resist. . . . 'It's my book,' he said in a voice of loud and angry complaint.

'Hush,' said Ruth, and stroked his head soothingly. He relinquished the book.

'Which shall it be?' asked Mrs. Escobar, turning over the pages of the volume. '"The Yonghy-Bonghy-Bo"? Or "The Pobble who has no Toes"? Or "The Dong"? Or "The Owl and the Pussy Cat"? Which?' She looked up, smiling enquiringly.

'"The Pobble,"' suggested Susan.

'I think "The Owl and the Pussy Cat" would be the best to begin with,' said Ruth. 'It's easier to understand than the others. You'd like to hear about the Pussy, wouldn't you, darling?'

The child nodded, unenthusiastically.

'Sweet pet!' said Mrs. Escobar. 'He shall have his Pussy. I love it too.' She found her place in the book. '"The Owl and the Pussy Cat,"' she announced in a voice more richly and cooingly vibrant than the ordinary. Mrs. Escobar had studied elocution with the best teachers, and was fond of acting, for charity. She had been unforgettable as Tosca in aid of the Hoxton Children's Hospital. And then there was her orthopaedic Portia, her tuberculous Mrs. Tanqueray (or was Mrs. Tanqueray for the incurables?).

'What's a owl?' asked Baby.

Interrupted, Mrs. Escobar began a preliminary reading of the poem to herself; her lips moved as she read.

'An owl's a kind of big funny bird,' his mother answered and put her arm round him. She hoped he'd keep quieter if she held him like this.

'Do nowls bite?'

'Owls, darling, not nowls.'

'Do they bite?'

'Only when people tease them.'

'Why do people tease them?'

'Sh-sh!' said Ruth. 'Now you must listen. Mrs. Escobar's going to read you a lovely story about an owl and a pussy.'

Mrs. Escobar, meanwhile, had been studying her poem. 'Too charming!' she said, to nobody in particular, smiling as she spoke with eyes and lips. 'Such poetry, really, though it is nonsense. After all, what is poetry but nonsense? Divine nonsense.' Susan nodded her agreement. 'Shall I begin?' Mrs. Escobar enquired.

'Oh, do,' said Ruth, without ceasing to caress the child's silky hair. He was calmer now.

Mrs. Escobar began:

'"The aul and the pooseh-cut went to sea
In a beautiful (after a little pause and with intensity) *pea-grreen* boat.
They took some honey and (the rich voice rose a tone and sank) plenty of money,
Wrapped (little pause) up (little pause) in a five-pound note."'

'What's a five-pound note?' asked Baby.

Ruth pressed her hand more heavily on the head, as though to squeeze down his rising curiosity. 'Sh-sh!' she said.

Ignoring the interruption, Mrs. Escobar went on, after a brief dramatic silence, to the second stanza.

'"The aul looked up to the starrs above (her voice thrilled deeply with the passion of the tropical and amorous night)
And sang to a small (little pause) guitarr . . ."'

'Mummy, what's a guit . . . ?'

'Hush, pet, hush.' She could almost feel the child's questioning spirit oozing out between her confining fingers.

With a green flash of emeralds, a many-coloured glitter of brilliants, Mrs. Escobar laid her long white hand on her heart and raised her eyes towards imaginary constellations.

'"Oh lovely poosseh, oh poosseh my love,
What a (from high, the voice dropped emphatically) *beau*tiful poosseh you are, you are,
What a *beau*tiful poosseh you are!"'

'But, mummy, do owls like cats?'

'Don't talk, darling.'

'But you told me cats eat birds.'

'Not this cat, my pet.'

'But you said so, mummy . . .'

Mrs. Escobar began the next stanza.

'"Said the cut to the aul, You elegant faul,
How charrmingly sweet you sing (Mrs. Escobar's voice became languishing).
Come, let us be murried; too long have we turried.
But *what* (pause; Mrs. Escobar made a despairing gesture, luminous with rings) shall we do (pause) for the (her voice rose to the question) rring, the rring?
But *what* shall we do for the rring?

'"So they sailed away for a yeerr and a day
To the lund where the bong-tree grows. . . ."'

'What's a bongtrygroze, mummy?'

Mrs. Escobar slightly raised her voice so as to cover the childish interruption and went on with her recitation.

'"And there (pause) in a wood (pause) a *Pig*gywig stood,
With a rring . . ."'

'But, mummy . . .'

'"With a rring (Mrs. Escobar repeated still more loudly, describing in the air, as she did so, a flashing circle) at the end of his nose, his nose . . ."'

'Mummy!' The child was furious with impatience; he shook his mother's arm. 'Why don't you say? What is a bongtrygroze?'

'You must wait, my pet.'

Susan put her finger to her lips. 'Sh-sh!' Oh, how she wished that he would be good! What would Mrs. Escobar think? And her reading was so beautiful.

'"With a rring (Mrs. Escobar described a still larger circle) at the end of his nose."'

'It's a kind of tree,' whispered Ruth.

'"Deerr peeg, arre you willing to sell for one shilling
Your rring? Said the Peeggy, I will.
So they took it a-way and were murried next day
By the turrkey who lives on the hill (the dreamy note in Mrs. Escobar's voice made the turkey's hill sound wonderfully blue, romantic and remote),
By the turrkey who lives on the hill.

'"They dined on mince and slices of quince,
Which they ate with a runcible spoon,
And . . ."'

'What's runcible?'

'Hush, darling.'

'". . . hand in hand (the voice became cooingly tender, bloomy like a peach with velvety sentiment) by the edge . . ."'

'But why do you say sh-sh, like that?' the little boy shouted. He was so angry, that he began to hit his mother with his fists.

The interruption was so scandalous, that Mrs. Escobar was forced to take notice of it. She contented herself with frowning and laying her finger on her lips.

'". . . by the edge of the sand (all the ocean was in Mrs. Escobar's voice),
They danced (how gay and yet how exquisitely, how nuptially tender!) by the light (she spoke very slowly; she allowed her hand, which she had lifted, to come gradually down, like a tired bird, on to her knee) of the moo-oon."'

If any one could have heard those final words, he would have heard interstellar space, and the mystery of planetary motion, and Don Juan's serenade, and Juliet's balcony. If any one could have heard them. But the scream which Baby uttered was so piercingly loud, that they were quite inaudible.

III

'I think you ought to talk to Ruth seriously one day,' said Mrs. Escobar, on the way back from Purlieu Villas, 'about Baby. I don't think she really brings him up at all well. He's spoiled.'

The accusation was couched in general terms. But Susan began at once to apologize for what she felt sure was Baby's particular offence.

'Of course,' she said, 'the trouble was that there were so many words in the poem he didn't understand.'

Mrs. Escobar was annoyed at having been too well understood.

'The poem?' she repeated, as though she didn't understand what Susan was talking about. 'Oh, I didn't mean that. I thought he was so good, considering, while I was reading. Didn't you?'

Susan blushed, guiltily. 'I thought he interrupted rather a lot,' she said.

Mrs. Escobar laughed indulgently. 'But what can you expect of a little child like that?' she said. 'No, no; I was thinking of his behaviour in general. At tea, for example. . . . You really ought to talk to Ruth about it.'

Susan promised that she would.

Changing the subject, Mrs. Escobar began to talk about Sydney Fell, who was coming to dinner that evening. Such a darling creature! She liked him more and more. He had a most beautiful mouth; so refined and sensitive, and yet at the same time so strong, so sensual. And he was so witty and such an accomplished amorist. Susan listened in misery and silence.

'Don't you think so?' Mrs. Escobar kept asking insistently. 'Don't you think he's delightful?'

Susan suddenly burst out. 'I hate him,' she said, and began to cry.

'You hate him?' said Mrs. Escobar. 'But why? Why? You're not jealous, are you?' She laughed.

Susan shook her head.

'You are!' Mrs. Escobar insisted. 'You are!'

Susan continued obstinately to shake her head. But Mrs. Escobar knew that she had got her revenge.

'You silly, silly child,' she said in a voice in which there were treasures of affection. She put her arm round the girl's shoulders, drew her gently and tenderly towards her and began to kiss her wet face. Susan abandoned herself to her happiness.

THE DWARFS

From 'Crome Yellow'

. . . THE INFANT who was destined to become the fourth baronet of the name of Lapith was born in the year 1740. He was a very small baby, weighing not more than three pounds at birth, but from the first he was sturdy and healthy. In honour of his maternal grandfather, Sir Hercules Occam of Bishop's Occam, he was christened Hercules. His mother, like many other mothers, kept a note-book, in which his progress from month to month was recorded. He walked at ten months, and before his second year was out he had learnt to speak a number of words. At three years he weighed but twenty-four pounds, and at six, though he could read and write perfectly and showed a remarkable aptitude for music, he was no larger and heavier than a well-grown child of two. Meanwhile, his mother had borne two other children, a boy and a girl, one of whom died of croup during infancy, while the other was carried off by smallpox before it reached the age of five. Hercules remained the only surviving child.

On his twelfth birthday Hercules was still only three feet and two inches in height. His head, which was very handsome and nobly shaped, was too big for his body, but otherwise he was exquisitely proportioned and, for his size, of great strength and agility. His parents, in the hope of making him grow, consulted all the most eminent physicians of the time. Their various prescriptions were followed to the letter, but in vain. One ordered a very plentiful meat diet; another exercise; a third constructed a little rack, modelled on those employed by the Holy Inquisition, on which young Hercules was stretched, with excruciating torments, for half an hour every morning and evening. In the course of the next three years Hercules gained perhaps two inches. After that his growth stopped completely, and he remained for the rest of his life a pigmy of three feet and four inches. His father, who had built the most extravagant hopes upon his son, planning for him in his imagination a military career equal to that of Marlborough, found himself a disappointed man. 'I have brought an abortion into the world,' he would say, and he took so violent a dislike to his son that the boy dared scarcely come into his presence. His temper, which had been serene, was turned by disappointment to moroseness and savagery. He avoided all company (being, as he said, ashamed to show himself, the father of a *lusus naturae*, among normal, healthy human beings), and took to solitary drinking, which carried him very rapidly to his grave; for the year before Hercules came of age his father was taken off by an apoplexy. His mother, whose love for him had increased with the growth of his father's unkindness, did not long survive, but little more than a year after her husband's death succumbed, after eating two dozen of oysters, to an attack of typhoid fever.

Hercules thus found himself at the age of twenty-one alone in the world, and master of considerable fortune, including the estate and mansion of Crome. The beauty and intelligence of his childhood had survived into his manly age, and, but for his dwarfish stature, he would have taken his place among the handsomest and most accomplished young men of his time. He was well read in the Greek and Latin authors, as well as in all the moderns of any merit who had written in English, French, or Italian. He had a good ear for music, and was no indifferent performer on the violin, which he used to play like a bass viol, seated on a chair with the instrument between his legs. To the music of the harpsichord and clavichord he was extremely partial, but the smallness of his hands made it impossible for him ever to perform upon these instruments. He had a small ivory flute made for him, on which, whenever he was melancholy, he used to play a simple country air or jig, affirming that this rustic music had more power to clear and raise the spirits than the most artificial productions of the masters. From an early age he practised the composition of poetry, but, though conscious of his great powers in this art, he would never publish any specimen of his writing. 'My stature,' he would say, 'is reflected in my verses; if the public were to read them it would not be because I am a poet, but because I am a dwarf.' Several MS. books of Sir Hercules's poems survive. A single specimen will suffice to illustrate his qualities as a poet.

In ancient days, while yet the world was young,
Ere Abram fed his flocks or Homer sung;
When blacksmith Tubal tamed creative fire,
And Jabel dwelt in tents and Jubal struck the lyre;
Flesh grown corrupt brought forth a monstrous birth
And obscene giants trod the shrinking earth,
Till God, impatient of their sinful brood,
Gave rein to wrath and drown'd them in the Flood.
Teeming again, repeopled Tellus bore
The lubber Hero and the Man of War;
Huge towers of Brawn, topp'd with an empty Skull,
Witlessly bold, heroically dull.
Long ages pass'd and Man grown more refin'd,
Slighter in muscle but of vaster Mind,
Smiled at his grandsire's broadsword, bow and bill,
And learn'd to wield the Pencil and the Quill.
The glowing canvas and the written page
Immortaliz'd his name from age to age,
His name emblazon'd on Fame's temple wall;

For Art grew great as Humankind grew small.
Thus man's long progress step by step we trace;
The Giant dies, the hero takes his place;
The Giant vile, the dull heroic Block:
At one we shudder and at one we mock.
Man last appears. In him the Soul's pure flame
Burns brightlier in a not inord'nate frame.
Of old when Heroes fought and Giants swarmed,
Men were huge mounds of matter scarce inform'd;
Wearied by leavening so vast a mass,
The spirit slept and all the mind was crass.
The smaller carcase of these later days
Is soon inform'd; the Soul unwearied plays
And like a Pharos darts abroad her mental rays.
But can we think that Providence will stay
Man's footsteps here upon the upward way?
Mankind in understanding and in grace
Advanc'd so far beyond the Giants' race?
Hence impious thought! Still led by GOD's own Hand,
Mankind proceeds towards the Promised Land.
A time will come (prophetic, I descry
Remoter dawns along the gloomy sky),
When happy mortals of a Golden Age
Will backward turn the dark historic page,
And in our vaunted race of Men behold
A form as gross, a Mind as dead and cold,
As we in Giants see, in warriors of old.
A time will come, wherein the soul shall be
From all superfluous matter wholly free;
When the light body, agile as a fawn's,
Shall sport with grace along the velvet lawns.
Nature's most delicate and final birth,
Mankind perfected shall possess the earth.
But ah, not yet! For still the Giants' race,
Huge, though diminish'd, tramps the Earth's fair face;
Gross and repulsive, yet perversely proud,
Men of their imperfections boast aloud.

Vain of their bulk, of all they still retain
Of giant ugliness absurdly vain;
At all that's small they point their stupid scorn
And, monsters, think themselves divinely born.
Sad is the Fate of those, ah, sad indeed,
The rare precursors of the nobler breed!
Who come man's golden glory to foretell,
But pointing Heav'nwards live themselves in Hell.

As soon as he came into the estate, Sir Hercules set about remodelling his household. For though by no means ashamed of his deformity—indeed, if we may judge from the poem quoted above, he regarded himself as being in many ways superior to the ordinary race of man—he found the presence of full-grown men and women embarrassing. Realizing, too, that he must abandon all ambitions in the great world, he determined to retire absolutely from it and to create, as it were, at Crome a private world of his own, in which all should be proportionable to himself. Accordingly, he discharged all the old servants of the house and replaced them gradually, as he was able to find suitable successors, by others of dwarfish stature. In the course of a few years he had assembled about himself a numerous household, no member of which was above four feet high and the smallest among them scarcely two feet and six inches. His father's dogs, such as setters, mastiffs, greyhounds, and a pack of beagles, he sold or gave away as too large and too boisterous for his house, replacing them by pugs and King Charles spaniels and whatever other breeds of dog were the smallest. His father's stable was also sold. For his own use, whether riding or driving, he had six black Shetland ponies, with four very choice piebald animals of New Forest breed.

Having thus settled his household entirely to his own satisfaction, it only remained for him to find some suitable companion with whom to share this paradise. Sir Hercules had a susceptible heart, and had more than once, between the ages of sixteen and twenty, felt what it was to love. But here his deformity had been a source of the most bitter humiliation, for, having once dared to declare himself to a young lady of his choice, he had been received with laughter. On his persisting, she had picked him up and shaken him like an importunate child, telling him to run away and plague her no more. The story soon got about—indeed, the young lady herself used to tell it as a particularly pleasant anecdote—and the taunts and mockery it occasioned were a source of the most acute distress to Hercules. From the poems written at this period we gather that he meditated taking his own life. In course of time, however, he lived down this humiliation; but never again, though he often fell in love, and that very passionately, did he dare to make any advances to those in whom he was interested. After coming to the estate and finding that he was in a position to create his own world as he desired it, he saw that, if he was to have a wife—which he very much desired, being of an affectionate and, indeed, amorous temper—he must choose her as he had chosen his servants—from among the race of dwarfs. But to find a suitable wife was, he found, a matter of some difficulty; for he would marry none who was not distinguished by beauty and gentle birth. The dwarfish daughter of Lord Bemboro he refused on the ground that besides being a pigmy she was hunchbacked; while another young lady, an orphan belonging to a very good family in Hampshire, was rejected by him because her face, like that of so many dwarfs, was wizened and repulsive. Finally, when he was almost despairing of success, he heard from a reliable source that Count Titimalo, a Venetian nobleman, possessed a daughter of exquisite beauty and great accomplishments, who was but three feet in height. Setting out at once for Venice, he went immediately on his arrival to pay his respects to the count, whom he found living with his wife and five children in a very mean apartment in one of the poorer quarters of the town. Indeed, the count was so far reduced in his circumstances that he was even then negotiating (so it was rumoured) with a travelling company of clowns and acrobats, who had had the misfortune to lose their performing dwarf, for the sale of his diminutive daughter Filomena. Sir Hercules arrived in time to save her from this untoward fate, for he was so much charmed by Filomena's grace and beauty, that at the end of three days' courtship he made her a formal offer of marriage, which was accepted by her no less joyfully than by her father, who perceived in an English son-in-law a rich and unfailing source of revenue. After an unostentatious marriage, at which the English ambassador acted as one of the witnesses, Sir Hercules and his bride returned by sea to England, where they settled down, as it proved, to a life of uneventful happiness.

Crome and its household of dwarfs delighted Filomena, who felt herself now for the first time to be a free woman living among her equals in a friendly world. She had many tastes in common with her husband, especially that of music. She had a beautiful voice, of a power surprising in one so small, and could touch A in alt without effort. Accompanied by her husband on his fine Cremona fiddle, which he played, as we have noted before, as one plays a bass viol, she would sing all the liveliest and tenderest airs from the operas and cantatas of her native country. Seated together at the harpsichord, they found that they could with their four hands play all the music written for two hands of ordinary size, a circumstance which gave Sir Hercules unfailing pleasure.

When they were not making music or reading together, which they often did, both in English and Italian, they spent their time in healthful outdoor exercises, sometimes rowing in a little boat on the lake, but more often riding or driving, occupations in which, because they were entirely new to her, Filomena especially delighted. When she had become a perfectly proficient rider, Filomena and her husband used often to go hunting in the park, at that time very much more extensive than it is now. They hunted not foxes nor hares, but rabbits, using a pack of about thirty black and fawn-coloured pugs, a kind of dog which, when not overfed, can course a rabbit as well as any of the smaller breeds. Four dwarf grooms, dressed in scarlet liveries and mounted on white Exmoor ponies, hunted the pack, while their master and mistress, in green habits, followed either on the black Shetlands or on the piebald New Forest ponies. A picture of the whole hunt —dogs, horses, grooms, and masters—was painted by William Stubbs, whose work Sir Hercules admired so much that he invited him, though a man of ordinary stature, to come and stay at the mansion for the purpose of executing this picture. Stubbs likewise painted a portrait of Sir Hercules and his lady driving in their green enamelled calash drawn by four black Shetlands. Sir Hercules wears a plum-coloured velvet coat and white breeches; Filomena is dressed in flowered muslin and a very large hat with pink feathers. The two figures in their gay carriage stand out sharply against a dark background of trees; but to the left of the picture the trees fall away and disappear, so that the four black ponies are seen against a pale and strangely lurid sky that has the golden-brown colour of thunder-clouds lighted up by the sun.

In this way four years passed happily by. At the end of that time Filomena found herself great with child. Sir

Hercules was overjoyed. 'If God is good,' he wrote in his day-book, 'the name of Lapith will be preserved and our rarer and more delicate race transmitted through the generations until in the fullness of time the world shall recognize the superiority of those beings whom now it uses to make mock of.' On his wife's being brought to bed of a son he wrote a poem to the same effect. The child was christened Ferdinando in memory of the builder of the house.

With the passage of the months a certain sense of disquiet began to invade the minds of Sir Hercules and his lady. For the child was growing with an extraordinary rapidity. At a year he weighed as much as Hercules had weighed when he was three. 'Ferdinando goes *crescendo*,' wrote Filomena in her diary. 'It seems not natural.' At eighteen months the baby was almost as tall as their smallest jockey, who was a man of thirty-six. Could it be that Ferdinando was destined to become a man of the normal, gigantic dimensions? It was a thought to which neither of his parents dared yet give open utterance, but in the secrecy of their respective diaries they brooded over it in terror and dismay.

On his third birthday Ferdinando was taller than his mother and not more than a couple of inches short of his father's height. 'To-day for the first time,' wrote Sir Hercules, 'we discussed the situation. The hideous truth can be concealed no longer: Ferdinando is not one of us. On this, his third birthday, a day when we should have been rejoicing at the health, the strength, and beauty of our child, we wept together over the ruin of our happiness. God give us strength to bear this cross.'

At the age of eight Ferdinando was so large and so exuberantly healthy that his parents decided, though reluctantly, to send him to school. He was packed off to Eton at the beginning of the next half. A profound peace settled upon the house. Ferdinando returned for the summer holidays larger and stronger than ever. One day he knocked down the butler and broke his arm. 'He is rough, inconsiderate, unamenable to persuasion,' wrote his father. 'The only thing that will teach him manners is corporal chastisement.' Ferdinando, who at this age was already seventeen inches taller than his father, received no corporal chastisement.

One summer holidays about three years later Ferdinando returned to Crome accompanied by a very large mastiff dog. He had bought it from an old man at Windsor who found the beast too expensive to feed. It was a savage, unreliable animal; hardly had it entered the house when it attacked one of Sir Hercules's favourite pugs, seizing the creature in its jaws and shaking it till it was nearly dead. Extremely put out by this occurrence, Sir Hercules ordered that the beast should be chained up in the stable-yard. Ferdinando sullenly answered that the dog was his, and he would keep it where he pleased. His father, growing angry, bade him take the animal out of the house at once, on pain of his utmost displeasure. Ferdinando refused to move. His mother at this moment coming into the room, the dog flew at her, knocked her down, and in a twinkling had very severely mauled her arm and shoulder; in another instant it must infallibly have had her by the throat, had not Sir Hercules drawn his sword and stabbed the animal to the heart. Turning on his son, he ordered him to leave the room immediately, as being unfit to remain in the same place with the mother whom he had nearly murdered. So awe-inspiring was the spectacle of Sir Hercules standing with one foot on the carcase of the gigantic dog, his sword drawn and still bloody, so commanding were his voice, his gestures, and the expression of his face, that Ferdinando slunk out of the room in terror and behaved himself for all the rest of the vacation in an entirely exemplary fashion. His mother soon recovered from the bites of the mastiff, but the effect on her mind of this adventure was ineradicable; from that time forth she lived always among imaginary terrors.

The two years which Ferdinando spent on the Continent, making the Grand Tour, were a period of happy repose for his parents. But even now the thought of the future haunted them; nor were they able to solace themselves with all the diversions of their younger days. The Lady Filomena had lost her voice and Sir Hercules was grown too rheumatical to play the violin. He, it is true, still rode after his pugs, but his wife felt herself too old and, since the episode of the mastiff, too nervous for such sports. At most, to please her husband, she would follow the hunt at a distance in a little gig drawn by the safest and oldest of the Shetlands.

The day fixed for Ferdinando's return came round. Filomena, sick with vague dreads and presentiments, retired to her chamber and her bed. Sir Hercules received his son alone. A giant in a brown travelling-suit entered the room. 'Welcome home, my son,' said Sir Hercules in a voice that trembled a little.

'I hope I see you well, sir.' Ferdinando bent down to shake hands, then straightened himself up again. The top of his father's head reached to the level of his hip.

Ferdinando had not come alone. Two friends of his own age accompanied him, and each of the young men had brought a servant. Not for thirty years had Crome been desecrated by the presence of so many members of the common race of men. Sir Hercules was appalled and indignant, but the laws of hospitality had to be obeyed. He received the young gentlemen with grave politeness and sent the servants to the kitchen, with orders that they should be well cared for.

The old family dining-table was dragged out into the light and dusted (Sir Hercules and his lady were accustomed to dine at a small table twenty inches high). Simon, the aged butler, who could only just look over the edge of the big table, was helped at supper by the three servants brought by Ferdinando and his guests.

Sir Hercules presided, and with his usual grace supported a conversation on the pleasures of foreign travel, the beauties of art and nature to be met with abroad, the opera at Venice, the singing of the orphans in the churches of the same city, and on other topics of a similar nature. The young men were not particularly attentive to his discourses; they were occupied in watching the efforts of the butler to change the plates and replenish the glasses. They covered their laughter by violent and repeated fits of coughing or choking. Sir Hercules affected not to notice, but changed the subject of the conversation to sport. Upon this one of the young men asked whether it was true, as he had heard, that he used to hunt the rabbit with a pack of pug dogs. Sir Hercules replied that it was, and proceeded to describe the chase in some detail. The young men roared with laughter.

When supper was over, Sir Hercules climbed down from his chair and, giving as his excuse that he must see how his lady did, bade them good-night. The sound of laughter followed him up the stairs. Filomena was not asleep; she had been lying on her bed listening to the sound of enormous laughter and the tread of strangely heavy feet on the stairs and along the corridors. Sir Hercules drew a chair to her bedside and sat there for a long time in silence, holding his wife's hand and sometimes gently squeezing it. At about ten o'clock they were startled by a violent noise. There was a breaking of glass, a stamping of feet, with an outburst of shouts and laughter. The uproar continuing for several minutes, Sir Hercules rose to his feet and, in spite of his wife's entreaties, prepared to go and see what was happening. There was no light on the staircase, and Sir Hercules groped his way down cautiously, lowering himself from stair to stair and standing for a moment on each tread before adventuring on a new step. The noise was louder here; the shouting articulated itself into recognizable words and phrases. A line of light was visible under the dining-room door. Sir Hercules tiptoed across the hall towards it. Just as he approached the door there was another terrific crash of breaking glass and jangled metal. What could they be doing? Standing on tiptoe he managed to look through the keyhole. In the middle of the ravaged table old Simon, the butler, so primed with drink that he could scarcely keep his balance, was dancing a jig. His feet crunched and tinkled among the broken glass, and his shoes were wet with spilt wine. The three young men sat round, thumping the table with their hands or with the empty wine bottles, shouting and laughing encouragement. The three servants leaning against the wall laughed too. Ferdinando suddenly threw a handful of walnuts at the dancer's head, which so dazed and surprised the little man that he staggered and fell down on his back, upsetting a decanter and several glasses. They raised him up, gave him some brandy to drink, thumped him on the back. The old man smiled and hiccoughed. 'Tomorrow,' said Ferdinando, 'we'll have a concerted ballet of the whole household.' 'With father Hercules wearing his club and lion-skin,' added one of his companions, and all three roared with laughter.

Sir Hercules would look and listen no further. He crossed the hall once more and began to climb the stairs, lifting his knees painfully high at each degree. This was the end; there was no place for him now in the world, no place for him and Ferdinando together.

His wife was still awake; to her questioning glance he answered, 'They are making mock of old Simon. To-morrow it will be our turn.' They were silent for a time.

At last Filomena said, 'I do not want to see to-morrow.'

'It is better not,' said Sir Hercules. Going into his closet he wrote in his day-book a full and particular account of all the events of the evening. While he was still engaged in this task he rang for a servant and ordered hot water and a bath to be made ready for him at eleven o'clock. When he had finished writing he went into his wife's room, and preparing a dose of opium twenty times as strong as that which she was accustomed to take when she could not sleep, he brought it to her, saying, 'Here is your sleeping-draught.'

Filomena took the glass and lay for a little time, but did not drink immediately. The tears came into her eyes. 'Do you remember the songs we used to sing, sitting out there *sulla terrazza* in summer-time?' She began singing softly in her ghost of a cracked voice a few bars from Stradella's '*Amor, amor, non dormir piu.*' 'And you playing on the violin. It seems such a short time ago, and yet so long, long, long. *Addio, amore. A rivederti.*' She drank off the draught and, lying back on the pillow, closed her eyes. Sir Hercules kissed her hand and tiptoed away, as though he were afraid of waking her. He returned to his closet, and having recorded his wife's last words to him, he poured into his bath the water that had been brought up in accordance with his orders. The water being too hot for him to get into the bath at once, he took down from the shelf his copy of Suetonius. He wished to read how Seneca had died. He opened the book at random. 'But dwarfs,' he read, 'he held in abhorrence as being *lusus naturae* and of evil omen.' He winced as though he had been struck. This same Augustus, he remembered, had exhibited in the amphitheatre a young man called Lucius, of good family, who was not quite two feet in height and weighed seventeen pounds, but had a stentorian voice. He turned over the pages. Tiberius, Caligula, Claudius, Nero: it was a tale of growing horror. 'Seneca, his preceptor, he forced to kill himself.' And there was Petronius, who had called his friends about him at the last, bidding them talk to him, not of the consolations of philosophy, but of love and gallantry, while the life was ebbing away through his opened veins. Dipping his pen once more in the ink he wrote on the last page of his diary: 'He died a Roman death.' Then, putting the toes of one foot into the water and finding that it was not too hot, he threw off his dressing-gown and, taking a razor in his hand, sat down in the bath. With one deep cut he severed the artery in his left wrist, then lay back and composed his mind to meditation. The blood oozed out, floating through the water in dissolving wreaths and spirals. In a little while the whole bath was tinged with pink. The colour deepened; Sir Hercules felt himself mastered by an invincible drowsiness; he was sinking from vague dream to dream. Soon he was sound asleep. There was not much blood in his small body.

POEMS

LEDA

BROWN and bright as an agate, mountain-cool,
Eurotas singing slips from pool to pool;
Down rocky gullies; through the cavernous pines
And chestnut groves; down where the terraced vines
And gardens overhang; through valleys grey
With olive trees, into a soundless bay
Of the Ægean. Silent and asleep
Lie those pools now: but where they dream most deep,
Men sometimes see ripples of shining hair
And the young grace of bodies pale and bare,
Shimmering far down—the ghosts these mirrors hold
Of all the beauty they beheld of old,
White limbs and heavenly eyes and the hair's river of gold,
For once these banks were peopled: Spartan girls
Loosed here their maiden girdles and their curls,
And stooping o'er the level water stole
His darling mirror from the sun through whole
Rapturous hours of gazing.
                                        The first star
Of all this milky constellation, far
Lovelier than any nymph of wood or green,
Was she whom Tyndarus had made his queen
For her sheer beauty and subtly moving grace—
Leda, the fairest of our mortal race.
Hymen had lit his torches but one week
About her bed (and still o'er her young cheek
Passed rosy shadows of those thoughts that sped
Across her mind, still virgin, still unwed,

For all her body was her own no more),
When Leda with her maidens to the shore
Of bright Eurotas came, to escape the heat
Of summer noon in waters coolly sweet.
By a brown pool which opened smooth and clear
Below the wrinkled water of a weir
They sat them down under an old fir tree
To rest: and to the laughing melody
Of their sweet speech the river's rippling bore
A liquid burden, while the sun did pour
Pure colour out of heaven upon the earth.
The meadows seethed with the incessant mirth
Of grasshoppers, seen only when they flew
Their curves of scarlet or sudden dazzling blue.
Within the fir tree's round of unpierced shade
The maidens sat with laughter and talk, or played,
Gravely intent, their game of knuckle-bones;
Or tossed from hand to hand the old dry cones
Littered about the tree. And one did sing
A ballad of some far-off Spartan king,
Who took a wife, but left her, well-away!
Slain by his foes upon their wedding-day.
'That was a piteous story,' Leda sighed,
'To be a widow ere she was a bride.'
'Better,' said one, 'to live a virgin life
Alone, and never know the name of wife
And bear the ugly burden of a child
And have great pain by it. Let me live wild,
A bird untamed by man!' 'Nay,' cried another,
'I would be wife, if I should not be mother.
Cypris I honour; let the vulgar pay
Their gross vows to Lucina when they pray.
Our finer spirits would be blunted quite
By bestial teeming; but Love's rare delight

Wings the rapt soul towards Olympus' height.'
'Delight?' cried Leda. 'Love to me has brought
Nothing but pain and a world of shameful thought.
When they say love is sweet, the poets lie;
'Tis but a trick to catch poor maidens by.
What are their boasted pleasures? I am queen
To the most royal king the world has seen;
Therefore I should, if any woman might,
Know at its full that exquisite delight.
Yet these few days since I was made a wife
Have held more bitterness than all my life,
While I was yet a child.' The great bright tears
Slipped through her lashes. 'Oh, my childish years!
Years that were all my own, too sadly few,
When I was happy—and yet never knew
How happy till to-day!' Her maidens came
About her as she wept, whispering her name,
Leda, sweet Leda, with a hundred dear
Caressing words to soothe her heavy cheer.
At last she started up with a fierce pride
Upon her face. 'I am a queen,' she cried,
'But had forgotten it a while; and you,
Wenches of mine, you were forgetful too.
Undress me. We would bathe ourself.' So proud
A queen she stood, that all her maidens bowed
In trembling fear and scarcely dared approach
To do her bidding. But at last the brooch
Pinned at her shoulder is undone, the wide
Girdle of silk beneath her breasts untied;
The tunic falls about her feet, and she
Steps from the crocus folds of drapery,
Dazzlingly naked, into the warm sun.
God-like she stood; then broke into a run,
Leaping and laughing in the light, as though

Life through her veins coursed with so swift a flow
Of generous blood and fire that to remain
Too long in statued queenliness were pain
To that quick soul, avid of speed and joy.
She ran, easily bounding, like a boy,
Narrow of haunch and slim and firm of breast.
Lovelier she seemed in motion than at rest,
If that might be, when she was never less,
Moving or still, than perfect loveliness.
At last, with cheeks afire and heaving flank,
She checked her race, and on the river's bank
Stood looking down at her own echoed shape
And at the fish that, aimlessly agape,
Hung midway up their heaven of flawless glass,
Like angels waiting for eternity to pass.
Leda drew breath and plunged; her gasping cry
Splashed up; the water circled brokenly
Out from that pearly shudder of dipped limbs;
The glittering pool laughed up its flowery brims,
And everything, save the poor fish, rejoiced:
Their idiot contemplation of the Moist,
The Cold, the Watery, was in a trice
Ended when Leda broke their crystal paradise.

Jove in his high Olympian chamber lay
Hugely supine, striving to charm away
In sleep the long, intolerable noon.
But heedless Morpheus still withheld his boon,
And Jove upon his silk-pavilioned bed
Tossed wrathful and awake. His fevered head
Swarmed with a thousand fancies, which forecast
Delights to be, or savoured pleasures past.
Closing his eyes, he saw his eagle swift,
Headlong as his own thunder, stoop and lift

On pinions upward labouring the prize
Of beauty ravished for the envious skies.
He saw again that bright, adulterous pair,
Trapped by the limping husband unaware,
Fast in each other's arms, and faster in the snare—
And laughed remembering. Sometimes his thought
Went wandering over the earth and sought
Familiar places—temples by the sea,
Cities and islands; here a sacred tree
And there a cavern of shy nymphs.
He rolled
About his bed, in many a rich fold
Crumpling his Babylonian coverlet,
And yawned and stretched. The smell of his own sweat
Brought back to mind his Libyan desert-fane
Of mottled granite, with its endless train
Of pilgrim camels, reeking towards the sky
Ammonian incense to his hornèd deity;
The while their masters worshipped, offering
Huge teeth of ivory, while some would bring
Their Ethiop wives—sleek wineskins of black silk,
Jellied and huge from drinking asses' milk
Through years of tropical idleness, to pray
For offspring (whom he ever sent away
With prayers unanswered, lest their ebon race
Might breed and blacken the earth's comely face).
Noon pressed on him a hotter, heavier weight.
O Love in Idleness! how celibate
He felt! Libido like a nemesis
Scourged him with itching memories of bliss.
The satin of imagined skin was sleek
And supply warm against his lips and cheek,
And deep within soft hair's dishevelled dusk

His eyelids fluttered; like a flowery musk
The scent of a young body seemed to float
Faintly about him, close and yet remote—
For perfume and the essence of music dwell
In other worlds among the asphodel
Of unembodied life. Then all had flown;
His dream had melted. In his bed, alone,
Jove sweating lay and moaned, and longed in vain
To still the pulses of his burning pain.
In sheer despair at last he leapt from bed,
Opened the window and thrust forth his head
Into Olympian ether. One fierce frown
Rifted the clouds, and he was looking down
Into a gulf of azure calm; the rack
Seethed round about, tempestuously black;
But the god's eye could hold its angry thunders back.
There lay the world, down through the chasmèd blue,
Stretched out from edge to edge unto his view;
And in the midst, bright as a summer's day
At breathless noon, the Mediterranean lay;
And Ocean round the world's dim fringes tossed
His glaucous waves in mist and distance lost;
And Pontus and the livid Caspian Sea
Stirred in their nightmare sleep uneasily.
And 'twixt the seas rolled the wide fertile land,
Dappled with green and tracts of tawny sand,
And rich, dark fallows and fields of flowers aglow
And the white, changeless silences of snow;
While here and there towns, like a living eye
Unclosed on earth's blind face, towards the sky
Glanced their bright conscious beauty. Yet the sight
Of his fair earth gave him but small delight
Now in his restlessness: its beauty could
Do nought to quench the fever in his blood.

Desire lends sharpness to his searching eyes;
Over the world his focused passion flies
Quicker than chasing sunlight on a day
Of storm and golden April. Far away
He sees the tranquil rivers of the East,
Mirrors of many a strange barbaric feast,
Where un-Hellenic dancing-girls contort
Their yellow limbs, and gibbering masks make sport
Under the moons of many-coloured light
That swing their lantern-fruitage in the night
Of overarching trees. To him it seems
An alien world, peopled by insane dreams.
But these are nothing to the monstrous shapes—
Not men so much as bastardy of apes—
That meet his eyes in Africa. Between
Leaves of grey fungoid pulp and poisonous green,
White eyes from black and browless faces stare.
Dryads with star-flowers in their woolly hair
Dance to the flaccid clapping of their own
Black dangling dugs through forests overgrown,
Platted with writhing creepers. Horrified,
He sees them how they leap and dance, or glide,
Glimpse after black glimpse of a satin skin,
Among unthinkable flowers, to pause and grin
Out through a trellis of suppurating lips,
Of mottled tentacles barbed at the tips
And bloated hands and wattles and red lobes
Of pendulous gristle and enormous probes
Of pink and slashed and tasselled flesh . . .
He turns
Northward his sickened sight. The desert burns
All life away. Here in the forkèd shade
Of twin-humped towering dromedaries laid,
A few gaunt folk are sleeping: fierce they seem

Even in sleep, and restless as they dream.
He would be fearful of a desert bride
As of a brown asp at his sleeping side,
Fearful of her white teeth and cunning arts.
Further, yet further, to the ultimate parts
Of the wide earth he looks, where Britons go
Painted among their swamps, and through the snow
Huge hairy snuffling beasts pursue their prey—
Fierce men, as hairy and as huge as they.

Bewildered furrows deepen the Thunderer's scowl;
This world so vast, so variously foul—
Who can have made its ugliness? In what
Revolting fancy were the Forms begot
Of all these monsters? What strange deity—
So barbarously not a Greek!—was he
Who could mismake such beings in his own
Distorted image. Nay, the Greeks alone
Were men; in Greece alone were bodies fair,
Minds comely. In that all-but-island there,
Cleaving the blue sea with its promontories,
Lies the world's hope, the seed of all the glories
That are to be; there, too, must surely live
She who alone can medicinably give
Ease with her beauty to the Thunderer's pain.
Downwards he bends his fiery eyes again,
Glaring on Hellas. Like a beam of light,
His intent glances touch the mountain height
With passing flame and probe the valleys deep,
Rift the dense forest and the age-old sleep
Of vaulted antres on whose pebbly floor
Gallop the loud-hoofed Centaurs; and the roar
Of more than human shouting underground
Pulses in living palpable waves of sound

From wall to wall, until it rumbles out
Into the air; and at that hollow shout
That seems an utterance of the whole vast hill,
The shepherds cease their laughter and are still.
Cities asleep under the noonday sky
Stir at the passage of his burning eye;
And in their huts the startled peasants blink
At the swift flash that bursts through every chink
Of wattled walls, hearkening in fearful wonder
Through lengthened seconds for the crash of thunder—
Which follows not: they are the more afraid.
Jove seeks amain. Many a country maid,
Whose sandalled feet pass down familiar ways
Among the olives, but whose spirit strays
Through lovelier lands of fancy, suddenly
Starts broad awake out of her dream to see
A light that is not of the sun, a light
Darted by living eyes, consciously bright;
She sees and feels it like a subtle flame
Mantling her limbs with fear and maiden shame
And strange desire. Longing and terrified,
She hides her face, like a new-wedded bride
Who feels rough hands that seize and hold her fast;
And swooning falls. The terrible light has passed;
She wakes; the sun still shines, the olive trees
Tremble to whispering silver in the breeze
And all is as it was, save she alone
In whose dazed eyes this deathless light has shone:
For never, never from this day forth will she
In earth's poor passion find felicity,
Or love of mortal man. A god's desire
Has seared her soul; nought but the same strong fire
Can kindle the dead ash to life again,
And all her years will be a lonely pain.

Many a thousand had he looked upon,
Thousands of mortals, young and old; but none—
Virgin, or young ephebus, or the flower
Of womanhood culled in its full-blown hour—
Could please the Thunderer's sight or touch his mind;
The longed-for loveliness was yet to find.
Had beauty fled, and was there nothing fair
Under the moon? The fury of despair
Raged in the breast of heaven's Almighty Lord;
He gnashed his foamy teeth and rolled and roared
In bull-like agony. Then a great calm
Descended on him: cool and healing balm
Touched his immortal fury. He had spied
Young Leda where she stood, poised on the river-side.

Even as she broke the river's smooth expanse,
Leda was conscious of that hungry glance,
And knew it for an eye of fearful power
That did so hot and thunderously lour,
She knew not whence, on her frail nakedness.
Jove's heart held but one thought: he must possess
That perfect form or die—possess or die.
Unheeded prayers and supplications fly,
Thick as a flock of birds, about his ears,
And smoke of incense rises; but he hears
Nought but the soft falls of that melody
Which is the speech of Leda; he can see
Nought but that almost spiritual grace
Which is her body, and that heavenly face
Where gay, sweet thoughts shine through, and eyes are bright
With purity and the soul's inward light.
Have her he must: the teasel-fingered burr
Sticks not so fast in a wild beast's tangled fur
As that insistent longing in the soul

Of mighty Jove. Gods, men, earth, heaven, the whole
Vast universe was blotted from his thought
And nought remained but Leda's laughter, nought
But Leda's eyes. Magnified by his lust,
She was the whole world now; have her he must, he
must . . .
His spirit worked; how should he gain his end
With most deliciousness? What better friend,
What counsellor more subtle could he find
Than lovely Aphrodite, ever kind
To hapless lovers, ever cunning, too,
In all the tortuous ways of love to do
And plan the best? To Paphos then! His will
And act were one; and straight, invisible,
He stood in Paphos, breathing the languid air
By Aphrodite's couch. O heavenly fair
She was, and smooth and marvellously young!
On Tyrian silk she lay, and purple hung
About her bed in folds of fluted light
And shadow, dark as wine. Two doves, more white
Even than the white hand on the purple lying
Like a pale flower wearily dropped, were flying
With wings that made an odoriferous stir,
Dropping faint dews of bakkaris and myrrh,
Musk and the soul of sweet flowers cunningly
Ravished from transient petals as they die.
Two stripling cupids on her either hand
Stood near with winnowing plumes and gently fanned
Her hot, love-fevered cheeks and eyelids burning.
Another, crouched at the bed's foot, was turning
A mass of scattered parchments—vows or plaints
Or glad triumphant thanks which Venus' saints,
Martyrs and heroes, on her altars strewed
With bitterest tears or gifts of gratitude.

From the pile heaped at Aphrodite's feet
The boy would take a leaf, and in his sweet,
Clear voice would read what mortal tongues can tell
In stammering verse of those ineffable
Pleasures and pains of love, heaven and uttermost hell.
Jove hidden stood and heard him read these lines
Of votive thanks—

Cypris, this little silver lamp to thee
I dedicate.
It was my fellow-watcher, shared with me
Those swift, short hours, when raised above my fate
In Sphenura's white arms I drank
Of immortality.

'A pretty lamp, and I will have it placed
Beside the narrow bed of some too chaste
Sister of virgin Artemis, to be
A night-long witness of her cruelty.
Read me another, boy,' and Venus bent
Her ear to listen to this short lament.

Cypris, Cypris, I am betrayed!
Under the same wide mantle laid
I found them, faithless, shameless pair!
Making love with tangled hair.

'Alas,' the goddess cried, 'nor god, nor man,
Nor medicinable balm, nor magic can
Cast out the demon jealousy, whose breath
Withers the rose of life, save only time and death.'
Another sheet he took and read again.

Farewell to love, and hail the long, slow pain
Of memory that backward turns to joy.
O I have danced enough and enough sung;
My feet shall be still now and my voice mute;
Thine are these withered wreaths, this Lydian flute,
Cypris; I once was young.

And piêtous Aphrodite wept to think
How fadingly upon death's very brink
Beauty and love take hands for one short kiss—
And then the wreaths are dust, the bright-eyed bliss
Perished, and the flute still. 'Read on, read on.'
But ere the page could start, a lightning shone
Suddenly through the room, and they were 'ware
Of some great terrible presence looming there.
And it took shape—huge limbs, whose every line
A symbol was of power and strength divine,
And it was Jove.
'Daughter, I come,' said he,
'For counsel in a case that touches me
Close, to the very life.' And he straightway
Told her of all his restlessness that day
And of his sight of Leda, and how great
Was his desire. And so in close debate
Sat the two gods, planning their rape; while she,
Who was to be their victim, joyously
Laughed like a child in the sudden breathless chill
And splashed and swam, forgetting every ill
And every fear and all, save only this:
That she was young, and it was perfect bliss
To be alive where suns so goldenly shine,
And bees go drunk with fragrant honey-wine,
And the cicadas sing from morn till night,
And rivers run so cool and pure and bright . . .
Stretched all her length, arms under head, she lay
In the deep grass, while the sun kissed away
The drops that sleeked her skin. Slender and fine
As those old images of the gods that shine
With smooth-worn silver, polished through the years
By the touching lips of countless worshippers,
Her body was; and the sun's golden heat

Clothed her in softest flame from head to feet
And was her mantle, that she scarcely knew
The conscious sense of nakedness. The blue,
Far hills and the faint fringes of the sky
Shimmered and pulsed in the heat uneasily,
And hidden in the grass, cicadas shrill
Dizzied the air with ceaseless noise, until
A listener might wonder if they cried
In his own head or in the world outside.
Sometimes she shut her eyelids, and wrapped round
In a red darkness, with the muffled sound
And throb of blood beating within her brain,
Savoured intensely to the verge of pain
Her own young life, hoarded it up behind
Her shuttered lids, until, too long confined,
It burst them open and her prisoned soul
Flew forth and took possession of the whole
Exquisite world about her and was made
A part of it. Meanwhile her maidens played,
Singing an ancient song of death and birth,
Seed-time and harvest, old as the grey earth,
And moving to their music in a dance
As immemorial. A numbing trance
Came gradually over her, as though
Flake after downy-feathered flake of snow
Had muffled all her senses, drifting deep
And warm and quiet.

From this all-but sleep
She started into life again; the sky
Was full of a strange tumult suddenly—
Beating of mighty wings and shrill-voiced fear
And the hoarse scream of rapine following near
In the high windlessness above her flew,

Dazzlingly white on the untroubled blue,
A splendid swan, with outstretched neck and wing
Spread fathom wide, and closely following
An eagle, tawny and black. This god-like pair
Circled and swooped through the calm of upper air,
The eagle striking and the white swan still
'Scaping as though by happy miracle
The imminent talons. For the twentieth time
The furious hunter stooped, to miss and climb
A mounting spiral into the height again.
He hung there poised, eyeing the grassy plain
Far, far beneath, where the girls' upturned faces
Were like white flowers that bloom in open places
Among the scarcely budded woods. And they
Breathlessly watched and waited; long he lay,
Becalmed upon that tideless sea of light,
While the great swan with slow and creaking flight
Went slanting down towards safety, where the stream
Shines through the trees below, with glance and gleam
Of blue aerial eyes that seem to give
Sense to the sightless earth and make it live.
The ponderous wings beat on and no pursuit:
Stiff as the painted kite that guards the fruit,
Afloat o'er orchards ripe, the eagle yet
Hung as at anchor, seeming to forget
His uncaught prey, his rage unsatisfied.
Still, quiet, dead . . . and then the quickest-eyed
Had lost him. Like a star unsphered, a stone
Dropped from the vault of heaven, a javelin thrown,
He swooped upon his prey. Down, down he came,
And through his plumes with a noise of wind-blown
flame
Loud roared the air. From Leda's lips a cry
Broke, and she hid her face—she could not see him die,

Her lovely, hapless swan.
Ah, had she heard,
Even as the eagle hurtled past, the word
That treacherous pair exchanged. 'Peace,' cried the swan;
'Peace, daughter. All my strength will soon be gone,
Wasted in tedious flying, ere I come
Where my desire hath set its only home.'
'Go,' said the eagle, 'I have played my part,
Roused pity for your plight in Leda's heart
(Pity the mother of voluptuousness).
Go, father Jove; be happy; for success
Attends this moment.'
On the queen's numbed sense
Fell a glad shout that ended sick suspense,
Bidding her lift once more towards the light
Her eyes, by pity closed against a sight
Of blood and death—her eyes, how happy now
To see the swan still safe, while far below,
Brought by the force of his eluded stroke
So near to earth that with his wings he woke
A gust whose sudden silvery motion stirred
The meadow grass, struggled the sombre bird
Of rage and rapine. Loud his scream and hoarse
With baffled fury as he urged his course
Upwards again on threshing pinions wide.
But the fair swan, not daring to abide
This last assault, dropped with the speed of fear
Towards the river. Like a winged spear,
Outstretching his long neck, rigid and straight,
Aimed at where Leda on the bank did wait
With open arms and kind, uplifted eyes
And voice of tender pity, down he flies.
Nearer, nearer, terribly swift, he sped

Directly at the queen; then widely spread
Resisting wings, and breaking his descent
'Gainst his own wind, all speed and fury spent,
The great swan fluttered slowly down to rest
And sweet security on Leda's breast.
Menacingly the eagle wheeled above her;
But Leda, like a noble-hearted lover
Keeping his child-beloved from tyrannous harm,
Stood o'er the swan and, with one slender arm
Imperiously lifted, waved away
The savage foe, still hungry for his prey.
Baffled at last, he mounted out of sight
And the sky was void—save for a single white
Swan's feather moulted from a harassed wing
That down, down, with a rhythmic balancing
From side to side dropped sleeping on the air.
Down, slowly down over that dazzling pair,
Whose different grace in union was a birth
Of unimagined beauty on the earth:
So lovely that the maidens standing round
Dared scarcely look. Couched on the flowery ground
Young Leda lay, and to her side did press
The swan's proud-arching opulent loveliness,
Stroking the snow-soft plumage of his breast
With fingers slowly drawn, themselves caressed
By the warm softness where they lingered, loth
To break away. Sometimes against their growth
Ruffling the feathers inlaid like little scales
On his sleek neck, the pointed finger-nails
Rasped on the warm, dry, puckered skin beneath;
And feeling it she shuddered, and her teeth
Grated on edge; for there was something strange
And snake-like in the touch. He, in exchange,
Gave back to her, stretching his eager neck,

For every kiss a little amorous peck;
Rubbing his silver head on her gold tresses,
And with the nip of horny dry caresses
Leaving upon her young white breast and cheek
And arms the red print of his playful beak.
Closer he nestled, mingling with the slim
Austerity of virginal flank and limb
His curved and florid beauty, till she felt
That downy warmth strike through her flesh and melt
The bones and marrow of her strength away.
One lifted arm bent o'er her brow, she lay
With limbs relaxed, scarce breathing, deathly still;
Save when a quick, involuntary thrill
Shook her sometimes with passing shudderings,
As though some hand had plucked the aching strings
Of life itself, tense with expectancy.
And over her the swan shook slowly free
The folded glory of his wings, and made
A white-walled tent of soft and luminous shade
To be her veil and keep her from the shame
Of naked light and the sun's noonday flame.

Hushed lay the earth and the wide, careless sky.
Then one sharp sound, that might have been a cry
Of utmost pleasure or of utmost pain,
Broke sobbing forth, and all was still again.

LEDA

A SUNSET

OVER against the triumph and the close—
  Amber and green and rose—
    Of this short day,

The pale ghost of the moon grows living-bright
  Once more, as the last light
    Ebbs slowly away.
Darkening the fringes of these western glories
  The black phantasmagories
    Of cloud advance
With noiseless footing—vague and villainous shapes,
  Wrapped in their ragged fustian capes,
    Of some grotesque romance.
But overhead where, like a pool between
  Dark rocks, the sky is green
    And clear and deep,
Floats windlessly a cloud, with curving breast
  Flushed by the fiery west,
    In god-like sleep . . .
And in my mind opens a sudden door
  That lets me see once more
    A little room
With night beyond the window, chill and damp,
  And one green-lighted lamp
    Tempering the gloom,
While here within, close to me, touching me
  (Even the memory
    Of my desire
Shakes me like fear), you sit with scattered hair;
  And all your body bare
    Before the fire
Is lapped about with rosy flame. . . . But still,
  Here on the lonely hill,
    I walk alone;
Silvery green is the moon's lamp overhead,
  The cloud sleeps warm and red,
    And you are gone.

FIRST PHILOSOPHER'S SONG

A POOR degenerate from the ape,
Whose hands are four, whose tail's a limb,
I contemplate my flaccid shape
And know I may not rival him,

Save with my mind—a nimbler beast
Possessing a thousand sinewy tails,
A thousand hands, with which it scales,
Greedy of luscious truth, the greased

Poles and the coco palms of thought,
Thrids easily through the mangrove maze
Of metaphysics, walks the taut
Frail dangerous liana ways

That link across wide gulfs remote
Analogies between tree and tree;
Outruns the hare, outhops the goat;
Mind fabulous, mind sublime and free!

But oh, the sound of simian mirth!
Mind, issued from the monkey's womb,
Is still umbilical to earth,
Earth its home and earth its tomb.

LEDA

FIFTH PHILOSOPHER'S SONG

A MILLION million spermatozoa,
All of them alive:
Out of their cataclysm but one poor Noah
Dare hope to survive.

And among that billion minus one
  Might have chanced to be
Shakespeare, another Newton, a new Donne—
  But the One was Me.

Shame to have ousted your betters thus,
  Taking ark while the others remained outside !
Better for all of us, froward Homunculus,
  If you'd quietly died !

LEDA

THEATRE OF VARIETIES

CIRCLE on circle the hanging gardens descend,
Sloping from upper darkness, each flower face
Open, turned to the light and laughter and life
Of the sun-like stage. And all the space between,
Like the hot fringes of a summer sky,
Is quick with trumpets, beats with the pulse of drums,
Athwart whose sultry thunders rise and fall
Flute fountains and the swallow flight of strings.
Music, the revelation and marvellous lie !
On the bright trestles tumblers, tamers of beasts,
Dancers and clowns affirm their fury of life.

  'The World-Renowned Van Hogen Mogen in
  The Master Mystery of Modern Times.'

He talks, he talks ; more powerfully than even
Music his quick words hammer on men's minds.
'Observe this hat, ladies and gentlemen ;
Empty, observe, empty as the universe
Before the Head for which this Hat is made
Was or could think. Empty, observe, observe.'

The rabbit kicks; a bunch of paper flowers
Blooms in the limelight; paper tape unrolls,
Endless, a clue. 'Ladies and gentlemen . . .'
Sharp, sharp on malleable minds his words
Hammer. The little Indian boy
Enters the basket. Bright, an Ethiop's sword
Transfixes it and bleeding is withdrawn.
Death draws and petrifies the watching faces.
'Ladies and gentlemen': the great Van Hogen Mogen
Smiles and is kind. A puddle of dark blood
Slowly expands. 'The irremediable
Has been and is no more.'
Empty of all but blood, the basket gapes.
'Arise!' he calls, and blows his horn. 'Arise!'
And bird-like from the highest gallery
The little Indian answers.
Shout upon shout, the hanging gardens reverberate.
Happy because the irremediable is healed,
Happy because they have seen the impossible,
Because they are freed from the dull daily law,
They shout, they shout. And great Van Hogen Mogen
Modestly bows, graciously smiles. The band
Confirms the lie with cymbals and bassoons,
The curtain falls. How quickly the walls recede,
How soon the petrified gargoyles re-become
Women and men! who fill the warm thick air
With rumour of their loves and discontents,
Not suffering even great Hogen Mogen—
Only begetter out of empty hats
Of rose and rabbit, raiser from the dead—
To invade the sanctity of private life.

The Six Aerial Sisters Polpetini
Dive dangerously from trapeze to far

Trapeze, like stars, and know not how to fall.
For if they did and if, of his silver balls,
Sclopis, the juggler, dropped but one—but one
Of all the flying atoms which he builds
With his quick throwing into a solid arch—
What panic then would shake the pale flower faces
Blooming so tranquilly in their hanging beds!
What a cold blast of fear! But patrons must not,
And since they must not, cannot be alarmed.
Hence Sclopis, hence (the proof is manifest)
The Six Aerial Ones infallibly
Function, and have done, and for ever will.

Professor Chubb's Automaton performs
Upon the viols and virginals, plays chess,
Ombre and loo, mistigri, tric-trac, pushpin,
Sings Lilliburlero in falsetto, answers
All questions put to it, and with its rubber feet
Noiselessly dances the antique heydiguy.
'Is it a man?' the terrible infant wonders.
And 'no,' they say, whose business it is
To say such infants nay. And 'no' again
They shout when, after watching Dobbs and Debs
Step simultaneously through intricate dances,
Hammer the same tune with their rattling clogs
In faultless unison, the infant asks,
'And they, are they machines?'

Music, the revelation and marvellous lie,
Rebuilds in the minds of all a suave and curving
Kingdom of Heaven, where the saxophone
Affirms everlasting loves, the drums deny
Death, and where great Tenorio, when he sings,
Makes Picardy bloom only with perfumed roses,

And never a rotting corpse in all its earth.
Play, music, play! In God's bright limelight eyes
An angel walks and with one rolling glance
Blesses each hungry flower in the hanging gardens.
'Divine,' they cry, having no words by which
To call the nameless spade a spade, 'Divine
Zenocrate!' There are dark mysteries
Whose name is beauty, strange revelations called
Love, and a gulph of pleasure and of awe
Where words fall vain and wingless in the dark;
The seen Ineffable, the felt but all-Unknown
And Undescribed, is God. 'Divine, divine!'
The god-intoxicated shout goes up.
'Divine Zenocrate!'
'Father,' the terrible infant's voice is shrill,
'Say, father, why does the lady wear no skirts?'
She wears no skirts; God's eyes have never been brighter.
The face flowers open in her emanation.
She is the suave and curving Kingdom of Heaven
Made visible, and in her sugared song
The ear finds paradise. Divine, divine!
Her belly is like a mound of wheat, her breasts
Are towers, her hair like a flock of goats.
    Her foot is feat with diamond toes
    And she—divine Zenocrate—
    And she on legs of ruby goes.
The face flowers tremble in the rushing wind
Of her loud singing. A poet in the pit
Jots down in tears the words of her Siren song.
    So every spirit as it is most pure,
    And hath in it the more of heavenly light,
    So it the rarer body doth procure
    To habit in, and is more fairly dight
    With cheerful grace and amiable sight:

For of the soul the body form doth take;
And soul is form and doth the body make.
'Now, boys, together. All with me,' she cries
Through the long sweet suspense of dominant chords;
'For of the soul,' her voice is paradise,
'For of the soul the body form doth take;
And soul is form and doth the body make.'
Zenocrate, alone, alone divine!

God save the King. Music's last practical joke
Still bugling in their ears of war and glory,
The folk emerge into the night.
Already next week's bills are being posted:—
Urim and Thummim, cross-talk comedians;
Ringpok, the Magian of Tibet;
The Two Bedelias; Ruby and Truby Dix;
Sam Foy and Troupe of Serio-Comic Cyclists . . .
Theatre of immemorial varieties,
Old mummery, but mummers never the same!
Twice nightly every night from now till doomsday
The hanging gardens, bedded with pale flower faces,
Young flowers in the old old gardens, will echo
With ever new, with ever new delight.

THE CICADAS

THE MOOR

Champion of souls and holiness, upholder
Of all the virtues, father of the Church,
Honest, honest, honest Iago! how
Crusadingly, with what indignant zeal
(*Ora pro nobis*), caracoling on
Your high horse and emblazoned, gules on white,

Did you ride forth (Oh, pray for us), ride forth
Against the dark-skinned hosts of evil, ride,
Martyr and saint, against those paynim hosts,
Having for shield all Sinai, and for sword,
To smite rebellion and avenge the Lord,
The sharp, the shining certainty of faith!
(*Ora pro nobis*) point us out the Way.

> 'Lily bright and stinking mud:
> Fair is fair and foul is ill.
> With her, on her, what you will.
> This fire must be put out with blood,
> Put out with blood.'

But for a glint, a hint of questing eyes,
Invisible, darkness through darkness goes
On feet that even in their victim's dreaming
Wake not an echo.
Lost, he is lost; and yet thus wholly in darkness
Melted, the Moor is more Othello than when,
Green-glittering, the sharp Venetian day
Revealed him armed and kingly and commanding
Captain of men.

How still she lies, this naked Desdemona,
All but a child and sleeping and alone,
How still and white!
Whose breast, whose arms, the very trustfulness
Of her closed eyelids and unhurried breath
More than a philtre maddeningly invite
Lust and those hands, those huge dark hands, and death.

> 'For oh, the lily and the mud!
> Fair is still fair and foulness, ill.
> With her, on her, what you will.
> This fire must be put out with blood.'

Well, now the fire is out, and the light too;
All, all put out. In Desdemona's place
Lies now a carrion. That fixed grimace
Of lidless eyes and starting tongue
Derides his foolishness. Cover her face;
This thing but now was beautiful and young.
Honest Iago's Christian work is over;
Short, short the parleying at the Golden Gate.
'For I am one who made the Night ashamed
Of his own essence, that his dark was dark;
One who with good St. Jerome's filthy tongue
Tainted desire and taught the Moor to scorn
His love's pale body, and because she had
Lain gladly in his arms, to call her whore
And strangle her for whoredom.' So he spoke,
And with majestic motion heaven's high door
Rolled musically apart its burnished vans
To grant him entrance.

Turning back meanwhile
From outer darkness, Othello and his bride
Perceive the globe of heaven like one small lamp
Burning alone at midnight in the abyss
Of some cathedral cavern; pause, and then
With face once more averted, hand in hand,
Explore the unseen treasures of the dark.

THE CICADAS

ORION

TREE-TANGLED still, autumn Orion climbs
Up from among the North Wind's shuddering emblems
Into the torrent void

And dark abstraction of invisible power,
The heart and boreal substance of the night.

Pleione flees before him, and behind,
Still sunken, but prophetically near,
Death in the Scorpion hunts him up the sky
And round the vault of time, round the slow-curving year,
Follows unescapably
And to the end, aye, and beyond the end
Will follow, follow; for of all the gods
Death only cannot die.

The rest are mortal. And how many lie
Already with their creatures' ancient dust!
Dead even in us who live—or hardly live,
Since of our hearts impiety has made,
Not tombs indeed (for they are holy; tombs
Secretly live with everlasting Death's
Dark and mysterious life),
But curious shops and learned lumber rooms
Of bone and stone and every mummied thing,
Where Death himself his sacred sting
Forgets (how studiously forgotten
Amid the irrelevant to and fro of feet!),
Where by the peeping and the chattering,
The loud forgetfulness seemingly slain,
He lies with all the rest—and yet we know,
In secret yet we know,
Death is not dead, not dead but only sleeping,
And soon will rise again.

Not so the rest. Only the Scorpion burns
In our unpeopled heaven of empty names
And insubstantial echoes; only Death

Still claims our prayers, and still to those who pray
Returns his own dark blood and quickening breath,
Returns the ominous mystery of fear.
Where are the gods of dancing and desire?
Anger and joy, laughter and tears and wine,
Those other mysteries of fire and flame,
Those more divine than Death's—ah, where are they?
Only a ghost between the shuddering trees,
Only a name and ghostly numbers climb;
And where a god pursued and fled,
Only a ghostly time, a ghostly place
Attends on other ghostly times and places.
Orion and the rest are dead.

And yet to-night, here in the exulting wind,
Amid the enormous laughters of a soul
At once the world's and mine,
God-like Orion and all his brother stars
Shine as with living eyes,
With eyes that glance a recognition, glance a sign
Across the quickened dark, across the gulphs
That separate no more,
But, like wide seas that yet bring home the freight
Of man's mad yearning for a further shore,
Join with a living touch, unbrokenly,
Life to mysterious life,
The Hunter's alien essence to my own.

Orion lives; yet I who know him living,
Elsewhere and otherwise
Know him for dead, and dead beyond all hope,
For 'tis the infertile and unquickening death
Of measured places and recorded times,
The death of names and numbers that he dies.

Only the phantom of Orion climbs.
Put out the eyes, put out the living eyes
And look elsewhere; yes, look and think and be
Elsewhere and otherwise.
But *here* and *thus* are also in their right,
Are in their right divine to send this wind of laughter
Rushing through the cloudless dark
And through my being; have a right divine
And imprescriptible now to reveal
The starry god, a right to make me feel,
As even now, as even now I feel,
His living presence near me in the night.

A curved and figured glass hangs between light and light,
Between the glow within us and the glow
Of what mysterious sun without?
Vast over earth and sky, or focussed burningly
Upon the tender quick, our spirits throw
Each way their images—each way the forms
O! shall it be of beauty, shall it be
The naked skeletons of doubt?
Or else, symbolically dark, the cloudy forms
Of mystery, or dark (but dark with death)
Shapes of sad knowledge and defiling hate?

'Lighten our darkness, Lord.' With what pure faith,
What confident hope our fathers once implored
The Light! But 'tis the shitten Lord of Flies
Who with his loathsome bounties now fulfils
On us their prayers. Our fathers prayed for light.
Through windows at their supplications scoured
Bare of the sacred blazons, but instead
Daubed with the dung-god's filth, all living eyes,
Whether of stars or men, look merely dead;

While on the vaulted crystal of the night
Our guttering souls project,
Not the Wild Huntsman, not the Heavenly Hosts,
But only times and places, only names and ghosts.

And yet, for all the learned Lord of Dung,
The choice is ours, the choice is always ours,
To see or not to see the living powers
That move behind the numbered points and times.
The Fly King rules; but still the choice remains
With us his subjects, we are free, are free
To love our fate or loathe it; to rejoice
Or weep or wearily accept; are free,
For all the scouring of our souls, for all
The miring of their crystal, free to give
Even to an empty sky, to vacant names,
Or not to give, our worship; free to turn
Lifewards, within, without, to what transcends
The squalor of our personal ends and aims,
Or not to turn; yes, free to die or live;
Free to be thus and passionately here,
Or otherwise and otherwhere;
Free, in a word, to learn or not to learn
The art to think and musically do
And feel and be, the never more than now
Difficult art harmoniously to live
All poetry—the midnight of Macbeth
And ripe Odysseus and the undying light
Of Gemma's star and Cleopatra's death
And Falstaff in his cups; the art to live
That discipline of flowers, that solemn dance
Of sliding weights and harnessed powers
Which is a picture; or to live the grave
And stoical recession, row on row,

Of equal columns, live the passionate leaping,
The mutual yearning, meeting, marrying,
And then the flame-still rapture, the fierce trance
Of consummation in the Gothic night.

The choice is always ours. Then, let me choose
The longest art, the hard Promethean way
Cherishingly to tend and feed and fan
That inward fire, whose small precarious flame,
Kindled or quenched, creates
The noble or the ignoble men we are,
The worlds we live in and the very fates,
Our bright or muddy star.

Up from among the emblems of the wind
Into its heart of power,
The Huntsman climbs, and all his living stars
Are bright, and all are mine.

THE CICADAS

SEPTEMBER

Spring is past and over these many days,
Spring and summer. The leaves of September droop,
Yellowing and all but dead on the patient trees.
Nor is there any hope in me. I walk
Slowly homewards. Night is as empty and dark
Behind my eyes as it is dark without
And empty round about me and over me.
Spring is past and over these many days,
But, looking up, suddenly I see
Leaves in the upthrown light of a street lamp shining,
Clear and luminous, young and so transparent,

They seem but the coloured foam of air, green fire,
No more than the scarce-embodied thoughts of leaves.
And it is spring within that circle of light.
Oh, magical brightness ! The old leaves are made new.
In the mind, too, some coloured accident
Of beauty revives and makes all young again,
A chance light shines and suddenly it is spring.

THE CICADAS

STORM AT NIGHT

Oh, how aquarium-still, how brooding-warm
This paradise ! How peacefully in the womb
Of war itself, and at the heart of storm
How safely—safely a captive, in a tomb—
I lie and, listening to the wild assault,
The pause and once-more fury of the gale,
Feel through the cracks of my sepulchral vault
The fine-drawn probe of air, and watch the pale
Unearthly lightnings leap across the sky
Like sudden sperm and die and leap again.
The thunder calls and every spasm of fire
Beckons, a signal, to that old desire
In calm for tempest and at ease for pain.
Dreaming of strength and courage, here I lie.

THE CICADAS

MIDSUMMER DAY

This day was midsummer, the longest tarrying
Time makes between two sleeps. What have I done
With this longest of so few days, how spent,

Dear God, the golden, golden gift of sun?
Virginal, when I rose, the morning lay
Ready for beauty's rape, for wisdom's marrying.
I wrote: only an inky spider went,
Smear after smear, across the unsullied day.
If there were other places, if there were
But other days than this longest of few;
If one had courage, did one dare to do
That which alone might kill what now defaces
This the one place of all the countless places,
This only day when one will never dare!

THE CICADAS

ALMERIA

WINDS have no moving emblems here, but scour
A vacant darkness, an untempered light;
No branches bend, never a tortured flower
Shudders, root-weary, on the verge of flight;
Winged future, withered past, no seeds nor leaves
Attest those swift invisible feet: they run
Free through a naked land, whose breast receives
All the fierce ardour of a naked sun.
You have the Light for lover. Fortunate Earth!
Conceive the fruit of his divine desire.
But the dry dust is all she brings to birth,
That child of clay by even celestial fire.
Then come, soft rain and tender clouds, abate
This shining love that has the force of hate.

THE CICADAS

THE CICADAS

SIGHTLESS, I breathe and touch; this night of pines
Is needly, resinous and rough with bark.
Through every crevice in the tangible dark
The moonlessness above it all but shines.

Limp hangs the leafy sky; never a breeze
Stirs, nor a foot in all this sleeping ground;
And there is silence underneath the trees—
The living silence of continuous sound.

For like inveterate remorse, like shrill
Delirium throbbing in the fevered brain,
An unseen people of cicadas fill
Night with their one harsh note, again, again.

Again, again, with what insensate zest!
What fury of persistence, hour by hour!
Filled with what devil that denies them rest,
Drunk with what source of pleasure and of power!

Life is their madness, life that all night long
Bids them to sing and sing, they know not why;
Mad cause and senseless burden of their song;
For life commands, and Life! is all their cry.

I hear them sing, who in the double night
Of clouds and branches fancied that I went
Through my own spirit's dark discouragement,
Deprived of inward as of outward sight:

Who, seeking, even as here in the wild wood,
A lamp to beckon through my tangled fate,
Found only darkness and, disconsolate,
Mourned the lost purpose and the vanished good.

Now in my empty heart the crickets' shout
Re-echoing denies and still denies
With stubborn folly all my learned doubt,
In madness more than I in reason wise.

Life, life ! The word is magical. They sing,
And in my darkened soul the great sun shines;
My fancy blossoms with remembered spring,
And all my autumns ripen on the vines.

Life ! and each knuckle of the fig tree's pale
Dead skeleton breaks out with emerald fire.
Life ! and the tulips blow, the nightingale
Calls back the rose, calls back the old desire:

And old desire that is for ever new,
Desire, life's earliest and latest birth,
Life's instrument to suffer and to do,
Springs with the roses from the teeming earth;

Desire that from the world's bright body strips
Deforming time and makes each kiss the first;
That gives to hearts, to satiated lips
The endless bounty of to-morrow's thirst.

Time passes, and the watery moonrise peers
Between the tree-trunks. But no outer light
Tempers the chances of our groping years,
No moon beyond our labyrinthine night.

Clueless we go ; but I have heard thy voice,
Divine Unreason ! harping in the leaves,
And grieve no more ; for wisdom never grieves,
And thou hast taught me wisdom ; I rejoice.

THE CICADAS

THE WORLD OF LIGHT*

A COMEDY IN THREE ACTS

The Characters

MRS. WENHAM	MAID
MR. WENHAM	BILL HAMBLIN
HUGO WENHAM	HUBERT CAPES
ENID DECKLE	MR. GRAY

ACT I

SCENE I

The drawing-room in the Wenhams' house in the country.

(MR. WENHAM *is sitting in front of the fire reading.* MRS. WENHAM *is writing letters. Silence for some seconds after the rise of the curtain.*)

MRS. WENHAM (*she is a woman of about thirty-five, handsome, large, commanding*). John dear. (*He looks up from his book.*) What's the time?

MR. WENHAM (*he is twenty-five years older than his wife, a well-preserved man, nice-looking in a grey suppressed way. His manner is very gentle*). Twenty to seven, dear.

MRS. WENHAM. I shall have to go and say good-night to the children in a moment.

MR. WENHAM. I'll come too. Whenever you give the word, my love.

MRS. WENHAM. As a matter of fact, John, I'd rather you

* The terms for the performance of this play may be obtained from James B. Pinker & Son, Talbot House, Arundel Street, Strand, London, W.C.2, to whom all applications for permission should be made. Copyright in the United States of America, 1931, by Aldous Huxley.

didn't come up. I'd like you to say a few words to Hugo when he arrives. About Enid.

MR. WENHAM (*nervously*). But, my dear, wouldn't it be better if you . . . I mean, a woman's touch . . . in these delicate matters . . .

MRS. WENHAM. One would think you were afraid of him, John. Afraid of your own son.

MR. WENHAM. No, no, my dear. It's not that. But one has a certain . . . a certain diffidence. Besides, I'm not very good at this sort of thing . . . I mean, discussing . . . well, shall we say, the affairs of the heart. So wouldn't it be better if you were to talk to him?

MRS. WENHAM (*firmly*). No, John, I'm afraid it must be you. After all, I'm only his stepmother, I can't speak to him as you can speak. And then, in the second place, I'm a woman, I'm a friend of Enid's. If I spoke to him, he might feel that it was a kind of feminine conspiracy to get him married, which would spoil everything. Because I *do* want him to get married. I really think it would be the making of him. Besides, there's *her* point of view to be considered. You see, it's really not fair on her. This friendship that's gone on ever since they were children and never quite turns into something else. Always on the brink. It's not fair. Don't you agree with me, John?

MR. WENHAM. Oh, quite, quite.

MRS. WENHAM. She has a right to expect Hugo to marry her. After all, she's nearly thirty, and I know for a fact that she's refused at least two other men. So you see, John, something ought to be done about it.

MR. WENHAM. Yes, I quite agree, my dear.

MRS. WENHAM. Hugo's been getting so unsettled recently. I don't like it. It's high time he got married. Besides, he's really rather a helpless person. He needs looking after. Enid would mother him. They *ought* to marry. Hugo's making quite a reasonable income now at Cambridge. Besides, Enid has three or four hundred of her own. And if necessary, you could always give him a little.

MR. WENHAM. Oh, one had always meant to, when Hugo . . . well, embarked on matrimony.

MRS. WENHAM. So you see there's no reason why they shouldn't get married. And a great many reasons why they should. As soon as possible. And that's what I want you to say to Hugo when he comes.

MR. WENHAM. Yes, dear. All the same, I do wish you could stay and help one to . . . explain it to him.

MRS. WENHAM. Out of the question, John.

MR. WENHAM. One's so loath to break in on a young man's . . . well, should one say his emotional privacies? . . .

MRS. WENHAM. There! I hear the car. Remember, John. I rely on you.

MR. WENHAM (*agitated*). Yes, dear. But really, it seems to me . . .

MRS. WENHAM. And say what you have to say as quickly as possible, dear. Because, you see, I arranged that Enid should come rather early, so that there'd be a chance of her being alone with Hugo, before dinner. So don't be too slow. And when Enid comes, just slip away. Tactfully, you know. Inconspicuously.

MR. WENHAM. Yes, but . . .

MRS. WENHAM. Say you've got to say good-night to the children.

(*Enter* HUGO WENHAM. *He is a man of about thirty, small, rather delicate-looking, with an ugly but sensitive, intelligent face, and a manner whose timidity is tempered by sudden spurts of brusque determination.*)

Ah, Hugo ! This is nice to see you. (*Holds out her hand.*) But you're icy. Come near the fire.

HUGO. Thank you. How are you, father ?

MR. WENHAM. As flourishing as can be expected. And you, dear boy ?

HUGO. Oh, all right. Rather tired, of course. But at the end of term one always is. Trying to make reluctant undergraduates understand Plato—God ! (*He shakes his head. To* MRS. WENHAM) How are the children, Alice ?

MRS. WENHAM. Very well, thanks. Peter's been having a bit of a sore throat. That's all. Which reminds me, I must go and say good-night to them. I'll leave you. Dinner's at half-past seven. Don't dress.

HUGO. Oh, talking of dinner, I hope you didn't mind my asking Bill Hamblin for this evening.

MRS. WENHAM. But we're delighted.

HUGO. He's leaving England to-morrow. It was my only chance of seeing him before he started. I hope you'll like him.

MRS. WENHAM. I'm sure we shall.

HUGO. Don't be *too* sure. But anyhow, you'll be amused, I think. I find him a real tonic (*laughs*), and after a spell of Cambridge one needs a tonic, I assure you.

MRS. WENHAM. He sounds charming. And as I wrote to you, I've asked Enid to drop in too. So it ought to be a delightful evening. But I must fly. (*She goes out.*)

(*Pause.*)

MR. WENHAM. Well, dear boy, it's pleasant to have you with us again.

HUGO. It's pleasant to be here. (*Another embarrassea pause.*) Been very busy lately, father ?

MR. WENHAM. Oh, the daily round, the common task.

HUGO. Yes, if only they could be a bit more irregular and extraordinary.

MR. WENHAM. I used to wish the same at your age. But one settles down; one gets to like the harness; one comes to realize that the daily and the common are . . . are sacred.

HUGO. Sacred? (*Makes a little grimace.*) I'd like to be able to feel that.

MR. WENHAM. Not the only sacred, of course. There's the other—the sublimer aspect of sacredness. (*He sighs.*) I wish I could persuade you to take more interest in spiritualism, dear boy.

HUGO. But I do. I read all the documents.

MR. WENHAM. Yes, but in what sort of spirit? Not as they ought to be read. You're detached. If you only knew how . . . how consoling and uplifting it was.

HUGO. I don't know that I awfully want to be consoled and uplifted. (*He begins walking up and down the room.*) And anyhow, if the common and the daily weren't so dismal, would one need all that consolation? I mean, couldn't one's whole life be made sacred in that sublimer, more exciting way? Here and now, without calling in the next world to redress the balance of this. The infinite in terms of the bounded and the relative —that's what I try to see my way towards. Gropingly. (*He breaks off to utter a constrained little laugh.*) Sorry I'm being a bit of a bore.

MR. WENHAM. But, no, dear boy. (*He lays a hand on his arm shyly.*) One's so happy to be allowed to . . . to share your thoughts. So happy and so . . . so proud.

HUGO (*very much embarrassed and trying to laugh it off*). Oh, there's not much to be proud of, I'm afraid.

MR. WENHAM. One understands so well what you mean.

That raising of life to a higher . . . well, level of significance . . . one's felt the need of that oneself. One has tried; one has, perhaps, to some extent, succeeded. (*A little pause.*) Listen, dear boy, I was wrong just now when I said that the common and the daily were sacred in themselves. Rather they become sacred when they're . . . they're shared with . . . well, somebody one's attached to; when they're made the . . . the foundation and background of . . . well, of love. That's the real point of marriage—its power to enrich ordinariness and make it sacred. Now, if you were to get married, dear boy . . .

HUGO (*laughing*). Do you think I'd begin to enjoy trying to make stupid undergraduates understand Plato? No, but seriously, I have thought about it.

MR. WENHAM. You have? That's good news. (*He hesitates, nervously.*) Very good news . . . because, you see, dear boy, one had been thinking about it so much oneself of late. You and our dear Enid . . .

HUGO. Enid?

MR. WENHAM. I mean, you've known her so long . . . such an intimate comradeship. It was hard to think of any one more suitable, more . . . well, suitable. And at the same time one hasn't been blind to the obvious fact that Enid herself is . . . well, devoted to you.

HUGO. Is that obvious?

MR. WENHAM. But surely, Hugo, you yourself must have seen . . . well, what one was saying.

(HUGO *shakes his head slowly.*)

No? Well, to other eyes, it has been plain enough. (*Pause.*) Dear boy, I don't exactly know what your feelings are in this matter.

HUGO (*laughs*). I wish I exactly knew myself.

MR. WENHAM. It's often difficult to know before one's . . . one's acted on the knowledge.

HUGO. On the knowledge one hasn't got?

MR. WENHAM. But one assumes it. And one acts on the assumption. And the result of the action is to prove . . . well, that the assumption was correct.

HUGO. Or incorrect. What happens in that case?

MR. WENHAM. One's never seen it proved incorrect.

HUGO. You mean that pretending to be in love always makes you really be in love?

MR. WENHAM. Not *pretending*, dear boy. The cases one was talking about are cases . . . cases where the old habit of companionship seems to exclude the possibility of a new revelation. All one was saying is that if you take a risk and give the new revelation a chance . . . well, it does manifest itself, in spite of the old habit. Always.

HUGO. All the same, there might be exceptions.

MR. WENHAM. And then, dear boy, there's Enid to be thought about. Would it be really . . . well, just to . . . to . . . I mean, *not* to marry her? (*Hastily, very embarrassed*) I mean if it were possible for you to marry her—possible as far as your own feelings went. Would it really be quite the . . . quite the . . . well, chivalrous thing?

HUGO. Chivalrous? But where have I been unchivalrous? Do you mean to imply . . . ?

MR. WENHAM. No, no, dear boy. One wasn't implying anything. Only there's this to be thought: that an old friendship like yours, a friendship with a woman, and a woman who's . . . who's . . . well, devoted to you, well, it . . . it automatically gives the friend to understand that . . . that she's more than a friend.

HUGO. But do you mean to say that Enid thinks . . . ? I mean, does she feel I've not been treating her fairly?

MR. WENHAM. Oh, no, she never says anything, of course not. All that one meant was that her present situation was—how shall I say it?—was in itself a kind of . . . of protest.

HUGO. You mean her life looks as though it had been spoilt?

MR. WENHAM. No, no. Hardly that. But it seems to me that it might come to be spoilt.

HUGO. If I didn't marry her?

MR. WENHAM. You or some one else. And one knows privately that she's refused several other offers of marriage.

HUGO. She never told me that.

MR. WENHAM. Of course she didn't. Do you think it would be like Enid to . . . to do anything that might look like . . . well, forcing your hand? But all the same, one happens to know from other sources that it's true. And the reason for it . . . well, dear boy, the reason is *you*. So that you see, in a way it's not quite fair to let things go on as they are. The right, the chivalrous thing to do would be either to stop seeing her altogether—that is, if you felt it was impossible to . . . well, feel more than friendship . . . or else . . .

HUGO. Yes, yes, I see. (*Pause.*)

MR. WENHAM. I think you ought to come to a decision, Hugo. (*The door opens and* ENID *enters quietly.*) You ought to make up your mind.

ENID (*she is a dark woman about twenty-eight, with large eyes and an emotional, intense expression*). Do you think Hugo can ever make up his mind?

(*The two men start and look round guiltily.*)

Oh, I'm sorry to have given you such a start. Good evening, Mr. Wenham. Well, Hugo?

(*They shake hands in silence.*)

(*Turning to* MR. WENHAM) What were you telling him to make up his mind about?

MR. WENHAM. Oh, nothing, my dear, nothing.

ENID. Those are the decisions he finds hardest to make. The ones about nothing. How I've suffered from his not knowing what restaurant he wants to go to for lunch, and when at last he does get somewhere, not being able to decide between the roast chicken and the veal cutlet. Terrible! Isn't it true, Hugo?

HUGO (*gloomily*). I suppose so.

ENID. To eat roast chicken or not to eat roast chicken, that is the question. But *I'm* like Lady Macbeth. Infirm of purpose, give *me* the menu. Poor old Hugo!

HUGO. Poor old everybody, it seems.

MR. WENHAM (*looking at his watch*). Oh, dear! One must be running up to say good-night to the children. I shall get into trouble if I'm late.

(*He goes out.*)

ENID (*going up to* HUGO *and examining him critically*). You look tired, Hugo.

HUGO. Mayn't I be tired? And anyhow, you needn't throw it in my teeth.

ENID. I was only throwing a little sympathy. You generally like it. Besides, you *do* look tired. A tonic—that's what you need. I'll get you a bottle of hypophosphates to-morrow.

HUGO (*with a kind of weary impatience*). No, don't. Please.

ENID (*playfully*). Yes, I will. And I'll stand over you to see that you take it.

(HUGO *says nothing, but his face shows that this spritely talk of tonics distresses him.*)

But what's the matter, Hugo?

HUGO. Nothing!

ENID. It must be a nasty sort of nothing. How's life?

HUGO (*shrugging his shoulders*). Oh, as usual. Rather like death.

ENID. I hate it when you say that sort of thing.

HUGO. I'm sorry. Would you like me to say that every day in every way it's getting better and better?

(ENID *says nothing.*)

What have you been up to since I saw you last? Bullying the deserving poor, as usual?

ENID. Yes, my old Charity Organization business. And parcels of books from Mudie's in the intervals.

HUGO. Bad novels to counteract the good works—I know. And then early service on Sunday morning, and 'Abide with me, fast falls the eventide,' on Sunday evening.

ENID. Which you needn't laugh at, Hugo.

HUGO. Oh, I don't. On the contrary. I wish *I* were a theolater.

ENID. A what?

HUGO. A theolater. A man who worships God.

ENID. How does any one contrive not to? God's there—it's so obvious.

HUGO. Yes, obvious, I know.

ENID. Then why?

HUGO. Because just knowing isn't any good. (*He laughs.*) I know I'm a man, for example; but that doesn't prevent me from often feeling a worm.

ENID. Which is just stupid, Hugo. You take a pleasure in feeling a worm. It's really rather disgusting.

HUGO. Yes, you're quite right. Disgusting. But then I do so enjoy being sorry for myself. It's a vice—something one hates and at the same time feels irresistibly attracted to. . . . Don't you ever feel sorry for yourself, Enid?

ENID. Oh, sometimes. But who doesn't?

HUGO. Well, what do you think about it?

ENID. Try to think about something else.

HUGO. God, for example? That's where theolatry must come in so useful. But that smell of a congregation on a wet Sunday morning—I wish *I* could feel it was the odour of sanctity. But, no. . . . (*He shakes his head.*) I really prefer the smell of cows. And then the service —so far as I'm concerned, the divinity it's addressed to is dead, stone-dead. If only I could find a live one.

ENID. You would if you looked.

HUGO (*he shakes his head*). Only a live man can find a live god. And when one's dead, as I am . . . There you are! Being sorry for myself again. But it happens to be true. I'm dead, I'm empty. A dead vacuum. How I'm enjoying this. And how you're hating it, Enid!

ENID. It just makes me feel miserable—miserable for your sake.

HUGO. Thank you. But I hope you also feel contemptuous. (*She shakes her head.*) No? Well, you ought to. (*Pause.*) I heard Mozart's G minor quintet last week. That's very nearly a living god—I mean, music like that.

ENID (*nodding and in a seriously ecstatic voice*). Yes, great music. . . .

HUGO (*made suddenly flippant by her earnestness*). And then what about great alcohol? I got absurdly tight when I was staying one week-end with Bill Hamblin. Perhaps champagne's another of the living gods. If only one could be permanently buffy! Bill Hamblin's in that state even when he's perfectly sober. Bubblingly alive and therefore surrounded by a whole pantheon of living gods. I envy him.

ENID. Do you think I'll like Bill Hamblin?

HUGO. You'll probably fall in love with him. Most women do.

ENID (*smiling sadly*). I'm afraid that's not very likely.

HUGO. Don't you be too sure. (*Pause.*) What about this love business, now? Is love also a dead god?

ENID. He's got to be born before he can die. You'd better first ask yourself if he's been born.

HUGO. I do, constantly. But I don't get any answer. But do you think he's got to be like the poets, *born*? I mean, can't he also be *made*? What do you think, Enid? Can love be made?

ENID. There'd have to be the makings first. Nothing can be made unless the makings are there first.

HUGO. And what are they? Affection, understanding, common tastes, a shared history—would you call those the makings of love?

ENID. I suppose so. But why do you ask me?

HUGO. What a stupid hypocritical question, Enid! You know quite well why I asked you.

ENID. I don't. But still . . .

HUGO. Well, if you don't, I may as well go on leaving you in the dark. (*Pause; he walks up and down, then at last, with the air of a man who has taken a decision, halts in front of her.*) Look here, Enid; suppose I were to say to you that I didn't love you, but that I had all the makings of love in me. And suppose that on the strength of those makings I were to ask you to marry me—which would be asking you to marry a dead man, but a dead man with a chance of coming to life, if he could love. Suppose all this; would you take a risk and try whether love and life could be made out of those makings, or else, if it couldn't be made —well, God knows what would happen if it couldn't be made. Would you take that risk, Enid?

ENID (*after a pause*). Would *you* take it, Hugo?

HUGO. I? It depends on how you feel about it.

ENID. Which depends on what *you* feel.

HUGO. No, I want to know what *your* feelings are.

ENID (*laughing and shaking her head*). Oh, Hugo, Hugo.

HUGO. No, don't laugh, Enid. Why do you laugh?

ENID. All this depending on other dependings. Why can't you make up your mind? It's the old story of the roast chicken and the veal cutlet.

HUGO (*hurt*). Well, if that's how you feel, I won't go on. I had an idea you cared. Otherwise I wouldn't . . . (*He is turning to walk away, when she catches his hand and kisses it.*)

ENID. Hugo! Don't be hurt. *Please.* (*Pause; they look at one another, after a moment his eyes flinch away from hers embarrassed.*) Oh, if you only knew, Hugo. How much, how much . . . (*Kisses his hand again; when she goes on speaking she keeps it pressed against her cheek.*) But I didn't want to tell you how much I cared. Not before you'd made up your mind. It would have been bullying you, bludgeoning you with my love. (*She laughs unsteadily.*) I don't want to be Lady Macbeth about *this.* When it's a question of chicken or veal cutlets, then it's all right my saying 'Give *me* the daggers.' But here—here you've got to decide. This is your risk. Where there's love there isn't any risk. Or at least the reward is so great, that the risk doesn't count. But there, I'm bullying you. I'm bludgeoning you with my feelings. Go, go. (*She pushes him away from her.*) Forget what I said. Don't be influenced by it. (*He moves back towards her; she pushes him away again.*) No, go. You must make up your mind at the other end of the room. Go.

(HUGO *stands hesitatingly for a few seconds, sheepishly, then moves away. The door opens.*)

MAID. Mr. Hamblin.

(*Enter* BILL HAMBLIN. *He is a young man of about* HUGO'S *age, thin, with an aquiline face and pale, silky hair. The skin is tanned till it is almost darker than the hair. The eyes are a very bright blue. His movements are quick and dancing. There is something gay and irresponsible about him, as though he were not quite human, a sort of fairy.*)

BILL. Well, Hugo, what fun to see you! Escaped from your ghastly academic prison? But you don't look as cheerful about it as I should have expected. Glum, boy, glum. (*Seeing* ENID) But I'm so sorry. Why didn't you introduce me, Hugo?

HUGO. You didn't give me time; Enid, this is Bill Hamblin. Miss Enid Deckle.

ENID (*as she shakes his hand*). I've heard so much about you from Hugo.

BILL. And yet you still shake me by the hand. You're discreet, Hugo, thank you. So am I, though. Not that there's any need for discretion in this case, Miss Deckle. Hugo's an absolute monster of honesty and temperance and chastity.

HUGO (*laughing*). Alas!

BILL. I've done my best for him. But it's no good. He's incorrigibly the good citizen. It's discouraging. What a charming dress you're wearing, if you'll allow me to say so.

ENID. I'm glad you like it.

BILL. Really ravishing. Don't you think so, Hugo?

HUGO. Well, now you mention it . . . As a matter of fact, I hadn't noticed.

ENID (*laughing*). Hugo never notices anything.

BILL. I know. These budding professors—they're above all that sort of thing. Or below it. But you should just listen to them chattering away together about the latest fashion in metaphysics. I hear that the Absolute is being worn rather short this year. Hugo, is that true?

HUGO. On the contrary, it's been lengthened.

BILL. Well, thank God for that. I was getting rather tired of these pragmatist fashions. I like my universe well draped with transcendental mysteries. Layers and layers of mystery, like petticoats. White mystery, black mystery. Have you ever been in a tropical forest, Miss Deckle?

ENID. Never.

BILL. Ah, you should go. Talk of black mysteries—it's like a cellar, like the crypt of a church—the devil's own cathedral. Nobody has a sufficient respect for the devil in our civilized temperate countries. You have to go to the tropics to see him functioning on the grand scale. The forests of Borneo, for example. Marvellous! Satan in all his grandeur. I went there an agnostic, but they converted me: I came back a convinced devil worshipper. I'm always telling Hugo that he ought to come to the tropics with me. No philosophy has ever been written in the jungle. And everything that's been written out of the jungle is just nonsense under the trees in the hothouse darkness. What an opportunity for somebody who wants to say something *new*! But Hugo prefers his rooms in Trinity. Well, well, there's no accounting for tastes. Particularly perverted tastes. Because, you know, he really hates being at Cambridge.

ENID. He only imagines he hates it. He'd be much wretcheder anywhere else.

BILL. What a man! Aren't you ashamed of yourself, Hugo?

HUGO. Why should I be?

BILL. For being unhappy. It's criminal, it's a vice. By the way, talking of vice, did I tell you that I'd bought a light amphibian?

HUGO. A what?

BILL. An amphibian. A seaplane that's also got wheels, so that you can come down on earth or water, which you like. Lovely little machine. I'm taking it with me to Guiana.

ENID. Are you going to Guiana, Mr. Hamblin?

(*As she speaks, enter* MR. *and* MRS. WENHAM.)

BILL. To-morrow morning, to be precise.

HUGO (*taking* BILL *by the arm and leading him forward*). Alice, this is Bill Hamblin. (*They shake hands.*) And my father.

BILL. How do you do, sir?

MR. WENHAM. How do you do? One's heard so much from Hugo . . .

BILL. Who's luckily so discreet, as I was saying to Miss Deckle.

MR. WENHAM. I hope we shall often have the pleasure of welcoming you here.

BILL. If and whenever I get back from Guiana.

(*Enter* MAID.)

ENID. Mr. Hamblin is taking an aeroplane with him.

MAID. Dinner is served.

MR. WENHAM. An aeroplane? You don't say so. How extremely . . .

MRS. WENHAM. Shall we go in to dinner? Come along, Enid.

(*They go out.*)

Curtain

SCENE II

A few seconds of darkness represents the lapse of three and a half hours.

(*The curtain rises again.* MR. *and* MRS. WENHAM *and* BILL *are sitting round the fire.*)

BILL (*politely*). You don't say so!

MR. WENHAM (*with triumph*). Ah, but that doesn't by any means exhaust the list of improvements. The art of accountancy is in full development. Consider ledger posting, for example. My firm now manufacture a machine for posting ledgers. One mechanical operation posts to a ledger account, adds up and works out the balance on the account, makes out the monthly statement, and at the same time records the total of all the items posted, so that . . .

MRS. WENHAM. Dear, I think I'll be going up to bed. I hope you'll excuse me, Mr. Hamblin, if I say good-night.

BILL. Good-night, Mrs. Wenham. (*They shake hands.*) And thank you so much for your charming hospitality.

MRS. WENHAM. Hugo ought to be back in quite a few minutes now. I'm sorry he should have been dragged away from you like this. But you'll understand, some one had to see Enid home. John, don't forget to offer Mr. Hamblin some whisky. Good-night, once more, Mr. Hamblin.

BILL. Good-night.

(*She goes out.*)

MR. WENHAM (*moving to the table on which stand the bottles and glasses*). A little of the . . . (*playfully*) the blood of John Barleycorn?

BILL. The what? Oh, whisky. Yes, I'd love a drop of whisky.

MR. WENHAM. Will you say when—I believe that's the correct expression. Or it used to be.

BILL. Still is—absolutely correct. When, when, when! (*He takes the glass and fills it up from the syphon.*) There's been regrettably little progress in the art of drinking, I'm afraid. Not like accountancy. But I'm sorry to see that you're not joining me.

MR. WENHAM. No. One has always found that one . . . one flourished just as well without alcohol as with.

BILL. You made the experiment?

MR. WENHAM. Once, with some cider. When I was quite a young man. But one found it didn't agree with one. And besides, one didn't even like it.

BILL. I'm not surprised. But did you never try anything else?

MR. WENHAM. Never. (*After a little pause he adds, hastily, afraid of having said something to embarrass his guest*) Not that one has any objection to other people partaking . . . I mean, in moderation.

BILL. Oh, in moderation, of course. I've often wondered if there isn't such a thing as an excess of moderation.

MR. WENHAM. I beg your pardon.

BILL. Oh, nothing. (*In another tone*) Hugo tells me that you take an interest in psychical research, Mr. Wenham. Is that true?

MR. WENHAM. A very deep interest.

BILL. And you've never travelled, have you? I mean, out of Europe.

MR. WENHAM. Alas, travel has been one of the luxuries one couldn't permit oneself.

BILL. Well, it's a pity if you're interested in the supernormal. I remember one time, for example, when I was with some howling dervishes near Ispahan . . .

MR. WENHAM. Ah, but you evidently approach the subject from the . . . how shall I say? . . . the ethnological position. I look at it from quite another standpoint. One regards spiritualism as the . . . the highest form of contemporary religion.

BILL. You think so?

MR. WENHAM. The highest because the most scientific. It brings actual proof—yes, actual visible and tangible proof of the great fact of eternal life. (*Pause. In a voice charged with emotion*) When I tell you that for the last six months I've been in almost constant communication with my mother . . .

BILL. Who, I take it, is dead.

MR. WENHAM. She passed on more than twenty years ago. And yet her . . . well, her presence was with me only yesterday at a séance I was attending in London. I had a long and . . . and intimate conversation with her.

BILL (*pause*). Tell me, Mr. Wenham, do you ever have long and intimate conversations with farm labourers, for example, or factory girls, or communist agitators, or society beauties?

MR. WENHAM. Well . . . no, I can't say that I do.

BILL. And don't particularly want to, I should imagine?

MR. WENHAM. Not particularly, I must admit.

BILL (*shaking his head*). I can't understand it. Taking all this trouble to have chats with ghosts and doing nothing about all the really extraordinary and fantastic living people in the world.

MR. WENHAM. But after all . . . the ghosts, as you choose to call them . . . though I object strongly to the expression, most strongly . . . they're our friends, our . . . our dear ones.

BILL. Yes, but the dear ones are dead—or if you object to *that* word, let's say that they're somewhere else, not here. Whereas the farm labourers and the society beauties and all the rest *are* here. Isn't it our business to make the best of this world while we're in it? Not the second-best—or more probably the millionth-best—of some other world. No, I must say, I'm all for the dead burying their dead.

MR. WENHAM. Jesus was a young man when he said that, Mr. Hamblin. It's easy to feel like that when one's young. But when you're my age . . .

(*The door opens while he speaks and* HUGO *enters.*)

Ah, but here's Hugo; well, dear boy, you've been gone a long time. We've missed you. Come and make yourself warm.

HUGO (*rubbing his hands in front of the fire*). It's vilely cold outside.

BILL. What you need is a drink. (*He goes to the table on which the glasses stand.*) Your father's been telling me the most fascinating things about book-keeping. Fascinating! Almost thou persuadest me to be an accountant, Mr. Wenham. Here's your whisky, Hugo. Lap it up. Did you know that it's possible to balance accounts by machinery? It's time some one invented a machine for teaching the young. A steel frame with a book at one end and a rapidly vibrating birch rod at the other. No more schoolmasters, no more dons or professors; you'd be free.

HUGO. To do what?

BILL. Whatever you liked.

HUGO. If one knew what one liked. And suppose one didn't like anything.

BILL. Then I should suggest putting your head in a gas oven.

MR. WENHAM (*rising*). Well, I think I'll leave you young men to your own devices. (*Playfully*) Repose for the aged bones. Good-night, Mr. Hamblin.

BILL. Good-night, sir.

MR. WENHAM (*laying his hand on* HUGO's *shoulder*). Good-night, dear boy. (*He goes out.*)

HUGO. I hope you weren't too bored by the paternal conversation.

BILL. On the contrary, I was charmed. One's too apologetic for fathers nowadays, though of course it is painfully obvious that you can't really hold any communication with any one over sixty. Strange, the way elderly people simply don't understand certain things. Psychological things, especially. How little they seem to realize motives—their own or any one else's. It's what comes of having been brought up before the discovery of the unconscious—when man was still a rational animal. Very queer. It's like talking to some specially foreign kind of foreigner. But there's a kind of innocence about them that's charming. And then how they work! Like ants! It's they who keep the world from collapsing.

HUGO. I sometimes wish it would collapse.

BILL. I don't. I like being free. You need a good strong social framework to be free inside—a framework of fathers all busily balancing accounts and doing their duty, in order that a few ne'er-do-weels like me can live in irresponsible freedom. No, I'm most grateful to your father and the other vertebrae in the social backbone. Grateful and, my God! sorry for them. It's not much fun being a vertebra.

HUGO. Don't tell *me* that. I'm a vertebra myself.

BILL. And on top of everything he's getting old, your poor father. He was saying something just as you came in—you interrupted him—something that made me shudder. We'd been talking about spiritualism.

HUGO. But I thought you'd been talking about accountancy?

BILL. Oh, we had. But the one led on to the other. Just as in your father's life. Led on inevitably. You can't specialize in accountancy without turning to some sort of compensation. And as he doesn't drink, it almost had to be spiritualism.

HUGO. Yes; that and marriage. I told you he'd been married three times, didn't I? My mother was his second wife.

BILL. Three times? Well, well. Another whisky? (*He holds up the bottle.*)

HUGO. Thanks.

(BILL *fills up his glass and afterwards his own.*)

BILL. Well, we'd been talking about spiritualism, and I'd said what I've always thought about these matters: let the dead bury their dead. Because even if it *is* all true, which I'm quite prepared to believe, well, what of it? It's the same with most of the facts of science. This chair—it's really a swarm of electrons whizzing about in a vacuum. But what of it? For all practical purposes of life it's got to be a solid chair. And so with souls. Souls may be really detachable like . . . like chintz covers . . . they may go on existing after we're dead. All right. But again, what of it? So let the dead bury their dead, and the electrons bury their electrons. I'm alive, and this thing I've got my bottom on is a chair.

HUGO. Well, as a professional metaphysician you can hardly expect me to agree with you there.

BILL. No, of course. But as a human being . . .

HUGO. I say, hear, hear! And as one of the dead I say we ought to be buried.

BILL. Well, when I said that to your father, do you know what he answered? 'Jesus was a young man when he said, "Let the dead bury their dead." It's easy to feel like that when you're young, but at *my* age . . .' And then you came in. He didn't go on. But he'd said enough to make the whole horror of growing old rise before me. Because when you're old, you obviously just can't let the dead bury their dead. I've never thought of that before. There are so many dead in an old man's universe, that he simply can't help thinking about them. Indeed, for a very old man, there are no living people at all. Every single one of the inhabitants of his world has gone. He's left with nothing, alone. You can't expect *him* to go about saying, 'Let the dead bury their dead.' Oh, it's a bad business this growing old.

HUGO. What do you propose to do about it?

BILL. What can one do, except make the best of one's youth. (*Turning on* HUGO *with sudden fierceness.*) Not make the worst of it like you. You know, Hugo, you're really intolerable. Sitting there at Cambridge enjoying your misery. It's disgusting. Why don't you throw it all up and come with me to-morrow?

HUGO. Well, to begin with, I simply haven't got the courage. After all, the job at Cambridge does mean a settled future.

BILL. But what sort of future? Just as awful as the past.

HUGO. But settled, at any rate. Absolutely settled.

BILL. Settled dreariness. You're a queer devil, Hugo! Deliberately choosing dreariness.

HUGO. Yes, but don't forget that in return for the dreariness I've got the certainty of never going hungry, of always being respectable . . .

BILL. Christ!

HUGO. Of always being able to afford to be honest. Of never having to commit a crime.

BILL. Not to mention never having to be a man.

HUGO (*after a little pause*). I suppose I'm a born coward?

BILL. Born? No. Made.

HUGO (*laughs*). Like love, eh?

BILL. Like what?

HUGO. Oh, nothing.

BILL. No, no, it's your education that's responsible. Thank God, I never had anything to do with respectable people. You've no idea what an advantage it is to be brought up by a jolly drunken spendthrift like my father.

HUGO. Not to mention the advantage of being born an aristocrat, with money in the background, generations of unearned increment.

BILL (*laughing*). My father got rid of most of that all right.

HUGO. Yes, but not all. And anyhow, the tradition of money persisted. Caste and money—between them they put a man above public opinion. Almost above fate—above all the fate, anyhow, that's embodied in society. You don't care about what the lower animals think. Well, when you're an aristocrat and rich, that's what the public is—a collection of lower animals; and public opinion is just a huge noise of mooing and bleating.

BILL (*laughing*). Not to mention grunting and braying, and howling and gibbering. But after all, you needn't be an aristocrat to think that. It's what any sensible man thinks about public opinion. It's what *you* think, for example.

HUGO. Yes, with my head. But the rest of me has a

kind of abject respect for the braying and the gibbering. Because, you see, the rest of me's bourgeois. Born and brought up amongst the lower animals, *as* a lower animal; in a world where people simply can't afford not to conform and be respectable. Playing for safety—that's what we lower animals are taught from the cradle. It becomes a second nature. And when one's a bit of a coward to start with, as I'm afraid I am . . . (*He shrugs his shoulders.*) Well, you understand why I am frightened of throwing up my job.

BILL (*holding out the bottle*). Then you'd better take a little more Dutch courage.

HUGO. No, really; I've had too much already.

BILL. Nonsense. Give me your glass.

(HUGO *holds out his glass.*)

You mustn't be like your father.

HUGO. I'm afraid I *am* rather like him.

BILL. Well, at any rate you've had enough imprudence to experiment with other things besides cider. Was he angry with you when you decided not to be a teetotaller?

HUGO. No, not angry.

BILL. More in sorrow than in anger, I take it.

HUGO. Oh, much more in sorrow. *Only* in sorrow. My father's never angry. That's one of his worst defects. Even when I was a child—and I was insufferable—he never lost his temper with me . . . always restrained himself. Yes, there was always restraint—in everything. Why is it that good people are so awful? I mean that sort of good people. I'm afraid it's my fate to be good.

BILL. Well, if you want it to be your fate, of course it will be.

HUGO. But I don't want it to be. God, how drunk you've

made me with all this whisky. (*Empties his glass.*) I absolutely don't want it to be.

BILL. And yet you're allowing it to become your fate. You're just letting yourself drift. And what makes it worse is that you know you're drifting; and worse still, that you like drifting, you want to destroy yourself.

HUGO (*suddenly laughing; he is rather tipsy*). Did I ever tell you that my father wrote verses for the magazines?

BILL. No.

HUGO. Secretly, under a pseudonym. Oh, the greasiest sentiments! and then a kind of arch playfulness. It's one of the penalties he pays for goodness, I suppose. Like his spiritualism. Think of sentimentalizing with the dead!

BILL. You'll be doing the same in a few years if you're not careful.

HUGO. No, no. I shall take to writing children's stories. Very charming and whimsical, you know. And I shall pinch little girls' legs in trains. (*Laughs extravagantly.*) And one day I shall get into the clutches of the police —'Serious charge against professor.' You can see the headlines. But all my friends will come and give evidence about my irreproachable morality. And I shall leave the court without a stain on my character. Yes, absolutely without a stain. Pure, my boy, pure. Chemically pure. *Du bist wie eine Blume, so hold und rein und schön.* Yes, I shall leave the court without a stain, and immediately rush off to find another little girl to pinch. And when I've pinched her I shall go home and write another of my sweet little whimsical children's stories. Much better than spiritualism, don't you think?

BILL (*after a pause, quietly and seriously*). Why don't you come with me to-morrow?

HUGO. I've told you.

BILL. Do you mean the question of courage? But I tell you it's not difficult to be courageous. Or at least it's not difficult to be foolhardy, and that's all you've got to be at the moment. Just shut your eyes and jump. It's nothing. And afterwards what happens, happens.

HUGO. But what happens to be happening to me at the moment is that I'm engaged to be married.

BILL. Since when?

HUGO (*looking at his wrist-watch*). Since about eleven-twenty-two.

BILL. You mean just now, with Miss What's-her-name?

HUGO. With Miss What's-her-name, precisely.

BILL. But I had no idea that you had any intention . . .

HUGO. Nor had I till this evening.

BILL. Or that you even . . . well, much cared.

HUGO (*laughing*). I don't. That's just the point. That's just the beauty of it!

BILL. Oh, God! I give you up, Hugo. You're really too awful. I think I'd better go home. (*Rises from his chair.*)

HUGO (*pushing him down again*). No, don't go, Bill. You mustn't go. Have another drink, do.

BILL. No, no, let me . . .

HUGO. Just one more. I beg you. (*Takes* BILL's *glass and fills it, then his own.*) The last drink together, Bill. Drink, drink for ever, for ever drink.

BILL. Oh, very well.

HUGO. The absolutely last. (*Raising his glass.*) To your adventures, Bill. To the tropics. Especially Capricorn, dear Capricorn, whom I shall never, never see. (*Drinks.*)

BILL. What do you expect *me* to drink to? To Cambridge? To metaphysics, to your pupils?

HUGO. Oh, all that, and my marriage. Bill, you're forgetting my marriage.

BILL. I wish I could forget it. As a matter of curiosity, Hugo—no, I'm not going to bully you about it—but just as a matter of curiosity, may I ask you why?

HUGO. Why not, after all?

BILL. If you don't care.

HUGO. Well, I wanted to make sure that I didn't, by experiment.

BILL. No, but seriously . . .

HUGO. Seriously, Bill, have you ever been blackmailed?

BILL (*shakes his head*). It's one of the advantages of not being afraid of public opinion.

HUGO. You needn't be. It's enough if you're afraid of your own better feelings. *They'll* blackmail you. God, what a fool I was! Because I saw it coming years ago.

BILL. Saw what coming?

HUGO. Why, the crisis, the . . . the . . . well, *this.* It was really so obvious that she was in love with me. I pretended that I didn't know when my father told me this evening. No, not pretended, because officially I didn't know.

BILL. Officially?

HUGO. Yes, like the communiqués during the war. 'Our forces are making a strategic retreat on a front of 350 miles.' You know. Official truth. And in the same way there's an official part of the mind that thinks and wishes the sort of things that people ought to think and wish. But there's also an unofficial part which doesn't believe in the communiqués, because it knows better—or anyhow it knows differently. Officially, Enid wasn't in love with me, because it would have been such a damned bore if she had been, but unofficially I knew she was, and I was pleased and flattered. Yes, and what's more, I did all I could to make her be more in love with me.

BILL. Even though you weren't in love with her yourself?

HUGO (*nods*). I don't think you can know what a luxury it is to have somebody in love with you.

BILL. Why shouldn't I know?

HUGO. Things you have every day aren't luxuries. You don't know what it is to be rather unattractive physically.

BILL. Nonsense.

HUGO. No, no. Unattractive, Bill, and shy, and frightened. You can't appreciate the luxury of discovering that there's at least *one* woman who can be in love with you. And the luxury of having one woman you're not more shy of because you've known her so long. For you it's so simple they should fall in love with you. Not for me. That's why . . .

BILL. That's why you encouraged her to go on loving you even though you weren't in love with her yourself. But, my good Hugo . . .

HUGO. Yes, I know it was idiotic.

BILL. Loving some one who doesn't love you—that's the worst thing, of course. But being loved by somebody you can't love in return, insistently and importunately loved—it's very nearly as bad.

HUGO. I know. I know. It's awful.

BILL. Then why . . . ?

HUGO. But because the other person's love blackmails you? Yes, blackmails you. Like the beastliest little professional lounger in Hyde Park. 'If you don't comply with what I demand,' that's what it says to you, 'I'll go straight off and tell your better self that you're a scoundrel; I'll go and torture your defenceless conscience.' That's why officially I never admitted that Enid was in love with me. I didn't want to be blackmailed. But to-day it all came out. There was no escape. I had to know officially. And the blackmail began immediately. 'She loves you, she loves you. If you don't do something about it, I'll go and stick pins into your conscience.' Rather than run the risk of that I proposed on the spot. But on the bloody spot. (*He drinks.*)

BILL. Don't be a clown, Hugo. It's not funny.

HUGO (*in a changed tone*). You're quite right. It wasn't. Do you know, Bill, I was terribly moved. I really believed for a moment that everything was coming right at last. I thought that if I tried hard enough to love her I should really find myself loving her—suddenly, like that—and be transfigured by loving; yes, and come alive. I thought all that, and it was moving, moving. And then, you know, at first she didn't want to say that she loved me—just because she realized it would be blackmailing me. Which touched me still more—it was so honest. And I insisted, and at last I succeeded. God! How well I succeeded! It was awful, awful!

BILL. Why?

HUGO. Why, because it was then, when she began loving me, that I really knew I didn't love her—couldn't love her. . . . And the more loving she was the more coldly certain I became that I could never love her. Never, never. Oh, God, when I took her home just now! (*He shakes his head sharply, shaking off the memory, shuts his eyes against an importunate inward vision.*) How dreadful that was. But the blackmailing went on. More effectively than ever, just because it was so awful. Well, in a few months we shall be married. (*Laughing*) Good luck to us. (*He raises his glass and drinks.)* We'll go to Venice for the honeymoon, I think.

BILL (*rising from his chair*). No, you won't.

HUGO. Not to Venice? But all the best German honeymooners go to Venice.

BILL. Possibly, but you're coming with me to-morrow, Hugo. The ship leaves Tilbury at eleven. Come along. (*Takes him by the arm and drags him out of his seat.*) You've got some letters to write.

HUGO. But what are you talking about?

(BILL *leads him across the room to the writing-table, and makes him sit down before it.*)

BILL. One to your College, resigning your tutorship. One to your father. Here's a pen and some paper.

HUGO. But seriously, Bill . . .

BILL. I'm not going to allow you to destroy either yourself or that girl. (*Offers him the pen.*) Take it.

HUGO. But I'm drunk, Bill. Wait till to-morrow morning. Let me think it over.

BILL. No, no, at once. You'd be sober in the morning. You'd be reasonable. Reasonable people never do anything. Now begin. I'll dictate.

HUGO. But it's madness.

BILL. I know. That's just what it ought to be. Write now. 'My dear father——'

HUGO. It's folly, it's criminal folly.

BILL. Good. 'My dear father——'

HUGO (*writes*). 'My dear father——' But I always write 'Dearest father——'

BILL. Never mind. He'll forgive you. 'My dear father, I have decided to accompany Bill Hamblin to-morrow. . . .'

HUGO. But I haven't.

BILL. You damned well have.

HUGO. I won't be bullied.

BILL. You will be bullied. (*He takes him by the shoulders and shakes him.*) Write, idiot, write!

HUGO. For God's sake, Bill . . .

BILL. Won't you be bullied?

HUGO. Yes, yes, I'll be bullied.

(BILL *stops shaking.*)

I've *been* bullied.

BILL. Good. Let's see now, where were we? Ah yes! 'I have decided to accompany Bill Hamblin.'

HUGO (*writing*). 'I have decided to accompany Bill Hamblin.'

Curtain

ACT II

SCENE I

SCENE—*The same.* TIME—*Two months later.*

(MRS. WENHAM *is sitting at her desk writing.* MR. WENHAM *enters, crosses the room and stands for a moment in nervous silence near her.* MRS. WENHAM *continues to write, then at last looks up.*)

MRS. WENHAM. Well, John?

MR. WENHAM. I didn't want to interrupt you, my dear.

MRS. WENHAM. You're not. What is it?

MR. WENHAM. One was wondering, dear, whether . . . whether you wouldn't care to . . . to join us in the library.

MRS. WENHAM. Join whom?

MR. WENHAM (*still more nervous*). Surely, my love, I thought you knew. Young Mr. Capes is here.

MRS. WENHAM. Mr. Capes?

MR. WENHAM. The young man through whom I've been receiving these . . . these communications from dear Hugo.

MRS. WENHAM. Oh, the medium. Yes, yes. I'd forgotten his name. No, I don't think I'll come, John.

MR. WENHAM. One would appreciate it so much if you did.

MRS. WENHAM. I really have no time.

MR. WENHAM. Not more than half an hour, my love.

MRS. WENHAM. Besides, John, I don't really much like that young man.

MR. WENHAM. No? One found him so . . . so charming oneself.

MRS. WENHAM. Too charming. That's the trouble. I don't like the butter laid on too thick.

MR. WENHAM. And gifted, wonderfully gifted. One simply can't doubt now that one's . . . well, in touch with poor Hugo.

MRS. WENHAM (*shrugs her shoulders*). All the same, John, I shall go on doubting until I hear definite news. After all, the only thing we know is that Hugo and Mr. Hamblin started out in their aeroplane to fly from Guiana to Cuba, and haven't been heard of since. But look at the map. There are hundreds of little islands where they could have come down. Besides, the machine had floats. It's only twelve days since they started. It seems to me still quite possible.

MR. WENHAM (*sighing and shaking his head*). One wishes one could think the same. There was really no hope. And now these communications through our young friend. . . . Well, they make it quite definite. The machine was forced down in a storm about thirty miles south of Haiti.

MRS. WENHAM. So he says. But why should one believe him?

MR. WENHAM. You'd know why, my love, if you'd only come and hear him. It's so obviously true—on the face of it. One can't doubt. That's why one was so anxious that you should . . .

MRS. WENHAM (*shaking her head*). I'd rather not.

MR. WENHAM. One had thought that perhaps . . . In this case . . . I mean, as it's dear Hugo——

MRS. WENHAM. No, dear. You know what I feel about it. Please don't insist. (*Looking out of the window.*) And here's Enid coming across the garden. Go and open the door for her. I think it's still locked.

(MR. WENHAM *goes and unlocks the French window.*)

Dressed in bright red to-day. She really is extraordinary.

(ENID *appears at the glass door and is let in by* MR. WENHAM.)

MR. WENHAM. Good-morning, my dear.

ENID (*her manner has a kind of defiant cheerfulness*). Good-morning. Good-morning, Alice. (*Turning back to* MR. WENHAM.) Any news yet?

MR. WENHAM (*shakes his head*). Not what *you* would call news, dear Enid. But so far as oneself is concerned . . .

ENID. What do you mean?

MRS. WENHAM. John means that he's had a message through the medium. It's supposed to be from Hugo.

ENID (*laughing with sudden violence—a laugh that is intended to be deliberately contemptuous, but rings a little hysterically, on the verge of going out of control*). Oh, if that's all.

MR. WENHAM (*gravely*). It's a very great deal, Enid dear. In fact, I'm afraid it's all we have now, all that's left. (*To* MRS. WENHAM) I shall be in the library if you want me, my love.

(MR. WENHAM *goes out. There is a silence.*)

MRS. WENHAM. I don't want to be critical and interfering, Enid; but I really do think it's rather a mistake to wear that red dress.

ENID. Why?

MRS. WENHAM. Well, surely the colour's a little inappropriate in the circumstances.

ENID. You'd like me to wear black, would you?

MRS. WENHAM. No, no. Only something rather quieter. It may be foolishness on my part; but it seems to me that in this dreadful uncertainty . . .

ENID. But I'm certain, Alice, absolutely certain. He isn't dead. (*She clasps her hands violently together.*) I know he isn't. He can't be. I won't let him be dead.

MRS. WENHAM. I only hope you're right.

ENID (*with sudden anger*). Why don't you say you *know* I'm right? Why do you doubt? You're killing him with all this doubt of yours. And his father's even worse. Deliberately killing him with denial. Yes, denial. He doesn't *want* Hugo to be alive. He'd like him to be dead, so that he can talk to him through these beastly mediums.

MRS. WENHAM. But, Enid, you're mad!

ENID (*beginning to break down uncontrollably*). You all want him to be dead.

MRS. WENHAM. You mustn't say such things.

ENID (*sobbing*). You want him to be dead, you want him to be dead.

(MRS. WENHAM *gets up and goes over to where* ENID *is sitting and stands by her with a hand on her shoulder.*)

(*Jerking herself away from under the touching hand*) No, don't.

MRS. WENHAM. My dear, my dear.

(ENID *suffers herself to be touched. There is a silence, broken only by the sound of* ENID'S *sobbing.*)

You know, I really think there's a good chance of Hugo's being all right.

(ENID *shakes her head.*)

I was saying so to John only a moment ago. One's only got to look at the map. All those hundreds of islands . . .

ENID. No, no. It's no good. I know he's dead, really. That's why I got so angry just now. I'm sorry. But if you knew how awful it was, Alice. (*She starts crying again.*)

MRS. WENHAM. Poor Enid. (*She pats her shoulder.*) Be brave. You must be brave.

ENID. I cared for him, so much, Alice. (*She puts her hand to her side.*) It's so awful, the pain. Like a kind of hole, where one's heart ought to be. Ever since he went away. Why did he go away, like that? Why, why?

MRS. WENHAM (*sighs and shakes her head*). Some mad idea. It was that wild young Hamblin, I suppose.

ENID (*after a pause. She is sitting bent forward, her elbows on her knees, her face between her hands.*) That morning when I came to tell you we were engaged and heard he was gone—that was when it began, this emptiness, I mean, this horrible, aching, anxious hole. Because I knew even then he'd gone for ever.

MRS. WENHAM. But, dear, you mustn't say that. There really *is* a chance. You're doing what you were reproaching us for doing a moment ago.

ENID. Gone for ever from *me*—that's what I meant. Because he didn't really love me, you know. He only wanted to love me, and perhaps he suddenly realized that he couldn't, simply couldn't. And that's why he went. I oughtn't to have said yes when he asked me. It was wrong, it was stupid; I ought to have realized.

MRS. WENHAM. But no, darling, we all know how deeply attached he was to you.

ENID (*nodding slowly*). You can be deeply attached and at the same time have a kind of hatred of the person you're attached to.

MRS. WENHAM. What nonsense!

ENID. A kind of fatal, uncontrollable, physical hatred. Perhaps that was why Hugo . . . No, it's dreadful, it's dreadful.

MRS. WENHAM. You mustn't think that sort of thing, Enid. It's stupid, it's morbid.

ENID. All the same, I do think it—constantly. I wonder and wonder. And the more I wonder, the worse it seems. (*Pause.*) No, I oughtn't to have said yes. It was madness. But I did care so much. Oh, Alice, I cared so terribly much.

MRS. WENHAM. And he cared too. It's absurd to say he didn't. And now I simply forbid you to go on thinking these horrible morbid thoughts any more.

ENID (*making an impatient gesture*). Oh, don't use that tiresome, stupid word, Alice.

MRS. WENHAM. What word? Morbid? But they *are* morbid; I'm sorry.

ENID. What you mean is that they're just thoughts you don't understand, thoughts you don't happen to have had yourself.

MRS. WENHAM. Thank goodness! I've no desire to have morbid thoughts. And I think that you ought to make an effort to keep your mind off them. It's almost all a question of will.

ENID (*uttering an ironic little laugh*). All right, I'll make an effort. (*She leans back in her chair and holds out her arms, clenching her fists as she does so.*) I'll will not to think about any truth that might be unpleasant.

There. What would you like me to talk about now? The weather? The latest Edgar Wallace?

MRS. WENHAM. Now really, dear, please. You ought to go home and rest. You're overwrought. I don't think it's good for you to go on talking. Not unless . . .

ENID. Not unless I can talk in a reasonable, polite, grey way to match the reasonable grey clothes I ought to be wearing, instead of this red. Poor Alice, what a bore you must think me. I'm sorry. There, it's really finished this time. Tell me, what was it Mr. Wenham wanted to say to me just now?

MRS. WENHAM. What about?

ENID. Something the medium had said.

MRS. WENHAM (*shrugging her shoulders*). Oh, some story about the aeroplane having come down in the sea near Haiti.

ENID. Do you believe in it, Alice?

MRS. WENHAM (*shakes her head*). No. Besides, it all seems so morbid to me. I don't like it.

ENID. Still, suppose it were true. Suppose one could go on being in touch with people. Even after . . . after . . .

MRS. WENHAM (*shakes her head again*). No; even if it were true, I still shouldn't like it.

ENID (*meditatively*). What bothers me is this. Do you think people would still be themselves if they were reduced to being just spirits? A person without his body—would it be the same person? (*Shaking her head*) I wonder. When I think of Hugo's hands, and the way he screwed up his face when he laughed, and his neck when he was wearing a shirt with an open collar—you know, where it joined his body, with that hollow like a deep thumb-print between the two tendons, and the ridges of bone going off to right and left. (*She closes her eyes as she speaks, her head tilted backwards, and her hands touch her own neck as she describes his.*) All those things meant such a lot, they were so much part of him, so essentially Hugo . . . (*Her voice trembles; she draws a deep breath, her hand goes up to her eyes.*) No, I can't feel that it would be the same person without a body. I can't, can't!

MRS. WENHAM. You may be right, dear. But I think it's the sort of subject it's better not to think about at all.

ENID (*her eyes still shut*). Do you remember, when he was thinking, that curious way he had of pinching his lip?

(*The door opens as she speaks and* MR. WENHAM *enters, followed by* HUBERT CAPES.)

Again and again. Do you remember? Like this.

MR. WENHAM (*advances silently across the room towards his wife, holding out a telegraph form. In a very low voice*). I've just received this.

(MRS. WENHAM *takes the paper, reads.*)

ENID (*re-opening her eyes, with a start*). What is it, Alice? A telegram?

MRS. WENHAM (*nodding*). It's from the British Consul at Port au Prince. (*Reading aloud.*) 'Wreckage Moth aeroplane found near Jacmel. Occupants presumed lost.' (*She folds up the telegram and hands it back to her husband.*)

(*There is a silence.*)

ENID (*in a flat voice*). Where is Jacmel?

MR. WENHAM. On the south coast of Haiti.

MRS. WENHAM. Haiti?

MR. WENHAM (*nodding*). Yes, Haiti. Our young friend here (*he indicates* CAPES) was quite right.

ENID (*with a sudden burst of angry, hysterical laughter*).

You're so pleased that he should be right. Much more pleased than you would be if the telegram had said that poor Hugo was safe and well. Yes, *much* more pleased.

MRS. WENHAM. Enid! How can you?

ENID. But it's true. (*She checks herself with an effort and is silent for a moment, biting her handkerchief; then in another voice*) I'm sorry, Mr. Wenham. I think I'd better go. Forgive me.

MR. WENHAM. There's nothing to forgive, my dear. One knows what you must be feeling. And there are no consolations, Enid dear, except the faith, the knowledge . . . well, that after all dear Hugo isn't dead . . . that his spirit is with us . . . still.

HUBERT (*in a rather unctuous, musical voice that harmonizes well with a darkly handsome, slightly clerical appearance*). Yes, his spirit is still with us.

ENID (*who has come to rest with her elbows on the mantelpiece, her face hidden*). Only his spirit. (*A pause; then breaking out*) But I don't want his spirit. I want Hugo, I want Hugo!

Curtain

SCENE II

SCENE—*The same.* TIME—*Ten months later*

(*Except for a few streaks of phosphorescent paint on various objects, the stage, when the curtain rises, is in darkness. The voices are heard, but the speakers are not seen.*)

MR. WENHAM. What do you think, Enid? Is it safe to turn on the light now?

ENID. Perhaps we'd better wait a moment longer. You know what a shock it is to him, when he's woken too quickly out of his trance.

MR. WENHAM. Oh, of course, one wouldn't dream of . . . of taking any risk at our young friend's expense. But it seems to me it must be the best part of five minutes since the last manifestation.

ENID. Do you think so? Time's apt to seem very long when one's sitting in the dark like this. Besides, he's always more tired when the séance has been a very successful one. So perhaps we ought to give him a little longer than usual.

MR. WENHAM. You're quite right, my dear. I wouldn't worry if it wasn't that Alice was expecting me to come up and say good-night to the children.

ENID (*impatiently*). After all, she can wait another minute or two.

MR. WENHAM. Yes, but one doesn't like to keep the little ones awake beyond the appointed hour.

ENID. Well, even they won't die of it.

MR. WENHAM. No, no, of course not. But all the same . . .

ENID. Wasn't he simply wonderful this evening? I don't think we've ever had such extraordinary physical manifestations as to-day.

MR. WENHAM. Yes, they were certainly very remarkable.

ENID. I've never known the table move so violently as it did this time. And then when the concertina started playing inside the cage—that was too extraordinary.

MR. WENHAM. And the phosphorescent paint made it quite easy to see. I was able to watch its movements very closely. Did you notice that it didn't just go in and out, but seemed to . . . well, to writhe from side to side as well?

ENID. Yes, I noticed that.

MR. WENHAM. Rather like a snake, if you were to hang it up by the tail. Very curious. I seemed to recognize the tune, by the way. Wasn't it something classical?

ENID. Yes, it was a bit of that air out of *Figaro*—you know, the duet of the letter. Hugo had a special liking for it, don't you remember? He was constantly whistling it.

MR. WENHAM. Of course. That was why one found it so familiar. I'd forgotten it completely. Strange that one should be reminded in this way. Very strange.

ENID. Very wonderful, I think. (*A little pause.*)

MR. WENHAM (*in a changed tone, preoccupied*). What about turning on the light now, Enid? It couldn't do any harm, and one really must be trotting up to the children.

ENID (*with a touch of contempt*). Oh, very well, then. Sit where you are. I'll do it.

(ENID *is heard fumbling in the darkness, then the room is suddenly flooded with light.* HUBERT CAPES *is seen lying back limply in a chair in the corner. The mediumistic apparatus is scattered round him, trumpets, tambourines, etc., and in a large parrot-cage, hanging vertically, a concertina.*)

MR. WENHAM (*blinking and holding his hands over his eyes*). It certainly does seem very bright all of a sudden.

ENID (*who has crossed the room and is bending over* HUBERT.) Hubert! (*She touches his shoulder, then his face.*) Hubert! (*To* WENHAM) It must have been a very deep trance.

MR. WENHAM (*rising*). Perhaps if one were to blow on his eyelids . . .

ENID. No, don't. He's beginning to wake up. Hubert!

(HUBERT *utters a deep sigh; his eyes begin to flutter open.*)

Wake up, Hubert, wake up!

HUBERT (*faintly*). Where am I? Oh, it's you. (*He takes her hand.*) I feel as though I've come back from a very long way this time. Enormously far. I feel sort of (*makes a vague gesture*)—I don't know what. Sort of not there. As though I've come to bits.

ENID. Poor Hubert! You were wonderful to-night. That's why you're so tired.

HUBERT. Did the spirits manifest well?

MR. WENHAM. Quite remarkably. There was a moment when the concertina began to play . . . but we'll discuss that later, if you don't mind. (*He looks at his watch.*) The children are expecting one to come and say good-night. Oh dear, oh dear, I'm ten minutes late already. Enid dear, see that our young friend has everything he wants. Forgive me. (*He hurries out of the room.*)

ENID. He's like a schoolboy. Too ridiculous, a man being frightened of his wife like that.

(HUBERT *sighs deeply and shuts his eyes again.*)

Poor Hubert! (*Her voice is tenderly solicitous, she lays her hand on his forehead.*) Are you terribly tired?

(HUBERT *nods without speaking.*)

Would you like me to get you a glass of wine, or some Bovril, or something?

(HUBERT *shakes his head.*)

You're sure you don't want anything? (ENID *sits down on the arm of his chair.*)

HUBERT. No, just keep your hand on my forehead, that's all. It's so soothing. I feel as though there were a kind of current of strength and serenity passing out from you. A river of healing. I shall be quite fresh and strong again in a few minutes. I think if some one were ill, you could cure him, just by touching him.

ENID. Do you think so?

HUBERT. I know it. I can feel it in myself.

ENID. Well, I'm glad. Because it means that I can make you some little return for what you did for me.

HUBERT. But I've done nothing.

ENID. Nothing, perhaps, so far as any one else is concerned. But you saved my life, Hubert. In those terrible days just after the news of poor Hugo's death, I wanted to die, I thought I was going to die; but I didn't. I suppose one doesn't die of unhappiness like that. One's tougher than one thinks. So I made up my mind to kill myself. Yes, and I should have killed myself if it hadn't been for you. You made me realize that he was not really dead, but still near, still interested and wanting me to go on living. Oh, I shall never forget that first message that you brought me! You saved me, Hubert.

HUBERT. Or rather, it was the truth that saved you—the truth expressing itself through me.

ENID. Yes, but you helped the truth, Hubert. You were so sweet to me, so divinely kind and good.

HUBERT (*making a gesture of deprecation*). No, no.

ENID. Yes, divinely. You were like some one sent from heaven to save me.

HUBERT. You mustn't talk so extravagantly. Though in one sense, of course, there's a certain truth in what you say. Because I'm a sort of instrument. Chosen for some inscrutable reason—in spite of unworthiness. Chosen to make known the truth. Chosen to help you and all who have an unhappiness like yours. Poor Enid! It made my heart bleed to see you so hopelessly and inconsolably miserable!

ENID. He seemed so utterably dead and gone. And yet I ought to have had faith. I believe in the resurrection of the body and the life everlasting. Haven't I been repeating that Sunday after Sunday, all my life? But when it came to the point I couldn't help feeling that death was the end of everything, just a black, ghastly pit.

HUBERT. What a terrible thing to believe!

ENID. You taught me more than all the books and creeds and churches ever taught me. I thought I believed; but I suppose I didn't really.

HUBERT. It's the difference between seeing in a glass darkly and seeing face to face. That's the wonderful thing about spiritualism: it can show you the dark truths of Christianity face to face, in the person of some one loved and believed lost and found again.

ENID. Yes, found again. I seemed to find everything, when you brought Hugo back to me—life, strength, peace, almost happiness; yes, actually happiness. I thought I should never be happy again. But it's come back to me—as he wanted it to come back. He said it again this evening, you know. 'I want you to be happy, Enid, I want you to live abundantly as I am living.'

HUBERT. Yes, the spirits always want that. More life. That's one of the reasons why they don't like us to grieve for them. Grief's a thing that numbs and deadens. . . . They want the people they love to be joyful. Did he say anything else?

ENID. Not much. Most of the manifestations were physical.

HUBERT. That explains why I am so tired. (*He sighs.*) You've no idea how exhausting these physical manifestations are for the medium. The spirits have to use such an enormous amount of our physical energy in order to produce them. One feels as though one had done a long day of the hardest manual labour when one comes to. (*He shuts his eyes and relaxes himself.*)

ENID. Poor Hubert! But you're better now, aren't you?

HUBERT. Yes, much better. But still tired. Deliciously tired, though. Don't take your hand away. (*He raises his own hand and lays it on* ENID'S, *pressing it against his forehead.*) I feel as though I were drawing life out of you, replenishing myself. (*He leans against her.*)

ENID. Try to go to sleep for a minute, try to rest. (*He leans still more confidingly, his head pillowed against her breast.*) Sleep, sleep.

HUBERT. I feel like a child . . . so dependent . . . like your child. (*He opens his eyes and smiles up at her.*)

ENID (*stroking his hair*). Go to sleep, then, go to sleep.

Slow Curtain

SCENE III

SCENE—*The Wenhams' drawing-room.*

TIME—*Fifteen months later.*

(*The tea-table is prepared. The room is empty when the curtain rises. Enter* ENID *and* HUBERT.)

ENID. Here. We shall be all right here. (*She is obviously agitated and on edge.*)

HUBERT. But don't you think we ought to go back to the library? I mean, wasn't it rather rude going in like that and dashing out again the moment we saw there were other people there?

ENID. Well, you didn't want to stay, did you?

HUBERT. No; but politeness . . .

ENID (*impatiently*). Politeness! One can't waste one's life being polite, particularly to that ghastly man Gray.

HUBERT. All the same, Enid . . .

ENID. No, no, no. (*Then looking at him intently*) Or do you *want* to get away from me?

HUBERT (*in a tone of complaining irritation*). But of course I don't!

ENID. Of course you don't! In *that* tone.

HUBERT. I'm sorry, I was on edge. But it was partly your fault. One doesn't like to be doubted and questioned, and cross-examined. Enid!

(HUBERT *holds out his arms to her, but* ENID *shakes her head and turns away. He lets his arms fall again rather sheepishly. There is a silence.*)

ENID (*almost meditatively*). And yet you used to care for me. At least I thought you did.

HUBERT. But, darling, I still do. What is this absurd, stupid idea you've got into your head?

ENID. It was you who put it there . . . by being so sweet to me when I was unhappy, so gentle and tenderly loving. Yes, you put it into my head by giving me something to compare the present with . . .

HUBERT. But the present's the same as the past. It's not as though we'd quarrelled or had a scene, or . . .

ENID. That's just what makes it so awful. I wish we had quarrelled. A quarrel would have been something definite, something to put one's finger on. But you've just noiselessly faded away from me. Faded away out of love, out of my life, like a ghost, like (*suddenly laughing hysterically*) . . . like the Cheshire cat.

HUBERT. But, Enid, it's not true.

ENID. Then why is it you make me feel that everything's changed?

HUBERT (*plaintively rational*). I really can't think. I suppose something must have changed in you.

ENID (*sarcastically laughing*). I like that; that's very good. But do you think a woman doesn't *feel* when a man has stopped loving her? Do you think it isn't obvious, even when he just quietly fades?

HUBERT. I'm sure it's obvious when it happens. But in this case . . . My darling! (*He makes an amorous movement towards her; anything to stop her talking.*)

ENID (*still savagely sarcastic*). Oh, I admit you still quite like going to bed with me.

HUBERT (*deeply shocked. He drops her hands which he had taken*). But, Enid, really! (*Looking round*) You must be careful. People might hear you.

ENID. Well, I don't care if they do. I'm not ashamed. Why should I be ashamed of loving you? You know I didn't want to at first because of Hugo. I tried to prevent myself caring for you. But Hugo himself wanted it. He is glad we love each other. Hasn't he said so again and again?

HUBERT (*hastily*). Yes, yes. All the same, people mightn't understand, they might so easily misinterpret . . .

ENID. Well, what does it matter? And anyhow, that's quite beside the point. The point is that you only like me in that way now. Just physically, that's all. When you happen to be feeling like it. No, no, don't deny it. You shrink from any other form of contact. You'd like never to see me in between whiles, in the day-time.

HUBERT. No, really. I . . .

ENID. You don't want to talk to me, or have any companionship, or feel anything for me but mere desire.

HUBERT. It's not true!

ENID. It *is* true, I tell you, it *is* true.

HUBERT. But I swear to you, darling . . .

ENID. Ah, now you're lying. Don't lie to me, Hubert.

HUBERT. I swear . . .

ENID (*in a rage*). Liar, liar !

HUBERT (*angered in his turn into a cynical sincerity*). All right, then. I'm a liar. In that case I think I'd better go back to the library at once. (*He moves towards the door.*)

ENID (*stands for a second or two looking after him, then hurries across the room to stop him*). Hubert ! (*She speaks imploringly, penitently.*) Don't go, please don't go. Oh, forgive me. It's as though I were possessed by a devil ; I can't help myself. I know it makes you hate me—you have every reason to hate me. But hate the devil that's in me. Oh, Hubert, please forgive me. (*She kisses his hand.*) I promise I won't ever do it again.

(*While she is speaking these words, the gong is heard outside, rising to a tremendous crescendo.* ENID *puts her hands to her ears. Her face is distorted with pain.*)

ENID. Oh, that noise ! That awful noise ! (*As the sound dies away*) But say you forgive me, Hubert.

HUBERT (*magnanimously, with a return of the clerical unctuousness*). But of course, I forgive you, my darling . . .

ENID. Kiss me. (*She clings to him.*)

HUBERT. But the gong's gone. Some one will be coming in.

ENID (*almost frantically*). Kiss me.

(HUBERT *kisses her.*)

Again !

(HUBERT *kisses her again and hastily disengages himself. As he does so the* MAID *enters with the silver kettle and teapot. They stand in silence, watching her place them on the table. She goes out again.*)

HUBERT. You see? We *must* be careful. (*He goes to her and pats her shoulder.*) Now, my darling, you've got to make an effort. Pull yourself together, control your nerves. They're just coming. (*He goes to a mirror hanging on the wall and standing before it, straightens his tie.*) You must be calm.

ENID. All right. (*She draws a deep breath. Her movements show that she is making a great effort to control herself. Then suddenly turning towards him she bursts out*) No, I simply can't face them. Besides, why should I? I won't, Hubert. Let's go quickly before they come. (*She takes his hand, and drags him protesting towards the door.*) Quickly, I simply must talk to you.

HUBERT. But, my darling . . .

ENID. Come.

(HUBERT *has taken a few reluctant steps, when the door opens and* MR. *and* MRS. WENHAM *enter, accompanied by* MR. GRAY. MR. GRAY *is a man between fifty and sixty, with a bright, sly, pig's eye actively alive in his fleshy red face.*)

MRS. WENHAM. Well, Enid? You're not going, are you?

ENID. Hubert thinks he ought to have half an hour's rest before the séance begins. You know how tired he gets. I was just taking him to the library.

MRS. WENHAM (*turning to* HUBERT). What, before you've had your tea?

HUBERT (*hesitant*). Well . . .

ENID. He doesn't feel like tea to-day. Shall we go, Hubert?

HUBERT (*unhappily*). Perhaps we'd better. (*He goes out.*)

MRS. WENHAM (*stopping* ENID *as she follows him, and speaking in a low voice*). Really, Enid, you mustn't exaggerate.

ENID. What do you mean?

MRS. WENHAM. There are limits.

ENID (*giving an angry shrug*). Oh, I don't care. (*She goes out.*)

MRS. WENHAM (*advancing to the tea-table, by which her husband and* MR. GRAY *have been standing*). Do make yourself comfortable, Mr. Gray.

MR. GRAY. Thank you. (*He sits down.*)

MRS. WENHAM. How do you like your tea? Strong or weak?

MR. GRAY. Oh, as it comes. And one lump of sugar, a little milk. Thank you.

MR. WENHAM (*passing a plate*). A scone while they're hot.

MR. GRAY. No, really. I never eat anything for tea. Doctor's orders, you know. Still, these look delicious. (*He helps himself.*) For once in a way.

MRS. WENHAM. Here's your tea, John.

MR. WENHAM. Thank you, dear.

MR. GRAY. Well, Mrs. Wenham, you'll be pleased to hear that the paper's ordered for the fourth edition of your husband's book. It's a triumph. Sixteen thousand copies of a guinea book—that's something that doesn't happen every day, I can tell you. Not every year even. I'm an old publisher, and I know. And I see no reason why we shouldn't touch the twenty thousand mark. No reason at all. After which we have the cheap edition to look forward to. Another twenty thousand at four-and-six—or why not six shillings while we're about it? It's a delightful prospect. (*He helps himself to a sandwich.*)

MRS. WENHAM. It certainly seems a great number, considering the subject of the book.

MR. GRAY. Oh, the subject's all right. Believe an old publisher, Mrs. Wenham. Spiritualism's one of the soundest of all non-fiction subjects. Almost as good as theology. Much sounder than politics, for example. Why, I'd far rather publish Mrs. Piper than Winston Churchill. No, it's the price I'm thinking of. It's considering the price that the sale's so remarkable.

MR. WENHAM (*uncomfortably—he does not like these commercial discussions*). One always did consider the price rather excessive.

MR. GRAY. I know you did. But admit, you were wrong. We asked a guinea, and sixteen thousand people have given it. *Vox populi, vox Dei.* Mrs. Wenham, I consider that it's a testimonial to the value of your husband's message. The truth about the Great Beyond —why, it's *worth* a guinea. People wouldn't pay a guinea for Edgar Wallace. To my mind, that's very significant. (*He helps himself to another sandwich.*)

MRS. WENHAM. Quite so. I see what you mean.

MR. GRAY (*his mouth full of sandwich*). And I don't mind admitting it, Mrs. Wenham; it was the popular response to your husband's book that finally converted me to spiritualism. Something that sixteen thousand men and women are prepared to pay a guinea for—and, mind you, there's nothing that people are so avaricious about as books—well, I said to myself, there must be something in it. Besides, when a man like your husband —an expert accountant, mark you!—affirms his belief in spiritualism, well, it's probable, to say the least of it, that spirits exist. It's practically certain, in fact. (*He takes a chocolate éclair.*) I think you'll agree with me, Mr. Wenham.

MR. WENHAM. Well, of course, one's ready to give more credit to a . . . well, a trained intelligence . . .

MR. GRAY. A trained intelligence; that's it exactly.

MR. WENHAM. But it's not simply a question of authority, of course. It's the facts that matter. The only merit one claims for one's book is that it's a collection of facts.

MR. GRAY. A positive mine.

MR. WENHAM. All one has done is to bring together the evidence. Dispassionately, as far as that's possible, with intelligence. . . .

MR. GRAY. The trained intelligence of the expert accountant. Don't forget that.

MR. WENHAM. But, of course, it's thanks to the powers of our young friend, Hubert Capes, that there's any evidence to collect. I consider him one of the most . . . the most richly talented of living mediums.

MR. GRAY. You don't say so.

MRS. WENHAM. Some more tea, Mr. Gray?

MR. GRAY. With pleasure. (*He passes his cup.*)

MRS. WENHAM. Cut Mr. Gray a slice of cake, John.

MR. WENHAM (*cutting*). You see, he's gifted in such a variety of ways. As a producer of physical manifestations, he's second to none. D. D. Home himself never excelled him. And at the same time he has an extraordinary receptivity for purely mental and spiritual communications. (*He hands the cake on the end of the knife to* MR. GRAY.) For book tests and cross-correspondence tests he's . . . well, unique. To one's own mind, some of the ones recorded in the book are even more . . . more convincing than Mrs. Verrall's and Mrs. Piper's.

MRS. WENHAM. Pass me your cup, John.

MR. GRAY (*with a sigh, profoundly*). Well, well, there are more things in heaven and earth, Horatio, than are dreamt of in *your* philosophy. . . . (*There is a silence. He eats his cake meditatively. Turning to* MRS. WENHAM) I suppose you share your husband's interests in this absorbing subject, Mrs. Wenham.

MRS. WENHAM (*coldly*). To some extent. But when one has a house to look after, and a couple of wild little boys, there isn't much time for spiritualism.

MR. GRAY. Quite, quite. A woman's work is never done, as the poet says.

MR. WENHAM (*changing the subject, with an artificial off-handedness*). It's a pity Miss Deckle had to run off like that; I'd have liked you to have a talk with her. A most interesting girl. She's been my . . . well, shall I be Irish and say she's been my right-hand man? The book would never have got written without her. She ought in justice to have her name on the title-page along with one's own. But she didn't want to.

MR. GRAY. A labour of love, in fact.

MR. WENHAM. In a very literal sense, even. She and my Hugo were actually . . . well, betrothed.

MR. GRAY. Poor girl, poor girl!

MR. WENHAM (*sighing*). She suffered very grievously, when Hugo passed on. A very highly strung, emotional nature, you know.

MR. GRAY. They're apt to be, these young people, I find. Rather morbid, even.

MR. WENHAM. It was a terrible blow, of course. But in the end suffering always purifies and uplifts.

MRS. WENHAM. Does it always? I sometimes wonder. (*She gets up.*) But I must go and see that my children aren't misbehaving. (*She moves towards the door.*)

MR. GRAY. Allow me. (*He hurries across the room to open for her.*)

MRS. WENHAM. Thank you. I'll see you later, Mr. Gray. (*She goes out.*)

MR. GRAY (*pulling out his case*). What do you say to a small cigar, Mr. Wenham?

MR. WENHAM. Thanks. One never smokes.

MR. GRAY (*selecting a cigar and lighting it*). Wise man. I wish I didn't (*leaning back in his chair and blowing a cloud of smoke into the air*). Well, well, it's all a very sad and touching story. That gallant youth lost there in the tropic seas. And this poor girl, waiting here. For men must work and women must weep. (*He shakes his head.*) Sad, very sad. Still, all's well that ends well. And I think we can say that this *has* ended pretty well, all things considered. Contact established with the dead . . . or rather (*he waves his cigar*) the happily living. Grief consoled. Tears, idle tears, completely dried. And finally, this extraordinary, this truly magnificent sale for your book. Sixteen thousand ! I shall be sending you another little cheque quite soon, you know. And not such a very little one either, my boy. (*He winks and shakes a fat forefinger at* MR. WENHAM.) Twelve hundred pounds. Not bad, eh ? It'll bring your royalties up to well over three thousand. Oh, I assure you, there are precious few of my authors who can make that with a single book—to say nothing of a first book, mark you. Why, if it weren't absolutely necessary that an author should begin writing some time, no publisher would ever look at a first book. Too risky, too unprofitable. And now you come along and prove the rule with a glorious exception. Sixteen thousand copies !

MR. WENHAM (*who has been listening with signs of embarrassment*). Of course, one's very pleased that so many people should . . . should be interested in the truth. (*He gets up and rings the bell*).

MR. GRAY. *Magna est veritas et praevalebit*, as we used to say at school. But at the same time, don't forget that the labourer is worthy of his hire. I'm so glad now that I was firm about the book being priced at a guinea. At twelve-and-six, sales would have been hardly any larger. We should just have lost forty per cent. of our profits. To no purpose. *Cui bono*, in a word.

MR. WENHAM. You may be right.

MR. GRAY. I know I'm right.

(*Enter the* MAID.)

MR. WENHAM (*to the* MAID). Will you clear away the tea things? (*To* GRAY) We might go into the library meanwhile.

MR. GRAY (*rising*). I'm at your disposition.

MR. WENHAM. I have some interesting early works on accountancy I'd like to show you.

(*They go out. The* MAID *is left. She hums to herself as she clears the table. She goes out with the cake-stand, returns, goes out again with the tray. During her second absence enter* HUBERT *and* ENID.)

ENID (*very much agitated*). It's really intolerable the way they chase one from room to room.

HUBERT. But mayn't Mr. Wenham go into his own library if he wants to? (*Goes over to the tea-table and looks round.*) Damn. I'd hoped there might be something left.

ENID (*who has not heard these last words*). He did it on purpose. He knew we were there.

HUBERT. What nonsense! (*His annoyance at not finding anything to eat has strengthened him against her. His tone is sharp.*) You saw how surprised and embarrassed he was.

ENID. *He* knew all right.

(*The* MAID *re-enters, silently.*)

I expect it was that cat Alice who sent him to . . .

HUBERT. Sh! Sh! (*Loudly*) The book seems to be doing very well. Gray was saying something about sixteen thousand copies when you interrupted him.

ENID. Isn't it simply disgusting, the way he says 'Sixteen thousand,' as though it were a mixture between something holy and something good to eat. Ugh!

HUBERT (*in a low voice, after glancing at the* MAID). I think perhaps it might be better . . .

ENID (*with contemptuous impatience*). All right, all right. (*Loudly*) Wasn't it nice and warm to-day? Or was it nice and cold? I forget which. (*She gets up, much agitated, and begins to walk about the room. A brief silence.*)

HUBERT. Decidedly warm. The thermometer was at seventy-two this morning.

(*Another silence. The* MAID, *who has been folding the cloth and putting away the tea-table, goes out.*)

ENID. At last! She was doing it on purpose, you know.

HUBERT. Doing what? (*His tone is snappy and resentful.*)

ENID. Being so slow. Just to spite us.

HUBERT. What a ridiculous exaggeration!

ENID. Exaggeration, exaggeration! Now you're beginning to talk like Alice.

HUBERT. Alice is quite right. (*He turns on her.*) And look here, Enid, I absolutely refuse to be made a fool of any more in this way.

ENID. What way?

HUBERT (*trembling with rage*). Being dragged out of rooms the moment any one comes in; and having my conversations interrupted; and being pulled here and pushed there; and having you answer for me and saying I don't want any tea—when I do.

ENID (*her anger fallen, in a sudden access of penitence*). But, my darling, I had no idea. Why didn't you say you were hungry? I'll ring and ask Mary to bring you something.

HUBERT (*checking her as she moves towards the bell*). Certainly not.

ENID. But if you want it.

HUBERT. It's too late now.

ENID. Not a bit.

HUBERT. Besides, I've lost my appetite. (*He turns away, a dignified martyr.*)

ENID. Oh, I'm so wretched.

HUBERT. A little late in the day.

ENID. It's this devil that possesses me. Making me do things that are stupid and harmful and against myself, against you. (*Appealingly*) Hubert!

HUBERT (*still averted*). And if you imagine that this sort of thing creates the right atmosphere for getting into touch with any one on the other side, you're very much mistaken.

ENID. Forgive me, Hubert.

HUBERT. What I need is soothing and sympathy and understanding. Instead of which I'm harried and shouted at as though I were a kind of criminal. I'm sure the séance this evening won't be a success. How can it be, with my nerves in this state? I've a good mind to tell Mr. Wenham that I can't do anything this evening.

ENID. Well, there's no reason why you should.

HUBERT. There *is* a reason. He's arranged specially for Gray to come.

ENID. That awful Gray? *He* doesn't matter. Let me go and tell Mr. Wenham that you can't manage a séance to-day.

HUBERT. No, no.

ENID (*rising*). You can rest here quietly, while I go.

HUBERT. No, I won't have it. Sit down. What would he think? He'd see there was something wrong. You'd have to explain. *I'd* have to explain. It would be very awkward. (*Resignedly heroic*) No, I'll go through with it somehow.

ENID (*takes his hand and strokes it. Almost whispering*). Forgive me, Hubert, forgive me. (*There is a long silence.*)

(*Enter* MR. WENHAM *and* MR. GRAY. *The others spring up and apart rather guiltily.*)

MR. WENHAM. One was wondering, Hubert, if you were ready to begin.

HUBERT (*breezily, with a smile*). Oh, whenever you like.

ENID (*anxiously*). You're sure you're feeling up to it? Hubert?

HUBERT (*annoyed*). Of course I am. (*To* MR. WENHAM) Shall we start at once?

MR. WENHAM. Well, why not? Turn on the light, Enid. I'm going to draw the curtains. (*He goes to the window.*)

HUBERT. Is this your first experience of this kind of thing, Mr. Gray?

MR. GRAY. Positively the first. To tell you the truth, I've not given the subject my serious consideration before reading our friend's book. I'd even been sceptical—the scepticism of ignorance. The book enlightened and convinced me! Truth is stranger than fiction. As an old publisher, I ought to have known it, of course. (*He shakes his head.*) Most extraordinary, most extraordinary.

HUBERT. Only because you're not used to it. If you lived as I do, on the borderland, so to speak, between the two worlds, you wouldn't find the other side any more extraordinary than this. Less, really. Because the other side is a moral world, and this isn't. What happens there is what ought to happen. So it seems more normal really than this world, where the things that ought to happen so seldom do happen.

MR. GRAY. Quite, quite. A most illuminating thought. (*To* ENID) What's that, may I ask, Miss Deckle?

ENID (*who is carrying a large box which she has taken out of a cupboard*). The musical-box. (*She puts it down on a small table.*)

MR. GRAY. A musical-box? What for?

ENID (*curtly—she cannot bear talking to him*). To make music.

HUBERT (*making up with a specially unctuous politeness for* ENID'S *bad manners*). It's kept going all through the séance. An atmosphere of harmonious sound. It helps me to get through.

MR. WENHAM (*who has finished with the curtains*). Music helps the medium to . . . well, I was going to say concentrate; but that's the wrong word; because you can't go into a trance without doing the exact opposite to concentrating. You've got to *ex*centrate, if you see what I mean—think of nothing. Music seems to help one to do that. (*To* HUBERT) You'll sit in your usual place, I suppose?

HUBERT. Yes.

MR. WENHAM. Put the trumpets and the accordion on the bookshelf, will you, Enid?

ENID. I'm just getting everything ready.

(ENID *goes back and forth to the cupboard, collecting various objects, such as tambourines, cardboard trumpets, a concertina, sheets of cardboard covered with luminous paint, etc.*)

MR. WENHAM (*to* MR. GRAY). We're just preparing for the simplest physical manifestations. For some one who's new to spiritualism, like yourself, they're . . . well, the most startling phenomena.

MRS. GRAY. Quite.

MR. WENHAM. Though not, of course . . . the most

significant as evidence of survival. Should we begin, Hubert?

HUBERT. Certainly, Mr. Wenham. (*He goes to his seat in the corner.*)

(*The others take chairs across the angle in front of him.* ENID *sits by the little table on which the musical-box stands.*)

ENID. I'll see to the music. (*She gives the handle a couple of turns; a few bars of a hymn tinkle out.*) That's working all right. Shall I turn off the light?

HUBERT (*who is lying back in his chair, relaxed, with closed eyes*). Yes, I'm ready.

(ENID *goes to the door and turns the switch. The room is plunged in darkness. Patches of phosphorescent paint gleam here and there.*)

MR. WENHAM. Can you find your way back, Enid?

ENID. Yes, thanks. Here I am. (*The music starts playing and tinkles on without interruption, the same hymn-tune, again and again.*)

MR. WENHAM. He's going off into a trance now. It generally takes a minute or two.

MR. GRAY. Oughtn't one to be silent, in that case?

MR. WENHAM. No, he prefers one to go on talking. Sometimes it even helps if one sings. Something simple that every one knows. A hymn, for example. 'Abide with me' always seems to be particularly . . . well . . . effective . . .

MR. GRAY. How can you tell when he's gone off into the trance?

MR. WENHAM. By the way he breathes. A certain . . . a certain stertorousness. And then, almost at once, you hear the voice of the control.

MR. GRAY. The who?

MR. WENHAM. The control, the spirit guide. Every

medium has a control on the other side. It's the control that . . . well, introduces the other spirits. In our young friend's case, the principal control is a certain Dr. Ledoux.

MR. GRAY. Yes, I remember your book. A Frenchman.

MR. WENHAM. Of French extraction. But he appears to have practised in London while he was . . . while he was . . . well, in a word, alive. An interesting personality. Rather eccentric. (*To* ENID) You're not getting tired turning that handle, are you, Enid?

ENID. No, thanks.

(*A silence. The hymn-tune tinkles out steadily, again and again.*)

MR. GRAY. It's a curious sensation, sitting here in the dark. One has a sort of expectant feeling that almost anything might happen. (*With a little laugh*) And in point of fact, it *does* happen.

MR. WENHAM. Well, not *any*thing. You mustn't imagine that the spirit world is . . . well, fantastic or irregular. It has its natural laws, like the material world. Little by little we're beginning to formulate them.

(*Silence. Curious sounds begin to come from the medium. The music stops.*)

Ah, do you hear? He seems to be going off.

MR. GRAY. Is he unconscious during the trance?

MR. WENHAM. The surface of his mind's asleep. But of course the deeper layers are unusually active.

HUBERT (*muttering in a voice quite unlike his normal voice, guttural, deep, with a foreign accent*). Good eve . . . good . . . goo . . . goo . . . (*stammering*) good eve . . .

MR. WENHAM. That's the control beginning to come through. (*In a loud and cheerful tone, rather like that which one uses to address a member of the lower classes*)

Good evening, Dr. Ledoux. It's nice to hear your voice again.

HUBERT. Good evening.

MR. WENHAM. And how are you? How are all our friends on the other side?

HUBERT. *Très bien, très bien, merci.* But there is a new face here to-night.

MR. WENHAM. Just a friend, Dr. Ledoux; an interested friend who wanted to see the manifestations.

MR. GRAY. In all reverence, mind you; not mere idle curiosity.

HUBERT. H'm, I do not much like him.

MR. WENHAM. Oh, come, Dr. Ledoux! (*To* MR. GRAY) I told you he was a most eccentric personality. (*To the medium*) Mr. Gray is deeply interested.

HUBERT. He is not grey, he is black. Enid! Why do you not speak to me this evening?

ENID. I was waiting till Mr. Wenham had finished. How is Hugo?

HUBERT. Hugo is *très bien, merci.*

ENID. Can you get him to come?

HUBERT. Yes, I think he will come. *Viens donc, viens. Mais, mais, mais, mais, qu'est-ce qu'il fait, ce garçon-la? Mais, mais, mais, mais . . .* (*The voice tails off into an incoherent mumble.*)

MR. GRAY. What's happened to him now?

MR. WENHAM. Oh, he's just gone back again for a moment. You mustn't mind if he's rude to you, by the way. Dr. Ledoux is often very rude. It's a certain perverted sense of humour in him. There's something . . . well, rather impish about him.

HUBERT. *Il va venir bientôt.* Not at present, though. He is thinking much of you, Mr. Wenham, much of Enid, too. More than usual. (*Calling sharply*) Black!

MR. GRAY. Does he mean me, do you think?

HUBERT. Yes, of course, I mean you. Why do you not ask me that question about your father?

MR. GRAY. Most extraordinary. I was just thinking of asking him if he knew my father's name. *Do* you happen to know it, Dr. Ledoux?

HUBERT. *Il s'appelle Alfred. Je le connais.* He asks if you still have *sa chaîne de montre en or et platine*?

MR. GRAY. His what?

ENID. His gold and platinum watch-chain.

MR. GRAY. But of course I've still got it. Tell him that I treasure it as one of the most precious, one of the most holy . . .

HUBERT. *Mais tais-toi, imbécile.*

MR. GRAY. What does he say?

HUBERT. *J'ai dit tais-toi, imbécile!*

MR. WENHAM. One gathers that he'd like you to be silent for the moment. (*To the medium*) Are there any other messages, Dr. Ledoux?

HUBERT. He says he is happy, *c'est tout.* Very happy.

MR. WENHAM. Tell him that we are happy in his happiness—in the happiness of all of them. (*Turning to* MR. GRAY*; his voice is charged with an ecstatic emotion*) Happy, happy. That's the refrain of all the spirits, Mr. Gray. Happiness and life, eternal happiness in eternal life. 'They are all gone into the world of light, and I alone sit lingering here.' You remember those beautiful lines of Vaughan. There are moments when one is almost . . . almost impatient to know it personally, that happiness—to experience it. Yes, almost impatient.

MR. GRAY. Well I can't say that I personally . . .

HUBERT (*muttering*). *Très bien, très bien.* (*Aloud*) *Il va venir.* Hugo says he is coming. But not at once.

MR. WENHAM. Well, we'll wait, Dr. Ledoux. We don't mind waiting. But perhaps it would be possible, meanwhile, to arrange a few physical phenomena. Our friend here would be so much interested.

MR. GRAY. Oh, yes. And I should feel it a privilege, I assure you, a real . . .

HUBERT. *Comme vous voudrez.* There are a lot of spirits here who would like to manifest. (*In a low voice, as though speaking intimately to a group of people near at hand*) Come along, come . . . *Par ici.* Yes, that's it. . . . *Tr-ès bien, tr-ès bien . . . Non. Non. Non. Comme ça, voyez-vous.* Yes, that's it. *Çà y est.*

MR. GRAY. What's that curious sort of cold draught that seems to be blowing . . . ?

HUBERT. *Tais-toi, tais-toi!* (*Silence—then a loud and startling rap—then several raps, from all over the room.*)

MR. GRAY. Oh! something hit me in the face.

HUBERT. Ha, ha, ha! (*A deep guttural peal of laughter from Dr. Ledoux.*)

(*There is a long silence broken by occasional raps. A luminous trumpet sails slowly through the air.*)

MR. GRAY. But this is amazing.

HUBERT. Hush! Hush! Watch the concertina.

(*There is a silence. The concertina, daubed with luminous paint, slowly rises and remains hanging in the middle of the room.*)

ENID. I believe it's going to play something.

HUBERT (*in a very muffled voice*). Yes, yes.

(*In complete silence all watch the faintly luminous concertina slowly contracting and expanding above them in the darkness. There is a long hush, then suddenly the thin wheezing sweetness of accordeon music. The tune is that of the letter duet in* Figaro—*Che soave zeffiretto.*)

ENID (*after the first few notes, whispering excitedly*). Do you recognize it, Mr. Wenham? That air out of *Figaro*?

MR. WENHAM. You mean the one that Hugo was so fond of?

ENID. Yes, the one that Hugo was always . . .

(*The door suddenly flies open, the figures of* HUGO *and* BILL *are seen silhouetted against the light outside.*)

HUGO. What on earth's happening here? (*He turns on the light.*)

(*The concertina falls with a crash to the ground.* HUBERT, *who is lying back limply in his chair, utters a cry of pain, covers his eyes with his hand, then slips sideways in a faint. The others spring up.*)

HUGO. Oh, a séance. I'm so sorry. Have I spoilt the best effect?

(*He advances into the room.*)

Well, father. Like the proverbial bad penny . . .

(MR. WENHAM *stands petrified.* ENID *steps forward.*)

ENID. Hugo!

HUGO. Why, Enid! I didn't know *you'd* taken to ghosts.

BILL (*in black spectacles, groping his way blindly after* HUGO). Hugo! Why the devil do you leave me alone here in the dark? (*He stumbles against a chair.*) Damnation! Where are you?

(ENID *stretches out her arm; he comes up against it.*)

Why . . . ?

HUGO (*meanwhile stepping back and taking him by the arm*). Here I am, Bill. (*Patting his arm. To* ENID) He can't see.

ENID. It's all right. Take my hand.

Curtain

ACT III

SCENE—*The same.* TIME—*The next morning.*

(MRS. WENHAM, HUGO *and* BILL, *standing near the French window by which* BILL *and* HUGO *have just entered.*)

MRS. WENHAM. But why, Hugo? Tell me why you never told us.

BILL (*who has been groping about with his hands, peevishly*). Can't you give me a chair, Hugo? For God's sake give me a chair.

HUGO. Sorry, Bill. (*Pushes up a chair.*)

(BILL *sits down.*)

There you are; make yourself comfortable.

BILL. None of your horrible bedside manner, now. I won't have you patronizing me.

HUGO. Sorry, I didn't mean to be bedside-ish.

BILL. That only makes it worse. It means you can't help being insulting.

MRS. WENHAM. But why, Hugo, tell me why?

HUGO. Why? Well, I don't know. Why did we go on letting people think we were dead, Bill?

BILL. Why not? Mayn't one play a practical joke if one wants to?

HUGO. Well . . . of course it sounds idiotic . . . but in a certain sense it *was* all a kind of joke. It seemed so amusing at the time. Bill and I—well, I don't exactly know how to describe it—we were kind of drunk with adventure. Weren't we, Bill?

BILL. Were we? (*Shrugs his shoulders.*) Anyhow, it's the morning after now.

HUGO. And then, of course, when one had carried on the joke for a certain time, it was difficult to go back.

One was a bit ashamed. So one felt one had to stick to it. If it hadn't been for Bill's accident, I suppose we'd still be playing our joke.

MRS. WENHAM. But what a horrible, wicked, cruel joke, Hugo!

HUGO. But how could I have foreseen that this would happen?

BILL (*laughing with sudden savagery*). The fun's really only just beginning.

MRS. WENHAM (*indignantly*). Mr. Hamblin!

(HUGO *makes an imploring gesture, begging her to be silent. She checks herself and turns to* HUGO.)

But even if your father hadn't written this book, Hugo—even then, it would have been a hateful, cruel thing to do.

HUGO. Oh, I know, I know. But there were also serious reasons, Alice. One's simply got to be cruel sometimes. There's a kind of ultimate selfishness that's sacred and imperative; I simply had to escape—go right away, be somebody else. It seemed a heaven-sent opportunity.

MRS. WENHAM. A heaven-sent opportunity to make your poor father suffer.

BILL. One for you, Mrs. Wenham!

MRS. WENHAM. I can't think how you did it, Hugo—you who used to be so considerate.

HUGO. Well, I suppose it was one of the things I learnt out there, Alice—*not* to be too considerate.

BILL. One for you, Hugo!

HUGO. And I can tell you, it was a difficult lesson. Learning to be hard, when one's naturally soft; learning to be clear and definite when one's native weather is fog—oh, it wasn't easy.

MRS. WENHAM. Now, Hugo, you can't expect me to discuss this sort of high-falutin nonsense. I know when a thing's wrong and I know when a thing's right.

BILL. You're uncommonly lucky, then.

MRS. WENHAM. However, I won't say anything more about it now. We've got other things to think about at the moment. But really, Hugo, really I do think it's disgraceful what you've done.

HUGO (*shrugging his shoulders*). I'm sorry.

MRS. WENHAM. As if that made any difference. The point is: what are we going to do now? You, I, your father, every one?

(MR. GRAY *enters while she is speaking.* MRS. WENHAM *sees him.*)

Perhaps you can help to answer that question, Mr. Gray. What are we going to do? What *are* we going to do?

MR. GRAY. Well, as a matter of fact, that was just what I was coming to ask of you, Mrs. Wenham. I've just been having a talk with your husband, and he tells me that he means to write to the papers about what's happened.

MRS. WENHAM. You mean, about their coming back?

(MR. GRAY *nods.*)

But what on earth for? Is he mad?

MR. GRAY. That's what I said, of course. But he declares it's a matter of principle. He can't go on sponsoring the untruth that's in the book. But, as I said to him: 'My dear Wenham,' I said . . .

BILL. Bow, wow, bow! (*With perfect gravity of manner.*)

MR. GRAY. What's that?

BILL. 'My dear Wenham,' you said. And what then? I haven't been so amused for weeks.

HUGO. Oh, for God's sake, Bill, be quiet.

BILL. Mayn't I even be amused?

MR. GRAY. Well, as I was saying: 'My dear Wenham,' I said . . .

MRS. WENHAM. But we simply must prevent him from sending that letter. Listen, Hugo, you've got to help us. You simply must.

HUGO. I'll do what I can.

MRS. WENHAM. Oh, how stupid it all is. Too utterly stupid! (*In an outburst of exasperation.*)

BILL. But that's just the beauty of it. That's . . .

HUGO. Come on Bill. Let's come and have breakfast. (*Laying his hand on* BILL'S *shoulder.*)

BILL. All right. I'll come quietly.

(*As they approach the door into the hall* MR. WENHAM *enters.*)

MR. WENHAM. Ah, good-morning, dear boy. Good-morning, Mr. Hamblin.

HUGO. Morning, father.

MR. WENHAM. Where are you off to?

HUGO. Going to have some breakfast.

MR. WENHAM. What, hasn't Mr. Hamblin had his breakfast yet?

HUGO. No, we went for a turn in the garden first. Come on, Bill.

BILL. You see, I make such a hoggish mess now when I eat. So I prefer doing it when nobody's there. I daresay the best thing would be if I had a little trough made for myself and ate off the floor. That would . . .

HUGO. Oh, come on, Bill. (*He leads him out.*)

MR. WENHAM (*advancing into the room and sitting down*). It really is too dreadful about that poor young man. Blinded like that, by the stupidest accident. And what makes it worse, he's so terribly . . . so terribly resentful about it. So bitter. That self-laceration . . . (*Passes his hand over his forehead.*) Oh, dear . . .

MRS. WENHAM. Mr. Gray tells me, dear, that you mean to write a letter to the papers about . . . well, about all this.

MR. WENHAM. Yes, one was just coming to tell you.

MRS. WENHAM. But is it necessary, John? Isn't it . . . isn't it simply madness?

MR. GRAY. Madness. I entirely agree with Mrs. Wenham.

MR. WENHAM. But don't you see, dear, one's in a false position. One's countenancing an untruth. It's a question of scientific good faith.

MRS. WENHAM. Oh, if it's only a question of science . . .

MR. WENHAM. Besides, one's actually obtaining money on false pretences. Every time somebody buys a copy of the book, one's committing a swindle. Can't you see? One *must* write that letter.

MRS. WENHAM. But, John, have you thought of the consequences?

MR. GRAY. Yes, the consequences, my dear Wenham.

MRS. WENHAM. They'll make a laughing-stock of you, an absolute laughing-stock. John, I beg you—please don't send that letter.

MR. WENHAM. But, dear, there's a principle at stake.

MRS. WENHAM. They'll be so horrible and beastly about it.

MR. WENHAM. Perhaps they will be. But after all, if it's right . . .

MRS. WENHAM. But it isn't right to go and destroy your whole life like this, deliberately. It isn't right. And destroy it for what? For nothing. For a lot of wretched ghosts. Because even if they did exist, what difference would it make?

MR. WENHAM. But surely, my dear . . .

MRS. WENHAM (*cutting him short*). Yes, what difference? Oh, I believe in the life to come and all that. I'm a good Christian. I go to church every Sunday. But

I've got my house to look after, and the children to think about, and you. I simply haven't got time for ghosts and séances and all the rest. I simply don't want to be interfered with by them, if you see what I mean.

MR. GRAY. How I agree with you, Mrs. Wenham! Religion is a wonderful thing in its proper place. But it should never be allowed to invade the sanctities of private life. Never. That's *my* opinion.

MRS. WENHAM. You've got no right to destroy real things for the sake of what isn't real. You've got no right to murder your happiness like this.

MR. WENHAM. But, dear, it isn't a question of happiness now. It's a question of honesty and good faith. After all, one can't think only of one's own feelings.

MRS. WENHAM. I quite agree. But what about other people's feelings, John? Think a little about my feelings, think a little of the children's feelings.

MR. GRAY. Think a little of *my* feelings.

MRS. WENHAM. Think of the boys at school, how they'll be teased and jeered at when your letter's published. Why should *we* be made to suffer?

MR. GRAY. Precisely.

MRS. WENHAM. It isn't only your own happiness that you're murdering.

MR. WENHAM (*gets up and walks restlessly about the room*). Do you think it will be as bad as all that?

MRS. WENHAM. I'm sure it will.

MR. GRAY. Worse even, I should say.

MR. WENHAM (*sitting down again, after a silence*). Still one *must* do what's right. Oh, if only one hadn't had the idea of publishing that book! But Capes seemed so perfectly all right. One could have sworn . . . Oh, God! I don't know, I don't know . . .

MRS. WENHAM (*insinuatingly*). Suppose you just quietly withdrew the book, John. Wouldn't that be enough?

MR. WENHAM. What difference would that make?

MRS. WENHAM. I should have thought it would make a great deal of difference. If people couldn't buy the book any more . . .

MR. WENHAM. But the lie would have been published just the same, and I shouldn't have contradicted it. It's a question of telling the truth.

MR. GRAY. Quite, quite. But not rashly, never rashly, my dear Wenham. Writing a letter to the papers—that's simply foolhardiness.

MRS. WENHAM. Mr. Gray's quite right, dear.

MR. GRAY. One should never do anything without carefully thinking it over first.

MR. WENHAM. Not even tell the truth?

MR. GRAY. Oh, the truth before everything, of course. *Magna est veritas*, as we used to say. But there are good ways and bad ways of telling it, there are auspicious moments and inauspicious moments. I think you'll agree with me, Mrs. Wenham?

MRS. WENHAM. Entirely.

MR. GRAY. And above all, anything like rashness, anything like precipitation must be avoided. It's like having a puncture when you're driving a car. If you're going at sixty miles an hour and your tyre bursts, it's dangerous, it's extremely dangerous. But a small hole, a gradual leak, that's quite harmless. It seems to me that that's what we ought to aim at in this case—just a very gradual leaking out of the truth. Because if it all came out at once, with a bang—well, really, I don't know what would happen. The book's selling with such a momentum, the publicity's at full throttle—everything's fairly whizzing along. And then, pop! You go and explode the truth on us. Why, there'd be the most hideous smash-up. Terrible! Of course, I'm not thinking about myself—though naturally it doesn't do any publisher much good to be openly made a fool of. I'm thinking of you. (*He pats* MR. WENHAM *on the shoulder.*)

MR. WENHAM (*shrinking deeper into his chair*). Most kind, I'm sure, but——

MR. GRAY. Yes, my dear Wenham, I'm thinking of you. *Your* reputation, *your* happiness, *your* position in the world, *your* . . .

(*He breaks off at the sight of* HUBERT CAPES, *who has entered from the hall and is standing hesitating on the threshold. In a portentous tone.*)

Good-morning, Mr. Capes.

HUBERT (*nervously*). Oh . . . Good-morning. I was just looking for Mr. Wenham. Good-morning, Mr. Wenham. But it doesn't matter. I'll wait till later on, when you're alone. (*He makes as if to retire.*)

MR. GRAY. Wait a minute, please, Mr. Capes. I'd like a word with you. We'd all like a word with you, I think.

(MRS. WENHAM *shrugs her shoulders and, turning away, leans against the mantelpiece. Huddled in his chair* MR. WENHAM *says nothing.*)

MR. GRAY (*bullyingly*). In fact we'd like several words.

HUBERT (*very nervously*). Well, I'm sure I shall be delighted.

MR. GRAY. I'm sure you *won't* be delighted. I certainly don't *want* you to be delighted. Because, young man, I consider you a low, dirty swindler.

HUBERT. No, really. I . . . I . . . Mr. Wenham, I beg you . . .

MR. WENHAM. After all, Gray, we don't know, we can't judge . . .

MR. GRAY. Leave this to me, Wenham. (*Turning back to* HUBERT, *thoroughly enjoying his righteous indignation.*) I repeat, sir, a low, dirty swindler. And I will add, a heartless cheat.

HUBERT (*plaintively indignant*). But . . . but this is dreadful. And if you knew how ill I felt. That shock I had last night . . . It's monstrous.

MR. GRAY. Monstrous. I quite agree. Exploiting the grief of a bereaved father, playing on the most sacred feelings for your own base and venial—I mean venal—purposes. Absolutely monstrous.

HUBERT. But it's not true, Mr. Gray. I never did that. I swear.

MR. GRAY. That's it, swear away. Add perjury to cheating.

HUBERT. But it wasn't cheating. I never did anything that wasn't absolutely straight. Did I, Mr. Wenham?

MR. WENHAM. Well, certainly one never . . . one never detected anything wrong.

MR. GRAY. Quite so. He was a very clever cheat. That's all *that* proves.

HUBERT. But on my word of honour, Mr. Gray . . .

MR. GRAY (*laughing*). On your word of honour! That's good, that's very good. Did you hear that, Mrs. Wenham? On his word of honour.

HUBERT. But it's true. Oh, Mrs. Wenham, do believe me.

MRS. WENHAM (*shrugging her shoulders without turning round*). What does it matter if I believe you or not? It won't make any difference to what's happened . . . to what's going to happen.

HUBERT. Yes, what *is* going to happen? What will people say about me if this gets known?

MR. GRAY. They'll say exactly what I've said, young

man. That you're an impudent and heartless swindler. Do you realize what you've let the unfortunate Mr Wenham in for? Do you realize?

HUBERT. It was a mistake, I swear. I simply can't think how it happened. The messages were so clear and definite . . . weren't they, Mr. Wenham?

MR. GRAY. Oh, stop that stupid canting! Clear and definite, indeed! Clear and definite swindling. The man ought to be horse-whipped, don't you agree, Mrs. Wenham? Soundly horse-whipped and then kicked out of the house. Do you hear what I say, sir? (*He advances menacingly towards* HUBERT, *who cowers away in abject terror.*)

HUBERT. No. Don't. Please. I'm so ill.

MR. WENHAM (*who has risen, speaking at the same time as* HUBERT). No, Gray, no.

(*While this has been going on,* HUGO *has entered and has advanced unnoticed into the room. He is already quite close to the shrinking* HUBERT *when he makes his presence known.*)

HUGO. But what on earth is happening here?

(HUBERT *turns round with a start, sees* HUGO *standing over him and immediately bolts behind the table.*)

HUBERT. No, no, please. Oh, it isn't fair. If you knew how bad my heart was. Really, I swear.

HUGO (*looking round in astonishment*). But has every one gone mad, or what?

HUBERT (*reassured, emerging from behind the table*). Goodness! I thought . . . my nerves are in such an awful state . . .

HUGO. Did you imagine I was going to set on you?

HUBERT. No, no. It was just my nerves. I'm sorry I was so foolish. Let's talk about something else.

HUGO. But I'm afraid I must talk about this. Because

if you imagined I was going to attack you, you must also imagine that I have some reason for attacking you.

MR. GRAY. It's his guilty conscience, Mr. Wenham. That's the reason. The man's a common swindler.

HUGO. But I don't agree with you, Mr. Gray. I don't believe for a moment that there's been any fraud.

HUBERT. There, you see!

MR. GRAY. No fraud? (*Spoken simultaneously with* HUBERT'S *words.*) But come, my dear sir, come. You're alive, aren't you? You're not a departed spirit?

HUGO. But that's only a detail.

MR. GRAY. Rather an important detail, I should have thought.

HUGO. Only from my point of view, not from Mr. Capes's.

MR. GRAY. But the fellow professed to be bringing messages from you in the next world.

HUGO. Well, it was just a little mistake, that's all. He was bringing them from me in this world. Do remember that spiritualism's only a theory for interpreting certain facts. There are other theories that fit the facts just as well—better, even. What's important is the facts.

MR. GRAY. You mean the concertina and all that sort of thing?

HUGO. Yes; and clairvoyance and telepathy and so on—those are the facts. If you like to say that they have something to do with dead people, you may. But it's purely a matter of taste. You can have all the facts and no belief in ghosts. Mediums who work for non-spiritualists never dream of having anything to do with ghosts. Whereas those who work for spiritualists—like you, father—well, naturally, they tend to find ghosts everywhere—swarms of them. It's only natural.

MR. WENHAM. Then you think that our young friend here . . .

HUGO. . . . is perfectly genuine. Only a bit mistaken in his interpretations. I hope you'll excuse my talking about you like this, Mr. Capes.

HUBERT. But of course. I'm so grateful for your support. I couldn't bear my honour being questioned. It's never happened before.

HUGO. Well, there's no reason why it should happen again if you stick to facts and avoid theories. You see, Mr. Gray, he's what's called a psychic subject—a man with certain special gifts. However, as he's always worked for spiritualists, he tends to attribute everything he does to ghosts. I mean, if a bell rings at a distance it's Napoleon or Joan of Arc. Or suppose the concertina plays something out of *Figaro*—then it's my ghost playing, because I happened to like the tune. But it isn't my ghost. It's Mr. Capes himself.

MR. GRAY. There, didn't I say so?

HUGO. Not the ordinary, waking Mr. Capes. Mr. Capes's unconscious mind influenced by my mind and using some sort of ectoplasm stuff to play the concertina with.

MR. GRAY. That's a bit far-fetched, isn't it?

HUGO. But you can take photographs of it, you know. Streams of ectoplasm guttering out of the medium's ears, or nose, or mouth. Great oozing tentacles of it, like the arms of an octopus. It makes the ghosts quite superfluous and unnecessary.

HUBERT. I can't quite agree with you there, of course. The spirits make use of the ectoplasm. (*Embarrassed*) At least they do in most cases. Don't they, Mr. Wenham?

MR. WENHAM. Well, one thought they did. One imagined

. . . but I don't know now, I don't know. (*Despairingly.*)

MR. GRAY. Then you really think there was no fraud in any of those messages?

HUGO. No fraud; only a misinterpretation. You see, father, you'd all got it so firmly into your heads that I was dead. Anything Mr. Capes extracted out of my mind by long-distance thought-reading you immediately put down as a communication from my departed spirit.

MR. GRAY. But do you think he really did get things out of your mind?

HUGO. Think? I know he did. I spent most of last night reading your book, father. It made me feel quite uncomfortable sometimes, as though I'd been living all this time with somebody's eye at the keyhole.

HUBERT. I'm most awfully sorry.

HUGO. It seemed so extraordinary that you should know so much about me, father—you of all people—forgive me for that.

MR. WENHAM. Yes, I of all people.

HUGO. You know, it's an extraordinarily good book. (*Looking at his father while he speaks.*)

MR. GRAY (*with an air of proprietorship*). I'm glad you think so, Mr. Wenham.

HUGO. I'd no idea you could write so well, father. I really congratulate you.

(MR. WENHAM *shakes his head and makes a gesture of negation.*)

MR. GRAY. You knew, of course, that it's been one of the great successes of the publishing season?

HUGO. No.

MR. GRAY. Sixteen thousand copies already sold.

HUGO (*whistles*). Whew!

MR. GRAY. At a guinea each, mark you.

HUGO. Well, there's an idea for a career. Why not take up spiritualism? I'd been wondering what I should do now.

MRS. WENHAM (*turning round sharply*). Listen, Hugo, it's time to speak seriously. All this talk about ghosts and ectoplasm and scientific theories may be very interesting. But it's out of place, it's beside the point. Your father is proposing to write to the papers to say that you've come back, that the book was all a mistake. . . .

HUBERT (*horrified*). You are not, Mr. Wenham! But it would be the ruin of me. It's too terrible, it's . . .

MRS. WENHAM (*coldly*). Perhaps you'll allow me to finish what I was saying, Mr. Capes. What we want to know now, Hugo, is not whether there are such things as ghosts, but whether your father still means to send that letter?

HUGO. Do you, father?

MR. WENHAM (*after a long pause, miserably*). One can't countenance an untruth, can one?

HUGO. But, after all, it isn't an untruth . . . not really. All the phenomena were perfectly genuine.

HUBERT. Absolutely, I swear it.

MR. WENHAM. But the interpretation—that was wrong. The world of light . . .

HUGO. Oh, I wouldn't bother about the world of light.

MR. WENHAM. I made statements which weren't true. One must do what's right.

MR. GRAY. But think of the consequences, my dear Wenham.

MRS. WENHAM. For all of us. Think of the children at school.

HUBERT. Think of me.

MRS. WENHAM. You know how malicious little boys are, how they'd jeer.

HUGO. And then think of poor Bill. It'll be so bad for him if you mix him up in a lot of excitement and publicity.

HUBERT. And it would be absolute ruin for me.

HUGO. Bill's nerves are in such a state.

MR. GRAY. And you know, we can easily withdraw the book. Just make it quietly disappear from the bookshops.

MRS. WENHAM. And then when the publicity has died down . . .

HUGO. You could write a second book, more cautious, so as to prepare the way.

MRS. WENHAM. And then . . .

MR. GRAY. Very, very gradually let the truth leak out.

HUBERT. Or not leak at all. Perhaps that would really be better.

MR. WENHAM (*getting up distracted*). I'm sorry, one can't stay. One's got to be alone. (*He moves towards the door.*)

MRS. WENHAM. But John, what about that letter?

MR. WENHAM. Oh, I don't know, one can't decide. One must think it over.

MR. GRAY. If you'll take my advice, Wenham . . .

MR. WENHAM. No, don't give it me now, Gray. Please don't. I don't think I could stand it. (*He hurries out through the door into the hall.*)

MR. GRAY. Do you think it would be a good thing if I followed him and—you know—rubbed in my arguments a little?

HUGO. No. No. Leave the poor man in peace for a moment.

MRS. WENHAM. But perhaps later on, if the matter's still undecided . . .

MR. GRAY. Yes, I'll rub it in.

MRS. WENHAM. Well, meanwhile one can only wait and hope. You'll withdraw the book anyhow, won't you, Mr. Gray?

MR. GRAY. It's the first thing I'll attend to when I get back to London. Which reminds me (*looking at his watch*)—nearly eleven. Perhaps I ought to go and pack my bag if I'm going to catch that five to twelve train.

MRS. WENHAM. And I must go and talk to the cook. Heaven and earth may pass away, but dinner's got to be ordered.

(MRS. WENHAM *goes out*, *followed by* MR. GRAY. *There is a silence.*)

HUGO (*shaking his head*). Well. It's a bad business, a thoroughly bad business.

HUBERT. It would have been still worse, so far as I'm concerned, if you hadn't come and taken my part. That was very kind of you, Hugo—I mean Mr. Wenham. I beg your pardon. I've been so used to calling you Hugo all this time. One's on more affectionate terms with the spirits, somehow. There's not so much etiquette on the other side.

HUGO. Well, I'm not a stickler for it even on this side.

HUBERT. Oh, dear, if only your father hadn't written that book! It's really terrible to think that a single mistake can ruin one's whole career. (*More clerically*) Besides, there's the Cause to think of. It would be awful if one had done anything, even accidentally, to injure the Cause.

HUGO. Oh, the Cause'll be all right. Don't you bother about the Cause, Mr. Capes. It's as safe as the Bank of England. Safer really, when you come to think of it. Another war might easily bust the Bank; but it could do nothing but good to spiritualism.

HUBERT (*unctuously*). At the great crises of history the great human truths have always come into their own.

HUGO. Quite, quite. (*After a little pause*) Tell me, as a matter of curiosity—was it genuine *every* time?

HUBERT (*indignantly*). Genuine? How can you ask such a question?

HUGO. Come now, don't take it badly. I know it was genuine most of the time. But weren't there occasions when . . . well, when the phenomena had to be helped out a little?

HUBERT. Certainly not.

HUGO. Strictly between ourselves, you know.

HUBERT. I'm ready to swear.

HUGO. No, please don't do that.

HUBERT. Every time—it was genuine every time. Even those messages for Enid.

HUGO. Which messages for Enid?

HUBERT (*embarrassed*). Well . . . it's rather difficult to explain.

HUGO (*looking at his watch*). Yes, quite. I really ought to go and see how poor old Bill's getting on.

HUBERT (*laying a hand on* HUGO'S *arm, as the latter moves towards the library door*). Just a minute, Mr. Wenham, I'd like to talk to you for a moment. About those messages—about Enid.

HUGO. Fire away, then.

HUBERT. Well . . . (*He coughs nervously.*) It's like this. You were engaged to Enid. You don't mind my being personal, I hope?

HUGO. Not *very* much.

HUBERT. You see, I know so many things about you. As though you were a historical character, if you see what I mean. It's strange, isn't it?

(HUGO *nods, making a wry face.*)

Well, as I say, you were engaged to Enid. Poor girl! The news of your death—I mean, what we thought was your death—naturally, it was a terrible shock to her. Terrible. (*Clerically*) It would have made your heart bleed to see her at that time.

HUGO. I'm glad I didn't. (*He gets up and takes one or two turns up and down the room.*) Was she really upset?

HUBERT. I was afraid she might do something desperate.

HUGO. What do you mean?

HUBERT. Kill herself, even. She confessed to me afterwards that she'd actually made up her mind. And she'd have done it, I believe, if it hadn't been for the new faith and hope that came to her with the séances. (*Embarrassed*) Well, in the circumstances it did look as though . . . I mean, they did seem to justify faith and hope . . .

HUGO. Quite, quite.

HUBERT. You understand?

(HUGO *nods.*)

And then I did my best, of course, to help her. (*Unctuously*) It was my duty; it's what I'm called and appointed to do—to help people in cases like this. Besides my heart bled for her.

(*Unseen by* HUBERT, HUGO *makes a grimace.*)

HUBERT. I talked to her, I tried to console her. And then . . . it's difficult to describe exactly how it came about . . . but gradually, little by little, well, our feelings began to change . . . without our being aware at first. You know how it happens.

HUGO (*looking greatly relieved*). Yes, I know how it happens. You fell in love with her, in fact. And she fell in love with you, I take it. Well, why not?

HUBERT (*taken aback*). Why not? But, after all, you were engaged.

HUGO. But only in a previous existence.

HUBERT. I . . . I thought you'd have minded. I mean, neither of us would have dreamt of . . . caring for one another, if it hadn't been for certain . . . certain . . . well, we thought they were messages from your spirit. Messages that encouraged us to . . . to . . . you see what I mean?

HUGO. Oh, perfectly.

HUBERT. Such definite messages.

HUGO. I'm sure they were.

HUBERT. And as it was really a question of saving her life . . .

HUGO. But why apologize like this? I can only wish you happiness.

HUBERT. But I wouldn't dream of standing in your way now.

HUGO. You're not standing in my way.

HUBERT (*growing almost desperate*). I mean, you have certain rights, certain prior claims.

HUGO. But what a way to speak of it, man! As though we were discussing house property!

HUBERT. What I meant to say was that I feel it as a duty. I'm ready to renounce . . .

HUGO. But, damn it, I don't ask you to renounce.

HUBERT. But I couldn't accept such sacrifices. I simply couldn't . . .

(*The door opens and* ENID *enters.* HUBERT *sees her at once.*)

Oh!

HUGO (*who has his back to the door, turns round*). Ah! here's Enid. (*His tone and expression are positively jolly. He has been steadily brightening throughout the previous conversation.*) Ought I to start congratulating . . . (*He is advancing towards her, but checks his movement; his words are abruptly frozen on his lips by the expression of stony misery on* ENID'S *face. She is dressed in black.*) I'm sorry, Enid.

ENID (*walks slowly into the middle of the room and sits down before answering*). Sorry, Hugo? What for?

HUGO. Well, I don't know. *You'll* have to tell me that. Sorry for being here, I suppose. For not being dead.

ENID. Oh, if only *I* were dead.

HUBERT. But you ought to be feeling thankful, Enid. It's really a miracle.

ENID (*with sudden anger*). Oh, be quiet, Hubert! Bleating away like a beastly little clergyman—it's disgusting! And the hypocrisy of it! Talking about thankfulness and miracles so as to avoid telling the real truth. Anything to avoid the truth. (*She checks herself.*) I'm sorry. But you did drive me to it. Thankfulness indeed! (*She laughs hysterically.*) That was really too much. (*She pulls herself together once more.*) Listen, Hugo, the truth's got to be told. I know Hubert won't tell it. And I rather doubt if you'll tell it. Besides, you don't know it all—only your part of it. I'm the only one who knows the whole of it. And I'm the only one who's got the courage to tell it. You're cowards, you know, both of you. Perhaps all men are a bit cowardly when it comes to facing the truth about feelings. And perhaps it's also because neither of you has suffered. You've only inflicted suffering. I'm the one it's been inflicted on. That's why I can tell the truth and you can't. Because I'm not ashamed. One isn't ashamed of suffering pain. One's only ashamed of inflicting it. You inflicted it. So you're ashamed, and it's that which prevents you from telling the truth. You're cowards through shame. Isn't that it?

HUGO. Yes, perhaps there's something in that.

HUBERT. Well, personally, I don't know of anything I've done that I need be ashamed of.

ENID (*with bitter irony*). No, of course you don't. Tell me, Hugo, don't you think I'm right? Isn't one always ashamed of inflicting pain, even when it isn't one's fault and one really can't help it? I mean, it wasn't your fault that you couldn't bear me. It wasn't your fault that you had that kind of instinctive physical horror of me. (*Her voice trembles.*)

HUGO (*greatly distressed*). Enid, don't! It's horrible. You're lacerating yourself.

ENID (*with a kind of laugh*). There! You see? You're shirking it again. You're ashamed of having hurt me, and therefore you haven't got the courage to tell the truth, or even to hear the truth. Because it *is* the truth, isn't it? Admit it. It *is* the truth.

HUGO (*after a pause*). Well, it's nearly the truth, I suppose.

ENID (*smiling sadly*). 'Nearly the truth.' You're getting braver, Hugo. Nearly the truth. And yet you liked me, in spite of everything. We were friends, weren't we? Even though I did bully you. Do you remember, you once said I ought to wear a stiff collar and cuffs like a nurse? Because I treated you as though you were a typhoid patient. Poor Hugo! I'm sorry. But you liked me all the same. Perhaps just because of the cuffs and collar. Secretly you rather enjoyed being bullied, didn't you?

HUGO. Did I?

ENID. Yes. But you hated it at the same time. And the hatred was made worse because of that kind of horror, that physical horror. Oh, I knew it all, I understood it all. And yet I'd forgotten, or rather I'd invented another past for myself, because I didn't like the real past. I'm a coward too, you see. Yes, a coward and a liar. Why are we all such cowards and liars, Hugo? I believe there's a cowardly lie at the bottom of every soul. Perhaps there's got to be. Perhaps it's the only condition on which we can ever be happy. Do you know, I've been lying to myself about you ever since you went away—or at least ever since we thought you were dead. Making a myth about you and our relations with each other. And I'd done it so successfully that last night, just before I went to sleep, I decided to come to you in the morning and suggest—can you guess what?

(HUGO *shakes his head.*)

That we should go away together and start a new life—like people in the movies! (*Laughs.*) Luckily I saw through the lie when I woke up this morning. Seven o'clock is a very truthful hour. What would you have done if I hadn't seen through it. I mean, supposing I'd come and asked you to take me—what *would* you have done? (*She leans forward with an ironical smile and yet desperately hopeful.*)

HUGO. Well . . . (*He hesitates.*) I really don't know. I mean . . .

ENID (*throwing herself back with a laugh that is the more mocking for covering a real disappointment*). You mean that you really know quite well, but don't want to hurt my feelings. Thank you for being a coward and liar again. It's well meant, I know. But all the same, if it had come to the point, you'd have told me to go to hell, wouldn't you?

HUGO. Come now, really!

ENID. Well, at any rate, you'd have run away again and left me here in hell, just as you did last time. Wouldn't you?

(*There is a pause.* HUGO *nods, slowly.*)

Yes, of course you would. Why should you want to stay in hell?

HUGO. But is it hell, Enid? I thought you . . . you . . . well, that you'd been happy. I mean, Capes was saying something to me just now . . .

ENID (*in a deliberately hard, flippant tone*). Oh, was he? What was he saying? That we'd slept together?

HUBERT (*genuinely shocked, as well as embarrassed*). Enid, how can you!

ENID (*mocking*). Yes, how *can* I? Isn't it shocking, to talk about the things we all do—isn't it disgustingly immoral?

HUBERT (*who has had time to adjust his face and manner*). It was the desecration I minded, the making light of something sacred.

ENID (*springing to her feet*). Something sacred? Oh, you're horrible, you're disgusting! Go away, you beast! (*She strikes him in the face.*)

(HUBERT *shrinks away, astonished, terrified, abject.*)

Go away! Get out of my sight. (*She makes as if to strike him again.* HUGO *lays a hand on her arm.*)

HUBERT. No, Enid, no.

ENID (*turning away from* HUBERT, *and walking back to her seat*). All right. But tell him to go away. I can't bear to see him.

HUGO. You'd better go, Capes.

HUBERT (*who has recovered from his first shock of terror and has become plaintively the sick man, brutally outraged. He keeps his hand pressed to his side*). It's my heart. You know, I nearly died. That shock . . . Mediums have been known to pass over when they're woken up like that. I think I'll go and lie down. (*He totters out.*)

HUGO (*comes back from shutting the door after showing

HUBERT *out, and sits down beside* ENID. *Silence. He lays his hand on* ENID'S *arm*). I'm sorry, Enid, I wish I could do something.

ENID. There isn't anything you can do. Nobody can do anything. I wish I were dead. What's the point of this stupid body going on when everything else is finished?

HUGO. But everything isn't finished, Enid.

ENID. Yes, it is, and if I had the courage, I'd finish myself too. But I haven't got the courage.

(*Enter from the library* MR. WENHAM *leading* BILL.)

MR. WENHAM. Here's Mr. Hamblin, Hugo. He was wondering what had become of you.

BILL. Wondering? I was damning your eyes. You really are disgusting, Hugo. Marooning me there alone in the library, not knowing how to get out, not knowing where the bell was.

HUGO. But you said you wanted to rest, Bill.

BILL. Yes, but I didn't say I wanted to be dumped like a bit of luggage and forgotten about. You really might think of me sometimes.

HUGO. But damn it all, Bill, I do think of you.

BILL. Every now and then, when it suits your convenience.

HUGO. But you know you don't like me to be hanging round you too attentively.

BILL. I don't like your beastly patronizing bedside manner, that's all. All that sort of 'How's-the-little-patient' business and 'We'll be up and about again next week.' It's intolerable; I don't want to have any of your damned encouragement. It's an impertinence, it's an insult.

MR. WENHAM. But you can't expect Hugo to talk discouragingly.

BILL. No, all I ask him to do is to talk naturally—as

he used to talk before this happened. (*He touches his spectacles.*) Like one normal human being to another. But then I'm not a normal human being now. I'm maimed. I'm a monster. So I suppose I can't expect people to talk naturally to me. Just because I happened to have fallen face first into a cactus-bush, am I to be patronized and insulted for the rest of my life? Well, I suppose I shall get used to it in time. But I must say, at present I find it pretty difficult to swallow. And then to be left like an old Gladstone bag in a corner of the room. And to be helpless, helpless, utterly helpless . . . (*He clenches his fists, his voice trembles.*)

HUGO. But, after all, Bill, you'll soon learn to be independent.

BILL. Oh, be quiet, Hugo! Be quiet! I will not be triumphed over and insulted. All this loathsome bedside encouragement—it's just people triumphing over the helpless. No healthy man can see a sick man without wanting to triumph over him. It may be disguised as Christian kindness. But it's always triumph underneath. (*Putting his hand to his collar.*) It's hot in here, it's stifling. I think it's partly the effect of being in the dark. As though one were inside an oven. Horrible. Will you take me out into the garden for a bit, Hugo?

HUGO. Well, if you'd like me to, if you don't think I shall just get on your nerves again.

ENID. Would you care to come with me, Mr. Hamblin? I was going out in any case.

BILL. Well, that's kind of you. You're sure it's not too much of a bore.

ENID. The pinks are all out, you know. (*She takes his arm.*) The scent of them is simply too delicious——

BILL. Well, at any rate I can still enjoy that.

ENID. And then, how lovely flowers feel! Pinks are feathery; so are cornflowers. The roses are like a very smooth, cool skin. And pansies are satiny—which is rather surprising, I always think, because pansies *look* like velvet.

BILL. Yes, that's true.

ENID (*opening the door*). A little step. That's it.

BILL (*turning back on the threshold*). Hugo?

HUGO. Yes, Bill?

BILL. I'm sorry I was so awful just now.

HUGO. Oh, that didn't matter, Bill.

(BILL *and* ENID *go out.*)

MR. WENHAM (*after a pause*). To see and yet be utterly in the dark, groping. In a certain sense, I wish . . . I almost wish I were physically blind, like poor young Hamblin. If one could suffer physically—perhaps it would be a kind of relief. At least it would be something definite to resist and be resigned to. It would be something one could be—well, it sounds a big word . . . one could be heroic about. Oedipus put out his own eyes. I can understand that. He wanted to match his spiritual blindness and perplexity with blindness in the flesh. Yes, I can understand that, now.

HUGO. But come, father, you're taking everything much too tragically.

MR. WENHAM. No, that's the trouble—I can't take it tragically enough. If only one *were* Oedipus! But one isn't. One's just—just an elderly manufacturer of office equipment wondering whether he'll have the courage to do what he ought to do.

HUGO. You mean, about that letter to the press?

MR. WENHAM (*nodding*). Yes.

HUGO. But honestly, father, I don't think you ought to send it, for Alice's sake to start with.

MR. WENHAM. Yes, I know. If it were physical pain, one could bear it alone. It would be entirely one's own private affair. But this . . . this can't be kept exclusively to oneself. And yet one *ought* to write that letter, one *ought* to publish the truth.

HUGO. Be careful, father. You're looking for excuses to suffer, you're trying to find justifications. Are any of those excuses and justifications good enough to allow you to make other people suffer?

MR. WENHAM. Were your excuses and justifications good enough, Hugo?

HUGO. Perhaps they weren't—though I feel that it would have been the sin against the Holy Ghost if I hadn't done the cruel thing I did.

MR. WENHAM. But perhaps it would be the sin against the Holy Ghost in this case too. Because I feel I *ought* to suffer. It's a question of—how shall I put it?—a question of concentrating a kind of—a kind of diffused misery and perplexity in a single focus—killing one kind of pain with another sharper pain. One could bear the pain; but the diffused misery—that's unbearable. Unbearable. It's as though . . . as though all one's light had gone suddenly dark. They are all gone into the world of light, and I alone sit lingering here. But perhaps they haven't gone into the world of light. Perhaps there isn't a world of light for them to go into? Do you remember those other verses later on in the poem?

> He that hath found some fledged bird's nest may know
> At first sight if the bird be flown;
> But what fair well or grove he sings in now,
> That is to him unknown.

But if there isn't a well or a grove or a bird to sing?

It's like a sudden darkness, it's like being blind . . . blind in a desert. It isn't pain. It's just emptiness and dryness and darkness. Just blindness in a desert.

HUGO (*deliberately brutal*). In a word, I spoilt your theory, and you'd rather have your theory than me.

MR. WENHAM. But that's not true, that's a cruel thing to say.

HUGO. But after all, it's natural enough. In a sense, the theory was always much more real than I was. So far as you're concerned, father, I've never really been there at all. I was a kind of ghost while I was alive . . . more of a ghost really than when I was dead. There was always a gulf fixed between us.

MR. WENHAM. Yes, there was always a gulf. (*Slowly, nodding his head.*)

HUGO. I suppose there's a gulf between most fathers and their sons.

MR. WENHAM. And yet, God knows, it wasn't from any lack of interest or . . . or affection on one's own part. Somehow, you know, it was easier when you were away, when we thought you were—well, that you had passed over. One seemed to be so much more intimate with you, dear boy.

HUGO. Thanks to young Capes. His messages made the ghost more real than the live man.

MR. WENHAM. But now the ghost has been made real, couldn't the live man be made real too? I mean, this new intimacy—why shouldn't it go on? One has never been much good at . . . well, at expressing one's feelings; but that didn't prevent them from existing. They were always there, they are still there. All one's pride in you, dear boy, all one's . . . one's anxious solicitude, all one's . . . (*He hesitates for a long time—embarrassed*) one's love. (*He lays his hand for a *moment, shyly, on* HUGO'S *knee. Awkwardly,* HUGO *touches his father's hand, then withdraws his own.*) And then I believe you really . . . well, you really care underneath, don't you?

(HUGO *nods.*)

So why shouldn't we go on from where we were when you were away? If I could feel that this thing had bridged the gulf I wouldn't mind anything else. If it had really given me back a son, I wouldn't care what it had taken away. Even if it had taken away the world of light. I shouldn't mind. I should even be glad. Don't you think we could go on, Hugo? Don't you think it would be possible?

HUGO. The gulf's still there, father.

MR. WENHAM. But that bridge one threw across?

HUGO. It only existed when I wasn't there, when you had Capes to build it.

MR. WENHAM. That intimacy?

HUGO. It was only an intimacy in absence. Now that we're together, can't you feel it? There's no contact any more, no flow between us.

MR. WENHAM. But perhaps that will pass, in time.

HUGO. No, it won't. It'll never pass.

MR. WENHAM. One doesn't like to say 'Never.'

HUGO. But one's got to say it, when it happens to be true.

MR. WENHAM. And you really think it's true?

HUGO. I know it's true. And so do you, father, when you're honest with yourself. (*Pause.*)

MR. WENHAM. Yes, I suppose that really I do know it's true. Even last night one really knew. And this morning—yes, one was certain, one was really certain. Certain of the darkness, certain of being blind, blind in a desert. 'Dear beauteous death'—do you remember that line in Vaughan's poem, 'Dear beauteous death, the jewel of the just'? That's how I feel about it now. 'Dear beauteous death'! But meanwhile . . . meanwhile . . .

(*Enter* MR. GRAY, *loudly*. MR. WENHAM *looks round.*)

Oh God! (*An expression of distress passes over his face.*)

MR. GRAY. Ah, here you are, my dear Wenham. I was coming to say good-bye. It's been a most delightful visit. Most eventful too. What with all these resurrections and returns of prodigal sons—eh, Mr. Wenham. (*This is spoken jocularly to* HUGO, *who does not answer.*)

MR. WENHAM. Well, one hopes you'll come again in less . . . less exceptional circumstances.

MR. GRAY. That's most kind of you, I'm sure. And if I may be permitted to give you a word of good advice about that letter to the press . . .

MR. WENHAM (*hastily*). Do you know, I really think you ought to be going. I'll go and see if I can find Alice to come and say good-bye to you. (*He goes out through the door into the hall.*)

MR. GRAY (*turning eagerly to* HUGO *the moment the door is closed*). I hope you persuaded him to delay the publication of that wretched statement. What does he mean to do?

HUGO (*shrugging his shoulders*). I don't know. I don't think he knows himself.

MR. GRAY. It would be madness if he did send it—criminal madness. What I always say is, let sleeping dogs lie.

HUGO (*averting his face with an expression of contemptuous dislike*). Yes, and let lying dogs sleep.

MR. GRAY. I beg your pardon?

HUGO. Oh, nothing.

(*A silence.* HUGO *stands meditatively frowning.* MR. GRAY *looks at his watch.*)

MR. GRAY. It's getting rather late. I wonder if your stepmother . . .

HUGO (*with sudden decision*). Listen, the tree shall be known by its fruits—isn't that it?

MR. GRAY (*surprised*). I believe that's correct.

HUGO. Well, if so, then no fruits, no tree. Isn't that obvious? If I weren't here . . . tell me, is the car at the door?

MR. GRAY. I saw them putting my luggage into it.

HUGO. Good! Then let's make a bolt for it.

MR. GRAY. What do you mean?

HUGO. I'm off again.

MR. GRAY (*his face brightening*). You mean to say . . . ?

HUGO. I'm better where I was—better anywhere rather than here. No fruits, no tree. And my God, what a tree it is!

MR. GRAY. But that's wonderful, my dear fellow! I mean we shall all be grieved to see you go. Terribly grieved. But still—well, it really is the best solution. I never ventured to suggest it; but of course I always thought . . .

HUGO (*laying a hand on his sleeve, cuts him short*). Listen. I shall need £500. Can you lend me that, Mr. Gray?

MR. GRAY (*alarmed*). Five hundred! That's a very big sum of money. (*His face brightening again*) But of course I could deduct it from your father's royalties on the book. (*Lavishly*) You shall have the money at once. More if you like. My dear chap, I'll make it a thousand.

HUGO. A thousand, then. I'm delighted. When can you let me have it?

MR. GRAY. This morning. We'll drive straight to the bank.

HUGO. Then come on. Quickly. Before my father comes back. (*He opens the hall door and puts his head out, listening.*) All clear. Sh-sh ! Don't make a noise in the hall. (*They tiptoe out of the room.* MR. WENHAM *re-enters from the library. He glances in astonishment round the empty room.*)

MR. WENHAM. Hugo? Hugo?

(*The car is heard off. He crosses to the window and looks out. The car hoots.*)

Curtain

GUIDE-BOOKS

For every traveller who has any taste of his own, the only useful guide-book will be the one which he himself has written. All others are an exasperation. They mark with asterisks the works of art which he finds dull, and they pass over in silence those which he admires. They make him travel long miles to see a mound of rubbish; they go into ecstasies over mere antiquity. Their practical information is invariably out of date. They recommend bad hotels and qualify good ones as 'modest.' In a word, they are intolerable.

How often I have cursed Baron Baedeker for sending me through the dust to see some nauseating Sodoma or drearily respectable Andrea del Sarto! How angry I have been with him for starring what is old merely because it is old! And how I have hated him for his lack of discrimination! He has a way of lumping all old things of one class together and treating them as if, being made at the same period, their merit were exactly equal. For example, the stained glass windows at Sens are treated by the guide-books as though they were just like all other stained glass of the fourteenth century, when in fact they are unique in boldness and beauty of design. Some very great artist made the series of Bible illustrations at Sens. The Baron speaks as highly of the competent craftsman's work at Chartres and Canterbury.

Similarly the monuments in the church of Brou and the choir screen at Chartres get as many stars as the tomb of Ilaria del Carretto at Lucca, or Della Robbia's bas-relief in the Opera del Duomo at Florence. They are all of them specimens of Renaissance sculpture. There is only this slight difference between them: that the Italian works happen to be consummate masterpieces, while the French are mere barbarisms—that at Brou positively and piercingly vulgar, that at Chartres well-meaning, laborious, and sincerely dull. And so totally does the Baron lack a sense of proportion that he gives as many stars to the church of Brou as to Bourges cathedral, recommending with equal enthusiasm a horrible little architectural nightmare and the grandest, the most strangely and fabulously beautiful building in Europe.

Imbecile! But a learned, and, alas, indispensable imbecile. There is no escape; one must travel in his company—at any rate on a first journey. It is only after having scrupulously done what Baedeker commands, after having discovered the Baron's lapses in taste, his artistic prejudices and antiquarian snobberies, that the tourist can compile that personal guide which is the only guide for him. If he had but possessed it on his first tour! But alas, though it is easy to take other people in by your picturesque accounts of places you have never seen, it is hard to take in yourself. The personal guide-book must be the fruit of bitter personal experience.

The only satisfactory substitute for a guide written by oneself is a guide which is copiously illustrated. To know the images of things is the next best to knowing the things themselves. Illustrations allow one to see what precisely it is that the Baron is recommending. A reproduction of those luscious Sodomas would enable one to discount the asterisks in the text. A few photographs of the tombs at Tarquinia would convince one that they were incomparably better worth looking at than the Forum. A picture of the church of Brou would excuse one from ever going near it. The best illustrated guide I know is Pampaloni's Road Book of Tuscany, in which the usual information is briefly summarized, the main routes from place to place described and nothing starred that is not reproduced in a photograph.

For some tastes, I know, Pampaloni seems a little too dry. All the cackle—even as much of it as gets into Baedeker—is cut, and one is left only with a telegraphic statement of facts and the photographs. Personally I have no great weakness for cackle (unless it be the cackle of genius) and so find Pampaloni perfectly satisfying. Many tourists, however, prefer a more literary guide. They like sentiment, and purple passages and states of soul in front of the Colosseum by moonlight, and all the rest. So do I—but not from the pens of the sort of people who write chatty guides. To me, even Baedeker seems at times rather too lyrical. I like my guides to be informative, unenthusiastic and, where practical matters are concerned, up-to-date—which Baedeker, by the way (reluctant, I suppose, for patriotic reasons to acknowledge the fact of the late War) is not. If I want cackle I take with me a better stylist than the Baron or his gushing substitutes.

The only literary guides I enjoy are the really bad ones—so bad that their badness makes, so to speak, a full circle and becomes something sublime. Your ordinary literary guides are never bad in this superlative way. Theirs is that well-bred, efficient mediocrity for which there is nothing whatever to be said. It is only in obscure local guides that one finds the sublimely ludicrous. In any town it is always worth taking a look at the local guide. If you are lucky you will find one in which a train is called ' Stephenson's magic babe.' Not often, I admit (for it is not every day that a genius is born who can hit on such felicities); but often enough to make the search worth while. I myself have found some notable passages in local Italian guides. This description of a sixth-rate ' Venus rising from the Sea ' is juicy : ' *Venere, abbigliata di una calda nudità, sorge dalle onde. . . . È una seducente figura di donna, palpitante, voluttuosa. Sembra che sotto l'epidermide pulsino le vene frementi e scorre tepido il sangue. L'occhio languido pare inviti a una dolce tregenda.'* D'Annunzio himself could hardly have done better. But the finest specimen of the guide-book style I have ever met with was in France. It is a description of Dijon. '*Comme une jolie femme dont une maturité savoureuse arrondit les formes plus pleines, la capitale de la Bourgogne a fait, en grandissant, éclater la tunique étroite de ses vieilles murailles ; elle a revêtu la robe plus moderne et plus confortable des larges boulevards, des places spacieuses, des faubourgs s'égrenant dans les jardins ; mais elle a gardé le corps aux lignes pures, aux charmants détails que des siècles épris d'art avaient amoureusement orné.*' Hats off to France ! It is with alacrity, on this occasion, that I accede to Lord Rothermere's request.

Old guide-books, so out of date as to be historical documents, make excellent travelling-companions. An early Murray is a treasure. Indeed, any volume of European travels, however dull, is interesting, provided that it be written before the age of railways and Ruskin. It is delightful to read on the spot the impressions and opinions of tourists who visited a hundred years ago, in the vehicles and with the aesthetic prejudices of the period, the places which you are visiting now. The voyage ceases to be a mere tour through space ; you travel through time and thought as well. They are morally wholesome reading too, these old books of travel ; for they make one realize the entirely accidental character of all our tastes and our fundamental intellectual beliefs. It seems to us axiomatic, for example, that Giotto was a great artist ; and yet Goethe, when he went to Assisi, did not even take the trouble to look at the frescoes in the church. For him, the only thing worth seeing at Assisi was the portico of the Roman temple. We for our part cannot get much pleasure out of Guercino ; and yet Stendhal was ravished by him. We find Canova 'amusing' and sometimes, as in the statue of Pauline Borghese, really charming in a soft, voluptuous way (the very cushion on which she reclines bulges out voluptuously; one is reminded of those positively indecent clouds over which Correggio's angels look down at one from the dome at Parma). But we cannot quite agree with Byron when he says 'Such as the Great of yore, Canova is to-day.' And yet after all, Goethe, Stendhal, and Byron were no fools. Given their upbringing, they could not have thought differently. We would have thought just as they did, if we had lived a hundred years ago. Our altered standards of appreciation and generally greater tolerance are chiefly the result of increased acquaintance with the art of every nation and period—an acquaintance due in its turn chiefly to photography. The vastly greater part of the world's art has been non-realistic; we know the world's art as our ancestors never did; it is therefore only to be expected that we should be much more favourably disposed to non-realistic art, much less impressed by realism as such than men who were brought up almost exclusively in the knowledge of Greek, Roman and modern realism. These old books teach us not to be too arrogant and cocksure in our judgments. We too shall look foolish in our turn.

There are so many of these old books and they are all so characteristic of their epoch, that one can select them almost at random from the shelves of a well-stocked library, certain that whatever one lights on will be entertaining and instructive reading. Speaking from my own personal experience, I have always found Stendhal particularly agreeable as an Italian companion. The *Promenades dans Rome* have accompanied me on many of my walks in that city and never failed to please. Very enjoyable too, when one is in Rome, is the too much neglected Veuillot. I will not pretend that Veuillot is a great writer. Indeed, much of his charm and apparent originality consists in the merely accidental fact that his prejudices were unlike those which most travellers bring with them to Italy. We are so much accustomed to hearing that the temporal power was an unmixed evil and that the priests were the cause of Italy's degradation, that a man who tells us the contrary seems startlingly original. After the denunciations of so many Protestants and freethinkers we read his book, if it be tolerably well written (and Veuillot was a first-rate journalist), with a special pleasure. (It is, in the same way, the unusualness of the point of view from which it is written that makes *Les Paysans* of Balzac seem an even more remarkable book than it really is. We are used to reading novels in which the humble virtues of the peasant are exalted, his hard lot deplored and the tyranny of the landlord denounced. Balzac starts with the assumption that the peasant is an unmitigated ruffian and demands our sympathy for the unhappy landlord, who is represented as suffering incessant and unmerited persecution at the hands of the peasants. Balzac's reading of social history may not be correct; but it is at least refreshingly unlike that of most novelists who deal with similar themes.) *Les Parfums de Rome* shares with *Les Paysans* the merit of being written from an unexpected point of view. Veuillot tours the papal states determined to see in them the earthly paradise. And he succeeds. His Holiness has only happy subjects. Outside this blessed fold prowl the wild beasts, Cavour, Mazzini, Garibaldi and the rest; it is the duty of every right-thinking man to see that they do not break in. This is his theme and he finds in everything he sees excuses for recurring to it. *Les Parfums de Rome* is written with a refreshing intemperance of language. Veuillot, like Zimmi, was

> So over violent or over civil,
> That every man with him was God or Devil.

Moreover he was logical and had the courage of his convictions. How admirable, for example, is his denunciation of all pagan art on the ground that it is not Christian! While all the rest of the world grovel before the Greeks and Romans, Veuillot, the logical ultramontanist, condemns them and all their works, on principle, contemptuously. It is delightful.

Of the other old travelling-companions who have given me pleasure by the way I can only mention a few. There is that mine of information, the Président des Brosses. No one is a better companion on the Italian tour. Our own Young is nearly as good in France. Miss Berry's journals of travel are full of interest. There are good things to be got from Lady Mary Montagu. Beckford is the perfect dilettante. But plain Bible-selling Borrow has the credit of being the first man to appreciate El Greco.

If pictures are not your chief interest, there is the admirable Dr. Burney, whose *Musical Tours* are as instructive as they are delightful. His Italian volumes are valuable, among many other reasons, because they make one realize what had happened, during the eighteenth century, to all the prodigious talent which had gone, in the past, to painting pictures, carving statues and building churches. It had all gone into music. The very street players were accomplished contrapuntists; the peasants sang divinely (you should hear the way they sing now!), every church had a good choir which was perpetually producing new masses, motets and oratorios; there was hardly a lady or gentleman who was not a first-rate amateur performer; there were innumerable concerts. Dr. Burney found it a musician's paradise. And what has happened to Italian genius nowadays? Does it still exist? or is it dead?

It still exists, I think; but it has been deflected out of music, as it was deflected out of the visual arts, into politics and, later, into business and engineering. The first two-thirds of the nineteenth century were sufficiently occupied in the achievement of freedom and unity. The sixty years since then have been devoted to the exploitation of the country's resources; and such energy as has been left over from that task has gone into politics. One day, when they have finished putting modern comfort into the old house, have turned out the obstreperous servants and installed a quiet, honest housekeeper—one day, perhaps, the Italians will allow their energy and their talent to flow back into the old channels. Let us hope they will.

ALONG THE ROAD

THE COUNTRY

It is a curious fact, of which I can think of no satisfactory explanation, that enthusiasm for country life and love of natural scenery are strongest and most widely diffused precisely in those European countries which have the worst climate and where the search for the picturesque involves the greatest discomfort. Nature worship increases in an exact ratio with distance from the Mediterranean. The Italians and the Spanish have next to no interest in nature for its own sake. The French feel a certain affection for the country, but not enough to make them desire to live in it if they can possibly inhabit the town. The south Germans and Swiss form an apparent exception to the rule. They live nearer to the Mediterranean than the Parisians, and yet they are fonder of the country. But the exception, as I have said, is only apparent; for owing to their remoteness from the ocean and the mountainous conformation of the land, these people enjoy for a large part of each year a climate that is, to all intents, arctic. In England, where the climate is detestable, we love the country so much that we are prepared, for the privilege of living in it, to get up at seven, summer and winter, bicycle, wet or fine, to a distant station and make an hour's journey to our place of labour. In our spare moments we go for walking tours, and we regard caravanning as a pleasure. In Holland the climate is far more unpleasant than in England and we should consequently expect the Dutch to be even keener country-fanciers than ourselves. The ubiquitous water makes it difficult, however, for season-ticket holders to settle down casually in the Dutch countryside. But if unsuitable as building land, the soggy meadows of the Low Countries are firm enough to carry tents. Unable to live permanently in the country, the Dutch are the greatest campers in the world. Poor Uncle Toby, when he was campaigning in those parts, found the damp so penetrating, that he was forced to burn good brandy in his tent to dry the air. But then my Uncle Toby was a mere Englishman, brought up in a climate which, compared with that of Holland, is balmy. The hardier Dutch camp out for pleasure. Of Northern Germany it is enough to say that it is the home of the wander-birds. And as for Scandinavia—it is well known that there is no part of the world, excluding the tropics, where people so freely divest themselves of their clothing. The Swedish passion for nature is so strong that it can only be adequately expressed when in a state of nature. 'As souls unbodied,' says Donne, 'bodies unclothed must be to taste whole joys.' Noble, nude and far more modern than any other people in Europe, they sport in the ivy waters of the Baltic, they roam naked in the primeval forest. The cautious Italian, meanwhile, bathes in his tepid sea during only two months out of the twelve; always wears a vest under his shirt and never leaves the town, if he can possibly help it, except when the summer is at its most hellish, and again, for a little while, in the autumn, to superintend the making of his wine.

Strange and inexplicable state of affairs! Is it that the dwellers under inclement skies are trying to bluff themselves into a belief that they inhabit Eden? Do they deliberately love nature in the hope of persuading themselves that she is as beautiful in the damp and darkness as in the sunlight? Do they brave the discomforts of northern country life in order to be able to say to those who live in more favoured lands: You see, our countryside is just as delightful as yours; and the proof is that we live in it!

But whatever the reason, the fact remains that nature worship does increase with distance from the sun. To search for causes is hopeless; but it is easy and at the same time not uninteresting to catalogue effects. Thus, our Anglo-Saxon passion for the country has had the result of turning the country into one vast town; but a town without the urban conveniences which makes tolerable life in a city. For we all love the country so much, that we desire to live in it, if only during the night, when we are not at work. We build cottages, buy season tickets and bicycles to take us to the station. And meanwhile the country perishes. The Surrey I knew as a boy was full of wildernesses. To-day Hindhead is hardly distinguishable from the Elephant and Castle. Mr. Lloyd George has built a week-end cottage (not, one feels, without a certain appositeness) at the foot of the Devil's Jumps; and several thousand people are busily following his example. Every lane is now a street. Harrod's and Selfridge's call daily. There is no more country, at any rate within fifty miles of London. Our love has killed it.

Except in summer, when it is too hot to stay in town, the French, and still more, the Italians, do not like the country. The result is that they still have country not to like. Solitude stretches almost to the gates of Paris. (And Paris, remember, still has gates; you drive up to them along country roads, enter and find yourself within a few minutes of the centre of the city.) The silence sleeps unbroken, except by the faint music of ghosts, within a mile of the Victor Emanuel monument at Rome.

In France, in Italy none but countrymen live in the country. Agriculture there is taken seriously; farms are still farms and not week-end cottages; and the corn is still permitted to grow on what, in England, would be desirable building land.

In Italy, despite the fact that the educated Italians like the country still less than the French, there are fewer complete solitudes than in France, because there are more countrymen. And how few there are in France! A drive from the Belgian frontier to the Mediterranean puts life and meaning into those statistics from which we learn, academically and in theory, that France is under-populated. Long stretches of open road extend between town and town.

> Like stones of worth they thinly placed are,
> Or captain jewels in the carcanet.

Even the villages are few and far between. And those innumerable farms which shine out from among the olive trees on Italian hillsides—one looks in vain for their French counterpart. Driving through the fertile plains of Central France, one can turn one's eyes over the fields and scarcely see a house. And then, what forests still grown on French soil! Huge tracts of uninhabited woodland, with not a week-ender or a walking tourist to be seen within their shades.

This state of things is delightful to me personally; for I like the country, enjoy solitude, and take no interest in the political future of France. But to a French patriot I can imagine that a drive across his native land must seem depressing. Huge populations, upon whose skulls the bump of philoprogenitiveness can be seen at a quarter of a mile, pullulate on the further side of almost every frontier. Without haste, without rest, as though by a steadily continued miracle, the Germans and the Italians multiply themselves, like loaves and fishes. Every three years a million brand new Teutons peer across the Rhine, a million Italians are wondering where they are going to find room, in their narrow country, to live. And there are no more Frenchmen. Twenty years hence, what will happen? The French Government offers prizes to those who produce large families. In vain; everybody knows all about birth control and even in the least educated classes there are no prejudices and a great deal of thrift. Hordes of blackamoors are drilled and armed; but blackamoors can be but a poor defence, in the long run, against European philoprogenitiveness. Sooner or later, this half-empty land will be colonized. It may be done peacefully, it may be done with violence; let us hope peacefully, with the consent and at the invitation of the French themselves. Already the French import, temporarily, I forget how many foreign labourers every year. In time, no doubt, the foreigners will begin to settle: the Italians in the south, the Germans in the east, the Belgians in the north, perhaps even a few English in the west.

Frenchmen may not like the plan; but until all nations agree to practise birth control to exactly the same extent, it is the best that can be devised.

The Portuguese who, in the later sixteenth and the seventeenth century, suffered acutely from under-population (half the able-bodied men had emigrated to the colonies, where they died in war or of tropical diseases, while those who stayed at home were periodically decimated by famine—for the colonies produced only gold, not bread) solved their problem by importing negro slaves to work the deserted fields. The negroes settled. They intermarried with the inhabitants. In two or three generations the race which had conquered half the world was extinct, and Portugal, with the exception of a small area in the north, was inhabited by a hybrid race of Eur-Africans. The French may think themselves lucky if, avoiding war, they can fill their depleted country with civilized white men.

Meanwhile, the emptiness of France is a delight to every lover of nature and solitude. But even in Italy, where farms and peasants and peasants' children are thick on the land, the lover of the country feels much happier than he does in what may actually be more sparsely inhabited districts of the home counties. For farms and peasants are country products, as truly native to the land as trees or growing corn, and as inoffensive. It is the urban interloper who ruins the English country. Neither he nor his house belong to it. In Italy, on the other hand, when the rare trespasser from the town does venture into the country, he finds it genuinely rustic. The country is densely populated, but it is still the country. It has not been killed by the deadly kindness of those who, like myself, are nature's townsmen.

The time is not far distant, I am afraid, when every countryside in Europe, even the Spanish, will be invaded by nature lovers from the towns. It is not so long ago, after all, since Evelyn was horrified and disgusted by the spectacle of the rocks at Clifton. Till the end of the eighteenth century every sensible man, even in England, even in Sweden, feared and detested mountains. The modern enthusiasm for wild nature is a recent growth and began—along with kindness to animals, industrialism and railway travelling—among the English. (It is, perhaps, not surprising that the people which first made their cities uninhabitable with dirt, noise and smoke should also have been the first to love nature.) From this island country sentiment has spread with machinery. All the world welcomed machinery with delight; but country sentiment has so far flourished only in the north. Still, there are evident signs that even the Latins are becoming infected by it. In France and Italy wild nature has become—though to a far less extent than in England—the object of *snobisme.* It is rather chic, in those countries, to be fond of nature. In a few years, I repeat, everybody will adore it as a matter of course. For even in the north those who do not in the least like the country are made to imagine that they do by the artful and never-ceasing suggestions of the people whose interest it is that the country should be liked. No modern man, even if he loathed the country, could resist the appeal of the innumerable advertisements, published by railways, motor-car manufacturers, thermos flask makers, sporting tailors, house agents and all the rest whose livelihood depends on his frequently visiting the country. Now the art of advertising in the Latin countries is still poorly developed. But it is improving even there. The march of progress is irresistible. Fiat and the State Railways have only to hire American advertising managers to turn the Italians into a race of week-enders and season-ticket holders. Already there is a *Città Giardino* on the outskirts of Rome; Ostia is being developed as a residential seaside suburb; the recently opened motor road has placed the Lakes at the mercy of Milan. My grandchildren, I foresee, will have to take their holidays in Central Asia.

ALONG THE ROAD

THE PALIO AT SIENA

OUR rooms were in a tower. From the windows one looked across the brown tiled roofs to where, on its hill, stood the cathedral. A hundred feet below was the street, a narrow canyon between high walls, perennially sunless; the voices of the passers-by came up, reverberating, as out of a chasm. Down there they walked always in shadow; but in our tower we were the last to lose the sunlight. On the hot days it was cooler, no doubt, down in the street; but we at least had the winds. The waves of the air broke against our tower and flowed past it on either side. And at evening, when only the belfries and the domes and the highest roofs were still flushed by the declining sun, our windows were level with the flight of the swifts and swallows. Sunset after sunset all through the long summer, they wheeled and darted round our tower. There was always a swarm of them intricately manoeuvring just outside the window. They swerved this way and that, they dipped and rose, they checked their headlong flight with a flutter of their long pointed wings and turned about within their own length. Compact, smooth and tapering they seemed the incarnation of airy speed. And their thin, sharp, arrowy cry was speed made audible. I have sat at my window watching them tracing their intricate arabesques until I grew dizzy; till their shrill crying sounded as though from within my ears and their flying seemed a motion, incessant, swift and bewilderingly multitudinous, behind my eyes. And all the while the sun declined, the shadows climbed higher up the houses and towers, and the light with which they were tipped became more rosy. And at last the shadow had climbed to the very top and the city lay in a grey and violet twilight beneath the pale sky.

One evening, towards the end of June, as I was sitting at the window looking at the wheeling birds, I heard through the crying of the swifts the sound of a drum. I looked down into the shadowy street, but could see nothing. Rub-a-dub, dub, dub, dub—the sound grew louder and louder, and suddenly there appeared round the corner where our street bent out of sight, three personages out of a Pinturicchio fresco. They were dressed in liveries of green and yellow—yellow doublets slashed and tagged with green, parti-coloured hose and shoes, with feathered caps of the same colours. Their leader played the drum. The two who followed carried green and yellow banners. Immediately below our tower the street opens out a little into a tiny piazza. In this clear space the three Pinturicchio figures came to a halt and the crowd of little boys and loafers who followed at their heels grouped themselves round to watch. The drummer quickened his beat and the two banner-bearers stepped forward into the middle of the little square. They stood there for a moment quite still, the right foot a little in advance of the other, the left fist on the hip and the lowered banners drooping from the right. Then, together, they lifted the banners and began to wave them round their heads. In the wind of their motion the flags opened out. They were the same size and both of them green and yellow, but the colours were arranged in a different pattern on each. And what patterns! Nothing more 'modern' was ever seen. They might have been designed by Picasso for the Russian Ballet. Had they been by Picasso, the graver critics would have called them futuristic, the sprightlier (I must apologize for both these expressions) jazz. But the flags were not Picasso's; they were designed some four hundred years ago by the nameless genius who dressed the Sienese for their yearly pageant. This being the case, the critics can only take off their hats. The flags are classical, they are High Art; there is nothing more to be said.

The drum beat on. The bannermen waved their flags, so artfully that the whole expanse of patterned stuff was always unfurled and tremulously stretched along the air. They passed the flags from one hand to the other, behind their backs, under a lifted leg. Then, at last, drawing themselves together to make a supreme effort, they tossed their banners into the air. High they rose, turning slowly, over and over, hung for an instant at the height of their trajectory, then dropped back, the weighted stave foremost, towards their throwers, who caught them as they fell. A final wave, then the drum returned to its march rhythm, the bannermen shouldered their flags, and followed by the anachronistic children and idlers from the twentieth century, Pinturicchio's three young bravos swaggered off up the dark street out of sight and at length, the drum taps coming faintlier and ever faintlier, out of hearing.

Every evening after that, while the swallows were in full cry and flight about the tower, we heard the beating of the drum. Every evening, in the little piazza below us, a fragment of Pinturicchio came to life. Sometimes it was our friends in green and yellow who returned to wave their flags beneath our windows. Sometimes it was men from the other *contrade* or districts of the town, in blue and white, red and white, black, white and orange, white, green and red, yellow and scarlet. Their bright pied doublets and particoloured hose shone out from among the drabs and funereal blacks of the twentieth-century crowd that surrounded them. Their spread flags waved in the street below, like the painted wings of enormous butterflies. The drummer quickened his beat, and to the accompaniment of a long-drawn rattle, the banners leapt up, furled and fluttering, into the air.

To the stranger who has never seen a Palio these little dress rehearsals are richly promising and exciting. Charmed by these present hints, he looks forward eagerly to what the day itself holds in store. Even the Sienese are excited. The pageant, however familiar, does not pall on them. And all the gambler in them, all the local patriot looks forward to the result of the race. Those last days of June before the first Palio, that middle week of August before the second, are days of growing excitement and tension in Siena. One enjoys the Palio the more for having lived through them.

Even the mayor and corporation are infected by the pervading excitement. They are so far carried away that, in the last days of June, they send a small army of men down in the great square before the Palazzo Comunale to eradicate every blade of grass or tuft of moss that can be found growing in the crannies between the flagstones. It amounts almost to a national characteristic, this hatred of growing things among the works of men. I have often, in old Italian towns, seen workmen laboriously weeding the less frequented streets and squares. The Colosseum, mantled till thirty or forty years ago with a romantic, Piranesian growth of shrubs, grasses and flowers, was officially weeded with such extraordinary energy that its ruinousness was sensibly increased. More stones were brought down in those few months of weeding than had fallen of their own accord in the previous thousand years. But the Italians were pleased; which is, after all, the chief thing that matters. Their hatred of weeds is fostered by their national pride; a great country, and one which specially piques itself on being modern, cannot allow weeds to grow even among its ruins. I entirely understand and sympathize with the Italian point of view. If Mr. Ruskin and his disciples had talked about my house and me as they talked about Italy and the Italians, I too should pique myself on being up-to-date; I should put in bathrooms, central heating and a lift, I should have all the moss scratched off the walls, I should lay cork lino on the marble floors. Indeed, I think that I should probably, in my irritation, pull down the whole house and build a new one. Considering the provocation they have received, it seems to me that the Italians have been remarkably moderate in the matter of weeding, destroying and rebuilding. Their moderation is due in part, no doubt, to their comparative poverty. Their ancestors built with such prodigious solidity that it would cost as much to pull down one of their old houses as to build a new one. Imagine, for example, demolishing the Palazzo Strozzi in Florence. It would be about as easy to demolish the Matterhorn. In Rome, which is predominantly a baroque, seventeenth-century city, the houses are made of flimsier stuff. Consequently, modernization progresses there much more rapidly than in most other Italian towns. In wealthier England very little antiquity has been permitted to stand. Thus, most of the great country houses of England were rebuilt during the eighteenth century. If Italy had preserved her independence and her prosperity during the seventeenth, eighteenth and nineteenth centuries, there would probably be very much less mediaeval or renaissance work now surviving than is actually the case. Money, then, is lacking to modernize completely. Weeding has the merit of being cheap and, at the same time, richly symbolic. When you say of a town that the grass grows in its streets you mean that it is utterly dead. Conversely, if there is no grass in its streets, it must be alive. No doubt the mayor and corporation of Siena did not put the argument quite so explicitly. But that the argument was put, somehow, obscurely and below the surface of the mind, I do not doubt. The weeding was symbolic of modernity.

With the weeders came other workmen who built up round the curving flanks of the great piazza a series of wooden stands, six tiers high, for the spectators. The piazza which is shaped, whether by accident or design I do not know, like an ancient theatre, became for the time being indeed a theatre. Between the seats and the central area of the place, a track was railed off and the slippery flags covered parsimoniously with sand. Expectation rose higher than ever.

And at last the day came. The swallows and swifts wove their arabesques as usual in the bright golden light above the town. But their shrill crying was utterly inaudible, through the deep, continuous, formless murmur of the crowd that thronged the streets and the great piazza. Under its canopy of stone the great bell of the Mangia tower swung incessantly backwards and forwards; it too seemed dumb. The talking, the laughter, the shouting of forty thousand people rose up from the piazza in a column of solid sound, impenetrable to any ordinary noise.

It was after six. We took our places in one of the stands opposite the Palazzo Comunale. Our side of the piazza was already in the shade; but the sun still shone on the palace and its tall slender tower, making their rosy brickwork glow as though by inward fire. An immense concourse of people filled the square and all the tiers of seats round it. There were people in every window, even on the roofs. At the Derby, on boat-race days, at Wembley I have seen larger crowds; but never, I think, so many people confined within so small a space.

The sound of a gunshot broke through the noise of voices; and at the signal a company of mounted carabiniers rode into the piazza, driving the loungers who still thronged the track before them. They were in full dress uniform, black and red, with silver trimmings; cocked hats on their heads and swords in their hands. On their handsome little horses, they looked like a squadron of smart Napoleonic cavalry. The idlers retreated before them, squeezing their way through every convenient opening in the rails into the central area, which was soon densely packed. The track was cleared at a walk and, cleared, was rounded again at the trot, dashingly, in the best Carle Vernet style. The carabiniers got their applause and retired. The crowd waited expectantly. For a moment there was almost a silence. The bell on the tower ceased to be dumb. Some one in the crowd let loose a couple of balloons. They mounted perpendicularly into the still air, a red sphere and a purple. They passed out of the shadow into the sunlight; and the red became a ruby, the purple a glowing amethyst. When they had risen above the level of the roofs, a little breeze caught them and carried them away, still mounting all the time, over our heads, out of sight.

There was another gunshot and Vernet was exchanged for Pinturicchio. The noise of the crowd grew louder as they appeared, the bell swung, but gave no sound, and across the square the trumpets of the procession were all but inaudible. Slowly they marched round, the representatives of all the seventeen *contrade* of the city. Besides its drummer and its two bannermen, each *contrada* had a man-at-arms on horseback, three or four halbardiers and young pages and, if it happened to be one of the ten competing in the race, a jockey, all of them wearing the Pinturicchian livery in its own particular colours. Their progress was slow; for at every fifty paces they stopped, to allow the bannermen to give an exhibition of their skill with the flags. They must have taken the best part of an hour to get round. But the time seemed only too short. The Palio is a spectacle of which one does not grow tired. I have seen it three times now and was as much delighted on the last occasion as on the first.

English tourists are often sceptical about the Palio. They remember those terrible 'pageants' which were all the rage some fifteen years ago in their own country, and they imagine that the Palio will turn out to be something of the same sort. But let me reassure them ; it is not. There is no poetry by Louis Napoleon Parker at Siena. There are no choruses of young ladies voicing high moral sentiments in low voices. There are no flabby actor-managers imperfectly disguised as Hengist and Horsa, no crowd of gesticulating supernumeraries dressed in the worst of taste and the cheapest of bunting. Nor finally does one often meet at Siena with that almost invariable accompaniment of the English pageant—rain. No, the Palio is just a show ; having no 'meaning' in particular, but by the mere fact of being traditional and still alive, signifying infinitely more than the dead-born English affairs for all their Parkerian blank verse and their dramatic re-evocations. For these pages and men-at-arms and bannermen come straight out of the Pinturicchian past. Their clothes are those designed for their ancestors, copied faithfully, once in a generation, in the same colours and the same rich materials. They walk, not in cotton or flannelette, but in silks and furs and velvets. And the colours were matched, the clothes originally cut by men whose taste was the faultless taste of the early renaissance. To be sure there are costumiers with as good a taste in these days. But it was not Paquin, not Lanvin or Poiret who dressed the actors of the English pageants ; it was professional wig-makers and lady amateurs. I have already spoken of the beauty of the flags—the bold, fantastic, 'modern' design of them. Everything else at the Palio is in keeping with the flags, daring, brilliant and yet always right, always irreproachably refined. The one false note is always the *Palio* itself—the painted banner which is given to the *contrada* whose horse wins the race. This banner is specially painted every year for the occasion. Look at it, where it comes along, proudly exposed on the great mediaeval war chariot which closes the procession—look at it, or preferably don't look at it. It is a typical property from the wardrobe of an English pageant committee. It is a lady amateur's masterpiece. Shuddering, one averts the eyes.

Preceded by a line of *quattrocento* pages carrying festoons of laurel leaves and escorted by a company of mounted knights, the war chariot rolled slowly and ponderously past, bearing aloft the unworthy trophy. And by now the trumpets at the head of the procession sounded, almost inaudibly for us, from the further side of the piazza. And at last the whole procession had made its round and was lined up in close order in front of the Palazzo Comunale. Over the heads of the spectators standing in the central area, we could see all the thirty-four banners waving and waving in a last concerted display and at last, together, all leaping high into the air, hesitating at the top of their leap, falling back, out of sight. There was a burst of applause. The pageant was over. Another gunshot. And in the midst of more applause, the racehorses were ridden to the starting place.

The course is three times round the piazza, whose shape, as I have said, is something like that of an ancient theatre. Consequently, there are two sharp turns, where the ends of the semicircle meet the straight diameter. One of these, owing to the irregularity of the plan, is sharper than the other. The outside wall of the track is padded with mattresses at this point, to prevent impetuous jockeys who take the corner too fast from dashing themselves to pieces. The jockeys ride bare-back; the horses run on a thin layer of sand spread over the flagstones of the piazza. The Palio is probably the most dangerous flat-race in the world. And it is made the more dangerous by the excessive patriotism of the rival *contrade*. For the winner of the race as he reins in his horse after passing the post, is set upon by the supporters of the other *contrade* (who all think that *their* horse should have won), with so real and earnest a fury that the carabiniers must always intervene to protect man and beast from lynching. Our places were at a point some two or three hundred yards beyond the post, so that we had an excellent view of the battle waged round the winning horse, as he slackened speed. Scarcely was the post passed when the crowd broke its ranks and rushed out into the course. Still cantering, the horse came up the track. A gang of young men ran in pursuit, waving sticks and shouting. And with them, their Napoleonic coat tails streaming in the wind of their own speed, their cocked hats bobbing, and brandishing swords in their white-gloved hands, ran the rescuing carabiniers. There was a brief struggle round the now stationary horse, the young men were repulsed, and surrounded by cocked hats, followed by a crowd of supporters from its native *contrada*, the beast was led off in triumph. We climbed down from our places. The piazza was now entirely shaded. It was only on the upper part of the tower and the battlements of the great Palazzo that the sun still shone. Rosily against the pale blue sky, they glowed. The swifts still turned and turned overhead in the light. It is said that at evening and at dawn these light-loving birds mount on their strong wings into the sky to bid a last farewell or earliest good-morrow to the sinking or the rising sun. While we lie sleeping or have resigned ourselves to darkness the swifts are looking down from their watch-tower in the height of heaven over the edge of the turning planet towards the light. Was it a fable, I wondered, looking up at the wheeling birds? Or was it true? Meanwhile, some one was swearing at me for not looking where I was going. I postponed the speculation.

ALONG THE ROAD

SABBIONETA

'THEY call it the Palazzo del Te,' said the maid at the little inn in the back street where we had lunch, 'because the Gonzaga used to go and take tea there.' And that was all that she, and probably most of the other inhabitants of Mantua, knew about the Gonzaga or their palaces. It was surprising, perhaps, that she should have known so much. Gonzaga—the name, at least, still faintly reverberated. After two hundred years, how many names are still remembered? Few indeed. The Gonzaga, it seemed to me, enjoy a degree of immortality that might be envied them. They have vanished, they are as wholly extinct as the dinosaur; but in the cities they once ruled their name still vaguely echoes, and for those who care to listen they have left behind some of the most eloquent sermons on the vanity of human wishes and the mutability of fortune that stones have ever mutely preached.

I have seen many ruins and of every period. Stonehenge and Ansedonia, Ostia and mediaeval Ninfa (which the duke of Sermoneta is busily turning into the likeness of a neat suburban park), Bolsover and the gruesome modern ruins in Northern France. I have seen great cities dead or in decay: Pisa, Bruges and the newly murdered Vienna. But over none, it seemed to me, did there brood so profound a melancholy as over Mantua; none seemed so dead or so utterly bereft of glory; nowhere was desolation more pregnant with the memory of splendour, the silence nowhere so richly musical with echoes. There are a thousand rooms in the labyrinthine Reggia at Mantua—Gothic rooms, rooms of the renaissance, baroque rooms, rooms rich with the absurd pretentious decorations of the first empire, huge presence chambers and closets and the horribly exquisite apartments of the dwarfs—a thousand rooms, and their walls enclosed an emptiness that is the mournful ghost of departed plenitude. It is through Mallarmé's *creux néant musicien* that one walks in Mantua.

And not in Mantua alone. For wherever the Gonzaga lived, they left behind them the same pathetic emptiness, the same pregnant desolation, the same echoes, the same ghosts of splendour.

The Palazzo del Te is made sad and beautiful with the same melancholy as broods in the Reggia. True, the stupid vulgarity of Giulio Romano was permitted to sprawl over its wall in a series of deplorable frescoes (it is curious, by the way, that Giulio Romano should have been the only Italian artist of whom Shakespeare had ever heard, or at least the only one he ever mentioned); but the absurdities and grossnesses seem actually to make the place more touching. The departed tenants of the palace become in a manner more real to one, when one discovers that their taste ran to *trompe l'œil* pictures of fighting giants and mildly pornographic scenes out of pagan mythology. And seeming more human, they seem also more dead; and the void left by their disappearance is more than ever musical with sadness.

Even the cadets of the Gonzaga house enjoyed a power of leaving behind them a more than Pompeian desolation. Twenty miles from Mantua, on the way to Cremona, is a village called Sabbioneta. It lies near the Po, though not on its banks; possesses, for a village, a tolerably large population, mostly engaged in husbandry; is rather dirty and has an appearance—probably quite deceptive—of poverty. In fact it is just like all other villages of the Lombard plain, but with this difference: a Gonzaga once lived here. The squalor of Sabbioneta is no common squalor; it is a squalor that was once magnificence. Its farmers and horse-copers live, dirtily and destructively, in treasures of late renaissance architecture. The town hall is a ducal palace; in the municipal school, children are taught under carved and painted ceilings, and when the master is out of the room they write their names on the marble bellies of the patient, battered caryatids who uphold the scutcheoned mantel. The weekly cinema show is given in an Olympic theatre, built a few years after the famous theatre at Vicenza, by Palladio's pupil, Scamozzi. The people worship in sumptuous churches, and if ever soldiers happen to pass through the town, they are billeted in the deserted summer palace.

The creator of all these splendours was Vespasiano, son of that Luigi Gonzaga, the boon companion of kings, whom, for his valour and his fabulous strength, his contemporaries nicknamed Rodomonte. Luigi died young, killed in battle; and his son Vespasiano was brought up by his aunt, Giulia Gonzaga, one of the most perfectly courtly ladies of her age. She had him taught Latin, Greek, the mathematics, good manners and the art of war. This last he practised with distinction, serving at one time or another under many princes, but chiefly under Philip II of Spain, who honoured him with singular favours. Vespasiano seems to have been the typical Italian tyrant of his period—cultured, intelligent and only just so much of an ungovernably ferocious ruffian as one would expect a man to be who has been brought up in the possession of absolute power. It was in the intimacy of private life that he displayed his least amiable characteristics. He poisoned his first wife on a suspicion, probably unfounded, of her infidelity, murdered her supposed lover and exiled his relations. His second wife left him mysteriously after three years of married life and died of pure misery in a convent, carrying with her into the grave nobody knew what frightful secret. His third wife, it is true, lived to a ripe old age; but then Vespasiano himself died after only a few years of marriage. His only son, whom he loved with the anxious passion of the ambitious parvenu who desires to found a dynasty, one day annoyed him by not taking off his cap when he met him in the street. Vespasiano rebuked him for this lack of respect. The boy answered back impertinently. Whereupon Vespasiano gave him such a frightful kick in the groin that the boy died. Which shows that, even when chastising one's own children, it is advisable to observe the Queensberry rules.

It was in 1560 that Vespasiano decided to convert the miserable village from which he took his title into a capital worthy of its ruler. He set to work with energy. In a few years the village of squalid cottages clustering round a feudal castle had given place to a walled town, with broad streets, two fine squares, a couple of palaces and a noble Gallery of Antiques. These last Vespasiano had inherited from his father, Rodomonte, who had been at the sack of Rome in 1527 and had shown himself an industrious and discriminating looter. Sabbioneta was in its turn looted by the Austrians, who carried off Rodomonte's spoils to Mantua. The museum remains; but there is nothing in it but the *creux néant musicien* which the Gonzaga alone, of all the princes in Italy, had the special art of creating by their departure.

We had come to Sabbioneta from Parma. In the vast Farnese palace there is no musically echoing void—merely an ordinary, undisturbing emptiness. Only in the colossal Estensian theatre does one recapture anything like the Mantuan melancholy. We drove through Colorno, where the last of the Este built a summer palace about as large as Hampton Court. Over the Po, by a bridge of boats, through Casalmaggiore and on, tortuously, by little by-roads across the plain. A line of walls presented themselves, a handsome gate. We drove in, and immediately faint ghostly oboes began to play around us; we were in Sabbioneta among the Gonzaga ghosts.

The central piazza of the town is oblong; Vespasiano's palace stands at one of the shorter ends, presenting to the world a modest façade, five windows wide, once rich with decorations, but now bare. It serves at present as town hall. In the waiting-room on the first floor, stand four life-sized equestrian figures, carved in wood and painted, representing four of Vespasiano's ancestors. Once there was a squadron of twelve; but the rest have been broken up and burned. This crime, together with all the other ravages committed by time or vandals in the course of three centuries, was attributed by the mayor, who personally did us the honours of his municipality, to the socialists who had preceded him in office. It is unnecessary to add that he himself was a fascista.

We walked round in the emptiness under the superbly carved and gilded ceilings. The porter sat among decayed frescoes in the Cabinet of Diana. The town council held its meetings in the Ducal Saloon. The Gallery of the Ancestors housed a clerk and the municipal archives. The deputy mayor had his office in the Hall of the Elephants. The Sala d'Oro had been turned into an infants' class-room. We walked out again into the sunlight fairly heart-broken.

The Olympic Theatre is a few yards down the street. Accompanied by the obliging young porter from the Cabinet of Diana, we entered. It is a tiny theatre, but complete and marvellously elegant. From the pit, five semicircular steps rise to a pillared loggia, behind which—having the width of the whole auditorium—is the ducal box. The loggia consists of twelve Corinthian pillars, topped by a cornice. On the cornice, above each pillar, stand a dozen stucco gods and goddesses. Noses and fingers, paps and ears have gone the way of all art; but the general form of them survives.

Their white silhouettes gesticulate elegantly against the twilight of the hall.

The stage was once adorned with a fixed scene in perspective, like that which Palladio built at Vicenza. The mayor wanted us to believe that it was his Bolshevik predecessors who had destroyed it; but as a matter of fact it was taken down about a century ago. Gone, too, are the frescoes with which the walls were once covered. One year of epidemic the theatre was used as a fever hospital. When the plague had passed, it was thought that the frescoes needed disinfecting; they were thickly white-washed. There is no money to scrape the white-wash off again.

We followed the young porter out of the theatre. Another two or three hundred yards and we were in the Piazza d'Armi. It is an oblong, grassy space. On the long axis of the rectangle, near one end there stands, handsomely pedestalled, a fluted marble column, topped by a statue of Athena, the tutelary goddess of Vespasiano's metropolis. The pedestal, the capital and the statue are of the late renaissance. But the column is antique, and formed a part of Rodomonte's Roman booty. Rodomonte was evidently no petty thief. If a thing is worth doing it is worth doing thoroughly; that, evidently, was his motto.

One of the long sides of the rectangle is occupied by the Gallery of Antiques. It is a superb building, architecturally by far the finest thing in the town. The lower storey consists of an open arcade and the walls of the gallery above are ornamented with blind arches, having well-proportioned windows at the centre of each and separated from one another by Tuscan pilasters. A very bold projecting cornice, topped by a low roof, finishes the design, which for sober and massive elegance is one of the most remarkable of its kind with which I am acquainted.

The opposite side of the piazza is open, a hedge separating

it from the back gardens of the neighbouring houses. It was here, I fancy, that the feudal castle originally stood. It was pulled down, however, during the eighteenth century (busy Bolsheviks !) and its bricks employed, more usefully but less aesthetically, to strengthen the dykes which defend the surrounding plain, none too impregnably, from the waters of the Po.

Its destruction has left Vespasiano's summer palace, or Palace of the Garden, isolated (save where it joins the Gallery of the Antiques), and rather forlorn at the end of the long piazza. It is a long, low building of only two storeys, rather insignificant from outside. It is evident that Vespasiano built it as economically as he could. For him the place was only a week-end cottage, a holiday resort, whither he could escape from the metropolitan splendour and bustle of the palace in the market-place, a quarter of a mile away. Like all other rulers of small states, Vespasiano must have found it extremely difficult to take an effective holiday. He could not go ten miles in any direction without coming to a frontier. Within his dominions it was impossible to have a change of air. Wisely, therefore, he decided to concentrate his magnificences. He built his Balmoral within five minutes' walk of his Buckingham Palace.

We knocked at the door. The caretaker who opened to us was an old woman who might have gone on to any stage and acted Juliet's Nurse without a moment's rehearsal. Within the first two minutes of our acquaintance with her she confided to us that she had just got married—for the third time, at the age of seventy. Her comments on the connubial state were so very Juliet's Nurse, so positively Wife-of-Bath, that we were made to feel quite early-Victorian in comparison with this robustious old gammer from the *quattrocento*. After having told us all that can be told (and much that cannot be told, at any rate in polite society) about the married state, she proceeded to do us the honours of the house. She led the way, opening the shutters of each room in the long suite, as we entered it. And as the light came in through the unglazed windows, what Gonzagesque ravishments were revealed to us. There was a Cabinet of Venus, with the remains of voluptuous nudes, a Hall of the Winds with puffing cherubs and a mantel in red marble; a Cabinet of the Caesars, floored with marble and adorned with medallions of all the ruffians of antiquity; a Hall of the Myths on whose ceiling, vaulted into the likeness of a truncated pyramid seen from within, were five delightful scenes from Lamprière—an Icarus, an Apollo and Marsyas, a Phaeton, an Arachne and, in the midst, a to me somewhat mysterious scene: a naked beauty sitting on the back, not of a bull (that would have been simple enough), but of a reclining horse, which turns its head amorously towards her, while she caresses its neck. Who was the lady and who the travestied god I do not rightly know. Vague memories of an escapade of Saturn's float through my mind. But perhaps I am slandering a respectable deity.

But in any case, whatever its subject, the picture is charming. Vespasiano's principal artist was Bernardino Campi of Cremona. He was not a good painter, of course; but at least he was gracefully and charmingly, instead of vulgarly mediocre, like Giulio Romano. About the Palazzo del Te there hangs a certain faded frightfulness; but the Giardino is all sweetness—mannered, no doubt, and rather feeble—but none the less authentic in its ruinous decay.

The old caretaker expounded the pictures to us as we went round—not out of any knowledge of what they represented, but purely out of her imagination, which was a good deal more interesting. In the Hall of the Graces, where the walls are adorned with what remains of a series of very pretty little *grotteschi* in the Pompeian manner, her fancy surpassed itself. These, she said, were the records of the Duke's dreams. Each time he dreamed a dream he sent for his painter and had it drawn on the walls of this room. These —she pointed to a pair of Chimaeras—he saw in a nightmare; these dancing satyrs visited his sleep after a merry evening; these four urns were dreamt of after too much wine. As for the three naked Graces, from whom the room takes its name, as for those—over the Graces she once more became too Wife-of-Bath to be recorded.

Her old cracked laughter went echoing down the empty rooms; and it seemed to precipitate and crystallize all the melancholy suspended, as it were, in solution within those bleared and peeling walls. The sense of desolation, vaguely felt before, became poignant. And when the old woman ushered us into another room, dark and smelling of mould like the rest, and threw open the shutters and called what the light revealed the 'Hall of the Mirrors,' I could almost have wept. For in the Hall of the Mirrors there are no more mirrors, only the elaborate framing of them on walls and ceiling. Where the glasses of Murano once shone are spaces of bare plaster that stare out like blind eyes, blankly and, it seems after a little, reproachfully. 'They used to dance in this room,' said the old woman.

ALONG THE ROAD

RIMINI AND ALBERTI

Rimini was honoured, that morning, by the presence of three distinguished visitors—ourselves and the Thaumaturgical Arm of St. Francis Xavier. Divorced from the rest of the saint's remains, whose home is a jewelled tabernacle in the church of Jesus at Old Goa, the Arm, like ourselves, was making an Italian tour. But while we poor common tourists were spending money on the way, the Thaumaturgical Arm—and this was perhaps its most miraculous achievement—was raking it in. It had only to show itself through the crystal window of the reliquary in which it travelled—a skeleton arm, with a huge amethyst ring still glittering on one of the fingers of its bony hand—to command the veneration of all beholders and a copper collection, thinly interspersed with nickel and the smallest paper. The copper collection went to the foreign missions: what happened to the veneration, I do not venture to guess. It was set down, no doubt, with their offered pence, to the credit of those who felt it, in the recording angel's book.

I felt rather sorry for St. Francis Xavier's arm. The body of the saint, after translation from China to Malacca and from Malacca to India, now reposes, as I have said, in the gaudy shrine at Goa. After a life so extraordinarily strenuous as was his, the great missionary deserves to rest in peace. And so he does, most of him. But his right arm has had to forgo its secular quiet; its missionary voyages are not yet over. In its gold and crystal box it travels indefatigably through catholic Christendom collecting pence—'for spoiling Indian innocence,' as Mr. Matthew Green tersely and rather tartly put it, two hundred years ago. Poor Arm!

We found it, that morning, in the church of San Francesco

at Rimini. A crowd of adorers filled the building and overflowed into the street outside. The people seemed to be waiting rather vaguely in the hope of something thaumaturgical happening. Within the church, a long queue of men and women shuffled slowly up into the choir to kiss the jewelled bone-box and deposit their *soldi.* Outside, among the crowd at the door of the church, stood a number of hawkers, selling picture postcards of the Thaumaturgical Arm and brief but fabulous biographies of its owner. We got into conversation with one of them, who told us that he followed the Arm from town to town, selling his wares wherever it stopped to show itself. The business seemed a tolerably profitable one ; it enabled him, at any rate, to keep a wife and family living in comfort at Milan. He showed us their photographs ; mother and children—they all looked well nourished. But, poor fellow ! his business kept him almost uninterruptedly away from home. 'What does one marry for ?' he said as he put the photographs back into his pocket. 'What ?' He sighed and shook his head. If only the Arm could be induced to settle down for a little !

During the lunch hour the Arm was taken for a drive round Rimini. Red and yellow counterpanes were hung out of all the windows in its honour ; the faithful waited impatiently. And at last it came, driving in a very large, very noisy and dirty old Fiat, accompanied, not, as one might have expected, by the ecclesiastical dignitaries of the city, but by seven or eight very secular young men in black shirts, with frizzy hair, their trousers pockets bulging with automatic pistols—the committee of the local fascio, no doubt.

The Arm occupied the front seat, next the driver : the fascists lolled behind. As the car passed, the faithful did a very curious thing ; mingling the gestures of reverence and applause, they fell on their knees and clapped their hands. The Arm was treated as though it were a combination of

Jackie Coogan and the Host. After lunch, it was driven rapidly away to Bologna. The vendors of sacred pictures followed as fast as the Italian trains would take them, the crowd dispersed and the church of San Francesco reverted to its habitual silence.

For this we were rather glad; for it was not to see a fragment of St. Francis Xavier that we had come to Rimini; it was to look at the church of St. Francis of Assisi. Sightseeing, so long as the Arm was there, had been impossible; its departure left us free to look round at our ease. Still, I was very glad that we had seen the peripatetic relic and its adorers in San Francesco. In this strange church which Malatesta found a Christian temple, rebuilt in pagan form and re-dedicated to himself, his mistress and the humanities, the scenes we had just witnessed possessed a certain piercing incongruousness that provoked—the wit of circumstances—a kind of meditative mirth. I tried to imagine what the first St. Francis would have thought of Sigismondo Malatesta, what Sigismondo thought of him and how he would have regarded the desecration of his Nietzschean temple by this posthumous visit of a bit of the second St. Francis. One can imagine a pleasant little Gobinesque or Lucianic dialogue between the four of them in the Elysian Fields, a light and airy skating over the most fearful depths of the spirit. And for those who have ears to hear there is eloquence in the dumb disputation of the stones. The Gothic arches of the interior protest against the Roman shell with which Alberti enclosed St. Francis's church; protest against Matteo de' Pasti's pagan decorations and Malatesta's blasphemous self-exaltation; protest, while they commend the missionary's untiring disinterestedness, against the excessive richness of his Jesuit reliquary. Grave, restrained, and intellectual, Alberti's classical façade seems to deplore the *naïveté* of the first St. Francis and the intolerant enthusiasms of the second, and, praising Malatesta's intelligence, to rebuke him for his lusts and excesses. Malatesta, meanwhile, laughs cynically at all of them. Power, pleasure and Isotta—these, he announces, through the scheme of decorations which he made Matteo de' Pasti carry out, these are the only things that matter.

The exterior of the church is entirely Alberti's. Neither St. Francis nor Malatesta are allowed to disturb its solemn and harmonious beauty. Its façade is a triumphal arch, a nobler version of that arch of Augustus which spans the street at the other end of Rimini. In the colossal thickness of the southern wall, Alberti has pierced a series of deep arched niches. Recessed shadow alternates harmoniously down a long perspective with smooth sunlit stone; and in every niche, plain and severe like the character of an early Roman in the pages of Plutarch, stands the sarcophagus of a scholar or a philosopher. There is nothing here of St. Francis's pre-lapsarian ingenuousness. Alberti is an entirely conscious adult; he worships, but worships reason, rationally. The whole building is a hymn to intellectual beauty, an exaltation of reason as the only source of human greatness. Its form is Roman; for Rome was the retrospective Utopia in which such men as Alberti, from the time of the Renaissance down to a much later date, saw the fulfilment of their ideals. The Roman myth dies hard, the Greek harder still; there are certain victims of a classical education who still regard the Republic as the home of all virtues and see in Periclean Athens the unique repository of human intelligence.

Malatesta would have got a better personal apotheosis if he had lived in a later century. Alberti was too severe and stoical an artist to condescend to mere theatrical grandiosity. Nor, indeed, was the art of being grandiose really understood till the seventeenth century, the age of baroque, of kingly and clerical display. The hard-working missionary, whose arm we had seen that morning in Malatesta's temple, reposes at Goa in the sort of surroundings that would be perfectly suitable in a tyrant's self-raised shrine. Alberti's monument, on the contrary, is a tribute to intellectual greatness. As a memorial to a particularly cunning and murderous ruffian it is absurd.

In the interior of the church, it is true, Malatesta had things all his own way. Alberti was not there to interfere in his scheme of decoration, so that Sigismondo was able to dictate to Matteo de' Pasti and his colleagues all the themes of their carving. The interior is consequently one vast personal tribute to Malatesta and Isotta, with an occasional good word in favour of the pagan gods, of literature, art and science. The too expressive theatrical gesture of the baroque architects and decorators had not yet been invented; Sigismondo's vulgar tyranny is consequently celebrated in the most perfect taste and in terms of a delicate and learned fantasy. Sigismondo got better than his deserts; he deserved Borromini, the Cavaliere Arpino and a tenth-rate imitator of Bernini. What he actually got, owing to the accident of his date, was Matteo de' Pasti, Piero della Francesca and Leon Battista Alberti.

Alberti's share in the monument, then, is a kind of hymn to intellectual beauty, a paean in praise of civilization, couched in the language of Rome—but freely and not pedantically employed, as the philosophers and the poets of the age employed the Latin idiom. To my mind, he was almost the noblest Roman of them all. The exterior of San Francesco at Rimini, the interior of Sant' Andrea at Mantua (sadly daubed about by later decorators and with Juvara's absurd high-drummed cupola in the midst instead of the saucer dome designed by Alberti himself) are as fine as anything in the whole range of renaissance architecture. What renders them the more remarkable is that they were without precedent, in his age. Alberti was one of the re-inventors of the style. Of his particular Roman manner, indeed (the manner which became the current idiom of the later renaissance) he was the sole re-discoverer. The other early renaissance manner, based, like Alberti's, on the classics—the manner of Brunelleschi—was doomed, so far at any rate as ecclesiastical architecture was concerned, to extinction. Sant' Andrea at Mantua is the model from which the typical churches of the later renaissance were imitated, not Brunelleschi's Florentine San Lorenzo or Santo Spirito.

A comparison between these nearly contemporary architects—Brunelleschi was born some twenty-five years before Alberti—is extremely interesting and instructive. Both were enthusiastic students of the antique, both knew their Rome, both employed in their buildings the characteristic elements of classical architecture. And yet it would be difficult to discover two architects whose work is more completely dissimilar. Compare the interiors of Brunelleschi's two Florentine churches with that of Alberti's Sant' Andrea. Brunelleschi's churches are divided into a nave and aisles by rows of tall slender pillars supporting round arches. The details are classical and so correct that they might have been executed by Roman workmen. But the general design is not Roman, but Romanesque. His churches are simply more spidery versions of eleventh-century basilicas, with 'purer' details. All is airiness and lightness; there is even a certain air of insecurity about these church interiors, so slender are the pillars, so much free space is to be seen.

What a contrast with Alberti's great church! It is built in the form of a Latin cross, with a single nave and side chapels. The nave is barrel-vaulted; over the crossing is a dome (Juvara's, unfortunately, not Alberti's); the altar is placed in an apse. The chapels open on to the central nave by tall, and proportionately wide, round-headed arches.

Between each of the chapels is a gigantic pier of masonry, as wide as the arches which they separate. A small door is pierced in each of these piers, giving access to subsidiary chapels hollowed out of their mass. But the doors are inconspicuous and the general effect is one of void and solid equally alternating. Alberti's is essentially the architecture of masses, Brunelleschi's of lines. Even to the enormous dome of Santa Maria del Fiore Brunelleschi contrives to impart an extraordinary lightness, as of lines with voids between them. The huge mass hangs aerially from its eight ribs of marble. A miracle is effortlessly consummated before our eyes. But a dome, however light you make it, is essentially an affair of masses. In designing his cupola for Santa Maria del Fiore Brunelleschi found the plastic view of things imposed upon him. That is why, it may be, the dome is so incomparably the finest thing he ever made. He was not permitted by the nature of the architectural problem to be solved to give free play to his passion for lightness and the fine line. He was dealing here with masses; it could not be escaped. The result was that, treating the mass of the dome as far as was possible in terms of light, strong, leaping lines, he contrived to impart to his work an elegance and an aerial strength such as have never been equalled in any other dome. The rest of Brunelleschi's work, however charming and graceful, is, to my mind at any rate, far less satisfying, precisely because it is so definitely an affair of lines. Brunelleschi studied the architecture of the Romans; but he took from it only its details. What was essential in it—its majestic massiveness—did not appeal to him. He preferred, in all his church designs, to refine and refine on the work of the Romanesque architects until at last he arrived at a slender and precarious elegance that was all vacuum and outline.

Alberti, on the other hand, took from the Romans their fundamental conception of an architecture of masses and developed it, with refinements, for modern, Christian uses. To my mind, he was the better and truer architect of the two. For I personally like massiveness and an air of solidity. Others, I know, prefer lines and lightness and would put the interior of San Lorenzo above that of Sant' Andrea, the Pazzi chapel above San Francesco at Rimini. We shall never be reconciled. All who practise the visual arts and, presumably, all who appreciate them must have some kind of feeling for form as such. But not all are interested in the same kind of forms. The lovers of pure line and the lovers of mass stand at opposite ends of an aesthetic scale. The aesthetic passion of one artist, or one art lover, is solidity; another is moved only by linear arabesques on a flat surface. Those formal passions may be misplaced. Painters may be led by their excessive love of three-dimensional solidity quite beyond the field of painting; Michelangelo is an obvious example. Sculptors with too great a fondness for mere linear effect cease to be sculptors, and their work is no more than a flat decoration in stone or metal, meant to be seen from only one point of view and having no depth; the famous Diana attributed to Goujon (but probably by Benvenuto Cellini) is one of these statues conceived in the flat. Just as painters must not be too fond of solidity, nor sculptors too much attached to flatness, so, it seems to me, no architect should be too exclusively interested in lines. Architecture in the hands of a linear enthusiast takes on the too slender, spidery elegance of Brunelleschi's work.

The psycho-analysts, who trace all interest in art back to an infantile love of excrement, would doubtless offer some simple faecal explanation for the varieties in our aesthetic passions. One man loves masses, another lines: the explanation in terms of coprophily is so obvious that I may be excused from giving it here. I will content myself by quoting from the works of Dr. Ernest Jones, the reason why the worship of form should come to be connected in so many cases with the worship of a moral ideal; in a word, why art is so often religious. 'Religion,' says Dr. Jones, 'has always used art in one form or another, and must do so, for the reason that incestuous desires invariably construct their phantasies out of the material provided by the unconscious memory of infantile coprophilic interests; that is the inner meaning of the phrase, "Art is the handmaid of Religion."' Illuminating and beautiful words! It is a pity they were not written thirty years ago. I should have liked to read Tolstoy's comments in *What is Art?* on this last and best of the aesthetic theories.

ALONG THE ROAD

POPULAR MUSIC

THERE is a certain jovial, bouncing, hoppety little tune with which any one who has spent even a few weeks in Germany, or has been tended in childhood by a German nurse, must be very familiar. Its name is 'Ach, du lieber Augustin.' It is a merry little affair in three-four time; in rhythm and melody so simple, that the village idiot could sing it after a first hearing; in sentiment so innocent that the heart of the most susceptible maiden would not quicken by a beat a minute at the sound of it. Rum ti-tiddle, Um tum tum, Um tum tum, Um tum tum: Rum ti-tiddle, Um tum tum, Um tum tum, TUM. By the very frankness of its cheerful imbecility the thing disarms all criticism.

Now for a piece of history. 'Ach, du lieber Augustin' was composed in 1770, and it was the first waltz. The first waltz! I must ask the reader to hum the tune to himself, then to think of any modern waltz with which he may be familiar. He will find in the difference between the tunes a subject richly suggestive of interesting meditations.

The difference between 'Ach, du lieber Augustin' and any waltz tune composed at any date from the middle of the nineteenth century onwards, is the difference between one piece of music almost completely empty of emotional content and another, densely saturated with amorous sentiment, languor and voluptuousness. The susceptible maiden who, when she hears 'Ach, du lieber Augustin,' feels no emotions beyond a general sense of high spirits and cheerfulness, is fairly made to palpitate by the luscious strains of the modern waltz. Her soul is carried swooning along, over waves of syrup; she seems to breathe an atmosphere heavy with ambergris and musk. From the jolly little thing it was at its birth, the waltz has grown into the voluptuous, heart-stirring affair with which we are now familiar.

And what has happened to the waltz has happened to all popular music. It was once innocent but is now provocative; once pellucid, now richly clotted; once elegant, now deliberately barbarous. Compare the music of *The Beggar's Opera* with the music of a contemporary revue. They differ as life in the garden of Eden differed from life in the artistic quarter of Gomorrah. The one is prelapsarian in its airy sweetness, the other is rich, luscious and loud with conscious savagery.

The evolution of popular music has run parallel on a lower plane, with the evolution of serious music. The writers of popular tunes are not musicians enough to be able to invent new forms of expression. All they do is to adapt the discoveries of original geniuses to the vulgar taste. Ultimately and indirectly, Beethoven is responsible for all the languishing waltz tunes, all the savage jazzings, for all that is maudlin and violent in our popular music. He is responsible because it was he who first devised really effective musical methods for the direct expression of emotion. Beethoven's emotions happened to be noble; moreover, he was too intellectual a musician to neglect the formal, architectural side of music. But unhappily he made it possible for composers of inferior mind and character to express in music their less exalted passions and vulgarer emotions. He made possible the weakest sentimentalities of Schumann, the baroque grandiosities of Wagner, the hysterics of Scriabine; he made possible the waltzes of all the Strausses, from the *Blue Danube* to the waltz from *Salome*. And he made possible, at a still further remove, such masterpieces of popular art as 'You made me love you' and 'That coal black mammy of mine.'

For the introduction of a certain vibrant sexual quality into music, Beethoven is perhaps less directly responsible than the nineteenth-century Italians. I used often to wonder why it was that Mozart's operas were less popular than those of Verdi, Leoncavallo and Puccini. You couldn't ask for more, or more infectiously 'catchy' tunes than are to be found in *Figaro* or *Don Giovanni.* The music though 'classical,' is not obscure, nor forbiddingly complex. On the contrary it is clear, simple with that seemingly easy simplicity which only consummate genius can achieve and thoroughly engaging. And yet for every time *Don Giovanni* is played, *La Bohème* is played a hundred. *Tosca* is at least fifty times as popular as *Figaro.* And if you look through a catalogue of gramophone records you will find that, while you can buy *Rigoletto* complete in thirty discs, there are not more than three records of *The Magic Flute.* This seems at first sight extremely puzzling. But the reason is not really far to seek. Since Mozart's day composers have learned the art of making music throatily and palpitatingly sexual. The arias of Mozart have a beautiful clear purity which renders them utterly insipid compared with the sobbing, catch-in-the-throaty melodies of the nineteenth-century Italians. The public, having accustomed itself to this stronger and more turbid brewage, finds no flavour in the crystal songs of Mozart.

No essay on modern popular music would be complete without some grateful reference to Rossini, who was, so far as I know, the first composer to show what charms there are in vulgar melody. Melodies before Rossini's day were often exceedingly commonplace and cheap; but almost never do they possess that almost indefinable quality of low vulgarity which adorns some of the most successful of Rossini's airs, and which we recognize as being somehow a modern, contemporary quality. The methods which Rossini employed for the achievement of his melodic vulgarity are not easy to analyse. His great secret, I fancy, was the very short and easily memorable phrase frequently repeated in different parts of the scale. But it is easiest to define by example. Think of Moses' first Aria in *Moses in Egypt*. That is an essentially vulgar melody; and it is quite unlike the popular melodies of an earlier date. Its affinities are with the modern popular tune. It is to his invention of vulgar tunes that Rossini owed his enormous contemporary success. Vulgar people before his day had to be content with Mozart's delicate airs. Rossini came and revealed to them a more congenial music. That the world fell down and gratefully worshipped him is not surprising. If he has long ceased to be popular, that is because his successors, profiting by his lessons, have achieved in his own vulgar line triumphs of which he could not have dreamed.

Barbarism has entered popular music from two sources—from the music of barbarous people, like the negroes, and from serious music which has drawn upon barbarism for its inspiration. The technique of being barbarous effectively has come, of course, from serious music. In the elaboration of this technique no musicians have done more than the Russians. If Rimsky-Korsakoff had never lived, modern dance music would not be the thing it is.

Whether, having grown inured to such violent and purely physiological stimuli as the clashing and drumming, the rhythmic throbbing and wailing glissandos of modern jazz music can supply, the world will ever revert to something less crudely direct, is a matter about which one cannot prophesy. Even serious musicians seem to find it hard to dispense with barbarism. In spite of the monotony and the appalling lack of subtlety which characterize the process, they persist in banging away in the old Russian manner, as though there were nothing more interesting or exciting to be thought of. When, as a boy, I first heard Russian music, I was carried off my feet by its wild melodies, its persistent, its relentlessly throbbing rhythms. But my excitement grew less and less with every hearing. To-day no music seems to me more tedious. The only music a civilized man can take unfailing pleasure in is civilized music. If you were compelled to listen every day of your life to a single piece of music, would you choose Stravinsky's 'Oiseau de Feu' or Beethoven's 'Grosse Fugue'? Obviously, you would choose the fugue, if only for its intricacy and because there is more in it to occupy the mind than in the Russian's too simple rhythms. Composers seem to forget that we are, in spite of everything and though appearances may be against us, tolerably civilized. They overwhelm us not merely with Russian and negroid noises, but with Celtic caterwaulings on the black notes, with dismal Spanish wailings, punctuated by the rattle of the castanets and the clashing harmonies of the guitar. When serious composers have gone back to civilized music—and already some of them are turning from barbarism—we shall probably hear a corresponding change for the more refined in popular music. But until serious musicians lead the way, it will be absurd to expect the vulgarizers to change their style.

ALONG THE ROAD

WORDSWORTH IN THE TROPICS

In the neighbourhood of latitude fifty north, and for the last hundred years or thereabouts, it has been an axiom that Nature is divine and morally uplifting. For good Wordsworthians—and most serious-minded people are now Wordsworthians, either by direct inspiration or at second hand—a walk in the country is the equivalent of going to church, a tour through Westmorland is as good as a pilgrimage to Jerusalem. To commune with the fields and waters, the woodlands and the hills, is to commune, according to our modern and northern ideas, with the visible manifestations of the 'Wisdom and Spirit of the Universe.'

The Wordsworthian who exports this pantheistic worship of Nature to the tropics is liable to have his religious convictions somewhat rudely disturbed. Nature, under a vertical sun, and nourished by the equatorial rains, is not at all like that chaste, mild deity who presides over the *Gemüthlichkeit*, the prettiness, the cosy sublimities of the Lake District. The worst that Wordsworth's goddess ever did to him was to make him hear

> Low breathings coming after me, and sounds
> Of undistinguishable motion, steps
> Almost as silent as the turf they trod;

was to make him realize, in the shape of 'a huge peak, black and huge,' the existence of 'unknown modes of being.' He seems to have imagined that this was the worst Nature *could* do. A few weeks in Malaya or Borneo would have undeceived him. Wandering in the hothouse darkness of the jungle, he would not have felt so serenely certain of those 'Presences of Nature,' those 'Souls of Lonely Places,' which he was in the habit of worshipping on the shores of Windermere and Rydal. The sparse inhabitants of the equatorial forest are all believers in devils. When one has visited, in even the most superficial manner, the places where they live, it is difficult not to share their faith. The jungle is marvellous, fantastic, beautiful; but it is also terrifying, it is also profoundly sinister. There is something in what, for lack of a better word, we must call the character of great forests—even in those of temperate lands—which is foreign, appalling, fundamentally and utterly inimical to intruding man. The life of those vast masses of swarming vegetation is alien to the human spirit and hostile to it. Meredith, in his 'Woods of Westermaine,' has tried reassuringly to persuade us that our terrors are unnecessary, that the hostility of these vegetable forces is more apparent than real, and that if we will but trust Nature we shall find our fears transformed into serenity, joy, and rapture. This may be sound philosophy in the neighbourhood of Dorking; but it begins to be dubious even in the forests of Germany—there is too much of them for a human being to feel himself at ease within their enormous glooms; and when the woods of Borneo are substituted for those of Westermaine, Meredith's comforting doctrine becomes frankly ridiculous.

It is not the sense of solitude that distresses the wanderer in equatorial jungles. Loneliness is bearable enough—for a time, at any rate. There is something actually rather stimulating and exciting about being in an empty place where there is no life but one's own. Taken in reasonably small doses, the Sahara exhilarates, like alcohol. Too much of it, however (I speak, at any rate, for myself), has the depressing effect of the second bottle of Burgundy. But in any case it is not loneliness that oppresses the equatorial traveller: it is too much company; it is the uneasy feeling that he is an alien in the midst of an innumerable throng of hostile beings.

To us who live beneath a temperate sky and in the age of Henry Ford, the worship of Nature comes almost naturally. It is easy to love a feeble and already conquered enemy. But an enemy with whom one is still at war, an unconquered, unconquerable, ceaselessly active enemy—no ; one does not, one should not, love him. One respects him, perhaps ; one has a salutary fear of him ; and one goes on fighting. In our latitudes the hosts of Nature have mostly been vanquished and enslaved. Some few detachments, it is true, still hold the field against us. There are wild woods and mountains, marshes and heaths, even in England. But they are there only on sufferance, because we have chosen, out of our good pleasure, to leave them their freedom. It has not been worth our while to reduce them to slavery. We love them because we are the masters, because we know that at any moment we can overcome them as we overcame their fellows. The inhabitants of the tropics have no such comforting reasons for adoring the sinister forces which hem them in on every side. For us, the notion 'river' implies (how obviously !) the notion 'bridge.' When we think of a plain, we think of agriculture, towns, and good roads. The corollary of mountain is tunnel ; of swamp, an embankment ; of distance, a railway. At latitude zero, however, the obvious is not the same as with us. Rivers imply wading, swimming, alligators. Plains mean swamps, forests, fevers. Mountains are either dangerous or impassable. To travel is to hack one's way laboriously through a tangled, prickly, and venomous darkness. 'God made the country,' said Cowper, in his rather too blank verse. In New Guinea he would have had his doubts ; he would have longed for the man-made town.

The Wordsworthian adoration of Nature has two principal defects. The first, as we have seen, is that it is only possible in a country where Nature has been nearly or quite enslaved to man. The second is that it is only possible for those who are prepared to falsify their immediate intuitions of Nature. For Nature, even in the temperate zone, is always alien and inhuman, and occasionally diabolic. Meredith explicitly invites us to explain any unpleasant experiences away. We are to interpret them, Pangloss fashion, in terms of a preconceived philosophy; after which, all will surely be for the best in the best of all possible Westermaines. Less openly, Wordsworth asks us to make the same falsification of immediate experience. It is only very occasionally that he admits the existence in the world around him of those 'unknown modes of being' of which our immediate intuitions of things make us so disquietingly aware. Normally what he does is to pump the dangerous Unknown out of Nature and refill the emptied forms of hills and woods, flowers and waters, with something more reassuringly familiar—with humanity, with Anglicanism. He will not admit that a yellow primrose is simply a yellow primrose—beautiful, but essentially strange, having its own alien life apart. He wants it to possess some sort of soul, to exist humanly, not simply flowerily. He wants the earth to be more than earthy, to be a divine person. But the life of vegetation is radically unlike the life of man: the earth has a mode of being that is certainly not the mode of being of a person. 'Let Nature be your teacher,' says Wordsworth. The advice is excellent. But how strangely he himself puts it into practice! Instead of listening humbly to what the teacher says, he shuts his ears and himself dictates the lesson he desires to hear. The pupil knows better than his master; the worshipper substitutes his own oracles for those of the god. Instead of accepting the lesson as it is given to his immediate intuitions, he distorts it rationalistically into the likeness of a parson's sermon or a professorial lecture. Our direct intuitions of Nature tell us that the world is bottomlessly strange: alien, even when it is kind and beautiful; having innumerable modes of being that are not our modes; always mysteriously not personal, not conscious, not moral; often hostile and sinister; sometimes even unimaginably, because inhumanly, evil. In his youth, it would seem, Wordsworth left his direct intuitions of the world unwarped.

> The sounding cataract
> Haunted me like a passion: the tall rock,
> The mountain, and the deep and gloomy wood,
> Their colours and their forms, were then to me
> An appetite; a feeling and a love,
> That had no need of a remoter charm,
> By thought supplied, nor any interest
> Unborrowed from the eye.

As the years passed, however, he began to interpret them in terms of a preconceived philosophy. Procrustes-like, he tortured his feelings and perceptions until they fitted his system. By the time he was thirty,

> The immeasurable height
> Of woods decaying, never to be decayed,
> The stationary blasts of waterfalls—
> The torrents shooting from the clear blue sky,
> The rocks that muttered close upon our ears,
> Black drizzling crags that spake by the wayside
> As if a voice were in them, the sick sight
> And giddy prospect of the raving stream,
> The unfettered clouds and regions of the heavens,
> Tumult and peace, the darkness and the light—
> Were all like workings of one mind, the features
> Of the same face, blossoms upon one tree,
> Characters of the great Apocalypse,
> The types and symbols of eternity,
> Of first, and last, and midst, and without end.

'Something far more deeply interfused' had made its appearance on the Wordsworthian scene. The god of Anglicanism had crept under the skin of things, and all the stimulatingly inhuman strangeness of Nature had become as flatly familiar as a page from a text-book of metaphysics or theology. As familiar and as safely simple. Pantheistically interpreted, our intuitions of Nature's endless varieties of impersonal mysteriousness lose all their exciting and disturbing quality. It makes the world seem delightfully cosy, if you can pretend that all the many alien things about you are really only manifestations of one person. It is fear of the labyrinthine flux and complexity of phenomena that has driven men to philosophy, to science, to theology—fear of the complex reality driving them to invent a simpler, more manageable, and, therefore, consoling fiction. For simple, in comparison with the external reality of which we have direct intuitions, childishly simple is even the most elaborate and subtle system devised by the human mind. Most of the philosophical systems hitherto popular have not been subtle and elaborate even by human standards. Even by human standards they have been crude, bald, preposterously straightforward. Hence their popularity. Their simplicity has rendered them instantly comprehensible. Weary with much wandering in the maze of phenomena, frightened by the inhospitable strangeness of the world, men have rushed into the systems prepared for them by philosophers and founders of religions, as they would rush from a dark jungle into the haven of a well-lit, commodious house. With a sigh of relief and a thankful feeling that here at last is their true home, they settle down in their snug metaphysical villa and go to sleep. And how furious they are when any one comes rudely knocking at the door to tell them that their villa is jerry-built, dilapidated, unfit for human habitation, even non-existent! Men have been burnt at the stake for even venturing to criticize the colour of the front door or the shape of the third-floor windows.

That man must build himself some sort of metaphysical shelter in the midst of the jungle of immediately apprehended reality is obvious. No practical activity, no scientific research, no speculation is possible without some preliminary hypothesis about the nature and the purpose of things. The human mind cannot deal with the universe directly nor even with its own immediate intuitions of the universe. Whenever it is a question of thinking about the world or of practically modifying it, men can only work on a symbolic plan of the universe, only on a simplified, two-dimensional map of things abstracted by the mind out of the complex and multifarious reality of immediate intuition. History shows that these hypotheses about the nature of things are valuable even when, as later experience reveals, they are false. Man approaches the unattainable truth through a succession of errors. Confronted by the strange complexity of things, he invents, quite arbitrarily, a simple hypothesis to explain and justify the world. Having invented, he proceeds to act and think in terms of this hypothesis, as though it were correct. Experience gradually shows him where his hypothesis is unsatisfactory and how it should be modified. Thus, great scientific discoveries have been made by men seeking to verify quite erroneous theories about the nature of things. The discoveries have necessitated a modification of the original hypotheses, and further discoveries have been made in the effort to verify the modifications—discoveries which, in their turn, have led to yet further modifications. And so on, indefinitely. Philosophical and religious hypotheses, being less susceptible of experimental verification than the hypotheses of science, have undergone far less modification. For example, the pantheistic hypothesis of Wordsworth is an ancient doctrine, which human experience has hardly modified throughout history. And rightly, no doubt. For it is obvious that there must be some sort of unity underlying the diversity of phenomena; for if there were not, the world would be quite unknowable. Indeed, it is precisely in the knowableness of things, in the very fact that they are known, that their fundamental unity consists. The world which we know, and which our minds have fabricated out of goodness knows what mysterious things in themselves, possesses the unity which our minds have imposed upon it. It is part of our thought, hence fundamentally homogeneous. Yes, the world is obviously one. But at the same time it is no less obviously diverse. For if the world were absolutely one, it would no longer be knowable, it would cease to exist. Thought must be divided against itself before it can come to any knowledge of itself. Absolute oneness is absolute nothingness: homogeneous perfection, as the Hindus perceived and courageously recognized, is equivalent to non-existence, is nirvana. The Christian idea of a perfect heaven that is something other than a non-existence is a contradiction in terms. The world in which we live may be fundamentally one, but it is a unity divided up into a great many diverse fragments. A tree, a table, a newspaper, a piece of artificial silk are all made of wood. But they are, none the less, distinct and separate objects. It is the same with the world at large. Our immediate intuitions are of diversity. We have only to open our eyes to recognize a multitude of different phenomena. These intuitions of diversity are as correct, as well justified, as is our intellectual conviction of the fundamental homogeneity of the various parts of the world with one another and with ourselves. Circumstances have led humanity to set an ever-increasing premium on the conscious and intellectual comprehension of things. Modern man's besetting temptation is to sacrifice his direct perceptions and spontaneous feelings to his reasoned reflections; to prefer in all circumstances the verdict of his intellect to that of his immediate intuitions. 'L'homme est visiblement fait pour penser,' says Pascal; 'c'est toute sa dignité et tout son mérite; et tout son devoir est de penser comme il faut.' Noble words; but do they happen to be true? Pascal seems to forget that man has something else to do besides think: he must live. Living may not be so dignified or so meritorious as thinking (particularly when you happen to be, like Pascal, a chronic invalid); but it is, perhaps unfortunately, a necessary process. If one would live well, one must live completely, with the whole being—with the body and the instincts, as well as with the conscious mind. A life lived, as far as may be, exclusively from the consciousness and in accordance with the considered judgments of the intellect, is a stunted life, a half-dead life. This is a fact that can be confirmed by daily observation. But consciousness, the intellect, the spirit, have acquired an inordinate prestige; and such is men's snobbish respect for authority, such is their pedantic desire to be consistent, that they go on doing their best to lead the exclusively conscious, spiritual, and intellectual life, in spite of its manifest disadvantages. To know is pleasant; it is exciting to be conscious; the intellect is a valuable instrument, and for certain purposes the hypotheses which it fabricates are of great practical value. Quite true. But, therefore, say the moralists and men of science, drawing conclusions only justified by their desire for consistency, therefore *all* life should be lived from the head, consciously, *all* phenomena should at *all* times be interpreted in terms of the intellect's hypotheses. The religious teachers are of a slightly different opinion. All life, according to them, should be lived spiritually, not intellectually. Why? On the grounds, as we discover when we push our analysis far enough, that certain occasional psychological states, currently called spiritual, are extremely agreeable and have valuable consequences in the realm of social behaviour. The unprejudiced observer finds it hard to understand why these people should set such store by consistency of thought and action. Because oysters are occasionally pleasant, it does not follow that one should make of oysters one's exclusive diet. Nor should one take castor-oil every day because castor-oil is occasionally good for one. Too much consistency is as bad for the mind as it is for the body. Consistency is contrary to nature, contrary to life. The only completely consistent people are the dead. Consistent intellectualism and spirituality may be socially valuable, up to a point; but they make, gradually, for individual death. And individual death, when the slow murder has been consummated, is finally social death. So that the social utility of pure intellectualism and pure spirituality is only apparent and temporary. What is needed is, as ever, a compromise. Life must be lived in different ways at different moments. The only satisfactory way of existing in the modern, highly specialized world is to live with two personalities. A Dr. Jekyll that does the metaphysical and scientific thinking, that transacts business in the city, adds up figures, designs machines, and so forth. And a natural, spontaneous Mr. Hyde to do the physical, instinctive living in the intervals of work. The two personalities should lead their unconnected lives apart, without poaching on one another's preserves or enquiring too closely into one another's activities. Only by living discretely and inconsistently can we preserve both the man and the citizen, both the intellectual and the spontaneous animal being, alive within us. The solution may not be very satisfactory; but it is, I believe now (though once I thought differently), the best that, in the modern circumstances, can be devised.

The poet's place, it seems to me, is with the Mr. Hydes of human nature. He should be, as Blake remarked of Milton, 'of the devil's party without knowing it'—or preferably with the full consciousness of being of the devil's party. There are so many intellectual and moral angels battling for rationalism, good citizenship, and pure spirituality; so many and such eminent ones, so very vocal and authoritative! The poor devil in man needs all the support and advocacy he can get. The artist is his natural champion. When an artist deserts to the side of the angels, it is the most odious of treasons. How unforgivable, for example, is Tolstoy! Tolstoy, the perfect Mr. Hyde, the complete embodiment, if ever there was one, of non-intellectual, non-moral, instinctive life—Tolstoy, who betrayed his own nature, betrayed his art, betrayed life itself, in order to fight against the devil's party of his earlier allegiances, under the standard of Dr. Jesus-Jekyll. Wordsworth's betrayal was not so spectacular: he was never so wholly of the devil's party as Tolstoy. Still, it was bad enough. It is difficult to forgive him for so utterly repenting his youthful passions and enthusiasms, and becoming, personally as well as politically, the anglican tory. One remembers B. R. Haydon's account of the poet's reactions to that charming classical sculpture of Cupid and Psyche. 'The devils!' he said malignantly, after a long-drawn contemplation of their marble embrace. 'The devils!' And he was not using the word in the complimentary sense in which I have employed it here: he was expressing his hatred of passion and life, he was damning the young man he had himself been—the young man who had hailed the French Revolution with delight and begotten an illegitimate child. From being an ardent lover of the nymphs, he had become one of those all too numerous

> woodmen who expel
> Love's gentle dryads from the haunts of life,
> And vex the nightingales in every dell.

Yes, even the nightingales he vexed. Even the nightingales, though the poor birds can never, like those all too human dryads, have led him into sexual temptation. Even the innocuous nightingales were moralized, spiritualized, turned into citizens and anglicans—and along with the nightingales, the whole of animate and inanimate Nature.

The change in Wordsworth's attitude towards Nature is symptomatic of his general apostasy. Beginning as what I may call a natural aesthete, he transformed himself, in the course of years, into a moralist, a thinker. He used his intellect to distort his exquisitely acute and subtle intuitions of the world, to explain away their often disquieting strangeness, to simplify them into a comfortable metaphysical unreality. Nature had endowed him with the poet's gift of seeing more than ordinarily far into the brick walls of external reality, of intuitively comprehending the character of the bricks, of feeling the quality of their being, and establishing the appropriate relationship with them. But he preferred to think his gifts away. He preferred, in the interests of a preconceived religious theory, to ignore the disquieting strangeness of things, to interpret the impersonal diversity of Nature in terms of a divine, anglican unity. He chose, in a word, to be a philosopher, comfortably at home with a man-made and, therefore, thoroughly comprehensible system, rather than a poet adventuring for adventure's sake through the mysterious world revealed by his direct and undistorted intuitions.

It is a pity that he never travelled beyond the boundaries of Europe. A voyage through the tropics would have cured him of his too easy and comfortable pantheism. A few months in the jungle would have convinced him that the diversity and utter strangeness of Nature are at least as real and significant as its intellectually discovered unity. Nor would he have felt so certain, in the damp and stifling darkness, among the leeches and the malevolently tangled rattans, of the divinely anglican character of that fundamental unity. He would have learned once more to treat Nature naturally, as he treated it in his youth; to react to it spontaneously, loving where love was the appropriate emotion, fearing, hating, fighting whenever Nature presented itself to his intuition as being, not merely strange, but hostile, inhumanly evil. A voyage would have taught him this. But Wordsworth never left his native continent. Europe is so well gardened that it resembles a work of art, a scientific theory, a neat metaphysical system. Man has re-created Europe in his own image. Its tamed and temperate Nature confirmed Wordsworth in his philosophizings. The poet, the devil's partisan were doomed; the angels triumphed. Alas!

DO WHAT YOU WILL

FASHIONS IN LOVE

HUMAN nature does not change, or, at any rate, history is too short for any changes to be perceptible. The earliest known specimens of art and literature are still comprehensible. The fact that we can understand them all and can recognize in some of them an unsurpassed artistic excellence is proof enough that not only men's feelings and instincts, but also their intellectual and imaginative powers, were in the remotest times precisely what they are now. In the fine arts it is only the convention, the form, the incidentals that change: the fundamentals of passion, of intellect and imagination remain unaltered.

It is the same with the arts of life as with the fine arts. Conventions and traditions, prejudices and ideals and religious beliefs, moral systems and codes of good manners, varying according to the geographical and historical circumstances, mould into different forms the unchanging material of human instinct, passion, and desire. It is a stiff, intractable material—Egyptian granite, rather than Hindu bronze. The artists who carved the colossal statues of Rameses II may have wished to represent the Pharaoh standing on one leg and waving two or three pairs of arms over his head, as the Indians still represent the dancing Krishna. But with the best will in the world they could not have imposed such a form upon the granite. Similarly, those artists in social life whom we call statesmen, moralists, founders of religions, have often wished to mould human nature into forms of superhuman elegance; but the material has proved too stubborn for them, and they have had to be content with only a relatively small alteration in the form which their predecessors had given it. At any given historical moment human behaviour is a compromise (enforced from without by law and custom, from within by belief in religious or philosophical myths) between the raw instinct on the one hand and the unattainable ideal on the other—a compromise, in our sculptural metaphor, between the unshaped block of stone and the many-armed dancing Krishna.

Like all the other great human activities, love is the product of unchanging passions, instincts, and desires (unchanging, that is to say, in the mass of humanity; for, of course, they vary greatly in quantity and quality from individual to individual), and of laws and conventions, beliefs and ideals, which the circumstances of time and place, or the arbitrary fiats of great personalities, have imposed on a more or less willing society. The history of love, if it were ever written (and doubtless some learned German, unread, alas, by me, *has* written it, and in several volumes), would be like the current histories of art—a record of succeeding 'styles' and 'schools,' of 'influences,' 'revolutions,' 'technical discoveries.' Love's psychological and physiological material remains the same; but every epoch treats it in a different manner, just as every epoch cuts its unvarying cloth and silk and linen into garments of the most diverse fashion. By way of illustration, I may mention that vogue of homosexuality which seems, from all accounts, to have been universal in the Hellenic world. Plutarch attributes the inception of this mode to the custom (novel in the fifth century, according to Thucydides) of exercising naked in the palestra.* But whatever may have been its origin, there

* Plutarch, who wrote some five hundred years after the event, is by no means an unquestionable authority. The habit of which he and Thucydides speak may have facilitated the spread of the homosexual fashion. But that the fashion existed before the fifth century is made sufficiently clear by Homer, not to mention Sappho. Like many modern oriental peoples, the ancient Greeks were evidently, in Sir Richard Burton's expressive phrase, 'omnifutuent.'

can be no doubt that this particular fashion in love spread widely among people who were not in the least congenitally disposed to homosexuality Convention and public opinion moulded the material of love into forms which a later age has chosen to call 'unnatural.' A recrudescence of this amorous mode was very noticeable in Europe during the years immediately following the war. Among the determining causes of this recrudescence a future Plutarch will undoubtedly number the writings of Proust and André Gide.

The present fashions in love are not so definite and universal as those in clothes. It is as though our age were dubiously hesitating between crinolines and hobble skirts, trunk hose and Oxford trousers. Two distinct and hostile conceptions of love coexist in the minds of men and women, two sets of ideals, of conventions, of public opinions, struggle for the right to mould the psychological and physiological material of love. One is the conception evolved by the nineteenth century out of the ideals of Christianity on the one hand and romanticism on the other. The other is that still rather inchoate and negative conception which contemporary youth is in process of forming out of the materials provided by modern psychology. The public opinion, the conventions, ideals, and prejudices which gave active force to the first convention and enabled it, to some extent at least, to modify the actual practice of love, had already lost much of their strength when they were rudely shattered, at any rate in the minds of the young, by the shock of the war. As usually happens, practice preceded theory, and the new conception of love was called in to justify existing post-war manners. Having gained a footing, the new conception is now a cause of new behaviour among the youngest adolescent generation, instead of being, as it was for the generation of the war, an explanation of war-time behaviour made after the fact.

Let us try to analyse these two coexisting and conflicting conceptions of love. The older conception was, as I have said, the product of Christianity and romanticism—a curious mixture of contradictions, of the ascetic dread of passion and the romantic worship of passion. Its ideal was a strict monogamy, such as St. Paul grudgingly conceded to amorous humanity, sanctified and made eternal by one of those terrific exclusive passions which are the favourite theme of poetry and drama. It is an ideal which finds its most characteristic expression in the poetry of that infinitely respectable rebel, that profoundly anglican worshipper of passion, Robert Browning. It was Rousseau who first started the cult of passion for passion's sake. Before his time the great passions, such as that of Paris for Helen, of Dido for Aeneas, of Paolo and Francesca for one another, had been regarded rather as disastrous maladies than as enviable states of soul. Rousseau, followed by all the romantic poets of France and England, transformed the grand passion from what it had been in the Middle Ages—a demoniac possession—into a divine ecstasy, and promoted it from the rank of a disease to that of the only true and natural form of love. The nineteenth-century conception of love was thus doubly mystical, with the mysticism of Christian asceticism and sacramentalism, and with the romantic mysticism of Nature. It claimed an absolute rightness on the grounds of its divinity and of its naturalness.

Now, if there is one thing that the study of history and psychology makes abundantly clear, it is that there are no such things as either 'divine' or 'natural' forms of love. Innumerable gods have sanctioned and forbidden innumerable kinds of sexual behaviour, and innumerable philosophers and poets have advocated the return to the most diverse kinds of 'nature.' Every form of amorous behaviour, from chastity and monogamy to promiscuity and the most fantastic 'perversions,' is found both among animals and men. In any given human society, at any given moment, love, as we have seen, is the result of the interaction of the unchanging instinctive and physiological material of sex with the local conventions of morality and religion, the local laws, prejudices, and ideals. The degree of permanence of these conventions, religious myths, and ideals is proportional to their social utility in the given circumstances of time and place.

The new twentieth-century conception of love is realistic. It recognizes the diversity of love, not merely in the social mass from age to age, but from individual to contemporary individual, according to the dosage of the different instincts with which each is born, and the upbringing he has received. The new generation knows that there is no such thing as Love with a large L, and that what the Christian romantics of the last century regarded as the uniquely natural form of love is, in fact, only one of the indefinite number of possible amorous fashions, produced by specific circumstances at that particular time. Psycho-analysis has taught it that all the forms of sexual behaviour previously regarded as wicked, perverse, unnatural, are statistically normal (and normality is solely a question of statistics), and that what is commonly called amorous normality is far from being a spontaneous, instinctive form of behaviour, but must be acquired by a process of education. Having contracted the habit of talking freely and more or less scientifically about sexual matters, the young no longer regard love with that feeling of rather guilty excitement and thrilling shame which was for an earlier generation the normal reaction to the subject. Moreover, the practice of birth-control has robbed amorous indulgence of most of the sinfulness traditionally supposed to be inherent in it by robbing it of its socially disastrous effects. The tree shall be known by its fruits: where there are no fruits, there is obviously no tree. Love has ceased to be the rather fearful, mysterious thing it was, and become a perfectly normal, almost commonplace, activity—an activity, for many young people, especially in America, of the same nature as dancing or tennis, a sport, a recreation, a pastime. For those who hold this conception of love, liberty and toleration are prime necessities. A strenuous offensive against the old taboos and repressions is everywhere in progress.

Such, then, are the two conceptions of love which oppose one another to-day. Which is the better? Without presuming to pass judgment, I will content myself with pointing out the defects of each. The older conception was bad, in so far as it inflicted unnecessary and undeserved sufferings on the many human beings whose congenital and acquired modes of love-making did not conform to the fashionable Christian-romantic pattern which was regarded as being uniquely entitled to call itself Love. The new conception is bad, it seems to me, in so far as it takes love too easily and lightly. On love regarded as an amusement the last word is surely this of Robert Burns:

> I waive the quantum of the sin,
> The hazard of concealing;
> But oh! it hardens all within
> And petrifies the feeling.

Nothing is more dreadful than a cold, unimpassioned indulgence. And love infallibly becomes cold and unimpassioned when it is too lightly made. It is not good, as Pascal remarked, to have too much liberty. Love is the product of two opposed forces—of an instinctive impulsion and a social resistance acting on the individual by means of ethical imperatives justified by philosophical or religious myths. When, with the destruction of the myths, resistance is removed, the impulse wastes itself on emptiness; and love, which is only the product of conflicting forces, is not born. The twentieth century is reproducing in a new form the error of the early nineteenth-century romantics. Following Rousseau, the romantics imagined that exclusive passion was the 'natural' mode of love, just as virtue and reasonableness were the 'natural' forms of men's social behaviour. Get rid of priests and kings, and men will be for ever good and happy; poor Shelley's faith in this palpable nonsense remained unshaken to the end. He believed also in the complementary paralogism that you had only to get rid of social restraints and erroneous mythology to make the Grand Passion universally chronic. Like the Mussets and Sands, he failed to see that the Grand Passion was produced by the restraints that opposed themselves to the sexual impulse, just as the deep lake is produced by the dam that bars the passage of the stream, and the flight of the aeroplane by the air which resists the impulsion given to it by the motor. There would be no air-resistance in a vacuum; but precisely for that reason the machine would not leave the ground, or even move at all. Where there are no psychological or external restraints, the Grand Passion does not come into existence and must be artificially cultivated, as George Sands and Musset cultivated it—with what painful and grotesque results the episode of Venice made only too ludicrously manifest.

'J'aime et je veux pâlir; j'aime et je veux souffrir,' says Musset, with his usual hysterically masochistic emphasis. Our young contemporaries do not wish to suffer or grow pale; on the contrary, they have a most determined desire to grow pink and enjoy themselves. But too much enjoyment 'blunts the fine point of seldom pleasure.' Unrestrained indulgence kills not merely passion, but, in the end, even amusement. Too much liberty is as life-destroying as too much restraint. The present fashion in love-making is likely to be short, because love that is psychologically too easy is not interesting. Such, at any rate, was evidently the opinion of the French, who, bored by the sexual licence produced by the Napoleonic upheavals, reverted (so far, at any rate, as the upper and middle classes were concerned) to an almost anglican strictness under Louis-Philippe. We may anticipate an analogous reaction in the not distant future. What new or what revived mythology will serve to create those internal restraints without which sexual impulse cannot be transformed into love? Christian morality and ascetic ideals will doubtless continue to play their part, but there will no less certainly be other moralities and ideals. For example, Mr. D. H. Lawrence's new mythology of nature (new in its expression, but reassuringly old in substance) is a doctrine that seems to me fruitful in possibilities. The 'natural love' which he sets up as a norm is a passion less self-conscious and high-falutin, less obviously and precariously artificial, than that 'natural love' of the romantics, in which Platonic and Christian notions were essential ingredients. The restraints which Mr. Lawrence would impose on sexual impulse, so as to transform it into love, are not the restraints of religious spirituality. They are restraints of a more fundamental, less artificial nature—emotional, not intellectual. The impulse is to be restrained from promiscuous manifestations because, if it were not, promiscuity would 'harden all within and petrify the feeling.' The restraint is of the same personal nature as the impulse. The conflict is between a part of the personality and the personality as an organized whole. It does not pretend, as the romantic and Christian conflict pretends, to be a battle between a diabolical Lower Self and certain transcendental Absolutes, of which the only thing that philosophy can tell us is that they are absolutely unknowable, and therefore, for our purposes, non-existent. It only claims to be, what in fact it is, a psychological conflict taking place in the more or less known and finite world of human interests. This doctrine has several great advantages over previous systems of inward restraint. It does not postulate the existence of any transcendental, non-human entity. This is a merit which will be increasingly appreciated as the significance of Kants and Nietzsche's destructive criticism is more widely realized. People will cease to be interested in unknowable absolutes; but they will never lose interest in their own personalities. True, that 'personality as a whole,' in whose interests the sexual impulse is to be restrained and turned into love, is, strictly speaking, a mythological figure. Consisting, as we do, of a vast colony of souls—souls of individual cells, of organs, of groups of organs, hunger-souls, sex-souls, power-souls, herd-souls, of whose multifarious activities our consciousness (the Soul with a large S) is only very imperfectly and indirectly aware—we are not in a position to know the real nature of our personality as a whole. The only thing we can do is to hazard a hypothesis, to create a mythological figure, call it Human Personality, and hope that circumstances will not, by destroying us, prove our imaginative guesswork too hopelessly wrong. But myth for myth, Human Personality is preferable to God. We do at least know something of Human Personality, whereas of God we know nothing and, knowing nothing, are at liberty to invent as freely as we like. If men had always tried to deal with the problem of love in terms of known human rather than of grotesquely imagined divine interests, there would have been less 'making of eunuchs for the kingdom of heaven's sake,' less persecution of 'sinners,' less burning and imprisoning of the heretics of 'unnatural' love, less Grundyism, less Comstockery, and, at the same time, less dirty Don-Juanism, less of that curiously malignant and vengeful love-making so characteristic of the debauchee under a Christian dispensation.

Reacting against the absurdities of the old mythology, the young have run into absurdities no less inordinate at the other end of the scale. A sordid and ignoble realism offers no resistance to the sexual impulse, which now spends itself purposelessly, without producing love, or even, in the long run, amusement, without enhancing vitality or quickening and deepening the rhythms of living. Only a new mythology of nature, such as, in modern times, Blake, Robert Burns, and Lawrence have defined it, an untranscendental and (relatively speaking) realistic mythology of Energy, Life, and Human Personality, will provide, it seems to me, the inward resistances necessary to turn sexual impulse into love, and provide them in a form which the critical intelligence of Post-Nietzschean youth can respect. By means of such a conception a new fashion in love may be created, a mode more beautiful and convenient, more healthful and elegant, than any seen among men since the days of remote and pagan antiquity.

DO WHAT YOU WILL

HOLY FACE

GOOD Times are chronic nowadays. There is dancing every afternoon, a continuous performance at all the picture-palaces, a radio concert on tap, like gas or water, at any hour of the day or night. The fine point of seldom pleasure is duly blunted. Feasts must be solemn and rare, or else they cease to be feasts. 'Like stones of worth they thinly placed are' (or, at any rate, they were in Shakespeare's day, which was the day of Merry England), 'or captain jewels in the carconet.' The ghosts of these grand occasional jollifications still haunt our modern year. But the stones of worth are indistinguishable from the loud imitation jewellery which now adorns the entire circlet of days. Gems, when they are too large and too numerous, lose all their precious significance; the treasure of an Indian prince is as unimpressive as Aladdin's cave at the pantomime. Set in the midst of the stage diamonds and rubies of modern pleasure, the old feasts are hardly visible. It is only among more or less completely rustic populations, lacking the means and the opportunity to indulge in the modern chronic Good Time, that the surviving feasts preserve something of their ancient glory. Me personally the unflagging pleasures of contemporary cities leave most lugubriously unamused. The prevailing boredom—for oh, how desperately bored, in spite of their grim determination to have a Good Time, the majority of pleasure-seekers really are!—the hopeless weariness, infect me. Among the lights, the alcohol, the hideous jazz noises, and the incessant movement I feel myself sinking into deeper and ever deeper despondency. By comparison with a night-club, churches are positively gay. If ever I want to make merry in public, I go where merrymaking is occasional and the merriment, therefore, of genuine quality; I go where feasts come rarely.

For one who would frequent only the occasional festivities, the great difficulty is to be in the right place at the right time. I have travelled through Belgium and found, in little market towns, kermesses that were orgiastic like the merry-making in a Breughel picture. But how to remember the date? And how, remembering it, to be in Flanders again at the appointed time? The problem is almost insoluble. And then there is Frogmore. The nineteenth-century sculpture in the royal mausoleum is reputed to be the most amazing of its amazing kind. I should like to see Frogmore. But the anniversary of Queen Victoria's death is the only day in the year when the temple is open to the public. The old queen died, I believe, in January. But what was the precise date? And, if one enjoys the blessed liberty to be elsewhere, how shall one reconcile oneself to being in England at such a season? Frogmore, it seems, will have to remain unvisited. And there are many other places, many other dates and days, which, alas, I shall always miss. I must even be resignedly content with the few festivities whose times I can remember and whose scene coincides, more or less, with that of my existence in each particular portion of the year.

One of these rare and solemn dates which I happen never to forget is September the thirteenth. It is the feast of the Holy Face of Lucca. And since Lucca is within thirty miles of the seaside place where I spend the summer, and since the middle of September is still serenely and transparently summer by the shores of the Mediterranean, the feast of the Holy Face is counted among the captain jewels of my year. At the religious function and the ensuing fair I am, each September, a regular attendant.

'By the Holy Face of Lucca!' It was William the Conqueror's favourite oath. And if I were in the habit of cursing and swearing, I think it would also be mine. For it is a fine oath, admirable both in form and substance. ‘ By the Holy Face of Lucca ! ’ In whatever language you pronounce them, the words reverberate, they rumble with the rumbling of genuine poetry. And for any one who has ever seen the Holy Face, how pregnant they are with power and magical compulsion ! For the Face, the Holy Face of Lucca, is certainly the strangest, the most impressive thing of its kind I have ever seen.

Imagine a huge wooden Christ, larger than life, not naked, as in later representations of the Crucifixion, but dressed in a long tunic, formally fluted with stiff Byzantine folds. The face is not the face of a dead, or dying, or even suffering man. It is the face of a man still violently alive, and the expression of its strong features is stern, is fierce, is even rather sinister. From the dark sockets of polished cedar wood two yellowish tawny eyes, made, apparently, of some precious stone, or perhaps of glass, stare out, slightly squinting, with an unsleeping balefulness. Such is the Holy Face. Tradition affirms it to be a true, contemporary portrait. History establishes the fact that it has been in Lucca for the best part of twelve hundred years. It is said that a rudderless and crewless ship miraculously brought it from Palestine to the beaches of Luni. The inhabitants of Sarzana claimed the sacred flotsam ; but the Holy Face did not wish to go to Sarzana. The oxen harnessed to the wagon in which it had been placed were divinely inspired to take the road to Lucca. And at Lucca the Face has remained ever since, working miracles, drawing crowds of pilgrims, protecting and at intervals failing to protect the city of its adoption from harm. Twice a year, at Easter time and on the thirteenth of September, the doors of its little domed tabernacle in the cathedral are thrown open, the candles are lighted, and the dark and formidable image, dressed up for the occasion in a jewelled overall and with a glittering crown on its head, stares down—with who knows what mysterious menace in its bright squinting eyes?—on the throng of its worshippers.

The official act of worship is a most handsome function. A little after sunset a procession of clergy forms up in the church of San Frediano. In the ancient darkness of the basilica a few candles light up the liturgical ballet. The stiff embroidered vestments, worn by generations of priests and from which the heads and hands of the present occupants emerge with an air of almost total irrelevance (for it is the sacramental carapace that matters; the little man who momentarily fills it is without significance), move hieratically hither and thither through the rich light and the velvet shadows. Under his baldaquin the jewelled old archbishop is a museum specimen. There is a forest of silvery mitres, spear-shaped against the darkness (bishops seem to be plentiful in Lucca). The choir boys wear lace and scarlet. There is a guard of halberdiers in a gaudily pied mediaeval uniform. The ritual charade is solemnly danced through. The procession emerges from the dark church into the twilight of the streets. The municipal band strikes up loud inappropriate music. We hurry off to the cathedral by a short cut to take our places for the function.

The Holy Face has always had a partiality for music. Yearly, through all these hundreds of years, it has been sung to and played at, it has been treated to symphonies, cantatas, solos on every instrument. During the eighteenth century the most celebrated *castrati* came from the ends of Italy to warble to it; the most eminent professors of the violin, the flute, the oboe, the trombone scraped and blew before its shrine. Paganini himself, when he was living in Lucca in the court of Elisa Bonaparte, performed at the annual concerts in honour of the Face. Times have changed, and the image must now be content with local talent and a lower standard of musical excellence. True, the good will is always there; the Lucchesi continue to do their musical best; but their best is generally no more nor less than just dully creditable. Not always, however. I shall never forget what happened during my first visit to the Face. The musical programme that year was ambitious. There was to be a rendering, by choir and orchestra, of one of those vast oratorios which the clerical musician, Dom Perosi, composes in a strange and rather frightful mixture of the musical idioms of Palestrina, Wagner, and Verdi. The orchestra was enormous; the choir was numbered by the hundred; we waited in pleased anticipation for the music to begin. But when it did begin, what an astounding pandemonium! Everybody played and sang like mad, but without apparently any reference to the playing and singing of anybody else. Of all the musical performances I have ever listened to it was the most Manchester-Liberal, the most Victorian-democratic. The conductor stood in the midst of them waving his arms; but he was only a constitutional monarch—for show, not use. The performers had revolted against his despotism. Nor had they permitted themselves to be regimented into Prussian uniformity by any soul-destroying excess of rehearsal. Godwin's prophetic vision of a perfectly individualistic concert was here actually realized. The noise was hair-raising. But the performers were making it with so much gusto that, in the end, I was infected by their high spirits and enjoyed the hullabaloo almost as much as they did. That concert was symptomatic of the general anarchy of post-war Italy. Those times are now past. The Fascists have come, bringing order and discipline—even to the arts. When the Lucchesi play and sing to their Holy Face, they do it now with decorum, in a thoroughly professional and well-drilled manner. It is admirable, but dull. There are times, I must confess, when I regret the loud delirious blaring and bawling of the days of anarchy.

Almost more interesting than the official acts of worship are the unofficial, the private and individual acts. I have spent hours in the cathedral watching the crowd before the shrine. The great church is full from morning till night. Men and women, young and old, they come in their thousands, from the town, from all the country round, to gaze on the authentic image of God. And the image is dark, threatening, and sinister. In the eyes of the worshippers I often detected a certain meditative disquiet. Not unnaturally. For if the face of Providence should really and in truth be like the Holy Face, why, then—then life is certainly no joke. Anxious to propitiate this rather appalling image of Destiny, the worshippers come pressing up to the shrine to deposit a little offering of silver or nickel and kiss the reliquary proffered to every almsgiver by the attendant priest. For two francs fifty perhaps Fate will be kind. But the Holy Face continues, unmoved, to squint inscrutable menace. Fixed by that sinister regard, and with the smell of incense in his nostrils, the darkness of the church around and above him, the most ordinary man begins to feel himself obscurely a Pascal. Metaphysical gulfs open before him. The mysteries of human destiny, of the future, of the purpose of life oppress and terrify his soul. The church is dark; but in the midst of the darkness is a little island of candlelight. Oh, comfort! But from the heart of the comforting light, incongruously jewelled, the dark face stares with squinting eyes, appalling, balefully mysterious.

But luckily, for those of us who are not Pascal, there is always a remedy. We can always turn our back on the Face, we can always leave the hollow darkness of the church. Outside, the sunlight pours down out of a flawless sky. The streets are full of people in their holiday best. At one of the gates of the city, in an open space beyond the walls, the merry-go-rounds are turning, the steam organs are playing the tunes that were popular four years ago on the other side of the Atlantic, the fat woman's drawers hang unmoving, like a huge forked pennon, in the windless air outside her booth. There is a crowd, a smell, an unceasing noise—music and shouting, roaring of circus lions, giggling of tickled girls, squealing from the switchback of deliciously frightened girls, laughing and whistling, tooting of cardboard trumpets, cracking of guns in the rifle-range, breaking of crockery, howling of babies, all blended together to form the huge and formless sound of human happiness. Pascal was wise, but wise too consciously, with too consistent a spirituality. For him the Holy Face was always present, haunting him with its dark menace, with the mystery of its baleful eyes. And if ever, in a moment of distraction, he forgot the metaphysical horror of the world and those abysses at his feet, it was with a pang of remorse that he came again to himself, to the self of spiritual consciousness. He thought it right to be haunted, he refused to enjoy the pleasures of the created world, he liked walking among the gulfs. In his excess of conscious wisdom he was mad; for he sacrificed life to principles, to metaphysical abstractions, to the overmuch spirituality which is the negation of existence. He preferred death to life. Incomparably grosser and stupider than Pascal, almost immeasurably his inferiors, the men and women who move with shouting and laughter through the dusty heat of the fair are yet more wise than the philosopher. They are wise with the unconscious wisdom of the species, with the dumb, instinctive, physical wisdom of life itself. For it is life itself that, in the interests of living, commands them to be inconsistent. It is life itself that, having made them obscurely aware of Pascal's gulfs and horrors, bids them turn away from the baleful eyes of the Holy Face, bids them walk out of the dark, hushed, incense-smelling church into the sunlight, into the dust and whirling motion, the sweaty smell and the vast chaotic noise of the fair. It is life itself; and I, for one, have more confidence in the rightness of life than in that of any individual man, even if the man be Pascal.

DO WHAT YOU WILL

PASCAL

I

§ 1. *The Orders*

'THE infinite distance which separates bodies from minds symbolizes the infinitely more infinite distance between minds and charity; for charity is supernatural.

All bodies, the firmament, the stars, earth and its kingdoms, are not worth the least of minds: for the mind knows all these things and itself; and bodies, nothing.

All bodies together, and all minds together, and all their productions, are not worth the least movement of charity. That belongs to an infinitely higher order.

Roll all the bodies in the world into one and you will not be able to get one little thought out of them. That is impossible, it belongs to another order. Similarly, from all bodies and minds you cannot draw a movement of true charity; for that too is impossible, that too belongs to another order, or supernatural order.'

It would be easy to criticize these affirmations. To begin with, it is obvious that Pascal has no right to say that it is *impossible* for bodies to think. He is simply promoting his ignorance and his metaphysical prejudices to the rank of a general law. He would certainly have been less dogmatic if he had seen the highly emotional plants at the Bose Institute or Warburg's breathing carbon. True, it was not his fault that he lived before these experiments were made. But it *was* his fault that he did not see the purely philosophical objections to his analysis of reality. The idea of orders of existence is profound and fruitful, but only on condition that you choose your orders so that they correspond with observed reality. The Christian-Pascalian orders do not. Body, mind, and charity are not realities, but abstractions from reality. The solutions of continuity, so conspicuous in human life, are not between body, mind, and charity, but between different states of the total reality from which these hypothetical entities have been arbitrarily abstracted. Reality, as we know it, is always a compound of the three elements into which Pascal divides it. And this in spite of idealism. For even if we grant the whole case of subjective idealism—and it is perhaps the only metaphysical system which is logically water-tight—we do nothing to diminish the importance of matter. Mind may be the creator of matter; but that does not mean that it can deny the existence of its creature. The habit of seeing and touching material objects is a habit of which the mind cannot break itself. Matter may be illusory; but it is a chronic illusion. Whether we like it or not, it is always there. So, for the benefit of the materialists, is mind. So are, intermittently, the psychological states which have been regarded, rightly or wrongly, as being states of contact with a higher spiritual world. For the purposes of classification we can divide the total reality into matter, mind, and, finally, charity, grace, the supernatural, God, or whatever other name you care to bestow on the third of the Pascalian orders. But we must beware of attributing actuality to these convenient abstractions; we must resist the temptation to fall down and worship the intellectual images carved by ourselves out of the world (whether objective or subjective, it makes no difference) with which experience has made us familiar. True the temptation is strong; for the intellect has a special weakness for its own creations. Moreover, in this case the abstractions have actually been made the basis of a social reality. Men have actually tried to realize their classification in the structure of society. Pascal's mistake consists in applying to individual psychology and the world at large the hierarchical classification of social functions into mechanic and liberal, spiritual and lay. Indeed, he did more than merely apply it: he assumed that it was inherent in human nature itself and even in non-human nature—that the caste system had an objective existence in the universe. A convenient social arrangement was thus promoted by him to the rank of a primordial fact of human psychology and cosmic structure. True, the particular social arrangement in question was a very convenient one. All the great qualitative civilizations have been hierarchical. The fine arts and the arts of life have flourished most luxuriantly in those societies in which a very sharp distinction was drawn between mechanic and liberal occupations. Our modern civilization is quantitative and democratic. We draw no distinctions between mechanic and liberal—only between rich and poor. Western society has been wholly laicized—with most depressing effects on those human activities hitherto regarded as the most valuable. America has twenty-five million motor-cars, but almost no original art.

Pascal took the social hierarchy for granted. Naturally. He had never heard of a society in which the distinction between the lay and the spiritual was not sharply drawn. But he was not for that reason justified in supposing that the hierarchy existed objectively in nature.

Reality, as we know it, is an organic whole. Separable in theory, the three Pascalian orders are in fact indissolubly wedded. Nor must we forget that matter, mind, and the supernatural are arbitrary abstractions from experience, and that other systems of classification are easily conceivable. The observed solutions of continuity are not, as Pascal maintains, between the three abstractions, which have no existence outside the classifying intellect. They are rather between different states of the total reality as experienced by different individuals, and by the same individual at different times.

Between the sick man and the healthy man, between the hungry and the full, the lustful and the satiated, the young and the old, between the normally and abnormally gifted, between the cultured European and the primitive Papuan, there yawn great gulfs of separation.

Those who would learn how far it is possible for some one with an unusual temperament to dissociate himself from the moral and intellectual reality accepted as normal by the majority of Europeans should read Dostoievsky's *Notes from Underground.* And what profoundly dissimilar universes may be inhabited by the same man at different seasons ! In the terrifying *Death of Ivan Ilyitch* Tolstoy has shown how deep, how wide, is the gulf which separates a man in health from the 'same man' when death has laid its hand upon him. These two works of fiction are worth a whole library of treatises on the theory of knowledge and the nature of reality. Most philosophical argument is argument at cross purposes ; it is the angry shouting at one another of two people who use the same words but mean different things by them. It is the hopeless and futile squabbling of beings who belong in taste and feeling to distinct zoological species. One philosopher abuses another for having stupid and wicked views about the nature of things, without realizing that the things about whose nature he has such decided opinions are entirely different from the things the other fellow has been discussing. Their universes are parallel to one another ; this side of infinity they do not meet.

§ 2. *Private Universes*

Now, the universe in which each individual lives is an affair partly of heredity, partly of acquired habit. A man may be born with a strong tendency to inhabit one kind of universe rather than another ; but this congenital tendency is never completely exclusive. The cosmos in which each of us lives is at least as much a product of education as of physiological inheritance; habit and a lifetime of repetitions determine its form and content. Its boundaries are fixed conventionally by a kind of inward Treaty of Versailles. It is a treaty, however, which Nature refuses to be rigidly and permanently bound by. When it suits the natural, hereditary man to recognize the Soviets of his own spirit, to make war on one of his Glorious Allies, or disestablish his private Church, he does so, with or without compunction, until the illegal action produces in due course a reaction towards legality, and he feels himself compelled once more to ratify his treaty. Men feel bound by a kind of intellectual and moral patriotism to defend in theory (even though in act they may betray it) the particular cosmos of their choice; they are jingo positivists, chauvinistically mystical. But if they were sincere with themselves they would realize that these patriotic ardours in matters of philosophy are not merely misplaced, but without justification. No man is by nature exclusively domiciled in one universe. All lives—even the lives of the men and women who have the most strongly marked congenital tendencies—are passed under at least two flags and generally under many more. Even the most ardent positivist is sometimes carried away by a wave of mystical emotion. Even the most frenzied absolute-hunters, aesthetes, and idealists must compromise with the gross world of relativity and practice to the extent of eating, taking shelter from the weather, behaving at least conventionally enough to keep out of the clutches of the police. Even Podsnap may once have had inklings of the nature of love and poetry. Even the healthiest man, the most bottomlessly 'average' and hard-headed of Ivan Ilyitches, feels the approach of death at least once in the course of his existence. Even the most pious Catholic is sometimes a Pyrrhonist—nay, *ought* to be a Pyrrhonist (it is Pascal himself who says it). The only completely consistent people are the dead; the living are never anything but diverse. But such is man's pride, such his intellectually vicious love of system and fixity, such his terror and hatred of life, that the majority of human beings refuse to accept the facts. Men do not want to admit that they are what in fact they are—each one a colony of separate individuals, of whom now one and now another consciously lives with the life that animates the whole organism and directs its destinies. They want, in their pride and their terror, to be monsters of stiff consistency; they pretend, in the teeth of the facts, that they are one person all the time, thinking one set of thoughts, pursuing one course of action throughout life. They insist on being *either* Pascal *or* Voltaire, *either* Podsnap *or* Keats, when in fact they are potentially always, and at different times actually, a little of what each of these personages symbolically stands for and a great deal more beside. My music, like that of every other living and conscious being, is a counterpoint, not a single melody, a succession of harmonies and discords. I am now one person and now another, 'aussi différent de moi-même,' in La Rochefoucauld's words, 'que des autres.' And I am always potentially and sometimes actually and consciously both at once. In spite or rather because of this (for every 'in spite' is really a 'because') I have tried to pretend that I was superhumanly consistent, I have tried to force myself to be an embodiment of a principle, a walking system. But one can only become consistent by becoming petrified; and a rigid philosophical system is only possible on condition that one refuses to consider all those necessarily numerous aspects of reality which do not permit themselves to be explained in terms of it. For me, the pleasures of living and understanding have come to outweigh the pleasures, the very real pleasures (for the consciousness of being a man of principle and system is extremely satisfying to the vanity), of pretending to be consistent. I prefer to be dangerously free and alive to being safely mummified. Therefore I indulge my inconsistencies. I try to be sincerely myself—that is to say, I try to be sincerely all the numerous people who live inside my skin and take their turn at being the master of my fate.

It is, then, as a mixed being, as a colony of free and living minds, not as a single mind irrevocably committed, like a fossil fly in amber, to a single system of ideas, that I now propose to write of Pascal. As a positivist first of all, for the rationalizing part is one I find only too easy to play. More sympathetically next, in the guise of a Pascalian; for I too have sometimes found myself in other worlds than those familiar to the positivist, I too have chased the absolute in those remote strange regions beyond the borders of the quotidian consciousness. And finally as a worshipper of life, who accepts all the conflicting facts of human existence and tries to frame a way of life and a philosophy (a necessarily inconsistent way, a realistically self-contradictory philosophy) in accordance with them. To make a map of a mountain, to fix its position in space, we must look at it from every side, we must go all round it, climb all over it. It is the same with a man as with a mountain. A single observation does not suffice to fix his form and define his position in relation to the rest of the world; he must be looked at from all sides. This is what I have tried to do with Pascal. There is little biography in this essay and no circumambient history. (To those who would see Pascal in relation to his own century I would recommend such works as Strowski's *Pascal et son Temps* and Chevalier's *Pascal.*) I have sought to situate him in the eternal landscape of human psychology, to fix his position in relation to its unchanging features—to the body, the instincts, the passions and feelings, the speculative mind. Indeed, to any one who takes the trouble to read this study it will be sufficiently apparent that its subject is not really Pascal at all, but this psychological landscape. Pascal is really only an excuse and a convenience. If I choose to write about him it is because he raises, either by implication in his life, or explicitly in his writings, practically all the major problems of philosophy and conduct. And raises them how masterfully ! Never has the case against life been put with such subtlety, such elegance, such persuasive cogency, such admirable succinctness. He explored the same country as I am now exploring ; went, saw, and found it detestable. He said so, exhaustively—for his quick eyes saw everything. All that, from his side, could be said, he said. His reports have accompanied me on my psychological travels ; they have been my Baedeker. I have compared his descriptions with the originals, his comments with my own reactions. In the margin of the guide-book I have pencilled a few reflections. This essay is made up of them. Pascal is only incidentally its subject.

§ 3. *The Riddle*

In the form in which men have posed it, the Riddle of the Universe requires a theological answer. Suffering and enjoying, men want to know why they enjoy and to what end they suffer. They see good things and evil things, beautiful things and ugly, and they want to find a reason—a final and absolute reason—why these things should be as they are. It is extremely significant, however, that it is only in regard to matters which touch them very closely that men look for theological reasons—and not only look, but find as well, and in what quantities ! With regard to matters which do not touch them to the quick, matters which are, so to speak, at a certain psychological distance from themselves, they are relatively incurious. They make no effort to find a theological explanation for them ; they see the absurdity, the hopelessness, of even looking for such an explanation. What, for example, is the final, the theological reason for grass being green and sunflowers yellow? One has only to put the question to perceive that it is quite unanswerable. We can talk about light-waves, vibrating electrons, chlorophyll molecules, and such like; but any explanation we may offer in terms of these entities will only be an explanation of *how* grass is green, not of *why* it is green. There is no 'why'—none, at any rate, that we can conceivably discover. Grass is green because that is how we see it; in other words, it's green because it *is* green. Now, there is no difference in kind between a green fact and a painful or beautiful fact, between a fact that is the colour of sunflowers and facts that are good or hellish: one class of facts is psychologically more remote than the other, that is all. Things are noble or agonizing because they are so. Any attempt to explain why they should be so is as inevitably predestined to failure as the attempt to explain why grass is green. In regard to greenness and other psychologically distant phenomena men have recognized the hopelessness of the task and no longer try to propound theological explanations. But they still continue to rack their brains over the riddles of the moral and aesthetic universes, they go on inventing answers and even believing in them.

§ 4. *Answers to the Riddle*

Pascal was well acquainted with the psychological reasons for the asking and answering of cosmic riddles. 'Il est bon,' he says, 'd'être lassé et fatigué par l'inutile recherche du vrai bien, afin de tendre les bras au Libérateur.' Borrowing a phrase from the Psalmist, he returns in another passage to the same theme. 'The waters of Babylon flow and fall and sweep away. O holy Zion, where all is stable and where nothing falls!' The words are Pascal's, but they express an ancient and almost universal yearning, the yearning that has given birth to all the Gods and Goods, all the Truths and Beauties, all the Justices, the Revelations, the Ones, the Rights of a bewildered and suffering humanity. For the Absolute has all too human parents. Fatigue and perplexity, wretchedness and the sentiment of transience, the longing for certainty, the desire for moral justification—these are its ancestors. 'Change and decay,' writes the author of the most popular of English hymns, 'change and decay in all around I see; O Thou who changest not, abide with me.' From the fact of change and decay the logic of desire deduces the existence of something changeless. Appearances are multiple and chaotic; if only things were simpler, easier to understand! The wish creates; it is desirable that there should be noumena; therefore noumena exist and the noumenal world is more truly real than the world of everyday life. *Quod erat demonstrandum.* A similar conjuring trick produces the One out of the deplorably puzzling Many, draws the Good and the Beautiful out of the seething hotch-potch of diverse human tastes and sensibilities and interests, deduces Justice from our actual inequalities, and absolute Truth from the necessary and unescapable relativities of daily life. It is by an exactly similar process that children invent imaginary playmates to amuse their solitudes and transform a dull, uninteresting piece of wood into a horse, a ship, a railway train—what you will. The difference between children and grown-ups is that children do not try to justify their compensatory imaginations intellectually; whereas grown-ups, or rather adolescents (for the vast majority of chronological adults have never grown, if they have emerged from childhood at all, beyond adolescence), do make the attempt. The newly conscious and the newly rational have all the defects of the newly rich; they make a vulgar parade of their possessions, they swaggeringly advertise their powers. They review all the biologically useful beliefs, all the life-stimulating fancies of individual or racial childhood, and pretentiously 'explain' them in terms of newly discovered rationalism. The gods and fairies are replaced by abstract noumena. Zeus fades away into Justice, Power, Oneness; Athene becomes Wisdom; Aphrodite degenerates into Intellectual Beauty. In recent times this replacement of the old deities by hypostasized abstractions has been called 'modernism,' and regarded, quaintly enough, as a spiritual advance, a liberation, a progress towards Truth. In reality, of course, the noumena invented by adolescent minds are, absolutely speaking, as false (or as true, there is no means of discovering which) as the mythological personages whose place they have usurped. As vital symbols they are much less adequate. The childish fancies are inspired directly by life. The adolescent noumena are abstractions from life, flights from diversity into disembodied oneness. The noumenal world is a most inadequate substitute for fairyland and Olympus.

§ 5. *Pascal and Rationalism*

Pascal was an intellectual adult who deliberately forced himself to think like a Christian philosopher—that is to say, like an unstably balanced compound of child and adolescent. Towards the complacencies of the full-blown adolescent he was ruthless. A critic so acute, so intellectually grown-up, could not be expected to swallow the pseudo-logical arguments of the rationalists. 'Laugh at philosophy,' was his advice, 'and you are a true philosopher.' He himself mocked wittily. 'Feu M. Pascal,' wrote a contemporary, 'appelait la philosophie cartésienne le *Roman de la Nature*, semblable à Don Quichotte.' What a high and, to my mind, what an undeserved compliment to Descartes! Most of those curious romances which we call philosophical systems are more like Sidney's *Arcadia* or the *Grand Cyrus* than *Don Quixote.* How proud I should be, if I were a metaphysician, to be mentioned in the same breath with Cervantes! But Descartes, if he had heard the sally, would certainly have been more pained by it than pleased. For Descartes was a rationalist; he believed in the reality of his abstractions. Inventing fictions, he imagined that he was revealing the Truth. Pascal knew better. Pascal was a critic and a realist; Pascal was intellectually grown-up. 'Our soul,' he said, 'is thrown into the body, where it finds matter, time, dimension. Thereon it reasons and calls that nature and necessity, and cannot believe in anything else.' And again: 'It is not in our capacity to know what God is, nor whether He exists.' We might be reading a discourse, mercifully abbreviated, by Kant. It is unnecessary for me to rehearse the arguments by means of which Pascal demolished the pretensions of the rationalists to attain by human means to the knowledge of any absolute whatever. Montaigne's armoury was conveniently at hand; he sharpened and envenomed the Pyrrhonian weapons with which it was stored. Elegantly, artistically, but without mercy, the rationalists were slaughtered. Rather more than a hundred years later they were slaughtered again by Kant, and, after the passage of another century, yet once more, and this time with a Tamburlane-like ferocity and thoroughness, by Nietzsche. Pragmatists, humanists, philosophers of science continue the massacre. Hewn down, the rationalists sprout again like the Hydra's heads. The learned and the unlearned world is crammed with them. This survival of rationalism in the teeth of an unescapable destructive criticism is a tribute, if not to humanity's intelligence, at least to its love of life. For rationalism, in its rather ponderous and silly way, is an illusion with a biological value, a vital lie. 'When the truth of a thing is unknown,' said Pascal, two hundred years before Nietzsche, 'it is good that there should be a common error to fix men's minds.' The only defect of rationalism as a vital lie is that it is insufficiently vital. Vital lie for vital lie, polytheistic mythology is preferable to the rationalists' system of abstractions. The falsehood of rationalism is manifest to any one who is ready to examine its paralogisms with the eyes of unprejudiced and dispassionate intelligence. If it stimulates life, it does so only feebly. Being in the most eminent degree intelligent, Pascal realized that there was no hope of attaining by rational means the absolutes for which he longed. A rational absolute is a contradiction in terms. The only absolute which a man of intelligence can believe in is an irrational one. It was his realization of the stupidity of rationalism that confirmed Pascal in his catholicism.

§ 6. *Revelation*

"C'est en manquant de preuves,' he says of the Christians, 'qu'ils ne manquent pas de sens.' The rationalists who are never in want of proofs thereby prove their own want of intelligence. Where absolutes are concerned, reason is unreasonable. 'Il n'y a rien si conforme à la raison que ce désaveu de la raison.' Being reasonable, Pascal disavowed rationalism and attached himself to revelation. The absolutes of revelation must be genuine absolutes, firm, eternal in the midst of life's indefinite flux, untainted with contingency. They *must* be genuine, because revelation is, by definition, non-human. But the definition of non-humanity is itself human; and the revelations are couched in human language, and are the work of individual human beings who lived all too humanly in space and time. We are fatally back again among the relativities. Nor will all the ingenious historical arguments contained in the later sections of the *Pensées* (arguments which Cardinal Newman was later to develop with his usual subtlety) do anything to get us out of the relativities. Pascal tried to demonstrate the Historical Truth of the Christian revelation. But, alas ! there is no such thing as Historical Truth—there are only more or less probable opinions about the past, opinions which change from generation to generation. History is a function, mathematically speaking, of the degree of ignorance and of the personal prejudices of historians. The history of an epoch which has left very few documents is at the mercy of archaeological research ; a happy discovery may necessitate its radical revision from one day to the next. In cases where circumstances seem to have condemned us to a definitive and permanent ignorance, we might expect historical opinions to be at least as settled as the historians' lack of knowledge. But this occurs only when the events in question are indifferent. So long as past events continue to possess a certain actuality their history will vary from age to age, and the same documents will be reinterpreted, the same definitive ignorance will be made the basis of ever new opinions. Where documents are numerous and contradictory (and such is the fallibility of human testimony that numerous documents are always contradictory), each historian will select the evidence which fits in with his own prejudices, and ignore or disparage all the rest. The nearest approach to Historical Truth is the fixed opinion entertained by successive historians about past events in which they take no vital interest. Opinions about mediaeval land tenure are not likely to undergo serious fluctuations, for the good reason that the question of mediaeval land tenure possesses, and will doubtless continue to possess, a purely academic interest. Christianity, on the other hand, is not an academic question. The documents dealing with the origins of the religion are therefore certain to undergo a constant process of reinterpretation. Doubtful human testimonies (all human testimony is doubtful) have given birth to, and will continue, so long as Christianity preserves a more than academic interest, to justify, a variety of opinions in variously constituted, variously prejudiced minds. This is the reality out of which Pascal tried to extract that non-existent thing, the Historical Truth.

§ 7. *Historical Grounds of Pascal's Faith*

It may seem strange that Pascal should not have realized the uselessness of trying to find an absolute even in revealed religion. But if he failed to treat catholicism as realistically as he treated other doctrines, that was because he wanted to believe in its absolutes. He felt a need for absolutes, and this temperamental need was stronger than his intelligence. Of Pascal's temperament, of that strange soul of his, 'naturaliter Christiana,' but with such a special and rather dreadful kind of Christianity, I shall speak later. In this place I shall only mention the external circumstances which quickened his desire to believe in the Catholic absolutes. Those middle years of the seventeenth century, which were the historical scene of Pascal's brief existence, were years, for Europe, of more than ordinary restlessness and misery. Germany was being devastated by the most bloodthirsty of religious wars. In England the Parliament was fighting with the King. France was agitated by the pointless skirmishing of the Fronde. It was the Europe, in a word, of Callot's etchings. Along its roads marched companies of hungry and marauding pikemen; its crows were busy on the carcases that dangled from the branches of every well-grown oak. There was raping and casual plundering, shooting and hanging in plenty, with torture to relieve the monotony and breakings on the wheel as a Sunday treat. To Pascal, as he looked at the world about him, peace seemed the supremely desirable thing, peace and order. The political situation was much the same as that which, in our own days, made Mussolini the saviour of his country, justified Primo de Rivera, and recruited so many adherents to the cause of the Action Française. Our modern anarchy has made of the unbelieving Charles Maurras an enthusiastic upholder of Catholicism. Pascal was a Maurras who believed in Catholicism to the point of thinking it true as well as politically useful, of regarding it as being good for himself as well as for the lower classes. Pascal's remedy for the disorders of his time was simple: passive obedience to the legally constituted authority—to the King in France, for example, to the Republic in Venice. For men to rebel against the masters Providence has given them is a sin; the worst of evils is civil war. It is the political wisdom of despair. To long, in the midst of anarchy, for peace and order at any price one need not be a Christian. Pascal's counsels of passive despair took their origin in political events, not in his Catholic convictions. But his Catholic convictions justified them. For man, being utterly corrupt, is incapable of bringing forth, without divine assistance, any good thing. It is therefore folly to rebel, folly to wish to change existing institutions; for the new state of things, being the work of corrupted human nature, must infallibly be as bad as that which it replaces. The wise man is therefore he who accepts the existing order, not because it is just or makes men happy, but simply because it exists and because no other order would be any juster or succeed in making men any happier.

History shows that there is a good deal of truth in Pascal's views. The hopes of revolutionaries have always been disappointed. But for any one who values life as life, this is no argument against attempting revolutions. The faith in the efficacy of revolutions (however ill-founded events may prove it to be) is a stimulus to present living, a spur to present action and thought. In the attempt to realize the illusory aims of revolution, men are induced to live more intensely in the present, to think, do, and suffer with a heightened energy; the result of this is that they create a new reality (very different, no doubt, from that which they had hoped to create, but that does not matter; the important fact is that it is new). The new reality imposes new hopes and faiths on those who live in the midst of it, and the new hopes and faiths stimulate men to intenser living and the creation of yet another new reality. And so on indefinitely. But this is an argument which would most certainly have failed to make Pascal a revolutionary. Pascal had no wish to have present living intensified. He detested present living. For present living is a tissue of concupiscences, and therefore thoroughly anti-Christian. He would have liked to see present living abolished; therefore he had no patience with any doctrine, religious, philosophical, or social, calculated to enhance the vital process. The Christianity which he chose to practise and believe in was duly anti-vital.

§ 8. *Personal Grounds: the Ecstasy*

It is, I repeat, in Callot's etchings of the Horrors of War that the political reasons for Pascal's Catholicism are to be found, just as it is in the newspaper man's snapshots of proletarian mobs 'demonstrating' in the industrial towns and capitalist mobs drearily and expensively amusing themselves at Monte Carlo, that we must look for an explanation of the Catholicism of M. Maurras. But Pascal had other, more cogent, personal reasons for believing. The record of his sudden apocalyptic conversion—that famous 'Memorial' which was found, after his death, sewn like a talisman in the lining of his clothes—is a document of the highest interest, not only for the light it throws on Pascal himself, but also for what it tells us of the mystical experience in general and of the way in which that experience is interpreted. I reproduce the text in its entirety:—

L'an de grace 1654.
Lundy 23 novembre, jour de St. Clement, pape
et martir et autres au martirologe
veille de St. Chrysogone martir, et autres
Depuis environ dix heures et demy du soir jusques environ
minuit et demy.

Feu

Dieu d'Abraham, Dieu d'Isaac, Dieu de Jacob
Non des philosophes et des sçavans
Certitude, certitude sentiment Joye Paix.
Dieu de Jésus Christ
Deum meum et Deum vestrum
Ton Dieu sera mon Dieu
Oubly du monde et de tout, hormis Dieu.
Il ne se trouve que par les voyes enseignées dans l'Evangile
Grandeur de l'ame humaine
Père juste, le monde ne t'a point connu, mais je t'ay connu
Joye, joye, joye, pleurs de joye
Je m'en suis separé
Dereliquerunt me fontem aquae vivae
Mon Dieu, me quitterez-vous ?
Que je n'en sois pas separé éternellement
Je m'en suis separé ; je l'ay fui renoncé crucifié
Que je n'en sois jamais separé
Il ne se conserve que par les voyes enseignées dans l'Evangile
Renonciation totalle et douce.
Soumission totale à Jésus Christ et mon directeur
Eternellement en joye pour un jour d'exercice sur la terre.
Non obliviscar sermones tuas. Amen.

To any one who reads this 'Memorial' with care it is at once obvious that its substance is not homogeneous. It is, so to speak, stratified, built up of alternate layers of direct experience and intellectual interpretations after the fact. Even the date is a mixture of straightforward chronology and Christian hagiography. Monday, November the twenty-third, is also the eve of St. Chrysogonus's day. With the first word, 'feu,' we are in the midst of pure experience. Fire—it is the mystical rapture in the raw, so to speak, and undigested. The next two lines are layers of interpretation. Meditating on that inward conflagration which burns in the 'feu' of the first line, Pascal comes to the conclusion that it has been lighted by 'the God of Abraham, Isaac, and Jacob, not of the philosophers and men of science.' There follows another stratum of pure experience. 'Certitude, certitude, feeling, joy, peace'; the violence of rapture has been succeeded by ecstatic calm. The mind once more steps in and explains these experiences in terms of a hypothesis which Pascal has telegraphically summarized in the words 'Dieu de Jésus Christ.'

With 'Oubly du monde et de toute, hormis Dieu' we move away from the realm of interpretation towards that of immediate psychological experience. Proceeding, we pass through several strata of doctrinal Meditations, to reach in 'Joye, joye, joye, pleurs de joye' yet another layer of pure experience. The next lines, from 'Je m'en suis separé' to 'Que je n'en sois pas separé éternellement,' are strata of mixed substance—records of direct or remembered experiences conditioned, as to mode and quality, by a theological hypothesis. For, it is obvious, emotional experience and intellectual interpretation of that experience cannot be kept permanently separated in alternating strata. Crudely and schematically, what happens is this: something is directly experienced; this experience is intellectually interpreted, generally in terms of some existing system of metaphysics or mythology; the myth, the philosophical system are regarded as true and become in their turn the source of new experiences and the channels through which the old emotions must pass. Pascal's 'Memorial' illustrates the whole process. In what I may call its upper strata we have alternating layers of pure experience and pure interpretation—fire and the God of Abraham; Certitude, Joy, Peace, and the God of Jesus Christ. Later on he gives expression to what I may call secondary emotions—emotions aroused in him by his reflections on the after-the-fact interpretation of the primary mystical emotions. He feels the terror of being separated from the God he has called in to explain his original sensations of joy and peace.

That the mystical experience need not necessarily be interpreted as Pascal interpreted it, is obvious. Substantially similar experiences have been explained in terms of Buddhism, Brahmanism, Mohammedanism, Taoism, Shamanism, Neo-Platonism, and countless other religions and philosophies. They have also frequently been left uninterpreted. In the correspondence of William James, for example, there is an interesting letter describing what is obviously a full-blown ecstasy, for which, however, James does not presume to suggest any metaphysical explanation. Wisely; for the mystical experience is like all other primary psychological facts, susceptible of none but a tautological explanation. These things happen because they do happen, because that is what the human mind happens to be like. Between the various explanatory hypotheses in terms of the 'God of Abraham,' Nirvana, Allah, and the rest, there is nothing to choose; in so far as each of them claims to be the unattainable Truth, and all of them postulate a knowledge of the unknowable Absolute, they are all equally ill-founded.

§ 9. *The Humanist and the Christian*

Pascal's metaphysic may be described as a kind of positivistic Pyrrhonism tempered, and indeed flatly denied, by dogmatic Christianity. His morality is similarly self-contradictory. For Pascal prescribes at the same time a more than Aristotelian moderation and a Christian excess. He rebukes men for pretentiously trying to be angels, and in the same breath rebukes them for being human. 'L'homme est ni ange ni bête, et le malheur veut que qui veut faire l'ange fait la bête.' Alas! the facts prove Pascal only too right. The would-be angels of this world 'font la bête' in every possible sense of the word: they become either beasts or silly—frequently both at once. The realistic wisdom of Pascal reveals itself in a remark like the following: 'I am perfectly willing to take my place in it [the middle, human world between beast and angel], and refuse to be at the lower end, not because it is low, but because it is an end; for I should equally refuse to be placed at the upper extremity.' And again: 'To step out of the middle way is to step out of humanity. The greatness of the human soul consists in knowing how to hold to the middle way.' Pascal lets fall many other aphorisms of the same kind. 'It is not good to be too free. It is not good to have all the necessities of life.' 'Les grands efforts de l'esprit, où l'âme touche quelquefois, sont choses où elle ne se tient pas; elle y saute quelquefois.' 'How much a man's virtue is capable of must be measured, not by his efforts, but by his ordinary behaviour.' And so on.

But this humanistic wisdom was, in Pascal, only occasional and theoretical. He himself did not practise what he preached. What he practised is admiringly recorded in his sister's biography. 'Always and in all things he used to act on principles. . . . It was not possible for him to abstain from using his senses; but when necessity obliged him to give them some pleasure he had a wonderful capacity for averting his spirit so that it should take no part in the pleasure. At meals we never heard him praise the viands that were served him. . . . And when anybody . . . admired the excellence of some dish, he could not abide it; for he called that "being sensual" . . . because, said he, it was a sign that one ate to please one's taste, a thing that was always wrong. . . . In the early days of his retreat he had calculated the amount of food required for the needs of his stomach, and from that time forward, whatever might be his appetite, he never passed that measure; and whatever disgust he might feel, he made a point of eating the quantity he had fixed.' His stomach was not the only part of him that Pascal mortified. 'The spirit of mortification, which is the very spirit of charity,' inspired him to have a spiked iron belt made for himself. This belt he would put on whenever a visitor came to see him, and when he found himself taking pleasure in the conversation, or feeling in the least vain of his powers as a spiritual guide, 'Il se donnait des coups de coude pour redoubler la violence des piqûres, et se faire ensuite ressouvenir de son devoir.' Later, when his illness made it impossible for him to concentrate on his studies, he wore the belt continually, that the pricking of it might excite his mind to continual fervour.

In the intervals of these ascetic practices Pascal wrote on the necessity of keeping to the middle road, of remaining human. But this was all abstraction and theory. Christianity would not permit him to behave hellenically, just as it would not permit him to think like a Pyrrhonist. Pascal, the philosopher, looked at the world and concluded that 'qui veut faire l'ange fait la bête.' But revealed religion insisted that he should try to be an angel of self-denial, of conscious and consistent other-worldliness. He made the effort and became—what? Perhaps an angel in some other world; who knows? The philosopher can only answer for this; and in this world the would-be angel duly and punctually 'faisait la bête.' That he had a horror of every form of sensuality goes without saying. He hated all lovers and their desires. He hated the beauty that inspired these impure longings. 'If I happened to say, for example, that I had seen a handsome woman,' writes Mme. Périer, 'he would reprimand me, saying that such a remark should never be made in the presence of servants and young people, as I did not know what thoughts it might excite in them.' Of marriage he said, in a letter to his sister, that it was 'une espèce d'homicide et comme un déicide.' For those who marry become exclusively interested in the creature, not the creator; the man who loves a woman kills God in his own mind and, by killing God, in the end kills himself—eternally.

He mistrusted even maternal love. 'Je n'oserais dire,' writes Mme Périer, 'qu'il ne pouvait même souffrir les caresses que je recevais de mes enfants ; il prétendait que cela ne pouvait que leur nuire, qu'on leur pouvait témoigner de la tendresse en mille autres manières.' Towards the end of his life this man of principles would not even permit himself the pleasure of being attached to his friends and relations, nor of being loved by them in return. 'It was one of the fundamental maxims of his piety never to allow any one to love him with attachment; and he gave it to be understood that this was a fault in regard to which men did not examine themselves with sufficient care, a fault that had serious consequences, and the more to be feared in that it often seemed to us devoid of all danger.' How dangerous Pascal himself considered it, may be judged from these words from a little memorandum which he carried about with him, and which was found on his person after his death: 'That people should attach themselves to me is not just. . . . I should be deceiving those in whom I inspired the wish to do so ; for I am no man's goal and have nothing wherewith to satisfy them. . . . If I make people love me, if I attract them to myself, I am guilty ; for their lives and all their cares should be devoted to attaching themselves to God or to seeking him.'

§ 10. *The Sick Ascetic*

Principles, the desire to be angelically consistent, caused him to 'faire la bête' outside the sphere of personal behaviour and human relations as well as within. Art, for example, he disliked because it was different from morality, and it was to morality that he had given his exclusive allegiance. In art, he says, 'la règle est [he means 'doit être'] l'honnêteté. Poète et non honnête homme.' How he hated the poets for having other rules than those of virtue and for behaving like men rather than like good men ! He felt all the Puritan's disapproval of the theatre because it made people think about love, and because it gave them pleasure. Anything that gave pleasure was odious to this great hater. That section of the *Pensées* which deals with worldly distractions is perhaps the most vigorous of the whole book; hatred improved his style. He loathed his fellows for being able to amuse themselves. He would have liked all men to be as he himself was—racked with incessant pain, sleepless, exhausted by illness. 'Sickness,' he affirmed, 'is the Christian's natural state; for in sickness a man is as he ought always to be—in a state, that is to say, of suffering, of pain, of privation from all the pleasures of the senses, exempt from all passions.' Such was the opinion of Pascal, the Christian dogmatist; Pascal, the philosopher, looked at the matter rather differently. 'We have another principle of error in our illnesses. They spoil our judgment and sense.' The Christian's natural state is therefore, philosophically, a state of chronic error. The sick man has no right to pass judgment on the activities of health. A man who has no ear is not the best critic of Mozart's quartets; and similarly a moralist 'deprived of all the pleasures of the senses, exempt from all passions,' is not the person best qualified to speak of 'temptations' and man's 'lower nature.' Only the musical can understand the significance of music, and only the sensual and the passionate can understand the significance of the senses and the passions. The sick ascetic can understand nothing of these things, for the simple reason that he cannot, or deliberately does not, experience the emotions or perform the acts which he sets out to criticize. He makes a virtue of necessity and calls his debility by sacred names. 'Those who restrain Desire,' says Blake, 'do so because theirs is weak enough to be restrained.' Pascal's sick body was *naturaliter Christianum.* 'Une douleur de tête comme insupportable, une chaleur d'entrailles et beaucoup d'autres maux,' would have made it extremely hard for him to be a pagan. Nietzsche would have been tempted by the very difficulty of the undertaking to try; for Nietzsche held that a sick man had no right to be an ascetic—it was too easy. Not so Pascal; he accepted his sickness, and even persuaded himself that he was grateful for the headache and the heat in the entrails. And not only did he accept sickness for himself; he even tried to impose it on other people. He demanded that every one should think and feel about the world at large as he did; he wanted to impose headaches, sleeplessness, and dyspepsia, with their accompanying psychological states, on all. Those of us, however, who are blessedly free from these diseases will refuse to accept Pascal's neuralgia-metaphysic, just as we refuse to accept the asthma-philosophy of a more recent invalid of genius, Marcel Proust.

II

§ 11. *Nature of the Normal Universe*

The second section of this essay shall begin where the first ended—with asthma and neuralgia, with heat in the entrails and insupportable pains in the head. Pascal, as we have seen, pronounced himself as contradictorily about sickness as about most other subjects. What he describes as one of the great sources of error is also the Christian's natural state. If he had been asked to reconcile the two pronouncements he would doubtless have replied that what seems error to the normal man, to a member of the 'omnitude,' is not necessarily error in the eyes of God—may, in fact, be the truth. For after all, what is our currently accepted 'reality'? What is 'the normal'? What is 'common sense'? What are the 'laws of thought' and the 'boundaries of the knowable'? They are merely more or less long-established conventions.

Our normal common-sense universe is the product of a particular habit of perception—perhaps a bad habit, who knows? A slight change in the nature of our sense organs would make it unrecognizably unlike its present self. Henri Poincaré has described some of the worlds which such changes in our structure would automatically call into existence. Extremely interesting in this context are certain recent studies of the universes inhabited by the lower animals. The world, for example, in which a sea-urchin has its being is a world, for us, of water, rocks, sand, weeds, and marine animals. For the urchin, however, not one of these things even exists. The universe perceived (which is the same thing as saying 'created') by its organs of touch is utterly unlike that in which we humans arbitrarily locate it. By modifying the apparatus with which we perceive (and the apparatus with which we perceive is the apparatus with which we create), sickness modifies the universe. For one man to impose his particular universe on another is almost as unjustifiable as it is for a man to impose a human universe on a sea-urchin.

In the course of the last century or two a considerable number of what once were necessities of thought and immutable laws of nature have been shown to be systems arbitrarily fabricated by human beings to serve particular human ends. Thus, God is no longer bound, as he once was, to obey the decrees promulgated by Euclid in 300 B.C. He can now take his choice among a variety of geometries. Geometries and laws of nature are among the latest products of the human spirit; they have not had time to take root. Such slightly formed habits are relatively easy to break. But there are habits of perception and thought incomparably more ancient, and so deeply ingrained that it seems hardly possible for us to interpret experience except in the terms of them. Thus, the habit of living in space and time is one which was evidently formed by our remotest ancestors. And yet men are now able, if not to live, at least to think in terms of a four-dimensional continuum; and when they deal with the sub-atomic world of electrons and protons, they must get rid of temporal and spatial notions altogether. The universe of the infinitely little is radically unlike the macroscopic universe which we inhabit. Modern physical theory shows that Pascal was quite right to insist on its strangeness. In the case of time it seems possible for us to *live* in a universe where the ordinary temporal relations do not hold. There is tolerably good evidence to show that the future is in certain circumstances foreseeable (especially in dreams, if we can believe Mr. Dunn, the author of that very interesting book, *An Experiment with Time*). It is quite conceivable that a technique of prevision may in time be perfected, and that the prophetic powers at present, it is to be presumed, latent in the vast majority of individuals will be actualized. In which case our normal universe would be changed out of all recognition.

§ 12. *The Sick Man's Universe: its Justification*

Sickness modifies our perceiving apparatus, and so modifies the universe in which we live. Which is more real, which is nearer to the thing in itself perceived by God—the healthy man's universe or the sick man's? It is clearly impossible to answer with certainty. The healthy man has the majority on his side. But *vox populi* is not *vox Dei*. For practical, social purposes the normal universe is certainly the most convenient we can inhabit; but convenience is not a measure of Truth. The healthy man labours under the grave disadvantage of not being disinterested. The world for him is a place to get on in, a place where the fittest to survive survive. Will he, nill he, he sees the utilitarian aspects of things. Sickness transports a man from the battlefield where the struggle for existence is being waged, into a region of biological detachment; he sees something other than the merely useful. Dostoievsky's Idiot, Prince Mishkin, was an epileptic. Each of his fits was preceded by an apocalyptic mystical experience. Thinkers of the Max Nordau school would 'explain' the experience in terms of the epilepsy—would explain it away, in fact. But the revelation is not the less credible for being accompanied by the fit; it is, on the contrary, more credible. For the fit detaches the mind from utilitarian reality and permits it to perceive, or create for itself, another reality, less superficial and tendencious than the normal utilitarian one of every day. (To be able to see things in the same disinterested way, with the eyes of a child, a god, a noble savage, is the mark and privilege of the artist. The artist is a man who has revelations without having to pay for them with epileptic fits.) The Nordauites, who see everything *sub specie Podsnapitatis* cannot forgive Mishkin, or for that matter, Shakespeare, Blake, Beethoven, for seeing them *sub specie Aeternitatis*. They refuse to admit the validity of Mishkin's experience. They might as well refuse to admit the validity of their own sense impressions. For the mystic or the artist his revelation is a psychological fact, like colour or sound. It is given: there is no getting away from it.

Men of talent may be described as a special class of chronic invalids. The one-and-a-half wit is as abnormal as the half-wit, and may as justifiably, since sanity is only a question of statistics, be called mad. There is a class of all-too-normal people who take a peculiar pleasure in asserting that all great men have been diseased and lunatic; it is their way of venting a natural but not very engaging envy, of avenging themselves on their superiors for being so manifestly superior. But even if it could be proved that these people were right and that all men of genius were neurotic, or syphilitic, or tuberculous, it would make not the slightest difference; Shakespeare may have been the sort of man that a good eugenist would castrate at sight, but that does not prevent him from being the author of *Antony and Cleopatra* and *Macbeth*. The canaille hates its betters for not being like itself. Its yapping can be ignored. All that its arguments amount to is simply this: that the men of talent are different from the Podsnapian canaille and have free access to universes which heredity and habit have closed to the common run of humanity. Illness may facilitate their entry into these non-Podsnapian universes of disinterested contemplation. If it does, then illness is a good. And in any case the acts and works of genius remain what they are, whatever the state of health of their authors. The medical denunciations of the all-too-normal are entirely irrelevant, and would be merely comic if the denouncers were not rendered dangerous by their numbers and influence. It is alarming, for example, to discover that the Eugenists are working to make the world safe for Podsnappery. According to Major Leonard Darwin, the fittest to survive are those who can earn most money. The deserving rich must be encouraged to propagate their kind; the poor, whatever the cause of their poverty, whether it be illness, eccentricity, too much or too little intelligence, must be discouraged and if necessary sterilized. If Major

Darwin gets his way, the world in a few generations will be peopled exclusively by Podsnaps and Babbitts. A consummation, it is obvious, devoutly to be hoped.

Pascal justified his asceticism on theological grounds. Christianity commands us to mortify the flesh and to be without concupiscence for the things of the world. Christianity is divinely inspired. Not to be ascetic is therefore an act of blasphemous rebellion. But asceticism can be justified without invoking the aid of a revelation which no amount of historical evidence can possibly guarantee. It can be justified on purely psychological grounds. Ascetic practices are methods for artificially inducing a kind of mental and physical abnormality or sickness. This sickness modifies the ascetic's perceiving apparatus, and his universe is consequently changed. Certain of his states are so strange that he feels, if he is religious, that he is in direct communication with the deity. (Which, of course, he may be. Or may not. We are not in a position to affirm or deny.) Anyhow, such states are felt by the ascetic to be of the highest value. This is a direct intuition, about which there can be no argument. If the ascetic feels that such states, along with the universe corresponding to them, are valuable, then he is obviously justified in continuing the practices which tend to induce them.

§ 13. *Pascal and Death*

With Pascal, as with all other mystics, ecstasy was only a very occasional state. So far as we know, indeed, he had only one experience of its joys. Only once was he touched with the divine fires. His daily, his chronic revelation was of darkness, and the source of that revelation was not the God of Life; it was Death.

After a moonless night the dawn is a kind of decadence. Darkness is limitless and empty; light comes, filling the void, peopling infinity with small irrelevancies, setting bounds to the indefinite. The deepest, the most utter darkness is death's; in the dark idea of death we come as near to a realization of infinity as it is possible for finite beings to come. Pascal early made the acquaintance of death. Through all the later years of his brief existence he lived surrounded by the bottomless obscurities of death. Those metaphysical gulfs which were said to have accompanied him wherever he went were openings into the pit of death. All his meditations on the infinities of littleness and greatness, on the infinite distance between body and mind and the infinitely more infinite distance between mind and charity, were inspired by death, were rationalizations of his sense of death. Death even prompted some of his mathematical speculations; for if it is true, in Pascal's words, that 'même les propositions géométriques deviennent sentiments,' the converse is no less certain. Sentiments are rationalized as geometrical propositions. When Pascal speculated on the mathematical infinite, he was speculating on that unplumbed darkness with which death had surrounded him. Pascal's thoughts become intelligible only on condition that we look at them against this background of darkness. A man who has realized infinity, not intellectually, but with his whole being, realized it in the intimate and terrifying realization of death, inhabits a different universe from that which is the home of the man to whom death and infinity are only names.

III

§ 14. *The God of Life*

But there is a revelation of life as well as a revelation of death; to Pascal that revelation was never vouchsafed. It seemed to him incredible that men should busy themselves with their petty affairs, their trivial pleasures, instead of with the huge and frightful problems of eternity. Himself hemmed in by the darkness of death, he was astonished that other people contrived to think of anything else. This disregard of death and infinity seemed to him so strange, that he was forced to regard it as supernatural. 'C'est un appesantissement de la main de Dieu,' was his conclusion. And he was right. God does lay his hand on those who can forget the darkness and death and infinity—but lays it upon them not in anger, not as a punishment, as Pascal imagined, but encouragingly, helpfully. For the God who forbids men to think incessantly of the infinite darkness is a God of Life, not of Death, a God of diversity, not of frozen unity. Pascal hates the world because it has 'le pouvoir de ne pas songer à ce qu'il ne veut pas songer.' But the God of Life demands that men shall live; and in order that they may live, they must have desire; and in order that they may have desire, they must live in a world of desirable things. But 'le fini s'anéantit en présence de l'infini, et devient un pur néant.' Therefore finite things must not be kept in contact with the infinite, because if they were they would lose their desirability and men would cease to desire them and so would cease to live. (Pascal's infinite, it should be noticed, is something external to the finite world. The spirit that sees infinity in a grain of sand and eternity in a flower is a life-worshipping spirit, not one enamoured of death.) Not to desire, not to live, would be a blasphemy and a rebellion against the God of Life. So the God of Life lays his hand upon men and gives them power not to think the thoughts they do not wish to have; he bestows the grace of life upon them that they may spend their little time on earth, not in trying to discover whether their eternal death-sentence has been passed, 'mais à jouer au piquet.' 'It is supernatural,' cries Pascal; and we can agree with him. The God of Life is a powerful God; Pascal knew it, and used all the arts of logic and persuasion to convert men from his worship to that of Death. But in vain. Men still refuse to spend their lives thinking of death, still refuse to contemplate that dark infinite whose enormousness reduces to nothingness all the objects of their finite desires; they prefer to think of 'dancing, of playing the lute, of singing, of making verses.' Even when their only son has died, they hunt the boar or play fives, or try to make themselves king. Why? Because life is diverse, because they are not always the same. They think of death when death is near, and of the boar when the boar is near. 'S'il ne s'abaisse pas à cela,' concludes Pascal, the philosopher, 'et veuille toujours être tendu, il n'en sera que plus sot, parce qu'il voudra s'élever au-dessus de l'humanité et il n'est qu'un homme.' In spite of which he demanded that men should raise themselves above humanity—or lower themselves beneath it—by becoming consistently Christians. He wanted them to deny their manifold being; he demanded that they should impose upon themselves a unity—his unity.

§ 15. *Unity and Diversity*

Now, it is obvious that men must organize their diversity into some kind of singleness. We cannot think successfully of the outside world unless we have some kind of unifying hypothesis as to its nature. (Would it, indeed, be possible to think of the external world as being one as well as diverse, if we had not previously conceived our own inward unity? I doubt it.) If we were without such a unifying hypothesis, if we never constrained ourselves to act the particular part which we have decided is peculiarly ours, social life and purposive action would be impossible. To-day's self would be unable to make any engagement for to-morrow's. As it is, when Tuesday's ego turns out to be different from Monday's, we make an effort to recapture the spirit of the earlier self, we loyally do our best (I speak at least for the conscientious, of whom unhappily I am one) to carry out the programme of thought or action elaborated on Monday, however repugnant it may seem to the Tuesday personage who has to do the carrying out. The task of unification is made easier by the fact that some sort of persistent identity does really underlie the diversities of personality. A collection of habits (among which, if we are good idealists, we must number the body), and a number of hereditary tendencies to form habits, persist as a gradually changing background to the diversities of personality. The colony of our souls is rooted in the stem of a single life. By a process of what Jules de Gaultier has called 'Bovarysm' (Mme Bovary, it will be remembered, was a lady who imagined herself other than what she really was) we impose upon ourselves a more or less fictitious personality and do our best consistently to act the imaginary part, whatever may be the real state of our psychology. The reality is often stronger than the imagination; in spite of all our earnest efforts to bovaryze ourselves into imaginary unity, human life constantly reveals itself as diverse and discontinuous. Pascal demands that all men shall imagine themselves to be ascetic despisers of the world; they must bovaryze their diversity into a conscious and consistent worship of death. The methods by means of which this bovaryzation is to be accomplished are the methods perfected through long ages of experience by the Catholic church. The external man, the machine, in Pascal's phrase, must perform the gestures of worship and renunciation, until a habit is formed, and the bovaric personage of the otherworldly hater of life is firmly established as an actualized imagination in the mind.

But not every man agrees with Pascal in finding life detestable. For those who love it his world-view and his way of life are a blasphemy and an ingratitude; let them therefore be anathema. What are the alternatives to Pascal's scheme?

To abandon ourselves completely to our natural diversity? Social existence and purposive individual activity would be rendered impossible by such an abandonment. Besides, we have a body, we have habits and memories that persist; we are conscious of being enduringly alive. Absolute diversity would be as difficult of achievement as absolute unity. The problem is obviously to discover just how much unifying requires to be done, and to see that it is done in the interests of life. A life-worshipping personage must be set up in opposition to the Pascalian worshipper of death, and the diversities of personality must be unified, so far as it is necessary to unify them, by being bovaryzed into a resemblance to this mythical personage.

§ 16. *The Life-Worshipper as Philosopher*

What are the principal features of the life-worshipper? I shall answer tentatively and only for my private personage. In these matters, it is obvious, no man has a right to speak for any one except himself and those who happen to resemble him. My objection to Pascal is not that he worships death. Every man has as good a right to his own particular world-view as to his own particular kidneys. Incidentally there is often, if we may judge from the case of Carlyle, of Pascal himself, and how many others, a very intimate connection between a man's viscera and his philosophy. To argue against Carlyle's 'fire-eyed despair' is futile, because it is to argue against Carlyle's digestion. I admit Carlyle's despair and Pascal's worship of death, just as I admit the shape of their noses and their tastes in art. What I object to is their claim to dictate to the world at large. I refuse to have death-worship imposed on me against my will. And conversely I have no desire to impose my particular brand of life-worship on any one else. In philosophical discussions the Sinaitic manner is ridiculous—as ridiculous as it would be in gastronomical discussions. It is not in terms of 'thus saith the Lord' that we talk, for example, of lobsters. Not now, at any rate; for it is worth remembering that Jehovah forbade the Chosen People to eat them—presumably because they divide the hoof but do not chew the cud. We admit that every man has a right in these matters to his own tastes. 'I like lobsters; you don't. And there's an end of it.' Such is the argument of gastronomers. In time, perhaps, philosophers will learn to treat one another with the same politeness and forbearance. True, I myself was impolite enough just now to anathematize Pascal's philosophy; but that was simply because he tried to force his opinions upon me. I can be civil to the lovers of semolina pudding so long as they do not want to make me share their peculiar tastes. But if they tried to force semolina down my throat, I should become extremely rude.

Briefly, then, these are my notions of the life-worshipper into whose likeness I myself should be prepared to bovaryze the diversities of my personality. His fundamental assumption is that life on this planet is valuable in itself, without any reference to hypothetical higher worlds, eternities, future existences. 'Is it not better, then, to be alone and love Earth only for its earthly sake?' It is, particularly if you have Blake's gift for seeing eternity in a flower and for 'making the whole creation appear infinite, and holy . . . by an improvement of sensual enjoyment.' The life-worshipper's next assumption is that the end of life, if we leave out of account for the moment all the innumerable ends attributed to it by living individuals, is more life, that the purpose of living is to live. God, for the life-worshipper, is of course life, and manifests himself in all vital processes, even those which, from our point of view, are most repulsive and evil. For the life-worshipper perceives, with Kant, that if man had no anti-social tendencies 'an Arcadian life would arise, of perfect harmony and mutual love, such as must suffocate and stifle all talents in their very germs'; and with Lotze that 'our virtue and happiness can only flourish amid an active conflict with wrong.' Following the Hindus, he realizes that perfection is necessarily Nirvana, and that the triumph of good would mean the total annihilation of existence. A homogeneously perfect life is a contradiction in terms. Without contrast and diversity life is inconceivable. Therefore he believes in having as much contrast and diversity as he can get; for not being a death-worshipper, like the Hindus, he will have nothing to do with a perfection that is annihilation; and not being illogical, like the Christians, he cannot believe in a perfection that is not a Nirvana of non-existence. It is in Blake's *Marriage of Heaven and Hell* that he finds the best statement of his own life-worshipper's metaphysic.

> Without contraries is no progression. Attraction and Repulsion, Reason and Energy, Love and Hate are necessary to Man's Existence.
>
> Man has no Body distinct from his Soul; for that call'd body is a portion of the Soul discern'd by the Senses, the chief inlets of spirit in this age. Energy is the only life and is from the body. . . . Energy is Eternal Delight.
>
> God alone Acts or is in existing beings or Men.

§ 17. *The Life-Worshipper as Moralist*

Blake is also the life-worshipper's favourite moralist.

> He who desires but acts not, breeds pestilence.

> Abstinence sows sand all over
> The ruddy limbs and flaming hair.
> But Desire gratified
> Plants fruits of life and beauty there.

Blake's value as a moralist would be higher if he had taken the trouble to explain how his admirable precepts could be carried out in practice within the bounds of a highly organized society. The life-worshipper completes Blake's teaching by showing how this may be done. He suggests a compromise which will enable the conscientious citizen of a modern industrialized state to be also a complete man, a creature with desires, passions, instincts, a body as well as a mind and a conscious will. This compromise is based on the recognition and deliberate organization of man's natural diversity. The life-worshipper is not, like Pascal, a man of principle; he is a man of many principles, living discontinuously. He does not select one single being from his colony of souls, call it his 'true self,' and try to murder all the other selves. Each self, he perceives, has as good a right to exist as all the others. Each one, so long as it is 'there' in possession of his consciousness, is his true self. To those who would object, in the name of the sense of values, to such a conclusion we can reply with a statement of the observable facts. The sense of values is something which persists, is an attribute of the single life in which the personal diversities are rooted. But the values of which we have a sense vary with our varying personality; what is good in the eyes of one self is bad in the eyes of another self. That which is given is the tendency to evaluate; the fixed standard of values is something which we arbitrarily impose on ourselves. We take the values of one out of our many personalities and call them absolute, and the values of our other personalities being different are therefore wrong. The life-worshipper cannot accept *a* philosophy and an ethic which are not in accord with the facts of experience. For him each self has the right to exist, the right to its own values. True, he does his best as a matter of practical politics to arrange that the appropriate self shall be there at the appropriate time. The murder of some importunate and momentarily unsuitable soul may sometimes be necessary; but he will not be a party to Pascal's daily slaughter of innocent selves, his chronic and continuous psychological pogroms. The life-worshipper's aim is to achieve a vital equilibrium, not by drawing in his diversities, not by moderating his exuberances (for Exuberance, in the words of Blake, is Beauty), but by giving them rein one against the other. His is the equilibrium of balanced excesses, the safest perhaps of all (is it not between the far-projecting extremities of a long pole that the tight-rope walker treads his spidery bridge?). Aristotle was also a preacher of moderation. Contradicting himself (it speaks well for Aristotle that he *could* contradict himself), he also extolled the delights of intellectual excess. But it is by his doctrine of the golden mean that he is best known as a moralist. As a later philosopher remarked of him, he was 'moderate to excess.' The life-worshipper's moderation is excessive in quite a different way. For the Aristotelian adorers of the mean (how aptly named in our ambiguous language!) the last word in human wisdom is to do everything by halves, to live in a perpetual state of compromise. Not for the life-worshipper; for the life-worshipper knows that nothing of any significance has ever been achieved by a man of moderation and compromise. Aristotle has influenced the world because he was excessively an intellectual, not because he preached and practised the Hellenic equivalent of gentlemanliness. The congenitally mediocre adorers of the mean exist to give stability to a world which might be easily upset by the violent antics of the excessive. Filled with divine madness, the excessive lay furiously about them; the great Leviathan of mediocre humanity presents its vast, its almost immovably ponderous bottom; there is a dull and suety thudding; the boot rebounds. Sometimes, when the kicks have been more than usually violent and well directed, the monster stirs a little. These are the changes which it has been fashionable, for the last hundred years or so, to describe as progress.

§ 18. *Balanced Excess*

The world has been moved, I repeat, only by those who have lived excessively. But this excessive life has been too often, from the point of view of the individual human being, a maimed, imperfect life. Living excessively only in one direction, the world-mover has been reduced from the rank of a complete human being to that of an incarnate function. How sterile, how terrifyingly inadequate as human existences, were the lives, for example, of Newton and Napoleon! Such men go through life without ever actualizing the greater number of their human potentialities; they keep all but one, or a very few, of their possible selves permanently smothered. It may be that such sacrifices are necessary and praiseworthy; it may be that the Genius of the Species demands psychological holocausts from those whom it has chosen to serve its ends. I do not pretend to be in the Genius's confidence. All I know is that a man has a perfect right to murder such of his personalities as he does not like or feel the need of—as good a right as he has, shall we say, to cut off his toes. He has no right, however, to impose his tastes on others, no right to go about saying, like Aunt Jobiska, 'that Pobbles are happier without their toes.' They aren't. He has no right to be a liar or a tyrannical enforcer of his own opinions. Conversely, those who want to live completely, realizing the potentialities of the whole man, have every right to do so without risk of physical or moral bullying from the specialists in one particular excess.

The aim of the life-worshipper is to combine the advantages of balanced moderation and excess. The moderate Aristotelian partially realizes all his potentialities; the man of excess fully realizes part of his potentialities; the life-worshipper aims at fully realizing all—at living, fully and excessively living, with every one of his colony of souls. He aspires to balance excess of self-consciousness and intelligence by an excess of intuition, of instinctive and visceral living; to remedy the ill effects of too much contemplation by those of too much action, too much solitude by too much sociability, too much enjoyment by too much asceticism. He will be by turns excessively passionate and excessively chaste. (For chastity, after all, is the proper, the natural complement of passion. After satisfaction, desire reposes in a cool and lucid sleep. Chastity enforced against desire is unquiet and life-destroying. No less life-destroying are the fulfilments of desires which imagination has artificially stimulated in the teeth of natural indifference. The life-worshipper practises those excesses of abstinence and fulfilment which chance and his unrestrained, unstimulated desire impose upon him.) He will be at times a positivist and at times a mystic; derisively sceptical and full of faith. He will live light-hearted or earnest and, when the sick Pascalian mood is upon him, correct his frivolities and ambitions with the thought of death. In a word, he will accept each of his selves, as it appears in his consciousness, as his momentarily true self. Each and all he will accept—even the bad, even the mean and suffering, even the death-worshipping and naturally Christian souls. He will accept, he will live the life of each, excessively.

The saints in the life-worshipper's calendar are mostly artists. His ideal of completeness, of moderation in terms of balanced excess, is realized by such men as Burns (about whom the respectable and the academic continue to write in the most nauseating tone of condescension and Pecksniffian forgiveness), as Mozart, as Blake, as Rubens, as Shakespeare, as Tolstoy before he deliberately perverted himself to death-worshipping consistency, as the adorable Chaucer, as Rabelais, as Montaigne. I need not lengthen the list. It contains the names of most of the few human beings for whom it is possible to feel admiration and respect. Those who are not in it are specialists in one exclusive excess. One can admire and respect a Newton, even a Napoleon. But one cannot propose them as models for those who would live well and with all their being.

There have been whole epochs during which the life-worshipper has been the representative man. Our own Renaissance, for example. Looking back, the modern historian finds himself utterly bewildered. Those brilliant and enigmatic personages who move across the Elizabethan scene—Essex, Marlowe, Donne, Elizabeth herself, Shakespeare, Raleigh, and how many others—they seem to him inexplicable beings. How is it possible for men to be at once so subtly refined and so brutal, so sensual and yet so spiritual, such men of action and so much enamoured of contemplation, so religious and so cynical? The modern historian, who is generally a professor, disapprovingly fails to understand. Pledged to a respectable consistency of professional thought and conduct, he is frightened by the spectacle of human beings who dared to be free, to realize all their natural diversity, to be wholly alive. Balanced between their inordinate excesses, they danced along the knife-edge of existence. We watch them enviously.

To the moralist the life-worshipper's doctrines may seem subversively dangerous; and, in effect, the 'Do what thou wilt' of Thelema was addressed only to 'men that are free, well-born, well-bred, and conversant in honest companies.' For the others, restraints from without in the shape of policemen, from within in the shape of superstitions, will always be necessary. The best life-worshippers are probably those who have been strictly educated in Christian or bourgeois morality, in the philosophy of common-sense tempered by religion, and have afterwards revolted against their upbringing. Their balancing-pole is weighted at opposite ends with the good social habits of their education and the anti-social habits of their revolt. For the well-born young aspirant to a cell in Gargantua's abbey I would recommend the most conventional of gentlemanly and Anglican public-school educations, followed, at the university, by an intensive course of theoretical Pyrrhonism and the practice of all Blake's most subversive precepts. The loss of his religious, intellectual, and moral faiths might lead him perhaps to neurasthenia or suicide; so much the worse for him. But if he were tough enough to survive, he could be confidently left to do what he liked. His public-school traditions would bring him honourably and sensibly through the affairs of social life, while his course of Pyrrhonism would have taught him to disregard the restraints imposed by these traditions on his activities as an individual, or colony of individuals.

§ 19. *Unbalanced Excess*

To those who object that it is impossible to obey Gargantua's commandment without behaving like a pig, 'Speak for yourselves,' is all that one can reply. If one is well-born and well-bred one does not behave like a pig; one behaves like a human being. In the case, moreover, of a sincere life-worshipper, his religion is a guarantee against swinishness. For swinishness is not a manifestation of life, but a blasphemy against it. Thus, swinish gluttony and swinish drunkenness are devices for lowering vitality, not enhancing it. Swinish promiscuity is not an expression of that spontaneous desire which 'plants fruits of life and beauty' in the human personality. Your Don Juans love from the head, artificially. They use their imagination to stimulate their desire, a self-conscious, unimpassioned, and so unjustified desire that humiliates, that diminishes, that 'sows sand all over' those who thus call it into action. Swinish avarice and covetousness limit vitality by canalizing its flow in a narrow and filthy channel. Cruelty, which is occasionally appropriate and necessary and is then life-enhancing, is life-limiting and life-destroying when it turns into a habitual reaction, when it becomes, in a word, swinish cruelty. Indeed, any course of behaviour pursued to the exclusion of all the other possible courses open to a normally diverse personality is obviously, according to our standards, immoral, because it limits and distorts the manifestations of life. In the eyes of the life-worshipper such exclusiveness is a sin. His doctrine of moderation demands that one excess shall be counterbalanced by another. To continue on principle or by force of habit in one course is to destroy that vital equilibrium whose name is virtue, and run into immorality. Pascal, it is obvious, was a horribly immoral man. He sinned against life by a consistent excess of holiness, in precisely the same way as gluttons sin by a consistent excess of greed, misers by avarice, and the lewd by unremitting lechery.

§ 20. *Life and the Routine of Living*

It is worth remarking that the revelation of life confirms many of the revelations of death.* The business and the distractions which Pascal hated so much, because they made men forget that they must die, are hateful to the life-worshipper because they prevent men from fully living. Death makes these distractions seem trivial and silly; but equally so does life. It was from pain and gradually approaching dissolution that Ivan Ilyitch learned to understand the futility of his respectable bourgeois career. If he had ever met a genuinely living man, if he had ever read a book, or looked

* I have borrowed the phrase from Shestov. 'La Révélation de la Mort' is the title, in its French translation, of one of his most interesting books.

at a picture, or heard a piece of music by a living artist, he would have learned the same lesson. But Pascal and the later Tolstoy would not permit the revelation to come from life. Their aim was to humiliate men by rolling them in the corruption of the grave, to inflict a defiling punishment on them; they condemned, not only the distracting, life-destroying futilities with which men fill their days, but also the life which those futilities destroyed. The life-worshipper agrees with them in hating the empty fooleries and sordidnesses of average human existence. Incidentally the progress of science and industry has enormously increased the element of foolery and sordidness in human life. The clerk and the taylorized workman leave their imbecile tasks to spend their leisure under the influence of such opiate distractions as are provided by the newspaper, the cinema, the radio; they are given less and less opportunity to do any active or creative living of their own. Pascal and Tolstoy would have led them from silliness to despair by talking to them of death; but 'memento vivere' is the life-worshipper's advice. If people remembered to live, they would abstain from occupations which are mere substitutes for life. However, most of them don't want to live, just as they don't want to die; they are as much afraid of living as of dying. They prefer to go on existing dimly in the semi-coma of mechanized labour and mechanized leisure. Gradually to putrefy is their ideal of felicity. If the life-worshipper objects, it is for his own sake. These people have every right to putrefy if they want to putrefy; but the trouble is, that they may infect those who don't wish to putrefy. A plague-pit is not the healthiest place to worship life in.

§ 21. *Life and the Future*

When he told his disciples to take no thought for the morrow, Jesus was speaking as a worshipper of life. To pay too much attention to the future is to pay too little to the present—is to pay too little, that is to say, to life; for life can only be lived in the present. Eternity conceived as existing apart from life is life's enemy; that was why Pascal laid so much stress on the eternal and infinite. The only eternity known to life is that present eternity of ecstatic timelessness which is the consummation of intense living. Pascal himself reproached men for being 'so imprudent that they wander through times that are not theirs and never think of the only time which belongs to them.' But, as usual, his principles and his physiology would not allow him to practise what his intelligence theoretically perceived to be right. He saw that it was stupid not to live in the only time which belonged to him, but nevertheless persisted in thinking of nothing but approaching death and posthumous futurity. Strangely enough, he seemed to have imagined that his death-worship was true Christianity. But 'let the dead bury their dead' was what the founder of the religion had said. Jesus had no patience (at that moment, at any rate) with the people who imagine that they have something better to do than to live.

Living too much in and for another time than the present is the source of other crimes than too much holiness. The undue interest in money derives from too exclusive and excessive a preoccupation with the future in this life, just as undue interest in death and the means of posthumous salvation derives from a preoccupation with the future in another life. Death-dealing holiness is rare in the contemporary West; but literally millions of men and women pass their time murdering themselves for the sake of their financial position in a worldly future, which the threats of wars and revolutions have rendered so precarious that one is amazed that any one in his senses can waste his time in taking laborious thought for it. The past is as fatal to life as the future.

Backward-looking artists who wander in times not their own invariably produce bad works: too much natural piety towards vanished things and people smothers present vitality in the pious. The life-worshipper lives as far as possible in the present—in present time or present eternity.

§ 22. *Habits*

'Two hundred and eighty sovereign goods in Montaigne.' Pascal uses the fact to support his argument in favour of the unique, divinely revealed Sovereign Good proposed to all men by the Catholic Church. 'We burn with desire,' he says, 'to find a fixed framework of reference, an ultimate and constant base.' But we burn in vain. Our unaided efforts result in the discovery only of uncertainty and multiplicity. Therefore, we must accept the divinely revealed doctrines of the Church. It is the appeal to fatigue and fear expressed in the form of an argument. The argument breaks down at several points. To begin with, there is no guarantee that the doctrines of the Church are of divine origin. And in the second place, do *we* (that is to say, all men) 'burn with desire' to find a fixed foundation of belief? All that I know with certainty is that *I* don't burn. And when Pascal says, 'Nous avons une idée de la vérité invincible à tout le pyrrhonisme,' I can only reply, 'Speak for yourself.' The fact is, of course, that these supposedly innate ideas and metaphysical desires are the fruit of habit. Pascal, as usual, understood it all theoretically, but refused to draw the necessary conclusions or to act on his own theory. (Was ever so penetrating an intelligence wedded to so perverse a will?) 'I am very much afraid,' he wrote, 'that this nature is only a first habit, as habit is a second nature.' And again: 'Habit is our nature. A man who has grown accustomed to the Faith believes it and cannot help being afraid of hell. . . . Who can doubt, then, that our souls, being accustomed to see number, space, movement, believe in these things and nothing but these things?' 'Our natural principles, what are they but the principles we have made a habit of? . . . A different habit would give us different natural principles; and if there are certain natural principles which habit cannot efface, there are also anti-natural principles of habit which cannot be effaced either by nature or by a second habit.' Our most ineffaceable habits are those of living in terms of space, time, and cause. But even these, as I have suggested earlier in this essay, can be shaken. Most of our other 'natural principles' date from a much later period in the mind's history than do these primeval habits of thought. When Pascal says that 'we' burn with desire to find a fixed foundation of belief, all that he means is that he, together with his friends and his favourite authors, happens to have been brought up in habits of doctrinal fixity. The desire for fixity is not the only metaphysical nostalgia attributed by Pascal to humanity. Men long to know the 'meaning' of events, to be told the 'answer to the riddle of the universe.' Christianity provides such an answer and satisfies these 'natural' longings: the fact has been regarded by its apologists as a proof of its divine origin and absolute truth. That Christianity should satisfy these longings will not surprise us when we realize that it was Christianity which first implanted them in the human mind and fixed them there as habits. 'Christian theology' (I quote from Bury's *Idea of Progress*) 'constructed a synthesis which for the first time attempted to give a definite meaning to the whole course of human events, a synthesis which represents the past as leading up to a definite and desirable goal in the future. Once this belief had been generally adopted and prevailed for centuries, men might discard it along with the doctrine of Providence on which it rested, but they could not be content to return again to such views as satisfied the ancients, for whom human history, apprehended as a whole, was a tale of little meaning. They must seek for a new synthesis to replace it.' Why must they seek for a new synthesis? Because Christianity has established in their minds a synthesis-habit, because the longing for a synthesis now seems 'natural.' But the ancients, as Bury shows, were quite happy with a history that was from the Christian's or the modern philosopher's point of view quite meaningless. Their habits were changed and they longed for meanings. Another change of habit may easily abolish that longing. In any case, however, the character of the longing does not affect the nature of the meaning that is longed for. We have only to observe ourselves and our fellows to discover that the universe has no single, pre-established 'meaning': its riddle is not a conundrum with only one correct answer. Meaning is a notion, like sourness or beauty.

§ 23. *Summary of the Life-Worshipper's Creed*

The life-worshipper's philosophy is comprehensive. As a manifold and discontinuous being, he is in a position to accept all the partial and apparently contradictory syntheses constructed by other philosophers. He is at one moment a positivist and at another a mystic: now haunted by the thought of death (for the apocalypse of death is one of the incidents of living) and now a Dionysian child of nature; now a pessimist and now, with a change of lover or liver or even the weather, an exuberant believer that God's in his heaven and all's right with the world. He holds these different beliefs because he is many different people. Each belief is the rationalization of the prevailing mood of one of these persons. There is really no question of any of these philosophies being true or false. The psychological state called joy is no truer than the psychological state called melancholy (it may be more valuable as an aid to social or individual living—but that is another matter). Each is a primary fact of experience. And since one psychological state cannot be truer than another, since all are equally facts, it follows that the rationalization of one state cannot be truer than the rationalization of another. What Hardy says about the universe is no truer than what Meredith says; if the majority of contemporary readers prefer the world-view expressed in *Tess of the D'Urbervilles* to the optimism which forms the background to *Beauchamp's Career*, that is simply because they happen to live in a very depressing age and consequently suffer from a more or less chronic melancholy. Hardy seems to them truer than Meredith because the philosophy of 'Tess' and 'Jude' is more adequate as a rationalization of their own prevailing mood than the philosophy of Richard Feverel or Beauchamp. What applies to optimism and pessimism applies equally to other trends of philosophical thought. Even the doctrines of 'fixed fate, free will, foreknowledge absolute,' for all the elaborateness of their form, are in substance only expression of emotional and physiological states. One feels free or one feels conditioned. Both feelings are equally facts of experience, so are the facts called 'mystical ecstasy' and 'reasonableness.' Only a man whose life was rich in mystical experiences could have constructed a cosmogony like that of Boehme's; and the works of Voltaire could have been written only by one whose life was singularly poor in such experiences. People with strongly marked idiosyncrasies of character have their world-view almost forced upon them by their psychology. The only branches of philosophy in regard to which it is permissible to talk of truth and falsehood are logic and the theory of knowledge. For logic and the theory of knowledge are concerned with the necessities and the limitations of thought—that is to say, with mental habits so primordial that it is all but impossible for any human being to break them. When a man commits a paralogism or lays claim to a more than human knowledge of the nature of things, we are justified in saying that he is wrong. I may, for example, admit that all men are mortal and that Socrates is a man, but nevertheless feel impelled to conclude that Socrates is immortal. Am I not as well justified in this opinion as I am in my optimism or pessimism, whichever the case may be? The answer is: no. I may have a personal taste for Socrates's immortality; but, in the syllogistic circumstances, the taste is so outrageously bad, so universally condemned, that it would be madness to try to justify it. Moreover, I should discover that, if I put my paralogistic theories into practice, I should find myself in serious trouble, not only with other human beings, but even with things. The hero of Dostoievsky's *Notes from Underground* protests against the intolerable tyranny of two and two making four. He prefers that they shall make five, and insists that he has a right to his preference. And no doubt he has a right. But if an express train happens to be passing at a distance of two plus two yards, and he advances four yards and a half under the impression that he will still be eighteen inches on the hither side of destruction, this right of his will not save him from coming to a violent and bloody conclusion.

Scientific thought is true or false because science deals with sense impressions which are, if not identical for all human beings, at least sufficiently similar to make something like universal agreement possible. The difference between a scientific theory and a metaphysical world-view is that the first is a rationalization of psychological experiences which are more or less uniform for all men and for the same man at different times, while the second is a rationalization of experiences which are diverse, occasional, and contradictory. A man may be a pessimistic determinist before lunch and an optimistic believer in the will's freedom after it; but both before and after his meal he will observe that the colour of the sky is blue, that stones are hard, that the sun gives light and warmth. It is for this reason that there are many philosophies, and only one science.

But even science demands that its votaries shall think, according to circumstances, in a variety of different ways. The mode of thinking which gives valid results when applied to objects of more than a certain size (in other words, to large numbers of objects; for anything big enough to be perceptible to our senses is built up, apparently, of enormous numbers of almost infinitesimal components) is found to be absolutely inapplicable to single objects of atomic or subatomic dimensions. About large agglomerations of atoms we can think in terms of 'organized common sense.' But when we come to consider individual atoms and their minuter components, common-sense gives results which do not square with the observed facts. (Nobody, of course, has ever actually observed an atom or an electron; but the nature of their behaviour can be inferred, with more or less probability, from such happenings on a macroscopical scale as accompany their invisible activity.) In the sub-atomic world practically all our necessities of thought become not only unnecessary but misleading. A description of this universe reads like a page from Lewis Carroll or Edward Lear.

Seeing, then, that even sense impressions not only can but must be rationalized in irreconcilably different ways, according to the class of object with which they are supposed to be connected, we need not be troubled or surprised by the contradictions which we find in the rationalization of less uniform psychological experiences. Thus, the almost indefinitely numerous rationalizations of the aesthetic and the mystical experiences not only contradict one another, but agree in contradicting those rationalizations of sense experience known as scientific theories. This fact greatly disturbed our grandfathers, who kept on losing their faith, sacrificing their reason, striking attitudes of stoical despair, and, in general, performing the most extraordinary spiritual antics, because of it. Science is ' true,' they argued ; therefore art and religion, therefore beauty and honour, love and ideals, must be ' false.' ' Reality ' has been ' proved ' by science to be an affair of space, time, mass, number, and cause ; therefore all that makes life worth living is an ' illusion.' Or else they started from the other end. Art, religion, beauty, love, make life worth living ; therefore science, which disregards the existence of these things, must be false. It is unnecessary for us to take so tragic a view. Science, we have come to realize, takes no cognizance of the things that make life worth living, for the simple reason that beauty, love, and so on, are not measurable quantities, and science deals only with what can be measured. One psychological fact is as good as another. We perceive beauty as immediately as we perceive hardness ; to say that one sensation is illusory and that the other corresponds with reality is a gratuitous piece of presumption.

Answers to the riddle of the universe often have a logical form and are expressed in such a way that they raise questions of epistemology and involve the acceptance or rejection of certain scientific theories. In substance, however, they are simply rationalizations of diverse and equally valid psychological states, and are therefore neither true nor false. (Incidentally, similar states are not necessarily or invariably rationalized in the same way. Mystical experiences which, in Europe, are explained in terms of a personal God are interpreted by the Buddhists in terms of an entirely godless order of things. Which is the truer rationalization ? God, or not-God, whichever the case may be, knows.) The life-worshipper who adopts in turn all the solutions to the cosmic riddle is committing no crime against logic or the truth. He is simply admitting the obvious fact that he is a human being

—that is to say, a series of distinct psychological states, a colony of diverse personalities. Each state demands its appropriate rationalizations; or, in other words, each personality has its own philosophies of life. Philosophical consistency had some justification so long as it could be imagined that the substance of one's world-view (as opposed to the logical trappings in which it was clothed and the problems of epistemology and science connected with it) was uniquely true. But if we admit, as I think we must, that one world-view cannot be truer than another, but that each is the expression in intellectual terms of some given and undeniable fact of experience, then consistency loses all philosophical merit. It is pointless to ignore all the occasions when you feel that the world is good, for the sake of being consistently a pessimist; it is pointless, for the sake of being consistently a positivist, to deny that your body is sometimes tenanted by a person who has mystical experiences. Pessimism is no truer than optimism, nor positivism than mysticism. Philosophically, there is no reason why a man should deny the thoughts of all but one of his potential selves. Each self on occasion exists; each has its feelings about the universe, its cosmic tastes—or, to put it in a different way, each inhabits its own universe. What relation these various private universes bear to the Universe in Itself, if such a thing exists, it is clearly impossible to say. We can believe, if we like, that each of them represents one aspect of the whole. 'In my Father's house are many mansions.' Nature has given to each individual the key to quite a number of these metaphysical mansions. The life-worshipper suggests that man shall make use of all his keys instead of throwing all but one of them away. He admits the fact of vital diversity and makes the best of it. In this he is unlike the general run of thinkers, who are very reluctant to admit diversity, and, if they do confess the fact, deplore it. They find diversity shocking, they desire at all costs to correct it. And even if it came to be universally admitted that no one world-view could possibly be true, these people would continue, none the less, to hold fast to one to the exclusion of all the rest. They would go on worshipping consistency, if not on philosophical, then on moral grounds. Or, in other words, they would practise and demand consistency through fear of inconsistency, through fear of being dangerously free, through fear of life. For morality is always the product of terror; its chains and strait-waistcoats are fashioned by those who dare not trust others, because they dare not trust themselves, to walk in liberty. By such poor terror-stricken creatures consistency in thought and conduct is prized among the highest virtues. In order to achieve this consistency they reject as untrue, or as immoral or anti-social (it matters not which; for any stick will serve to beat a dog), all the thoughts which do not harmonize with the particular system they have elected to defend; they do their best to repress all impulses and desires which cannot be fitted into their scheme of moral behaviour. With what deplorable results!

§ 24. *Pascal, the Death-Worshipper*

The consistent thinker, the consistently moral man, is either a walking mummy or else, if he has not succeeded in stifling all his vitality, a fanatical monomaniac. (By the admirers of consistency the mummies are called 'serene' or 'stoical,' the monomaniacs 'single-minded'—as though single-mindedness were a virtue in a being to whom bountiful nature has given a multiple mind! Single-mindedness is all very well in cows or baboons; in an animal claiming to belong to the same species as Shakespeare it is simply disgraceful.)

In spite of all his heroic efforts, Pascal never succeeded in entirely suppressing the life that was in him. It was not in his power to turn himself into a pious automaton. Vitality continued to flow out of him, but through only one channel. He became a monomaniac, a man with but one aim—to impose the death of Christian spirituality on himself and all his fellows. 'What religion,' he asks, 'will teach us to cure pride and concupiscence?' In other words, what religion will cure us of living? For concupiscence, or desire, is the instrument of life, and 'the pride of the peacock is the glory of God'—not of Pascal's God, of course, but of the God of Life. Christianity, he concludes, is the only religion which will cure men of living. Therefore all men must become Christians. Pascal expended all his extraordinary powers in trying, by persuasion, by argument, to convert his fellows to consistent death-worship. It was with the *Provincial Letters* that he opened the campaign. With what consummate generalship! The casuists were routed with terrific slaughter. Entranced by that marvellous prose, we find ourselves even now believing that their defeat was merited, that Pascal was in the right. But if we stop our ears to the charmer's music and consider only the substance of what he says, we shall realize that the rights were all on the side of the Jesuits and that Pascal was using his prodigious talents to make the worse appear the better cause. The casuists were often silly and pedantic. But their conception of morality was, from a life-worshipper's point of view, entirely sound. Recognizing the diversity of human beings, the infinite variety of circumstances, they perceived that every case should be considered on its own merits. Life was to be tethered, but with an elastic rope; it was to be permitted to do a little gambolling. To Pascal this libertarianism seemed horrible. There must be no compromise with life; the hideous thing must be ruthlessly suppressed. Men must be bound down by rigid commandments, coffined in categorical imperatives, paralysed by the fear of hell and the incessant contemplation of death, buried under mounds of prohibitions. He said so with such exquisite felicity of phrase and cadence that people have gone on imagining, from that day to this, that he was upholding a noble cause, when in fact he was fighting for the powers of darkness.

After the *Letters* came the *Pensées*—the fragmentary materials of what was to have been a colossal work of Christian apology. Implacably the fight against life continued. 'Admiration spoils everything from childhood onwards. Oh, isn't he clever ! Isn't he good ! The children of the Port Royal school, who are not urged on with this spur of envy and glory, sink into indifference.' Pascal must have been delighted. A system of education which resulted in children sinking into 'la nonchalance' was obviously, in his eyes, almost ideal. If the children had quietly withered up into mummies, it would have been absolutely perfect. The man was to be treated to the same deadening influences as the child. It was first to be demonstrated that he lived in a state of hopeless wretchedness. This is a task which Pascal undertook with the greatest satisfaction. All his remarks on the 'misère de l'homme' are magnificent. But what is this misery ? When we examine Pascal's arguments we find that man's misery consists in not being something different from a man. In not being simple, consistent, without desires, omniscient and dead, but on the contrary alive and full of concupiscence, uncertain, inconsistent, multiple. But to blame a thing for not being something else is childish. Sheep are not men ; but that is no reason for talking about the 'misère du mouton.' Let sheep make the best of their sheepishness and men of their humanity. But Pascal does not want men to make the best of their human life ; he wants them to make the worst of it, to throw it away. After depressing them with his remarks about misery, he brings them into paralysing contact with death and infinity ; he demonstrates the nothingness, in the face of this darkness, these immensities, of every thought, action, and desire. To clinch the argument he invokes the Jansenist God, the Christian revelation. If it is man's true nature to be consistent and undesiring, then (such is Pascal's argument) Jansenistic death-worship is a psychological necessity. It is more than a psychological necessity; death-worship has been made obligatory by the God of Death in person, has been decreed in a revelation which Pascal undertakes to prove indubitably historical.

§ 25. *Pascal's Universe*

The spectacle of so much malignity, so much hatred, is profoundly repulsive. Hate begets hate, and it is difficult not to detest Pascal for his venomous detestation of everything that is beautiful and noble in human existence. It is a detestation, however, which must be tempered with pity. If the man sinned against the Holy Ghost—and surely few men have sinned like Pascal, since few indeed have been endowed with Pascal's extraordinary gifts—it was because he could not help it.

His desires, in Blake's words, were weak enough to be restrained. Feeble, a sick man, he was afraid of life, he dreaded liberty. Acquainted only with the mystical states that are associated with malady and deprivation, this ascetic had never experienced those other, no less significant, states that accompany the fulfilment of desire. For if we admit the significance of the mystical rapture, we must equally admit the significance of the no less prodigious experiences associated with love in all its forms, with the perception of sensuous beauty, with intoxication, with rhythmic movement, with anger, with strife and triumph, with all the positive manifestations of concupiscent life. In the second section of this essay I stated the psychological case for asceticism.

Ascetic practices produce a condition of abnormality and so enable the ascetic to get out of the ordinary world into another and, as he feels, more significant and important universe. Anger, the feeling inspired by sensuous beauty, the orgasm of amorous desire, are abnormal states precisely analogous to the state of mystical ecstasy, states which permit the angry man, the aesthete, the lover, to become temporary inhabitants of non-Podsnapian universes which are immediately felt (just as the mystic's universe is immediately felt) to be of peculiar value and significance. Pascal was acquainted with only one abnormal universe—that which the ecstatic mystic briefly inhabits. Of all the rest he had no personal knowledge; his sickly body did not permit of his approaching them. We condemn easily that which we do not know, and with pleasure that which, like the fox who said the grapes were sour, we cannot enjoy.

To a sickly body Pascal joined an extraordinarily powerful analytical intellect. Too acute to be taken in by the gross illusions of rationalism, too subtle to imagine that a home-made abstraction could be a reality, he derided the academic philosophers. He perceived that the basis of reason is unreasonable; first principles come from 'the heart,' not from the mind. The discovery would have been of the first importance if Pascal had only made it with the right organ. But instead of discovering the heart with the heart, he discovered it with the head. It was abstractly that he rejected abstractions, and with the reason that he discovered unreason. His realism was only theoretical; he never lived it. His intelligence would not permit him to find satisfaction in the noumena and abstractions of rationalist philosophy. But for fixed noumena and simple unchanging abstractions he none the less longed. He was able to satisfy these longings of an invalid philosopher and at the same time to salve his intellectual conscience by choosing an irrational abstraction to believe in—the God of Christianity. Marooned on that static Rock of Ages, he felt himself safe—safe from the heaving flux of appearances, safe from diversity, safe from the responsibilities of freedom, safe from life. If he had allowed himself to have a heart to understand the heart with, if he had possessed a body with which to understand the body, and instincts and desires capable of interpreting the meaning of instinct and desire, Pascal might have been a life-worshipper instead of a devotee of death. But illness had strangled the life out of his body and made his desires so weak that to resist them was an easy virtue. Against his heart he struggled with all the force of his tense and focussed will. The Moloch of religious principle demanded its sacrifice. Obediently, Pascal performed the rite of harakiri. Moloch, unsatisfied, demanded still more blood. Pascal offered his services; he would make other people do as he had done. Moloch should be glutted with entrails. All his writings are persuasive invitations to the world to come and commit suicide. It is the triumph of principle and consistency.

§ 26. *Musical Conclusion*

And yet the life-worshipper is also, in his own way, a man of principles and consistency. To live intensely—that is his guiding principle. His diversity is a sign that he consistently tries to live up to his principles; for the harmony of life—of the single life that persists as a gradually changing unity through time—is a harmony built up of many elements. The unity is mutilated by the suppression of any part of the diversity. A fugue has need of all its voices. Even in the rich counterpoint of life each separate small melody plays its indispensable part. The diapason closes full in man. In *man*. But Pascal aspired to be more than a man. Among the interlaced melodies of the human counterpoint are love songs and anacreontics, marches and savage dance-rhythms, hymns of hate and loud hilarious chanties. Odious voices in the ears of one who wanted his music to be wholly celestial! Pascal commanded them to be still and they were silent. Bending towards his life, we listen expectantly for a strain of angelic singing. But across the centuries what harsh and painful sounds come creaking down to us!

DO WHAT YOU WILL

FROM 'JESTING PILATE'

THE DIARY OF A JOURNEY

PORT SAID

THE after-hatch was off. Hung high above the opening, the electric lights glared down into the deep square well of the hold. The watcher, leaning over the brink of the well, shouted and waved his arms. The donkey-engine rattled responsively. Twenty sacks of potatoes came rushing up from the depths. Ten feet above the level of the deck, they were swung sideways by the transverse pull of a second rope, hung suspended for a moment beyond the gunwale, then, at another signal from the watcher, dropped down into the waiting lighter. The watcher raised his hand again; again the engine rattled. Two empty loops of rope came up over the ship's side, whipped across the deck and went down, writhing like living snakes, into the well. At the bottom, far down, little men caught at the trailing ropes, piled up the sacks, made fast. The watcher shouted. Yet another quintal of potatoes came rushing up, swung sideways, dropped out of sight over the edge of the ship. And so it continued, all the night. Curiously, admiringly, and at last with a growing sense of horror, I looked on. Moving bits of matter from one point of the world's surface to another—man's whole activity. And the wisdom of the East, I reflected, consists in the affirmation that it is better to leave the bits of matter where they are. Up to a point, no doubt, the sages of the East are right. There are many bits of matter which might be left in their place and nobody would be any the worse. These particles of ink, for example, which I so laboriously transfer from their bottle to the surface of the paper. . . .

We landed—in what a sink! At Port Said they speak all languages, accept every currency. But their exchange is robbery and they employ their gift of tongues only for cheating. The staple industry of the place seems to be the manufacture and sale of indecent photographs. They are stocked in almost every shop; they are pressed upon you—at prices that decline astonishingly, as you walk away, from a sovereign to half a crown—by every loafer. The copiousness of the supply is proof of a correspondingly large demand for these wares by passing travellers. In these matters, it seems, many people are more agreeably excited by the representation—whether pictorial or verbal—than by carnal reality. It is a curious psychological fact, for which I can find no complete explanation.

IN THE RED SEA

Talking with Europeans who live and work in the East, I find that, if they love the East (which they mostly do), it is always for the same reason. In the East, they say, a man is somebody; he has authority and is looked up to; he knows all the people who matter and is known. At home, he is lost in the crowd, he does not count, he is nobody. Life in the East satisfies the profoundest and most powerful of all the instincts—that of self-assertion. The young man who goes out from a London suburb to take up a clerkship in India finds himself a member of a small ruling community; he has slavish servants to order about, dark-skinned subordinates to whom it is right and proper to be rude. Three hundred and twenty million Indians surround him; he feels incomparably superior to them all, from the coolie to the maharaja, from the untouchable to the thoroughbred Brahmin, from the illiterate peasant to the holder of half a dozen European degrees. He may be ill-bred, stupid, uneducated; no matter. His skin is white. Superiority in India is a question of epiderms. No wonder if he loves the East. For the European, Eastern conditions of life are a kind of intoxicant. But the tipsiness they produce is more satisfactory than that which results from the absorption of whiskey. Alcohol, as the anonymous poet has said:

> Bids valour burgeon in strong men,
> Quicken's the poet's wit and pen,
> Despises fate.

But the sense of power which it gives, the feeling of grandeur and importance, are purely illusory and do not last. The intoxication of the East is permanent, and the sense of greatness is not entirely an illusion. The commercial traveller who goes East is really a greater man (so long as he remains in the East) than his colleague in patent medicines at home. Sobriety supervenes only when he returns to Europe. In the West he finds his natural place in the social hierarchy. One out of London's suburban millions, he feels homesick for the East. It is not to be wondered at. What man likes to be sediment, when he might float gallantly on the sunlit surface?

BOMBAY

In the lounge of the hotel is a bookstall, stocked with periodicals and novels—my own, I was gratified to see, among them. One whole section of the bookstall is devoted to the sale of English and American technical journals—but technical journals of a single, rather special kind. Journals of gynaecology, of obstetrics, of sexual psychology, of venereal disease. Rows of them, and dozens of copies of each. The hotel lounge is not specially frequented by doctors; it is the general public which buys these journals. Strange, strange phenomenon! Perhaps it is one of the effects of the climate.

BOMBAY

FROM its island body, Bombay radiates long tentacles of suburban squalor into the land. Mills and huge grey tenements, low huts among the palm trees flank the outgoing roads for miles, and the roads themselves are thronged with the coming and going of innumerable passengers. Driving out of Bombay along one of these populous highways, I felt (but more acutely) that amazement which often overwhelms me when I pass through the sordid fringes of some European city—amazement at my own safety and comfort, at the security of my privileges, at the unthinking and almost unresentful acceptance by millions of my less fortunate fellow-beings of my claim to be educated, leisured, comparatively wealthy. That I and my privileged fellows should be tolerated by our own people seems to me strange enough. But that our pretensions, which are still higher in India than in Europe, should be allowed by these innumerable dark-skinned strangers, over whom we rule, strikes me as being still more extraordinary.

We are accepted much as paper money is accepted, because there is a general belief that we are worth something. Our value is not intrinsic, but borrowed from the opinion of the world. We live and rule on credit and are respected, not so much because we are really formidable (though our power is great) as because there exists a convention that we should be respected. The less fortunate majority is carefully educated in this useful opinion.

Our paper currency has begun to lose its conventional value in Europe. We still continue to offer ourselves (often with a certain secret diffidence) as five-pound notes; but the more sceptical of our 'inferiors' refuse to regard us as anything more precious than waste paper. When the same thing begins to happen in India, when the credit on which the white man has been living and ruling for so long is withdrawn, what then? Without any violence, merely by quietly refusing to accept the white man at his own valuation, merely by declining to have anything to do with him, the Indian can reduce British rule to impotence. Non-co-operation has failed, up till now, owing to inefficiency of organization and a lack of public spirit on the part of the Indians. But efficient organization and public spirit are the products of a special education. When the masses have received that education, when the paper money of European prestige has been systematically discredited and individual Europeans are boycotted and left suspended in a kind of social and economic vacuum, the Indians will be able to get whatever they ask for. (The mere disappearance of all Indian servants would be almost enough in itself to bring the white man to terms. Faced with the prospect of having to empty his own slops, a Viceroy would begin to listen with an increased sympathy to Swarajist demands.) Whether the Indians will succeed any better than the English in the task of governing India, is another question. Swaraj may prove a blessing, or it may turn out to be a catastrophe. But in any case it will be obtained whenever a sufficient number of India's three hundred and twenty millions make up their minds systematically to ask for it; the thing is obvious. They have only to be incredulous of the white man's pretensions, they have only to ignore his almost invisible presence among their multitudes; that is all.

In the meantime, however, our credit holds, at any rate among the masses. The educated Indian may doubt whether our five-pound notes are worth more than an equal area snipped out of the *Daily Mail*; but his uneducated brother still accepts us at our face value. Thin-legged pedestrians salute me as I pass. Through the squalor of suburban Bombay, I carry my privileges of comfort, culture, and wealth in perfect safety. They are still secure, more or less, even in the suburbs of an English manufacturing town. For how long? Rolling along between the palm trees, I wonder.

BOMBAY

THIS evening a congratulatory address was presented to Mr. Patel, the new Speaker of the Legislative Assembly, by the members of his community, an agricultural sub-caste of Gujarat. Other members of the community have broken through the traditionary trammels—the hall was full of men who had left the ancestral plough for work in the city—but none has previously risen to a position so exalted as that attained by Mr. Patel. 'From Plough-boy to President'—Indian journalists, like their colleagues across the sea, have a weakness for phrases—was the phrase in which the newspapers summed up Mr. Patel's career.

We accompanied Mrs. Naidu to the function and, as her guests, found ourselves sitting in places of honour on the platform. The hall was crowded. The heat, though the sun had set, was prodigious. (It is one of the peculiarities of the Bombay climate that the temperature rises, or at any rate seems to rise, during the first hours of the night.) In the garden outside, a band was playing the fox-trots of two or three seasons ago.

The programme of the function had been carefully worked out. A chorus of children was to sing during the period of waiting before Mr. Patel entered. Somebody was to recite a congratulatory poem when he had taken his seat. Then there were to be speeches, with Mr. Patel's reply and the presentation of the address in its silver casket to finish off the proceedings. A perfect programme, on paper; but in practice, as it turned out, not quite so good as it might have been. For the band played and the audience talked all through the children's singing; indeed, it was only quite by chance, because I happened to notice that they were opening and shutting their mouths in an unnatural, fish-like sort of way, that I came to know that the children were singing at all. And when the reciter began intoning his congratulatory poem, the indefatigable band struck up the tune of 'Why did you kiss that Girl?'—the poem was lost. But by this time some few thousands of Bombay's innumerable population of crows had settled in the trees outside the hall and were discussing the question, as gregarious birds will do at sunset, of retiring for the night. Their cawing was portentous. Never in Europe have I heard anything like it. I was sitting on the platform, within a few feet of the speakers; but their voices were quite inaudible, even to me. It was only some half an hour later, when the crows had dropped off to sleep, that any word can have reached the audience. After that the proceedings went off pretty smoothly, and with only a little hitch or two about the reading of the address and the presentation of the casket to mar the solemnity of the occasion.

I was reminded very much of analogous functions in Italy. There is no word of which Italian journalists are fonder than the word *solenne*. Every ceremony of which you read an account in an Italian newspaper is solemn—solemn foundation-stone layings, solemn depositings of wreaths on tombs, solemn celebrations of centenaries, solemn royal entrances and exits. In the papers, as I say, all these things are solemn. In practice, however, they are rarely anything but slipshod, haphazard, and to northern eyes at any rate, ineffective and unimpressive. The good Catholic who comes to Rome in the hope of seeing noble and soul-stirring religious ceremonies, generally returns disappointed to his own country. The fact is that they order these things better in France, in England, in Belgium, in Germany—in any northern land. We Northerners stage-manage our effects more professionally than do the people of the south. We take pains to impress ourselves; and at the same time we give the ceremony which we have staged every chance of seeming impressive to us by deliberately throwing ourselves into a serious state of mind and consistently keeping our seriousness till the function is over. The Southerner declines to take trouble over the details of stage-management, and will not be bothered to hold one mental attitude for a long time at a stretch. To us, in consequence, he seems disgracefully slipshod, cynical, and irreverent.

But we must not be over-hasty in our judgments. The Southerner has his own traditions about these matters, and they happen to be different from ours. In this respect, I should guess, his habits of thought and feeling are nearer to the Oriental's than to ours. Let us try to understand before we condemn.

We call the Southerner slipshod because he tolerates shabbiness among his grandeurs, and permits his solemnities to be marred by a ludicrous inefficiency. But he could retort by calling us crassly unimaginative because we are incapable of seeing the fine intention through the inadequate medium of its expression, of appreciating the noble general effect in spite of the shabbiness of the details. For in matters of art, he would argue (and a religious ceremony, a civic or political function are forms of art, being only solemn ballets and symbolical charades), it is the intention and the general effect that count. Those little struts and flying buttresses of marble, with which the Greeks strengthened their statues, are absurd, if you choose to consider them closely. But they are meant to be ignored. Structurally, a sham façade is ludicrous; the Southerner knows it, of course, just as well as Mr. Ruskin. But, more wise than Ruskin, he does not fly into a passion of moral indignation over the falsehood of it; he permits himself to enjoy the genuine grandiosity of its appearance when seen from the right angle. In church, the priest may gabble, as though he were trying to break a world's record, the acolytes may pick their noses, the choir-boys sing out of tune, the vergers spit; we Northerners are revolted, but the wisely indulgent Southerner passes over these trivial details, and enjoys the fine general effect of the ecclesiastical ballet in spite of its little blemishes. But if he enjoys it, the Northerner now asks, why doesn't he at least sit still and refrain from laughing chatter, why doesn't he try to look, and looking, make himself feel, consistently serious? To which the other will retort by deriding the Northerner's slowness and inelasticity of mind, his pomposity, his incapacity for frankly feeling two emotions at once, or at any rate in very rapid succession. 'I can see ludicrous and shabby details just as clearly as you do,' he will say, 'and, like you, I deplore them. But I keep my sense of proportion, and do not permit mere details to interfere with my appreciation of the general effect. You have a talent for high seriousness; but I can smile and feel solemn within the same minute. In church I pray fervently at one moment, I am transported by the beauty of the ceremonial (in spite of the shoddy details), and the next I make eyes at the young woman across the aisle or talk to my neighbour about the price of rubber shares.

Operatic airs, I know, are stagey and conventional, and I deride the ludicrously strutting tenor who sings them; but at the same time I rapturously applaud his bawling and abandon myself, even while I mock, to the throaty passion of the music. Your mind is clumsier, more stiffly starched than mine. You can only be one thing at a time, and you regard as shocking the nimble emotional antics of those more fortunately endowed than yourself or more reasonably brought up. For my part I can only pity you for your limitations.'

The speeches, all but that of Mrs. Naidu, who gave us English eloquence, were in Gujarati, and for me, therefore, no better than gibberish. I amused myself by listening for the occasional English words with which the incomprehensibility was powdered. 'Gibber gibber gibber Bombay Presidency'; it was thus that I should have reported a typical speech of the evening. 'Gibber gibber committee, gibber gibber gibber minority report, gibber gibber Government of India, gibber gibber gibber George Washington, gibber Edmund Burke, gibber gibber gibber Currency Commission, gibber gibber gibber gibber . . .' It was thus, I reflected, that our Saxon fathers borrowed from the invaders' speech the words for which they could find no equivalent in their own debased, post-Conquest English. Listening to the incomprehensible chatter of his foreign vassals, the Norman baron would have been amused to catch, every now and then, the sound of such familiar words as 'army,' 'castle,' 'law.'

The function came to an end. Festooned with flowers —for there had been a generous distribution of garlands, by which even we, albeit quite undeserving, had profited —we followed our hostess into the garden. There under palm trees, we drank a kind of richly perfumed soda-water, we ate strange dumplings stuffed with mincemeat that was at once sweet and violently peppery—chopped mutton mixed with a vitriolic jam—and tried to take the burning taste of them away with little cakes and sandwiches, slabs of almond icing and fried savouries. At the other side of the garden, safely removed from possible contamination, the orthodox refreshed themselves with special foods prepared by cooks of guaranteed good family. White-bearded and most majestically robed, Mr. Patel moved among the guests, looking like a minor, even a major, prophet—but a prophet, as we saw when he sat down at table, with a most reassuringly humorous twinkle in his eyes.

It was nearly nine when we got back to the hotel. Coming up from dinner, an hour later, we found our room magically perfumed by the tuberoses and champaks of our garlands. That night, and all next day, till they were quite withered, the flowers poured out their scent, and the wind driven down on us by the electric fan in the ceiling was a warm air impregnated with strange and tropical sweetness.

SRINAGAR

In the autumn great flocks of teal and mallard come through Kashmir, on their way from the breeding-grounds to their winter home in Northern India. Some breed in the recesses of Ladakh, a few hundred miles only from the Kashmir valley; but the majority, it is said, go farther afield into Central Asia, possibly even into Siberia, where so many migrants pass the brief but generous summer. In the autumn they fly southwards, over the Himalayas, into India. Some varieties of these water-fowl cross the range at the eastern end, some to the west. Thus the cotton-tail, I am assured by sportsmen, is found in Assam and Bengal, but not in the Panjab; while the mallard is seen only in the west. How these birds, which normally spend their lives in the plain, contrive to pass the Himalayas without dying of mountain-sickness or asphyxiation on the way, is something of a mystery. Most small animals, when taken up suddenly to a height of fifteen or twenty thousand feet—and many of the Himalayan passes touch these heights—simply die. The migrating duck, if it really does come down from Central Asia, must be flying at these altitudes for miles at a stretch. Physiologically, the feat seems almost as extraordinary as that of the eel, which leaves its native pond or river to breed, two or three thousand miles away, in the deep water of the ocean.

It would be interesting to know the feelings of a migrant animal, when the moment has arrived for it to perform its journey. The swallow at the end of the summer, the salmon when, having attained its maximum weight, it feels that the time has come for it to go up into the rivers, the fresh-water eel at the approach of its first and final breeding season, must feel, I imagine, much as a man might feel when suddenly converted, or who finds himself compelled by an irresistible sense of duty to perform some hazardous and disagreeable enterprise. Some power within them—an immanent god—commands them to change their comfortable way of life for a new and arduous existence. There is no disobeying the command; the god compels. If eels could formulate their theories of ethics, they would be eloquent, I am sure, about the categorical imperative and the compulsive character of the sense of duty.

Our categorical imperatives, like those of eels and swallows, are generally backed by the forces of an instinct. Our social instinct deters us from doing what we think would be condemned, and encourages us to do what we think would be commended by our equals, by our moral superiors, by our 'better selves,' by 'God.' But there are occasions, curiously enough, when the categorical imperative to do or refrain from doing seems to have no connection with a compulsive instinct. For example, a man writes two letters, addresses two envelopes, puts the letters into the envelopes, and seals them up. He is extremely careful when inserting the letters, to see that each goes into its proper envelope. Nevertheless, a few minutes later, he is seized by an irresistible desire to reopen the envelopes so as to make sure that the letter to his mistress is not in the envelope addressed to his maiden aunt, and *vice versa*. He knows that each letter is where it should be. But despite his conviction, despite the derisive comments of the rational part of his mind, he does reopen the envelopes. The categorical imperative is stronger than reason. It may be so strong that after five more minutes, he will open the envelopes a second time.

What gives the imperative its strength in cases such as this, I am at a loss to imagine. The August cuckoo takes wing for Africa at the command of a special migratory instinct. A desire born of his social instinct, to win the approval of his fellows, of some hypostasized 'better self' or 'personal god,' makes a man act honourably in circumstances where it would be more profitable and more convenient to act dishonourably. But when a man reopens an envelope to see if it contains the letter he *knows* it does contain, when he gets out of bed on a cold night to make sure that he has switched off the light and bolted the doors which he clearly remembers turning out and bolting ten minutes before, no primary instinct can be invoked to account for the compulsive nature of the desire to do these irrational things. In such cases the categorical imperative seems to be morally senseless and psychologically unaccountable. It is as though a god were playing practical jokes.

SRINAGAR

It takes the Tartar traders six weeks of walking to get from Kashgar to Srinagar. They start with their yaks and ponies in the early autumn, when the passes are still free from snow and the rivers, swollen in summer by its melting, have subsided to fordableness. They walk into Kashmir, and from Kashmir into India. They spend the winter in India, sell what they have brought, and in the following spring, when the passes are once more open, go back into Turkestan with a load of Indian and European fabrics, velvet and plush and ordinary cotton, which they sell for fabulous profit in their own country.

We paid a visit to the Central Asian *sarai* at Srinagar where the Tartars halt for a rest on their way down into India. A dozen merchants with their servants were encamped there: strange Mongolian men, high-booted, trousered, jerkined in thick cloth or sheepskin. They showed us their wares: carpets, costly and cheap, from Kashgar and the other oasis cities of the Tarim basin; coarse felt mats, on which were rudely printed in red and blue the most exquisite designs; hand-woven and hand-printed cottons from Turkestan; Chinese silks, jade and crystal; furs. We bought a rug of the poorest quality, a thing of more cotton than wool, but superbly patterned in colours that were none the less beautiful for being manifestly aniline. Also a felt mat in the design of which a Greek decorative motive played a leading part. That identity of the contemporary with the ancient and classical form—was it due to the coincidence of reinvention, to a modern importation from the West? Or was it due, as I liked to think it was, to the survival, through centuries of change and tumult and in spite of invasions and slaughters, of the art which Alexander's adventurous successors, the despots of

Central Asia, implanted in that once flourishing land beyond the mountains?

I do not know why it should be so; but there is something peculiarly romantic about caravans and the slow commerce of pedestrians. The spectacle of a hundred laden yaks or ponies is enough to fire the imagination; of a hundred laden trucks leaves us entirely cold. We take no interest in the merchant who sends his goods by train; but the pedestrian merchant seems to us an almost beautiful and heroic figure. And the aura of romance which surrounded the Tartars was brightened in our eyes when they showed us their medium of exchange. Diving down into the recesses of their greasy clothing, they pulled out for our inspection glittering handfuls of gold. We examined the coins. They were Russian ten-rouble pieces of before the Revolution, all bright and new. The head of the Tsar stood sharply out on them, as though they had but yesterday issued from the Imperial mint.

BETWEEN PESHAWAR AND LAHORE

At Peshawar we were seized with one of our periodical financial panics. Money, in this country, slips rapidly between the fingers, particularly between the fingers of the tourist. Great wads of it have to be handed out every time one gets into the train; for fares are high and distances enormous. No place in India seems to be less than three hundred miles from any other place; the longer journeys have to be measured in thousands. Financial panics are justifiable. We decided to travel second-class as far as Lahore.

For the first hour or so we were alone in our compartment. We congratulated ourselves on having secured all the comfort and privacy of first-class travelling at exactly half the price. In future, we decided, we would always travel second. But nature abhors a vacuum, and our compartment was evidently the object of her special abhorrence. When the train stopped at Campbellpur, we were invaded. In the twinkling of an eye our luxurious emptiness was filled to overflowing with luggage and humanity. And what queer specimens of humanity ! The leader of the party which now entered the compartment was a middle-aged man wearing a yellow robe and, on his head, a kind of quilted bonnet with hanging ear-flaps. He was profusely garlanded with yellow chrysanthemums, and had been followed on to the platform by a large crowd of flower-bearing admirers and devotees. Our ignorance of the language did not permit us to discover who this exalted person might be. But he was evidently some kind of high priest, some Hindu pope of considerable holiness, to judge by the respect which was paid him by his numerous retinue and his admirers. His passage along the line must have been well advertised; for at every station our compartment was invaded by a swarm of devotees who came to kiss the great man's feet and to crave a blessing, which in most cases he seemed too lazy to give. Even the guards and ticket-collectors and stationmasters came in to pay their respects. The enthusiasm of one ticket-collector was so great that he travelled about thirty miles in our already packed compartment, simply in order to be near the holy man. He, meanwhile, passed the time by counting his money, which was contained in a large brass-bound box, by loudly eating and, later, dozing. Even at the stations he did not take the trouble to rouse himself, but reclined with closed eyes along his seat, and passively permitted the faithful to kiss his feet. When one is as holy as he evidently was, it is unnecessary to keep up appearances, behave decently, or do anything for one's followers. Office and hereditary honour claim the respect of a believing people quite as much as personal merit.

Judging by appearances, which are often deceptive, I should say that this particular holy man had no personal merit, but a very great office. His face, which had the elements of a fine and powerful face, seemed to have disintegrated and run to fat under the influence of a hoggish self-indulgence. To look at, he was certainly one of the most repulsive human specimens I have ever seen. But of course he may in reality have been a saint and an ascetic, a preacher and a practiser of the moral doctrines formulated in the Gita, or even one of those pure-souled Oriental mystics who, we are told, are to leaven the materialism of our Western civilization. He may have been, but I doubt it. All that we could be certain of was that he looked unpleasant, and was undoubtedly dirty; also that he and his admirers exhaled the sour stink of garments long unwashed.

Tolstoy objected to too much cleanliness on the ground that to be too clean is a badge of class. It is only the rich who can afford the time and money to wash their bodies and shift their linen frequently. The labourer who sweats for his living, and whose house contains no bathroom, whose wardrobes no superfluous shirts, must stink. It is inevitable, and it is also right and proper, that he should. Work is prayer. Work is also stink. Therefore stink is prayer. So, more or less, argues Tolstoy, who goes on to condemn the rich for not stinking, and for bringing up their children to have a prejudice against all stinks however natural and even creditable. The non-stinker's prejudice against stink is largely a class prejudice, and therefore to be condemned.

Tolstoy is quite right, of course. We, who were brought up on open windows, clean shirts, hot baths, and sanitary plumbing, find it hard to tolerate twice-breathed air and all the odours which crowded humanity naturally exhales. Our physical education has been such that the majority of our fellow-beings, particularly those less fortunately circumstanced than ourselves, seem to us slightly or even extremely disgusting. A man may have strong humanitarian and democratic principles; but if he happens to have been brought up as a bath-taking, shirt-changing lover of fresh air, he will have to overcome certain physical repugnances before he can bring himself to put those principles into practice to the extent, at any rate, of associating freely with men and women whose habits are different from his own. It is a deplorable fact; but there it is. Tolstoy's remedy is that we should all stink together. Other reformers desire to make it economically possible for every man to have as many hot baths and to change his shirt as often as do the privileged non-stinkers at the present day. Personally, I prefer the second alternative.

Meanwhile, the crowd in our compartment increased. The day, as it advanced, grew hotter. And suddenly the holy man woke up and began to hoick and spit all over the compartment. By the time we reached Rawal Pindi we had decided that the twenty-two rupees we should economize by remaining seven hours longer among our second-class brothers were not enough. We had our luggage transferred into a first-class carriage and paid the difference. The only other occupant of the compartment was an English official of the Kashmir State, bound for his winter headquarters at Jammu. He was a dim little man; but at any rate his linen was clean, and he was not in the least holy. Nobody came in to kiss his feet.

For the rest of the journey I ruminated my anti-clericalism. Indian friends have assured me that the power of the priests is less than it was, and goes on rapidly waning.

I hope they are right and that the process may be further accelerated. And not in India alone. There is still, for my taste, too much kissing of amethyst rings as well as of slippered feet. There are still too many black coats in the West, too many orange ones in the East. *Écrasez l'infâme.* My travelling companion had made me, for the moment, a thorough-going Voltairian.

It is a simple creed, Voltairianism. In its simplicity lies its charm, lies the secret of its success—and also of its fallaciousness. For, in our muddled human universe, nothing so simple can possibly be true, can conceivably 'work.'

If the *infâme* were squashed, if insecticide were scattered on all the clerical beetles, whether black or yellow, if pure rationalism became the universal faith, all would automatically be well. So runs the simple creed of the anti-clericals. It is too simple, and the assumptions on which it is based are too sweeping. For, to begin with, is the *infâme* always infamous, and are the beetles invariably harmful? Obviously not. Nor can it be said that the behaviour-value of pure rationalism (whatever the truth-value of its underlying assumptions) is necessarily superior to the behaviour-value of irrational beliefs which may be and, in general, almost certainly are untrue. And further, the vast majority of human beings are not interested in reason or satisfied with what it teaches. Nor is reason itself the most satisfactory instrument for the understanding of life. Such are a few of the complications which render so simple a formula as the anti-clerical's inapplicable to our real and chaotic existence.

Man's progress has been contingent on his capacity to organize societies. It is only when protected by surrounding society from aggression, when freed by the organized labour of society from the necessity of hunting or digging for his food, it is only, that is to say, when society has tempered and to a great extent abolished the struggle for personal existence, that the man of talent can exercise his capacities to the full. And it is only by a well organized society that the results of his labours can be preserved for the enrichment of succeeding generations. Any force that tends to the strengthening of society is, therefore, of the highest biological importance. Religion is obviously such a force. All religions have been unanimous in encouraging within limits that have tended to grow wider and ever wider, the social, altruistic, humanitarian proclivities of man, and in condemning his anti-social, self-assertive tendencies. Those who like to speak anthropomorphically would be justified in saying that religion is a device employed by the Life Force for the promotion of its evolutionary designs. But they would be justified in adding that religion is also a device employed by the Devil for the dissemination of idiocy, intolerance, and servile abjection. My fellow-passenger from Campbellpur did something, no doubt, to encourage brotherly love, forbearance, and mutual helpfulness among his flock. But he also did his best to deepen their congenital stupidity and prevent it from being tempered by the acquirement of correct and useful knowledge, he did his best to terrify them with imaginary fears into servility and to flatter them with groundless hopes into passive contentment with a life unworthy of human beings. What he did in the name of the evolutionary Life Force, he undid in the name of the Devil. I cherish a pious hope that he did just a trifle more than he undid, and that the Devil remained, as the result of his ministry, by ever so little the loser.

LAHORE

By the kindness of our hospitable friends at Lahore, we were able to hear a good deal of Indian music, both classical and popular. Indian music is innocent of any harmony more subtle than that with which the bagpipe has made us familiar—the drone on the dominant. It knows of no form more highly organized than that of the air with variations. It is played on but few instruments (two kinds of lute and a kind of wire-stringed viola are the commonest), and these few are, alas, rapidly being ousted by a form of miniature American harmonium, pumped with one hand and played with one finger of the other. Yet, in spite of these limitations, Indian music is surprisingly rich and various. How rich and how various depends entirely upon the individual player. For in India, where music has never been committed to writing, but is an affair of tradition tempered by personal inspiration, the part of the interpreter is more important even than with us. Of European music even a bad player can give us some idea; and those who have acquired the art of reading a score can get their musical pleasure through the eye alone. Not so in India. Here the performer is all-important. He is everything; not only the interpreter, but also the repository and publisher of music—Breitkopf and Hartel as well as Paganini; not only the guardian of ancient tradition, but also the inspired improvisatore. The bad performer can give you nothing of Indian music.

At Lahore, we were fortunate in hearing a most accomplished performer on the sitar or Indian lute. He was a middle-aged man with a walrus moustache and an explosion of most musical long hair, in the centre of which he wore a red plush cap embroidered with gold. He looked, I thought, like a reproduction in brown of an old-fashioned

German pianist. But how humble, in comparison with the lordly artists of Europe, how very definitely an inferior the poor man was! He sat on the floor awaiting our good pleasure, played when he was told, stopped at a word in the middle of a musical phrase, played on uncomplainingly through our conversation. Music in India has strangely come down in the world. From being, it is said, the accomplishment of princesses, it has come to be the monopoly of prostitutes. Courtesans are the only professional female musicians in India, and very many of the male professionals are only the hereditary teachers of courtesans. Our musician had climbed a little way above his congenital station in life; he gave lessons to amateurs.

The sitar is a long-necked guitar, bellied with the half of a bisected pumpkin (and having, sometimes the second half attached like a goitre to its neck), wire-strung, and played with a plectrum. From this lute a skilled musician can draw an extraordinary variety of sounds—from sharp staccato to notes long-drawn, as though produced by a bow; from clear, full, ringing sounds to a whining slither through fractions of a tone; from loudly martial to sweet and tender. The melody is played only on the first string, the remaining wires (tuned to sound the dominant, in various octaves, of the key to whose tonic the first string is tuned) being used to produce the accompanying drone.

Our lutanist's repertory was large, and he was prepared to play anything we asked for. Folk-songs in the pentatonic black-note scale—first cousins, these, to what we are accustomed to regard as characteristically Scottish airs—were followed by classical pieces, in which the most elaborate variations were embroidered on themes that sounded now Gregorian, now like a rambling and, to our ears, rather tuneless Western folk-song. We heard specimens of the music that is supposed to be played only in the morning, and specimens of that which is intended for the night. We heard the delightful song that is meant to be sung in cloudy weather. We heard the snake-charmer's music, built up round a most snaky phrase of descending semitones, and the camel-driver's song, wailing and romantic. Generally the instrument sounded alone. But sometimes the minstrel lifted his shaggy head and gave vent to shrill tenor notes, neighed out from somewhere between the nose and the upper gullet. Strange sounds, and to our ears somewhat ludicrous, particularly when taken in conjunction with certain nods and vibrations of the head, certain almost girlishly coquettish gestures made with a hand that was lifted for the purpose from the sounding strings.

I was able to understand and appreciate the music tolerably well. All of it, that is, except the music played, traditionally, when a man gives up the world for the life of meditation. One of these renunciatory pieces—a most elaborate, classical affair—was played for our benefit. But I must confess that, listen as I might, I was unable to hear anything particularly mournful or serious, anything specially suggestive of self-sacrifice in the piece. To my Western ears it sounded much more cheerful than the dance which followed it.

Emotions are everywhere the same; but the artistic expression of them varies from age to age and from one country to another. We are brought up to accept the conventions current in the society into which we are born. This sort of art, we learn in childhood, is meant to excite laughter, that to evoke our tears. Such conventions vary with great rapidity, even in the same country. There are Elizabethan dances that sound as melancholy to our ears as little funeral marches. Conversely, we are made to laugh by the 'Anglo-Saxon attitudes' of the holiest personages in the drawings and miniatures of earlier centuries. Only with the aid of a historically trained imagination can we see or hear as our ancestors heard or saw. Remoteness in space divides no less than remoteness in time, and to the untrained auditor or spectator the artistic conventions of strangers are as little comprehensible as those of his own fathers.

It is in the visual arts that the conventions for the expression of emotions vary most widely. This is due, I suppose, to two main causes, of a character respectively physiological and intellectual. Form and colour have very little direct physiological effect upon the perceiving organism. Sounds, on the other hand, act directly on the nerves and can stimulate, exasperate, daze, bemuse, as forms and colours can never do. Certain types of rhythmical sounds produce certain almost specific effects upon the nervous system. It is obvious that in forming his conventions of expressions the musician must take into account these specific physiological effects of sound. Drum-beats and loud brassy notes sounded in regular, even time are specifically exciting; it therefore follows that the convention for expressing the martial emotions can never involve slow croonings of violins in an undulating three-four time, or elaborate bird-like, warblings on the flute. Thus it comes about that there is a certain family likeness common to the conventions of expression of every system of music—a family likeness which does not exist among the conventions of the various systems of pictorial art. But even in music the differences between the conventions of expression are very great. Music affects us physiologically through rhythm and the volume and quality of sounds. Conventions, which we have come to regard as fundamental, but which do not involve these particular factors, are found, when we compare them with the conventions of other systems, to be purely arbitrary. Thus, what we regard as the fundamental difference between major and minor keys—the minor being for us essentially melancholy—is not fundamental at all, but the result of a recent and arbitrary convention of Western musicians. Before the seventeenth century the convention did not exist even in European music, and in Oriental music it is not thought of, the most cheerful, jolly, and martial music being pitched in the minor.

So much for physiology. There are other and purely intellectual reasons why the conventions of expression should vary more widely in the different systems of visual art than they do in the systems of music. The visual arts lend themselves to story-telling and the symbolical exposition of philosophical theories and religious dogmas. Music does not. Thus, to Western eyes, the picture of a man with four arms, an elephant's head, and a lotus growing out of his navel seems grotesque. But an orthodox Hindu would see nothing comical in it. To us pictures of monsters and impossible hybrids are by convention, funny. To him they are symbolical of the highest truths.

AMRITSAR

THE Golden Temple of the Sikhs is genuinely eighteen-carat. It is also exceedingly sacred. Holiness and costliness make up for any lack of architectural merit. For architecturally the temple is less than nothing. We went in bare-footed—the Sikhs insist on this sign of respect. Picking our way among the bird droppings and expectorated betel that strewed the causeway, we advanced gingerly towards the most golden and holiest of the shrines which stands islanded in the middle of the sacred tank. In the holy of holies three magnificent old men were chanting ecstatically to the accompaniment of a small portable harmonium, which was being played with one finger by a fourth, yet more superbly patriarchal. We listened with reverence, were offered by the verger some sugar-plums —symbolical, no doubt, of something—deposited an alms and retraced our squeamish steps along the causeway.

In the street a young beggar, half-witted, or feigning imbecility, pursued us, pitiably moaning as though he were being tortured. Bearded Akalis passed us carrying their swords. A group of male prostitutes, painted, jewelled, and dressed like women, loitered at a street corner. We turned down a narrow passage and found ourselves in the Jalianwalla Bagh, the scene of General Dyer's exploits in 1919. It is a piece of waste ground enclosed by walls and houses. The narrow passage down which we had come appeared to be the only entrance. A bad place for a crowd to be caught and fired on with machine-guns. One could kill more people here, and in a shorter time, than in most plots of ground of equal area. General Dyer proved it experimentally.

Dyer's reversion to the old-fashioned methods of Aurangzeb evoked a good deal of unfriendly comment at home. It was found shocking and un-English. At the same time, it had to be admitted that his ruthlessness had achieved what it had been intended to achieve. It put a stop to what might have turned into a revolution. The blood of the martyrs is by no means invariably the seed of the church. The victims of the Inquisition died in vain; Protestantism disappeared from Spain as completely as the Albigensian faith from Southern France, or as Christianity from North Africa. Persecution can always succeed, provided that it is sufficiently violent and long-drawn. The Romans persecuted feebly and by fits—enough to stimulate the persecuted to fresh efforts, but not enough to destroy them; enough to arouse sympathy for their victims, but not enough to deter the sympathizers. That was why the blood of the early Christian martyrs was indeed the seed of their church. If the Romans had been as systematically ruthless as the Christians were to show themselves in future centuries, the infant church could never have survived. Anybody who has the power and is prepared to go on using it indefinitely and without compunction, can force his will on the whole world. It is obvious.

It was rarely in the past that any one possessed of power showed himself in the least reluctant to use it to the full. If the Romans failed to persecute Christianity with an adequate ferocity, that was due to their failure to realize its anti-Imperial significance, not to any conscientious dislike to violent persecution as such. Things are different now, at any rate in the West. Men have become reluctant to use their power to the full, to carry authority to its logical conclusion in brute force. Those who possessed power have voluntarily abstained from making full use of it, have even deprived themselves of their power for the benefit of the powerless. Oligarchs have granted privileges to the disinherited; industrialists have passed laws to restrain themselves from exploiting to excess their workmen. Instead of shooting their unwilling subjects wholesale, the owners of colonies have dealt out constitutions. The criminal is no longer cruelly punished, and even the domestic animal is now legally protected from the violences of its human master.

Living as we do in the midst of this historical process, which we vaguely call 'the humanitarian movement,' we are unable to realize the strangeness and fundamental novelty of it. Tennyson warned us against 'the craven fear of being great' (at other people's expense); but the craven fear has gone on steadily growing, in spite of him. What seems to us extraordinary to-day is not some symptom of reluctance to use power, but its ruthless, full, and unhesitating employment. We are amazed, not by President Wilson, but by Mussolini; not by Chelmsford and Montagu, but by Dyer. At any other period of the world's history than this, Dyer and Mussolini would have seemed the normal ones.

In Europe the new feelings about force and power have gradually grown up, the new policy which is the result of them has been developed by degrees. We have been brought up with them; they seem natural to us. We are too familiar with them to realize them. The anti-democratic reaction in Italy and Spain and Russia has made many of us for the first time acutely conscious of these humanitarian feelings, has rendered the nature of this democratic policy explicitly clear.

Nowhere is the contrast between old and new more striking than in India. For humanitarian feelings are not native to the Indian soil. The life of a cow, it is true, is respected, but not the life of a man. Humanitarian feelings with regard to men have been introduced artificially, from outside. And the democratic system of policy in which these feelings normally result has been grafted suddenly on another system, whose general benevolence of intention made it none the less despotic. Old and new strangely coexist, and India is ruled in accordance with two completely incompatible theories of government: that of Akbar, shall we say, and that of Woodrow Wilson. On Monday the watchword of the Executive is 'Reform and Responsible Self-Government'; like Oliver Twist, the Indians immediately ask for more; their demands become alarmingly insistent, and the Government nervously decides to be firm. On Tuesday some General Dyer rivals the exploits of the Moguls; repressive legislation is passed, the gaols are crowded. On Wednesday the Government is seized with conscientious qualms; remembering what

Mr. Gladstone said in 1882 and why the Great War was fought, it makes a 'generous gesture.' The response is so unenthusiastic that it becomes necessary on Thursday to suspend the Habeas Corpus Act and imprison several thousand suspects without a trial. By the end of the week, everybody, including the Government itself, is feeling rather muddled. And what about next week, and the week after that, and all the other weeks that are to follow?

FATEHPUR SIKRI

AKBAR built the city as a small personal tribute to himself. The vanity of Indian potentates had a way of running to brand new cities. Witness Jai Singh's Jaipur, five miles from the existing and perfectly satisfactory town of Amber; Jodha's Jodhpur, an hour's walk from Mandor; the Udaipur of Udai Singh next door to Arh. An expensive form of royal vanity; but one for which the modern tourist should be grateful. There is nothing more picturesque than a deserted city, nothing more mournfully romantic. These deserted cities of Northern India are particularly romantic because, being relatively modern, they are all in an excellent state of preservation. For a building that is intact, but deserted, is much more romantic, more picturesquely melancholy than a deserted ruin. One expects a ruin to be deserted; nobody, it is obvious, could possibly live in Pompeii, or among the roofless remains of an English abbey. But in a building that is intact one expects to find inhabitants. When such a building is deserted, we are mournfully surprised; and the contrast between its emptiness and intactness strikes us as being strange and suggestive.

Fatehpur is less than four hundred years old, and, so far as the principal buildings are concerned, it is in a state of perfect preservation. The red sandstone which Akbar used in the building of his city is a hard, weather-resisting rock. The sculpture, the mouldings are still clean-edged and sharp. There has been no blurring of outlines, no crumbling, no leprous decay. Akbar's red city stands to-day in the condition in which he left it—and stands empty, untenanted even by the monkeys which inhabit so many of India's deserted palaces and temples.

To those whom the dry and sterile elegance of Shah Jahan's Agra has left unsatisfied, the architecture of Fateh-pur Sikri will seem refreshing. For the greatest of the alien Mohammedan emperors was a patron of the indigenous Hindu art of India, and the architecture of his capital is marked by something of the genuine Hindu vigour and wealth of imagination. The *liwan* or covered portion of the mosque is particularly fine. It is divided up into three square chambers, in line and communicating; and the characteristically Hindu ceilings of these chambers are supported by a number of very tall Hindu columns. The building is superb in proportion and detail, and is certainly one of the finest pieces of interior architecture on a large scale to be seen in Upper India. And yet, such is the prestige of expensive material that poor uninteresting buildings, wholly lacking in grandeur or originality, like the Pearl Mosque at Agra, the pavilions by the lake at Ajmere, are much more widely celebrated. They are of marble; Fatehpur is only of sandstone.

It was late in the afternoon when we left the deserted city. The walls and domes glowed more rosily than ever in the light of the almost level sun. It had become a city of coral. There was a screaming in the air above us. Looking up we saw a flock of parrots flying across the pale sky. The shadow of the enormous Gate of Victory was upon them; but a moment later they emerged from it into the bright transfiguring sunlight. Over the courts of that deserted city of coral and ruddy gold a flight of emerald birds passed glittering and was gone.

JAIPUR

At Jaipur we were fortunate in having an introduction to one of the great *thakurs* of the State. He was a mighty landholder, the owner of twenty villages with populations ranging from five hundred to as many thousands, a feudal lord who paid for his fief (until, a year or two ago, a somewhat simpler and more modern system of tenure was introduced) by contributing to the State army one hundred and fifty armed and mounted men. This nobleman was kind enough to place his elephant at our disposal.

It was a superb and particularly lofty specimen, with gold-mounted tusks; ate two hundredweight of food a day and must have cost at least six hundred a year to keep. An expensive pet. But for a man in the *thakur's* position, we gathered, indispensable, a necessity. Pachyderms in Rajputana are what glass coaches were in Europe a century and a half ago—essential luxuries.

The *thakur* was a charming and cultured man, hospitably kind as only Indians can be. But at the risk of seeming ungrateful, I must confess, that, of all the animals I have ever ridden, the elephant is the most uncomfortable mount. On the level, it is true, the motion is not too bad. One seems to be riding on a small chronic earthquake; that is all. The earthquake becomes more disquieting when the beast begins to climb. But when it goes downhill, it is like the end of the world. The animal descends very slowly and with an infinite caution, planting one huge foot deliberately before the other, and giving you time between each calculated step to anticipate the next convulsive spasm of movement—a spasm that seems to loosen from its place every organ in the rider's body, that twists the spine, that wrenches all the separate muscles of the loins and thorax. The hills round Jaipur are not very high. Fortunately; for by the end of the three or four hundred feet of our climbing and descending, we had almost reached the limits of our endurance. I returned full of admiration for Hannibal. He crossed the Alps on an elephant.

We made two expeditions with the pachyderm; one—over a rocky pass entailing, there and back, two climbs and two sickening descents—to the tanks and ruined temples of Galta, and one to the deserted palaces of Amber. Emerging from the palace precincts—I record the trivial and all too homely incident, because it set me mournfully reflecting about the cosmos—our monster halted and, with its usual deliberation, relieved nature, portentously. Hardly, the operation over, had it resumed its march when an old woman who had been standing at the door of a hovel among the ruins, expectantly waiting—we had wondered for what—darted forward and fairly threw herself on the mound of steaming excrement. There was fuel here, I suppose, for a week's cooking. 'Salaam, Maharaj,' she called up to us, bestowing in her gratitude the most opulent title she could lay her tongue to. Our passage had been to her like a sudden and unexpected fall of manna. She thanked us, she blessed the great and charitable Jumbo for his Gargantuan bounty.

Our earthquake lurched on. I thought of the scores of millions of human beings to whom the passage of an unconstipated elephant seems a godsend, a stroke of enormous good luck. The thought depressed me. Why are we here, men and women, eighteen hundred millions of us, on this remarkable and perhaps unique planet? To what end? Is it to go about looking for dung—cow dung, horse dung, the enormous and princely excrement of elephants? Evidently it is—for a good many of us, at any rate. It seemed an inadequate reason, I thought, for our being here—immortal souls, first cousins of the angels, own brothers of Buddha and Mozart and Sir Isaac Newton.

But a little while later I saw that I was wrong to let the consideration depress me. If it depressed me, that was only because I looked at the whole matter from the wrong end, so to speak. In painting my mental picture of the dung-searchers I had filled my foreground with the figures of Sir Isaac Newton and the rest of them. These, I perceived, should have been relegated to the remote background and the foreground should have been filled with cows and elephants. The picture so arranged, I should have been able to form a more philosophical and proportionable estimate of the dung-searchers. For I should have seen at a glance how vastly superior were their activities to those of the animal producers of dung in the foreground. The philosophical Martian would admire the dung-searchers for having discovered a use for dung; no other animal, he would point out, has had the wit to do more than manufacture it.

We are not Martians and our training makes us reluctant to think of ourselves as animals. Nobody inquires why cows and elephants inhabit the world. There is as little *reason* why we should be here, eating, drinking, sleeping and in the intervals reading metaphysics, saying prayers, or collecting dung. We *are* here, that is all; and like other animals we do what our native capacities and our environment permit of our doing. Our achievement, when we compare it with that of cows and elephants, is remarkable. They automatically make dung; we collect it and turn it into fuel. It is not something to be depressed about; it is something to be proud of. Still, in spite of the consolations of philosophy, I remained pensive.

BIKANER

THE desert of Rajputana is a kind of Sahara, but smaller and without oases. Travelling across it, one looks out over plains of brown dust. Once in every ten or twenty yards, some grey-green plant, deep-rooted, and too thorny for even camels to eat, tenaciously and with a kind of desperate vegetable ferocity struggles for life. And at longer intervals, draining the moisture of a rood of land, there rise, here and there, the little stunted trees of the desert. From close at hand the sparseness of their distantly scattered growth is manifest. But seen in depth down the long perspective of receding distance, they seem—like the in fact remotely scattered stars of the Milky Way—numerous and densely packed. Close at hand the desert is only rarely flecked by shade; but the farther distances seem fledged with a dense dark growth of trees. The foreground is always desert, but on every horizon there is the semblance of shadowy forests. The train rolls on, and the forests remain for ever on the horizon; around one is always and only the desert.

Bikaner is the metropolis of this desert, a great town islanded in the sand. The streets are unpaved, but clean. The sand of which they are made desiccates and drinks up every impurity that falls upon it. And what astonishing houses flank these streets! Huge *palazzi* of red sandstone, carved and fretted from basement to attic, their blank walls—wherever a wall has been left blank—whitewashed and painted with garishly ingenuous modern frescoes of horses, of battles, of trains running over bridges, of ships. These houses, the like of which we had seen in no other city, are the palaces of the Marwari merchants, the Jews of India, who go forth from their desert into the great towns, whence they return with the fruits of their business ability to their native place. Some of them are said to be fabulously wealthy, and Bikaner has, I suppose, more millionaires per thousand of population than any other town in the world.

We were shown over the country villa of one of these plutocrats, built in the desert a mile or two beyond the city wall. Costly and unflagging labour had created and conserved in the teeth of the sand, the scorching wind of summer and the winter frosts, a garden of trees and lawns, of roses and English vegetables. It is the marvel of Bikaner.

The sun was setting as we reached the bungalow. A little army of coolies was engaged in covering the lawns with tarpaulin sheets and fitting canvas greatcoats on all the shrubs. The night frosts are dangerous at this season. In summer, on the other hand, it is by day that the verdure must be jacketed. Such is horticulture in Rajputana.

I had hoped, too optimistically, to find in the Marwari plutocrats the modern equivalents of the Florentine merchant-princes of the *quattrocento.* But this pleasing bubble of illusion burst, with an almost audible pop, as we passed from the millionaire's garden into his house. The principal drawing-room was furnished almost exclusively with those polychromatic *art nouveau* busts that issue from the workshops of the tombstone manufacturers of Carrara, and with clockwork toys. These last had all been set going, simultaneously, in our honour. A confused ticking and clicking filled the air, and wherever we looked our eyes were dizzied by movement. Tigers, almost life size, nodded their heads. Pink *papier-mâché* pigs opened and shut their mouths. Clocks in the form of negroes rolled their eyes; in the form of fox-terriers wagged their tails and, opening their jaws to bark, uttered a tick; in the form of donkeys agitated their long ears sixty times a minute. And, preciously covered by a glass dome, a porcelain doll, dressed in the Paris fashions of 1900, jerkily applied a powder-puff to its nose, and jerkily reached back to the powder-box—again and again. These, evidently, are the products of our Western civilization which the East really admires. I remembered a certain brooch which I had seen one evening, at a dinner-party, on the *sari* of an Indian lady of great wealth and the highest position—a brooch consisting of a disc of blue enamel surrounded by diamonds, on the face of which two large brilliants revolved, by clockwork, in concentric circles and opposite directions. It was an eight-day brooch, I learned, wound every Sunday night.

JODHPUR

It was late in the afternoon when we drove past the Courts of Justice. The day's business was over and the sweepers were at work, making clean for the morrow. Outside one of the doors of the building stood a row of brimming waste-paper baskets, and from these, as from mangers, two or three sacred bulls were slowly and majestically feeding. When the baskets were empty officious hands from within replenished them with a fresh supply of torn and scribbled paper. The bulls browsed on; it was a literary feast.

Watching them at their meal, I understood why it is that Indian bulls are so strangely mild. On a diet of waste-paper, it would be difficult for them to be anything but disciples of Gandhi, devotees of non-violence and *ahimsa.* I also understood why it is that Indian cows yield so little milk and, further, why the cattle of either six are so often afflicted with hiccoughs. Before I came to India, I had never heard a bull hiccoughing. It is a loud and terrifying sound. Hearing behind me that explosive combination of a bellow and a bark, I have often started in alarm, thinking I was on the point of being attacked. But looking round, I would find that it was only one of the mild, dyspeptic totems of the Hindus, gorged with waste-paper and painfully, uncontrollably belching as it walked.

The effects on horses of a certainly insufficient and probably also unnatural diet are different. They do not hiccough—at least I never heard them hiccoughing. But as they trot the withered and emptily sagging entrails in their bellies give forth, at every step, a strange sound like the leathery creaking of organ bellows. It is a most distressing sound, but one to which all those who drive in Indian tongas must learn to accustom themselves.

PUSHKAR LAKE

THE holiest waters in India are mantled with a green and brilliant scum. Those who would bathe must break it, as hardy swimmers, in our colder countries, break the ice, before they can reach the spiritually cleansing liquid. Coming out of the water, bathers leave behind them jagged rifts of blackness in the green; rifts that gradually close, if no more pilgrims come down to bathe, till the green skin of the lake is altogether whole again.

There were but few bathers when we were at Pushkar. The bathing ghats going down in flights of white steps to the water were almost deserted and the hundred temples all but empty. We were able to walk easily and undisturbed along the little stone embankments connecting ghat with ghat. Here and there, on the lowest steps, a half-naked man squatted, methodically wetting himself with the scummy water, a woman, always chastely dressed, methodically soaked her clothes. On days of little concourse the bathers do not venture far out into the lake. Death lurks invisible under the green scum, swims noiselessly inshore, snaps, drags down. We saw him basking on a little shrine-crowned island a hundred yards from land, monstrous and scaly, grinning even in his sleep—a crocodile. Pushkar is so holy that no life may be taken within its waters or on its banks, not even the man-eater's. A dozen pilgrims disappear each year between those enormous jaws. It is considered lucky to be eaten by a crocodile at Pushkar.

Behind the ghats rises a charming architecture of temples and priestly houses and serais for the pilgrims—all white, with little domes against the sky, and balconies flowering out of high blank walls, and windows of lattice-work, and tunnelled archways giving a glimpse, through shadow, of sunlight beyond. Nothing very old, nothing very grand; but all exceedingly pretty, with a certain look of the Italian Riviera about it. Italian, too, are the innumerable shrines —in little niches, in ornamental sentry-boxes of stucco, under domed canopies of stone-work. Looking into them, I almost expected to see a mouldering plaster Crucifixion, an Annunciation in painted terra-cotta, a blue-robed Madonna with her Child. And it came each time as something of a shock to discover among the sacred shadows of the shrine a rough-hewn cow of marble or red sandstone, kneeling reverently before a bi-sexual phallic symbol and gazing at it with an expression on its ingenuously sculptured face of rapt ecstatic adoration.

CHITOR

A VISIT to India makes one realize how fortunate, so far at any rate as the arts are concerned, our Europe has been in its religions. The Olympian religion of antiquity and, except occasionally, the Christianity which took its place, were both favourable to the production of works of art, and the art which they favoured was, on the whole, a singularly reasonable and decent kind of art. Neither paganism nor Christianity imposed restrictions on what the artist might represent; nor did either demand of him that he should try to represent the unrepresentable. The Olympian deities were men made gods; the Saviour of the Christians was God made man. An artist could work to the greater glory of Zeus or of Jesus without ever going beyond the boundaries of real and actual human life.

How different is the state of things in India. Here, one of the two predominant religions forbids absolutely the representation of the human form, and even, where Muslim orthodoxy is strict, of any living animal form whatever. It is only occasionally, and then in purely secular art and on the smallest of scales, that this religious injunction is disobeyed. Mohammedan art tends, in consequence, to be dry, empty, barren, and monotonous.

Hinduism, on the other hand, permits the representation of things human, but adds that the human is not enough. It tells the artist that it is his business to express symbolically the superhuman, the spiritual, the pure metaphysical idea. The best is always the enemy of the good, and by trying to improve on sober human reality, the Hindus have evolved a system of art full of metaphysical monsters and grotesques that are none the less extravagant for being symbolical of the highest of 'high' philosophies. (Too high, I may add parenthetically, for my taste. Philosophies, like pheasants, can be hung too long. Most of our highest systems have been pendant for at least two thousand years. I am plebeian enough to prefer my spiritual nourishment fresh. But let us return to Hindu art.)

Readers of the *Bhagavad Gita* will remember the passage in the Eleventh Discourse, where Krishna reveals himself to Arjuna in a form hitherto unbeheld by mortal eyes :—

> 'With mouths, eyes, arms, breasts multitudinous . . .
> Long-armed, with thighs and feet innumerable,
> Vast-bosomed, set with many fearful teeth. . . .'

And further: 'With many divine ornaments, with many upraised divine weapons, wearing divine necklaces and vestures, anointed with divine unguents, the God all-marvellous, boundless, with face turned every way.' And so on. The catalogue of Krishna's members, features and wardrobe covers several pages of Mrs. Besant's translation of the *Gita*. We recognize the necessarily inadequate embodiment of the description in innumerable Indian statues and paintings. And what is the significance of these grotesque and repulsive monsters? Krishna himself explains it. 'Here today,' he says to Arjuna, 'behold the whole universe, movable and immovable, standing in one in my body.' These many-limbed monsters are symbolic, then, of the cosmos. They are the One made manifest, the All in a nutshell. Hindu artists are trying to express in terms of form what can only be expressed—and not very clearly at that, for it is difficult to speak lucidly about things of which one knows nothing—in words. The Hindus are too much interested in metaphysics and ultimate Reality to make good artists. Art is not the discovery of Reality—whatever Reality may be, and no human being can possibly know. It is the organization of chaotic appearance into an orderly and human universe.

CAWNPORE

Personally I have little use for political speaking. If I know something about the question at issue, I find it quite unnecessary to listen to an orator who repeats in a summarized, and generally garbled, form the information I already possess; knowing what I do, I am quite capable of making up my own mind on the subject under discussion without listening to his rhetorical persuasions. If, on the other hand, I know nothing, it is not to the public speaker that I turn for the information on which to base my judgment. The acquisition of full and accurate knowledge about any given subject is a lengthy and generally boring process, entailing the reading of many books, the collating of numerous opinions. It therefore follows, inevitably, that the imparting of knowledge can never be part of a public speaker's work, for the simple reason that if his speeches are boring and lengthy—and boring and lengthy they must be, if he is to give anything like a fair and full account of the facts—nobody will listen to him. Now it happens that I have a prejudice in favour of information. I like to know what I am doing and why. Hence, when I am ignorant, I go to the library, not to the public meeting. In the library, I know, I shall be able to collect enough facts to permit me to form an opinion of my own. At the public meeting, on the other hand, the speaker will give me only a garbled selection of the available facts, and will devote the bulk of his time and energies to persuading me by means of rhetoric to adopt his opinions. Political speaking is thus of no use to me. Either I know enough about the point at issue to make the oratory of politicians entirely superfluous; or else I know so little that their oratory is apt to be misleading and dangerous. In the first case I am in a position to make up my own mind; in the second I am not, and I do not desire to have my mind made up for me.

The All-India Congress at Cawnpore lasted for three days, and in the course of those three days I listened to more political speeches than I had previously listened to in all the years of my life. Many of them were in Hindi and therefore, to me, incomprehensible. Of the speeches in English most were eloquent; but for the reasons I have set out above they were of little use to me. If the Congress was impressive—and it did impress me, profoundly—it was not by reason of the oratory of the delegates. Oratory in large quantities is always slightly ridiculous. Particularly if it is the oratory of people who are not in a position to give effect to their words. The English in India are very quick in seeing this absurdity. Possessing as they do the power to act, they have no need to talk. It is easy for them to mock the powerless and disinherited Indians for the luxuriant copiousness of their eloquence. The Indians themselves are quite aware of the absurdity of so much oratory. 'We talk too much,' an old Indian said to me. 'But at least that's doing something. In my young days we didn't even talk.' In the beginning was the word . . . Words are creative. In the long run they have a way of generating actions. But it was not, I repeat, by the oratory that I was impressed. It was by the orators and by their audience.

Imagine an enormous tent, a hundred yards or more in length by sixty in width. Looking up, you could see, through the thin brown canvas of its roof, the shadows of wind-blown flags, and from time to time the passing silhouette of a kite or slowly soaring vulture. The floor of the tent and the platform were decently covered with matting, and it was on this matting—for there were no chairs—that the delegates sat, and sat unflinchingly, I may add, from before noon till long after sunset, six hours, seven hours and, on the last day, nearly nine. Those nine foodless hours of squatting on the floor were very nearly my last. By the time they were over, I was all but dead of sheer fatigue. But the delegates seemed positively to enjoy every moment of them. Comfort and regular meals are Western habits, which few, even of the wealthy, have adopted in the East. The sudden change to discomfort and protracted starvation is very painful to Western limbs and loins, Western hams, and Western stomachs.

It was a huge crowd. There must have been seven or eight thousand delegates packed together on the floor of the tent. In the old days, I was told, it would have been a variegated crowd of many-coloured turbans and fezes, interspersed with European hats and sun helmets. But now, since the days of non-co-operation, nobody wears anything but the white cotton 'Gandhi cap.' It is an ugly headgear, like a convict's cap. The wearers of it find the similitude symbolic. All India, they say, is one great gaol; for its inhabitants the convict's is the only suitable, the only logical uniform. From our exalted seats on the platform we looked down over what seemed a great concourse of prisoners.

It was the size of the crowd that first impressed me. Mere quantity is always impressive. The human observer is small and single. Great numbers, huge dimensions overawe him into feeling yet more solitary and minute. In the world of art even ugliness and disproportion can impress us, if there be but enough of them. The buildings which flank Victoria Street in London are architecturally monstrous; but they are so high, and the monotonous stretch of them is so long, that they end by taking on a certain grandeur. The individuals composing a Derby or Cup Final crowd may be repulsive both in appearance and character; but the crowd is none the less a magnificent and impressive thing. But at Cawnpore it was not only the quantity of humanity assembled within the Congress tent that impressed; it was its quality too. Looking through the crowd one was struck by the number of fine, intelligent faces. These faces were particularly plentiful on and in the neighbourhood of the platform, where the leaders and the more important of their followers were assembled. Whenever I remarked a particularly sensitive, intelligent or powerful face, I would make inquiries regarding its owner. In almost every case I found he had spent at least six months in gaol for a political offence. After a little practice, I learned to recognize the 'criminal type' at sight.

CAWNPORE

EDWARD LEAR has a rhyme about

> an old man of Thermopylae,
> Who never did anything properly.

To the Westerner all Indians seem old men of Thermopylae. In the ordinary affairs of life I am a bit of a Thermopylean myself. But even I am puzzled, disquieted, and rather exasperated by the Indians. To a thoroughly neat-minded and efficient man, with a taste for tidiness and strong views about respectability and the keeping up of appearances, Indians must be literally maddening.

It would be possible to compile a long and varied list of what I may call Indian Thermopylisms. But I prefer to confine my attention to the Thermopylean behaviour of Indians in a single sphere of activity—that of ceremonial. For it is, I think, in matters of ceremonial and the keeping up of appearances that Indians most conspicuously fail, in our Western opinion, 'to do anything properly.' Nobody who has looked into a temple or witnessed the ceremonies of an Indian marriage can fail to have been struck by the extraordinary 'sloppiness' and inefficiency of the symbolical performances. The sublime is constantly alternated with the ridiculous and trivial, and the most monstrous incongruities are freely mingled. The old man of Thermopylae is as busy in the palace as in the temple; and the abodes of Indian potentates are an incredible mixture of the magnificent and the cheap, the grandiose and the ludicrously homely. Cows bask on the front steps; the anteroom is filthy with the droppings of pigeons; beggars doze under the gates, or search one another's heads for lice; in one of the inner courts fifty courtesans from the city are singing interminable songs in honour of the birth of the Maharaja's eleventh grandchild; in the throne room, nobody quite knows why, there stands a brass bedstead with a sham mahogany wardrobe from the Tottenham Court Road beside it; framed colour prints from the Christmas number of the *Graphic* of 1907 alternate along the walls with the most exquisite Rajput and Persian miniatures; in the unswept jewel room, five million pounds' worth of precious stones lies indiscriminately heaped; the paintings are peeling off the walls of the private apartments, a leprosy has attacked the stucco, there is a hole in the carpet; the marble hall of audience is furnished with bamboo chairs, and the Rolls Royces are driven by ragged chauffeurs who blow their noses on the long and wind-blown end of their turbans. As an Englishman belonging to that impecunious but dignified section of the upper middle-class which is in the habit of putting on dress-clothes to eat—with the most studied decorum and out of porcelain and burnished silver—a dinner of dish-water and codfish, mock duck and cabbage, I was always amazed, I was pained and shocked by this failure on the part of Eastern monarchs to keep up appearances, and do what is owing to their position.

I was even more helplessly bewildered by the Thermopylean behaviour of the delegates at the Cawnpore Congress during Mr. Gandhi's speech on the position of Indians in South Africa. The applause when he ascended the rostrum was loud—though rather less loud than a Western observer might have expected. Indian audiences are not much given to yelling or hand-clapping, and it is not possible, when one is sitting on the floor, to stamp one's feet. But though the noise was small, the enthusiasm was evidently very great. And yet, when the Mahatma began to speak, there was more talking and fidgeting, more general inattention than during any other speech of the day. True, it was late in the afternoon when Mr. Gandhi made his speech. The delegates had spent a long and hungry day sitting on a floor that certainly grew no softer with the passage of the hours. There was every reason for their feeling the need to relax their minds and stretch their cramped legs. But however acute its weariness had become, a Western audience would surely have postponed the moment of relaxation until the great man had finished speaking. Even if it had found the speech boring, it would have felt itself bound to listen silently and with attention to a great and admired national hero. It would have considered that chattering and fidgeting were signs of disrespect. Not so, evidently, the Indian audience. To show disrespect for the Mahatma was probably the last thing in the world that the Cawnpore delegates desired. Nevertheless they talked all through the speech, they stretched their stiff legs, they called for water, they went out for little strolls in the Congress grounds and came back, noisily. Knowing how Englishmen could comport themselves during a speech by a national hero, combining in his single person the sanctity of the Archbishop of Canterbury with the popularity of the Prince of Wales, I was astonished, I was profoundly puzzled.

In an earlier entry in this diary I attributed the Thermopylism of the Indians to a certain emotional agility (shared, to some extent, by the natives of Southern Europe), to a capacity for feeling two things at once or, at least, in very rapid succession. Indians and Neapolitans, I pointed out, can reverence their gods even while spitting, jesting, and picking their noses. But this explanation does not go far enough; it requires itself to be explained. How is it that, while we are brought up to practise consistency of behaviour, the children of other races are educated so as to be emotionally agile? Why are we so carefully taught to keep up the appearances which to others seem so negligible?

Reflecting on my observations in Italy and in India, I am led to believe that these questions must be answered in one way for the Southern Europeans, in another for the Indians. The emotional agility of the Italians is due to the profound 'realism' of their outlook, coupled with their ingrained habit of judging things in terms of aesthetics. Thus, the Southern European may admire a religious service or a royal procession as works of art, while holding strong atheistical and anti-monarchical opinions; he will be able to mock and to admire simultaneously. And perhaps he is not an atheist or a republican at all. But however ardently a Christian or a monarchist, he will always find himself able to reflect—while he kneels before the elevated Host or cheers the royal barouche—that the priest and the king make a very good thing out of their business, and that they are, after all, only human, like himself—probably all too human. As for the shabbinesses and absurdities of the performance, he will ignore them in his appreciation of the grandiose intention, the artistic general effect. And he will regard the Northerner who wants the performance to be perfect in every detail as a laborious and unimaginative fool. Nor will he understand the Northerner's passion for keeping up appearances in ordinary daily life.

The Southerner has a liking for display; but his display is different from ours. When we go in for keeping up appearances, we do the job, not showily, but thoroughly, and at every point. We want all the rooms in our house to look 'nice,' we want everything in it to be 'good'; we train our servants to behave as nearly as possible like automatons, and we put on special clothes to eat even the worst of dinners. The Southerner, on the other hand, concentrates his display into a single splendid flourish. He likes to get something spectacular for his money, and his aim is to achieve, not respectability, but a work of art. He gives his house a splendid façade, trusting that every lover of the grandiose will be content to contemplate the marble front, without peering too closely at the brick and rubble behind. He will furnish one drawing-room in style, for state occasions. To keep up appearances at every point —for oneself and one's servants, as well as for the outside world—seems to him a folly and a waste of spirit. Life is meant to be enjoyed, and occasional grandiosities are part of the fun. But on ordinary days of the week it is best enjoyed in shirt sleeves.

The Indian's Thermopylisms are due, it seems to me, to entirely different causes. He is careless about keeping up appearances, because appearances seem to him as nothing in comparison with 'spiritual reality.' He is slack in the performance of anything in the nature of symbolic ceremonial, because the invisible thing symbolized seems to him so much more important than the symbol. He is a Thermopylean, not through excess of 'realism' and the aesthetic sense, but through excess of 'spirituality.' Thus the Maharaja does not trouble to make his surroundings look princely, because he feels that princeliness lies within him, not without. Marriages are made in heaven; therefore it is unnecessary to take trouble about mere marriage ceremonies on earth. And if the soul of every Indian is overflowing with love and respect for Mahatma Gandhi, why should Congress delegates trouble to give that respect the merely physical form of silence and motionlessness?

Such arguments, of course, are never consciously put. But the training of Indians is such that they act as though in obedience to them. They have been taught that this present world is more or less illusory, that the aim of every man should be to break out of the cycle of recurrent birth, that the 'soul' is everything and that the highest values are purely 'spiritual.' Owing to their early inculcation, such beliefs have tended to become almost instinctive, even in the minds of those whose consciously formulated philosophy of life is of an entirely different character. It is obvious that people holding such beliefs will attach the smallest importance to the keeping up of appearances.

In these matters we Northerners behave like Behaviourists—as though the visible or audible expression of an idea were the idea itself, as though the symbol in some sort created the notion symbolized. Our religious rites, our acts of 'natural piety,' are solemnly performed, and with an almost military precision. The impressive service, we have found, actually manufactures God; the memorial ceremony creates and conserves our interest in the dead. Our royal pageantry is no less rich, no less consistently effective; for the pageant *is* the king. Our judges are wigged and magnificently robed. Absurd survival! But no; the majesty of the law consists in the wigs and the ermine. The gentry keeps up appearances to the limit of its financial means and beyond. It is a folly, protests the believer in 'spiritual' realities. On the contrary, it is profound wisdom, based on the instinctive recognition of a great historical truth. History shows us that there were rites before there were dogmas, that there were conventions of behaviour before there was morality. Dogmas, indeed, have often been the children of rites—systems of thought called into existence to explain gestures. Morality is the theory of pre-existing social habits. (In the same way some of the greatest advances in mathematics have been due to the invention of symbols, which it afterwards became necessary to explain; from the minus sign proceeded the whole theory of negative quantities.) To sceptics desirous of believing, catholic directors of conscience prescribe the outward and visible practice of religion; practice, they know, brings forth faith; the formal appearance of religion creates its 'spiritual' essence. It is the same with civilization; men who practise the conventional ritual of civilization become civilized. Appearing to be civilized, they really are so. For civilization is nothing but a series of conventions; being civilized is obeying those conventions, is keeping up the appearances of culture, prosperity, and good manners. The more widely and the more efficiently such appearances are kept up, the better the civilzation. There can never be a civilization that ignores appearances and is wholly 'spiritual.' A civilization based on Quaker principles could not come into existence; Quakerism in all its forms is the product, by reaction, of a civilization already highly developed. Before one can ignore appearances and conventions, there must be, it is obvious, conventions and appearances to ignore. The Simple Life is simple only in comparison with some existing life of complicated convention. If Quaker principles ceased to be the luxury of a refined few, and were accepted by the world at large, civilization would soon cease to exist: freed from the necessity of keeping up the appearance of being civilized, the majority of human beings would rapidly become barbarous.

Admirers of India are unanimous in praising Hindu

'spirituality.' I cannot agree with them. To my mind 'spirituality' (ultimately, I suppose, the product of the climate) is the primal curse of India and the cause of all her misfortunes. It is this preoccupation with 'spiritual' realities, different from the actual historical realities of common life, that has kept millions upon millions of men and women content, through centuries, with a lot unworthy of human beings. A little less spirituality, and the Indians would now be free—free from foreign dominion and from the tyranny of their own prejudices and traditions. There would be less dirt and more food. There would be fewer Maharajas with Rolls Royces and more schools. The women would be out of their prisons, and there would be some kind of polite and conventional social life—one of those despised appearances of civilization which are yet the very stuff and essence of civilized existence. At a safe distance and from the midst of a network of sanitary plumbing, Western observers, disgusted, not unjustifiably, with their own civilization, express their admiration for the 'spirituality' of the Indians, and for the immemorial contentment which is the fruit of it. Sometimes, such is their enthusiasm, this admiration actually survives a visit to India.

It is for its 'materialism' that our Western civilization is generally blamed. Wrongly, I think. For materialism—if materialism means a preoccupation with the actual world in which we live—is something wholly admirable. If Western civilization is unsatisfactory, that is not because we are interested in the actual world; it is because the majority of us are interested in such an absurdly small part of it. Our world is wide, incredibly varied and more fantastic than any product of the imagination. And yet the lives of the vast majority of men and women among the Western peoples are narrow, monotonous, and dull. We are not materialistic enough; that is the trouble. We do not interest ourselves in a sufficiency of this marvellous world of ours. Travel is cheap and rapid; the immense accumulations of modern knowledge lie heaped up on every side. Every man with a little leisure and enough money for railway tickets, every man, indeed, who knows how to read, has it in his power to magnify himself, to multiply the ways in which he exists, to make his life full, significant, and interesting. And yet, for some inexplicable reason, most of us prefer to spend our leisure and our surplus energies in elaborately, brainlessly, and expensively murdering time. Our lives are consequently barren and uninteresting, and we are, in general, only too acutely conscious of the fact. The remedy is more materialism and not, as false prophets from the East assert, more 'spirituality' —more interest in this world, not in the other. The Other World—the world of metaphysics and religion—can never possibly be as interesting as this world, and for an obvious reason. The Other World is an invention of the human fancy and shares the limitations of its creator. This world, on the other hand, the world of the materialists, is the fantastic and incredible invention of—well, not in any case of Mrs. Annie Besant.

CAWNPORE

Serfs, burghers, nobles—we read about them in our history books; but we find it difficult to realize what mediaeval society was really like. To understand our European Middle Ages, one should go to India. Hereditary aristocracies still exist in the West—exist, but *pour rire*; they are scarcely more than a joke. It is in India that one learns what it meant, six hundred years ago, to be a villein, a merchant, a lord. Aristocracy, there, exists in fact, as well as in name. Birth counts. You come into the world predestined to superiority or abjection; it is a kind of social Calvinism. Some are born with Grace; they are Brahmins or Kshatriyas. The rest are damned from the beginning. Outcasts, peasants, money-lenders, merchants—the Indian hell has lower and higher circles; but even the upper circles are only the attics of the social abyss.

Almost without exception Indian politicians profess democratic principles. They envisage a popularly governed British dominion, ultimately a republic. Government by the people, for the people, and so on. But the majority of the influential ones are members of the highest castes, hereditary wise men and warriors. Their principles may be democratic, but their instincts remain profoundly aristocratic. Transplant a few mediaeval cardinals and dukes across the centuries into modern Europe; you might convince them that democracy was a good thing, but you could hardly expect them to forget from one day to the next their prejudices about villeins and burgesses, their conviction of their own inherent nobility. I have seen high-caste educated Indians treating their inferiors in a way which to a bourgeois like myself, born in even so moderately democratic a society as that of England, seemed unthinkably high-handed. I envied them the sense of assured and inalienable superiority which enabled them so naturally to play the part of the mediaeval noble.

That the lower-caste masses would suffer, at the beginning, in any case, from a return to Indian autonomy seems almost indubitable. Where the superiority of the upper classes to the lower is a matter of religious dogma, you can hardly expect the governing few to be particularly careful about the rights of the many. It is even something of a heresy to suppose that they have rights. Any indigenous government under Swaraj would necessarily be in the nature of a despotic oligarchy—that is, until education has spread so widely that another and more democratic form of government becomes practicable. One can only hope, piously, that the despotism will be paternal and that the education will spread quickly.

CAWNPORE

FROM its advertisements much may be learned of a nation's character and habits of thought. The following brief anthology of Indian advertisements is compiled from newspapers, magazines, medical catalogues, and the like. Several of the most characteristic specimens are taken from the *Cawnpore Congress Guide*, an official publication intended for the use of delegates and interested visitors. It is with one of these appeals to India's most enlightened public that I make a beginning.

> Beget a son and Be Happy by using the 'SON BIRTH PILLS,' my special secret Hindu Shastrick preparation, according to directions. Ladies who have given birth to daughters only WILL SURELY HAVE SONS NEXT, and those who have sons MUST HAVE MALE ISSUES ONCE AGAIN by the Grace of God. Fortunate persons desirous of begetting sons are bringing this marvellous Something into use for brightening their dark homes and making their lives worth their living. It is very efficacious and knows no failure. Self praise is no recommendation. Try and be convinced. But if you apply, mentioning this publication, with full history of your case, along with a consultation fee of Rupees Ten (Foreign one guinea) only giving your 'Word of Honour' to give me a SUITABLE REWARD (naming the amount) according to your means and position in life, just on the accomplishment of your desire in due course of time, you can have the same Free, ABSOLUTELY FREE. Act immediately, for this FREE OFFER may not remain open indefinitely.

Here are some pleasing Hair-oil advertisements from various sources :—

> Dr. ——'s Scented Almond Oil. Best preparation to be used as hair-oil for men who do mental work. The effects of almond oil on brain are known to everybody.

> Jabukusum is a pure vegetable oil, to which medicinal ingredients and the perfume have been added to prevent all affectations (*sic*) of the hair and the brain.

There are several panaceas on the Indian market. There is, for example, Sidda Kalpa Makaradhwaja which 'is a sure and infallible specific for all Diseases, and it never fails to effect a satisfactory cure in the patient, be his ailment whatever it may. Among the various diseases amenable to its administration, to state a few, are the following :—Debility, general or nervous, including Nervous Prostration, due to whatever cause, Loss of Memory, Giddiness and Insanity . . . Asthma and Consumption, all stomach troubles . . . Cholera . . . all Kidney and Bladder Troubles . . . all Acute and Chronic Venereal Diseases . . . Leprosy of all kinds, White, Black, Red, etc. . . . Rheumatism, Paralysis, Epilepsy . . . Hysteria, Sterility . . . and all Fevers, including Malaria, Pneumonia, Influenza, and such other poisonous ones.'

Not a bad medicine, but I prefer the 'Infallible Cure for Incurable Diseases, Habits, and Defects' advertised in the *Cawnpore Guide*. The announcement runs as follows :—

> I have discovered the natural system of cure for all diseases, habits, defects, failings, etc., without the use of deleterious and pernicious drugs or medicines. Being Scientific, it is absolutely safe, simple, painless, pleasant, rapid, and infallible. Diseases like hysteria, epilepsy, rheumatism, loss of memory, paralysis, insanity and mania ; addiction to smoking, opium, drink etc. ; impotence, sterility, adultery, and the like can

be radically cured duly by My System. Come to me after every one else has failed to do you good. I guarantee a cure in every case undertaken. Every case needs to be treated on its special merits, and so applicants should furnish me with the complete history of the health of the patient and general occupation from birth, height, measurement over chest or bust, waist and hips, and a photograph with as little dress on as possible, along with a consultation fee of Rupees Five, without which no replies can be sent.

If the buying of a postal order were not so insuperable a nuisance, I should send five rupees to get the details of the adultery cure. So much cheaper than divorce.

The following are characteristic of a large class of Indian advertisements :—

WONDERFUL WORK ! ! !

Works wonders in the earthly pleasure.

MARAD MITRA LAPE

Will make you a man in one day

MARAD MITRA YAKUTI

Renews all your lost vigour and enables you to enjoy the pleasure with increased delights. Try once. 1 Bottle Rs. 10. ½ Bottle Rs. 5.

FREE ! FREE ! !

Do you want 'Secret of Happiness from Conjugal Encounter' and 'Good Luck'? If so, apply for the illustrated literature to ——.

The enormous number of such advertisements testifies to the disastrous effect on Indian manhood of the system of child marriages. The effects, as Gandhi has pointed out in his autobiography, would probably be still worse, if it were not for the fact that Hindu girl wives generally spend at least half the year with their own parents, away from their schoolboy husbands.

The testimonials of Indian sufferers relieved by patent medicines are generally of a most lyrical character, and the oddity of the English in which they are written gives them an added charm. Here is one from an Indian Christian :—

> I can say really the medicine —— is sent by Lord Jesus Christ to the sinful world to save the poor victims from their dreadful diseases. In my 8 years' experience in medical line I have come across many preparations of medicine, but I have not seen such a wonderful medicine as ——. Please send 10 phials more.

Another pious gentleman writes :—

> I am living to see that I am what I am by the wonderful cure these pills wrought in me by the Grace of God, who I think has put the wisdom of preparing such pills into the head of our Venerable Pundit ——.

Another has 'no hesitation in recommending it to the suffering humanity.'

Yet another writes as follows :—

> Several of my friends and myself have been using your —— for over four months for Influenza, Lumbago, Dyspepsia, Syphilis, Rheumatism and Nervous Debility with complete success. There has not been a case in which it failed. I will call it an Ambrosia.

The classical allusion is elegant and apt. One is not surprised to find that the author of the testimonial is a Bachelor of Arts.

BENARES

January 14, 1926

IT was said that the eclipse of the sun would be visible from Benares. But it needed more than smoked glass to see it; the eye of faith was also indispensable. That, alas, we did not possess. Partial to the point of being non-existent, the eclipse remained, for us at least, unseen. Not that we minded. For it was not to look at the moon's silhouette that we had rowed out that morning on the Ganges; it was to look at the Hindus looking at it. The spectacle was vastly more extraordinary.

There were, at the lowest estimate, a million of them on the bathing ghats that morning. A million. All the previous night and day they had been streaming into the town. We had met them on every road, trudging with bare feet through the dust, an endless and silent procession. In bundles balanced on their heads they carried provisions and cooking utensils and dried dung for fuel, with the new clothes which it is incumbent on pious Hindus to put on after their bath in honour of the eclipsed sun. Many had come far. The old men leaned wearily on their bamboo staves. Their children astride of their hips, the burdens on their heads automatically balanced, the women walked in a trance of fatigue. Here and there we would see a little troop that had sat down to rest—casually, as is the way of Indians, in the dust of the road and almost under the wheels of the passing vehicles.

And now the day and the hour had come. The serpent was about to swallow the sun. (It was about to swallow him in Sumatra, at any rate. At Benares it would do no more than nibble imperceptibly at the edge of his disk. The serpent, should one say, was going to try to swallow the sun.) A million of men and women had come together at Benares to assist the Light of Heaven against his enemy.

The ghats go down in furlong-wide flights of steps to the river, which lies like a long arena at the foot of enormous tiers of seats. The tiers were thronged to-day.

Floating on the Ganges, we looked up at acres upon sloping acres of humanity.

On the smaller and comparatively unsacred ghats the crowd was a little less densely packed than on the holiest steps. It was at one of these less crowded ghats that we witnessed the embarkation on the sacred river of a princess. Canopied and curtained with glittering cloth of gold, a palanquin came staggering down through the crowd on the shoulders of six red-liveried attendants. A great barge, like a Noah's ark, its windows hung with scarlet curtains, floated at the water's edge. The major-domo shouted and shoved and hit out with his rod of office; a way was somehow cleared. Slowly and with frightful lurchings, the palanquin descended. It was set down, and in the twinkling of an eye a little passage-way of canvas had been erected between the litter and the door of the barge. There was a heaving of the cloth of gold, a flapping of the canvas; the lady—the ladies, for there were several of them in the litter—had entered the barge unobserved of any vulgar eye. Which did not prevent them, a few minutes later when the barge had been pushed out into mid-stream, from lifting the scarlet curtains and peering out with naked faces and unabashed curiosity at the passing boats and our inquisitive camera. Poor princesses! They could not bathe with their plebeian and unimprisoned sisters in the open Ganges. Their dip was to be in the barge's bilge-water. The sacred stream is filthy enough under the sky. What must it be like after stagnating in darkness at the bottom of an ancient barge?

We rowed on towards the burning ghats. Stretched out on their neat little oblong pyres, two or three corpses were slowly smouldering. They lay on burning faggots, they were covered by them. Gruesomely and grotesquely, their bare feet projected, like the feet of those who sleep uneasily on a bed too short and under exiguous blankets.

A little farther on we saw a row of holy men, sitting like cormorants on a narrow ledge of masonry just above the water. Cross-legged, their hands dropped limply, palm upwards, on the ground beside them, they contemplated the brown and sweating tips of their noses. It was the Lord Krishna himself who, in the *Bhagavad Gita*, prescribed that mystic squint. Lord Krishna, it is evident, knew all that there is to be known about the art of self-hypnotism. His simple method has never been improved on; it puts the mystical ecstasy *à la portée de tous*. The noise of an assembled million filled the air; but no sound could break the meditative sleep of the nose-gazers.

At a given moment the eye of faith must have observed the nibblings of the demoniacal serpent. For suddenly and simultaneously all those on the lowest steps of the ghats threw themselves into the water and began to wash and gargle, to say their prayers and blow their noses, to spit and drink. A numerous band of police abbreviated their devotions and their bath in the interest of the crowds behind. The front of the waiting queue was a thousand yards wide; but a million people were waiting. The bathing must have gone on uninterruptedly the whole day.

Time passed. The serpent went on nibbling imperceptibly at the sun. The Hindus counted their beads and prayed, made ritual gestures, ducked under the sacred slime, drank, and were moved on by the police to make room for another instalment of the patient million. We rowed up and down, taking snapshots. West is West.

In spite of the serpent, the sun was uncommonly hot on our backs. After a couple of hours on the river, we decided that we had had enough, and landed. The narrow lanes that lead from the ghats to the open streets in the centre of the town were lined with beggars, more or less holy. They sat on the ground with their begging bowls before them; the charitable, as they passed, would throw a few grains of rice into each of the bowls. By the end of the day the beggars might, with luck, have accumulated a square meal. We pushed our way slowly through the thronged alleys. From an archway in front of us emerged a sacred bull. The nearest beggar was dozing at his post —those who eat little sleep much. The bull lowered its muzzle to the sleeping man's bowl, made a scouring movement with its black tongue, and a morning's charity had gone. The beggar still dozed. Thoughtfully chewing, the Hindu totem turned back the way it had come and disappeared.

Being stupid and having no imagination, animals often behave far more sensibly than men. Efficiently and by instinct they do the right, appropriate thing at the right moment—eat when they are hungry, look for water when they feel thirst, make love in the mating season, rest or play when they have leisure. Men are intelligent and imaginative; they look backwards and ahead; they invent ingenious explanation for observed phenomena; they devise elaborate and roundabout means for the achievement of remote ends. Their intelligence, which has made them the masters of the world, often causes them to act like imbeciles. No animal, for example, is clever and imaginative enough to suppose that an eclipse is the work of a serpent devouring the sun. That is the sort of explanation that could occur only to the human mind. And only a human being would dream of making ritual gestures in the hope of influencing, for his own benefit, the outside world. While the animal, obedient to its instinct, goes quietly about its business, man, being endowed with reason and imagination, wastes half his time and energy in doing things that are completely idiotic. In time, it is true, experience teaches him that magic formulas and ceremonial gestures do not give him what he wants. But until experience has taught him—and he takes a surprisingly long time to learn—man's behaviour is in many respects far sillier than that of the animal.

So I reflected, as I watched the sacred bull lick up the rice from the dozing beggar's bowl. While a million people undertake long journeys, suffer fatigue, hunger, and discomfort in order to perform, in a certain stretch of very dirty water, certain antics for the benefit of a fixed star ninety million miles away, the bull goes about looking for food and fills its belly with whatever it can find. In this case, it is obvious, the bull's brainlessness causes it to act much more rationally than its masters.

To save the sun (which might, one feels, very safely be left to look after itself) a million of Hindus will assemble on the banks of the Ganges. How many, I wonder, would assemble to save India? An immense energy which, if it could be turned into political channels, might liberate and transform the country, is wasted in the name of imbecile superstitions. Religion is a luxury which India, in its present condition, cannot possibly afford. India will never be free until the Hindus and the Moslems are as tepidly enthusiastic about their religion as we are about the Church of England. If I were an Indian millionaire, I would leave all my money for the endowment of an Atheist Mission.

LUCKNOW

At the end of the second day of the All-India Musical Conference, I declared a strike. Accustomed to the ordinary three-hour day of the European concert-goer, I found myself exhausted by the seven or eight hours of daily listening imposed on me by the makers of the Lucknow programme. There was one long concert every morning, another every afternoon, a third at night. It was too much. After the second day I would not go again. Still, before I struck, I had had sixteen hours of Indian music—enough, at home, to hear all the symphonies of Beethoven, with a good sprinkling of characteristic specimens from Mozart and Bach thrown in. Sixteen hours of listening should be enough to give one at least the hang of an unfamiliar music.

Professional musicians, mostly attached to the courts of reigning princes, had come to Lucknow from every part of India. There were accomplished singers and celebrated players of every Indian instrument—including even the harmonium, which, to my great astonishment and greater disgust, was permitted to snore and whine in what I was assured was the very sanctuary of Indian music. I listened to all the virtuosity of India. That it touched me less than the more modest accomplishment of the old Lahore musician was due, I think, to purely physical causes. The vina and the sitar must be heard at close quarters. All the expression and feeling that a performer puts into his playing evaporates at a distance, and nothing can be heard beyond the jangle of the plucked strings. At Lahore I had been amazed by the richness and variety of the tone that came out of the old musician's sitar. At Lucknow, where the concerts were held in a large tent, I was wearied by its tinkling monotony. Space had sucked the soul out of the music; it came to me dry and dead.

Much is enthusiastically talked about the use of quartertones in Indian music. I listened attentively at Lucknow in the hope of hearing some new and extraordinary kind of melody based on these celebrated fractions. But I listened in vain. The scales in which Indian music is written are of quite familiar types. The pentatonic or black-note scale, for example, seems to be a favourite; and any one learned in ancient European music would probably find no difficulty in labelling with their modal names the various melodies of India. The quarter-tone makes its appearance only in the slurred transition from one note of the fundamental scale to another. The sentimental tzigane violinist and the jazz-band player make just as free a use of quarter-tones as do the Indians, and in precisely the same way.

DELHI

THE wars of Troy had their Homer. But other and more significant events, other cities vastly greater, have remained uncommemorated in the outer darkness that lies beyond the frontiers of the little luminous world of art. Men, places, and happenings do not always and necessarily get the chroniclers they deserve. Shakespeare is without his Boswell and his Holbein. The European War has not, as yet at any rate, produced its Tolstoy or its Goya. No Swift has reacted to modern America. Nor, finally, has contemporary Delhi, nor the new India of which it is the capital and epitome, evolved its Marcel Proust.

How often, while at Delhi, I thought of Proust and wished that he might have known the place and its inhabitants. For the imperial city is no less rich in social comedy than Paris; its soul is as fertile in snobberies, dissimulations, prejudices, hatreds, envies. Indeed, I should say that in certain respects the comedy of Delhi is intrinsically superior to that which Proust found in the Faubourg Saint-Germain and so minutely analysed. The finest comedy (I speak for the moment exclusively as the literary man) is the most serious, the most nearly related to tragedy. The comedy of Delhi and the new India, however exquisitely diverting, is full of tragic implications. The dispute of races, the reciprocal hatred of colours, the subjection of one people to another—these things lie behind its snobberies, conventions, and deceits, are implicit in every ludicrous antic of the comedians. Sometimes, when a thunderstorm is approaching, we may see a house, a green tree, a group of people illuminated by a beam of the doomed sun, and standing out with a kind of unearthly brightness against the black and indigo of the clouds. The decaying relics of feudalism, the Dreyfus case, the tragedies of excessive leisure—these form the stormy background to the Proustian comedy. The clouds against which imperial Delhi appears so brilliantly comical are far more black, far more huge and menacing.

In India I was the spectator of many incidents that might have come straight out of '*A la Recherche du Temps Perdu*'; trivial incidents, but pregnant with the secret passions and emotions which Proust could always find, when they were there, beneath the most ordinary gestures, the most commonplace and innocuous words. I remember, for example, the behaviour of an Indian guest at a certain hotel, where the European manager made a habit of strolling about the dining-room during meals, superintending the service, chatting with the diners and, when they rose to leave, opening the door to let them out. The Indian, I noticed, never gave the manager a chance of opening the door for him. When he wanted to leave the dining-room, he would wait till the manager's back was turned and then fairly run to the door, turn the handle and slip through, as though the devil were after him. And indeed the devil *was* after him —the devil in the form of a painful suspicion that, if he gave the manager an opportunity of opening the door for him, the fellow might make a humiliating exception to his rule of courtesy and leave it conspicuously shut.

I remember a dinner-party at Delhi, at which the embarrassment was all on the other side. An Indian politician was the host; the guests, two other politicians, a high English official, and ourselves. It was a cheerful evening. With the roast, the Indians began talking of the time they had spent in gaol during the Non-Co-operation Movement. It had been for them a not too uncomfortable and even rather comical experience. They were men of standing; it was only natural that they should have been exceptionally well treated. 'Besides, the eldest and most eminent of the politicians explained, parodying the words of a Great Mogul, 'rivers of champagne had flowed between me and Sir ——, who was the governor of the province.' Rivulets, one gathered, continued to flow, even in the prison. The conversation was entirely good-humoured, and was punctuated with laughter. But the English official listened with a certain embarrassment. He was, after all, a member of the executive which had had these men thrown into gaol; and the fact that they had, on the whole, enjoyed themselves in prison did not diminish his indirect responsibility for their having been sent there. Nor were the comments of the Indians on the paternal and imprisoning government any the less scathing for being uttered with a laugh of good-natured derision. I did not envy the official; his situation was dreadfully ticklish. He was a guest, to begin with; moreover, the post he had occupied since the introduction of the Montford Reforms officially imposed upon him a behaviour towards Indian politicians of more than ordinary courtesy and cordiality. He existed, officially, to make the Legislative Assembly work; he was there to lubricate the ill-designed and creaking machinery of Indian parliamentary government. It was impossible for him either in his public or his private capacity to protest against the remarks of the Indian politicians. At the same time it was no less impossible for him, as a member of the British executive, to accept or agree with them. He adopted the only possible course, which was to disassociate himself completely from the conversation, to be as though he were not. He did it, I must say, marvellously well; so well, indeed, that there was a certain moment (the Government was catching it particularly hot) when he seemed on the point of becoming invisible, of fading out altogether, like the Cheshire Cat. I admired his tact and thanked God that I was not called upon to exercise it. The lot of the modern I.C.S. official is not entirely enviable.

And then there were the Maharajas. The Chamber of Princes—that remarkable assembly, attended every year by a steadily diminishing number of Indian rulers—was holding its sittings while we were at Delhi. For a week Rolls Royces were far more plentiful in the streets than Fords. The hotels pullulated with despots and their viziers. At the Viceroy's evening parties the diamonds were so large that they looked like stage gems; it was impossible to believe that the pearls in the million-pound necklaces were the genuine excrement of oysters. How hugely Proust would have enjoyed the Maharajas! Men with a pride of birth more insensate than that of Charlus; fabulously rich, and possessing in actual fact all the despotic power of which the name of Guermantes is only the faint hereditary symbol; having all the idiosyncrasies and eccentricities of Proust's heroes and none of their fear of public opinion; excessive and inordinate as no aristocrat in the modern West could hope to be; carrying into Napoleonic or Neronian actuality the poor potential velleities towards active greatness or vice that are only latent in men who live in and not above society. He would have studied them with a passionate interest, and more especially in their relations—their humiliating and gravely ludicrous relations—with the English. It would have charmed him to watch some Rajput descendant of the Sun going out of his way to be agreeable to the official who, though poor, insignificant, of no breeding, is in reality his master; and the spectacle of a virtuous English matron, doing her duty by making polite conversation to some dark and jewelled Heliogabalus, notorious for the number of his concubines and catamites, would have delighted him no less. How faithfully he would have recorded their words, how completely and with what marvellous intuition he would have divined the secret counterpoint of their thoughts! He would have been deeply interested, too, in that curious unwritten law which decrees that European women shall dance in public with no Indian below the rank of Raja. And it would, I am sure, have amused him to observe the extraordinarily emollient effects upon even the hardest anti-Asiatic sentiments of the possession of wealth and a royal title. The cordiality with which people talk to the dear Maharaja Sahib—and even, occasionally, about him—is delightful. My own too distant and hurried glimpses of the regal comedies of India made me desire to look more lingeringly, more closely, and with a psychological eye acuter than that with which nature has grudgingly endowed me.

I remember so many other pregnant trifles—The pathetic gratitude of a young man in an out-of-the-way place, to whom we had been ordinarily civil, and his reluctance to eat a meal with us, for fear that he should eat it in an un-European fashion and so eternally disgrace himself in our eyes. The extraordinarily hearty, back-slapping manner of certain educated Indians who have not yet learned to take for granted their equality with the ruling Europeans and are for ever anxious loudly to assert it. The dreadfully embarrassing cringing of others. The scathing ferocity of the comments which we overheard, in the gallery of the Legislative Assembly, being made on the Indian speakers by the women-folk of certain Government members. Listening, I was reminded of the sort of things that were said by middle-class people in England about the workmen at the time of the coal strike. People whose superiority is precarious detest with passion all those who threaten it from below.

Nor must I forget—for Proust would have devoted a score of pages to it—the noble Anglo-Indian convention of dressing for dinner. From the Viceroy to the young clerk who, at home, consumes high tea at sunset, every Englishman in India solemnly 'dresses.' It is as though the integrity of the British Empire depended in some directly magical way upon the donning of black jackets and hard-boiled shirts. Solitary men in dak bungalows, on coasting steamers, in little shanties among the tiger-infested woods, obey the mystical imperative and every evening put on the funereal uniform of English prestige. Women, robed in the latest French creations from Stratford-atte-Bowe, toy with the tinned fish, while the mosquitoes dine off their bare arms and necks. It is magnificent.

Almost more amazing is that other great convention for the keeping up of European prestige—the convention of eating too much. Five meals a day—two breakfasts, luncheon, afternoon tea, and dinner—are standard throughout India. A sixth is often added in the big towns where there are theatres and dances to justify late supper. The Indian who eats at the most two meals a day, sometimes only one—too often none—is compelled to acknowledge his inferiority. In his autobiography Gandhi records his youthful lapses—after what frightful wrestlings with his conscience !—into meat eating. A fellow-schoolboy led him into the sin. Meat, the tempter speciously argued, was the secret of English supremacy. The English were strong because they ate so much. If Indians would stuff themselves as imperially, they would be able to turn the English out of India. Gandhi was struck; he listened, he allowed himself to be convinced. He ate—three or four times, at least. Perhaps that is why he came as near as he did to turning the English out of India. In any case, the story proves how deeply the Indians are impressed by our gastronomic prowess. Our prestige is bound up with overeating. For the sake of the Empire the truly patriotic tourist will sacrifice his liver and his colon, will pave the way for future apoplexies and cancers of the intestine. I did my best while I was in India. But at the risk of undermining our prestige, of bringing down the whole imperial fabric in ruins about my ears, I used from time to time unobtrusively to skip a course. The spirit is willing, but the flesh, alas, is weak.

ON THE HOOGLY

THE ship slides down the Hoogly, between the mudbanks and the palms. Every now and then we pass a village, a huge white jute mill. Above the flat plain of the delta the sky is enormous and peopled with majestic clouds. After these months lived under a perpetually flawless blue, the spectacle of clouds is a delight and a refreshment. I understand, now, the inspiration of those Mogul paintings, which represent princesses and great lords looking at the clouds. A dry season in India makes one long for a break in the monotony of too perfect weather. Cloud-gazing when at last the approaching rains render it possible, must be a most delicious pastime, particularly when combined (as the Moguls in the paintings combine it) with dalliance, the sipping of sherbet, and the slow deliberate smoking of an enormous hubble-bubble.

These clouds are messengers from the world that lies beyond the borders of India; my pleasure at seeing them is symbolical. For, to tell the truth, I am glad to be leaving India. I have met old friends in India, and made new friends; I have seen many delightful and interesting things, much beauty, much that is strange, much that is grotesque and comical. But all the same I am glad to be going away. The reasons are purely selfish. What the eye does not see, the heart does not grieve over. It is because I do not desire to grieve that I am glad to be going. For India is depressing as no other country I have ever known. One breathes in it, not air, but dust and hopelessness. The present is unsatisfactory, the future dubious and menacing. The forces of the West have been in occupation for upwards of a century and a half. And yet five generations of peace and settled government have made the country, as a whole, no more prosperous than it was in the days of anarchy; according to some authorities, such as Digby, they have made it much poorer. Millions, at any rate, are still admittedly without enough to eat, all their lives. Custom and ancient superstition are still almost as strong as they ever were, and after a century and a half of Western government, nine Indians out of ten cannot read or write, and the tenth, who can, detests the Europeans who taught him. The educated and politically conscious profess democratic principles; but their instincts are profoundly and almost ineradicably aristocratic. They desire, theoretically, to see the country 'progressing' in the Western sense of the term; but the practical ambition of most of them is to secure a quiet job without responsibilities or risks.

Meanwhile the mountains of unnecessary labour, of

evitable hardship and superfluous suffering, are piled up, patiently, higher and ever higher. Millions upon millions are born and painfully live—to what end? God knows, it is hard enough to find a reason anywhere, West or East. But in India there is no conceivable answer to the question, at any rate in terms of the present existence. Metempsychosis had to be invented, and the doctrine of *karma* elaborated with a frightful logic, before the serried, innumerable miseries of India could be satisfactorily accounted for.

The ship goes sliding down-stream. The clouds seem to beckon and lead on, away. To-morrow we shall be at sea.

ON THE IRRAWADDY

My reading on the Irrawaddy was *The Glass Palace Chronicle of the Kings of Burma*. This curious work was prepared in 1829 at the command of King Bagyidaw, who appointed a committee of the most famous scholars to compile a definitive and authoritative chronicle from the existing records. The result is probably the most learned edition of a fairy tale that has ever been published.

The Burmese fancy has a peculiar flavour of its own. In the reigns of the good kings, for example, there were repeated showers of gems, a phenomenon of which I do not remember to have read in the fabulous history of any other people. And what remarkable things happened whenever a king died! Sometimes it was merely a matter of smoke issuing from the palace. But it was seldom that the country got off so lightly; a royal death ordinarily produced effects of a much more disturbing character. Planets and even the Pleiades would pass across the disk of the moon, or remain stationary for as much as seven months at a stretch. Sometimes the river would flow up country and light would stream from the earth. Sometimes —a mystery which the translator does not condescend to explain—the *deinnatthè* coincided with the *thingyan.* But perhaps the most unpleasant incident of all occurred when King Hkanlat died. 'About the time of his death an ogre wandered laughing over the whole country for full seven days; and the people who heard the ogre's laugh durst not sleep.' Long live the King; the Burmese must have repeated the loyal formula with a special and peculiar fervour.

This random selection of incidents from Burmese history is sufficient, I think, to indicate the character of the chronicle as a whole. It is a collection of fabulous anecdotes. But the charm of the fabulous quickly palls, and it would be impossible to read more than a very few pages of the *Glass Palace Chronicle*, if it were not for the solemn absurdities introduced into it by the compiling scholars. These learned men collated the several sources of their chronicle with the most laudable industry; they weighed the credibility of varying texts; they applied the principles of Higher Criticism to the ancient records and were bold to reject even that which was old, if it offended against reason and authoritative tradition. How learnedly and with what sober criticism do they deal, for example, with the story of the Naga princess who had an affair with the Sun Prince and, in consequence, laid a number of eggs which hatched out, some into human children and some, surprisingly, into iron and rubies! The comments of the scholars are too long and too intricately learned to be quoted in full. But this is how they deal with the question of the Naga princess's eggs:—

'As for the statement that a human being was born from the union of the Sun Prince and a female Naga, these are the only parallel instances in the books: in the *Bhuridatta*

Jataka, the birth of a human being after the father's kind from the union of a human prince with a female Naga and the birth of a Naga after the father's kind from the union of Dhattharattha, the Naga King, with the Princess Samuddaja; and in the *Mahavamsa*, such tales as the birth of Prince Sihabahu after the mother's kind from the union of the human princess, daughter of King Vangaraja, with a lion. Even if there were real union between the Sun Prince and the female Naga, either a spirit or a Naga should have been born, after the kind either of the father or the mother. Therefore, that a human son was born and not a spirit, nor a Naga, is contrary to reason, and this is a point of variance with the books.

'As for the statement that one golden egg broke in the land of Mogok Kyappyin and became stone, iron and ruby, this land of Mogok Kyappyin being thus singled out from among the fifty-six places of precious stones on the surface of Jambadapa, it is worth considering whether, in other places also, the various kinds of gems, stones, iron, ruby, gold and silver, and pearl, were likewise the result of the breaking of a Naga egg. Not a shadow, not a hint,' the scholars vehemently conclude, 'appears in the books that in all these fifty-six places a Naga egg broke and became stone, iron, or ruby.'

It is crushing, it is utterly conclusive. The female Naga and all her eggs must be rejected. Reason and authority demand that we should accept a more probable account of the origin of the young Pyusawhti, the Prince who killed, with a magic bow, the Great Boar, the Great Bird, the Giant Tiger and the Monstrous Flying Squirrel.

It is as though a committee of Scaligers and Bentleys had assembled to edit the tales of the nursery. Perrault's chronicle of Red Riding Hood is collated with Grimm's, the variants recorded, the credibility of the two several versions discussed. And when that little matter has been satisfactorily dealt with, there follows a long and incredibly learned discussion of the obscure, the complex and difficult problems raised by Puss in Boots. What language did the cat talk? And was he black or tortoise-shell, ginger or common tabby? Scaliger inclines to Latin and tortoise-shell. Bentley, with more weight of evidence, prefers black and Hebrew. A pleasing fancy. But when we pass from Red Riding Hood and Puss in Boots to the fables of the Old Testament, the fancy becomes a fact. In America, it would appear, there are still people who can discuss the first chapter of Genesis, the stories of Noah and Joshua, with all the earnest gravity of Burmese pandits discussing the Sun Prince and the eggs of the female Naga.

SINGAPORE

CLEARED of the forests, tamed into park and garden, this tropical land seems, under its perennially clouded skies, a piece of temperate Europe. From our windows we looked out on to sloping lawns, set here and there with huge umbrageous trees that looked almost like elms and oaks. The clouds swam indolently overhead. A thin haze stippled the distances and made them tenderly dim. We might have been looking out over a park in the Thames valley, but a Thames valley, as you saw at a second glance, deliriously dreaming of palm trees and orchids, and where the air was as warm as blood. It was into an equatorial England that we had suddenly stepped.

BATAVIA, JAVA

NEAR the Penang Gate lies an old brass cannon, half buried in the mud. It has no history, it is quite unornamental. A more commonplace piece of ordnance never issued from an eighteenth-century arsenal. The world is full of such old brass cannons. By all the rules it should have been melted down long ago or stuck muzzle downwards into the ground to serve as a post, or mounted on a little wooden carriage and left in the weather outside the door of a museum. But destiny decreed otherwise. Instead of suffering any of the ignominies usually reserved for its kind, this superannuated popgun was turned into a god. It lies there in the mud, wreathed with gardenias and orchids and a whole conservatory of paper flowers. The ground all about it is planted with long-stemmed paper lanterns, and incense burns perpetually before its muzzle. Two or three hawkers are encamped all day beside it, under the trees, like the sellers of books and plaster saints and candles in the shadow of a cathedral. The gun god's worshippers are numerous; they do a roaring trade in offerings and souvenirs. Great is the Cannon of the Batavians.

The Javanese were once Hindus, as their neighbours of Bali are to this day. But now, with the other Malayan peoples of Sumatra and the peninsula, they are Mohammedans. Mohammedans in name, at any rate; for their monotheism is hardly more than a varnish spread over cults much more ancient and, in the tropical circumstances, much more apposite. Pure monotheism is probably the last religion that would suggest itself to the minds of men living near the equator. In a tropical jungle, only a blind deaf-mute could be a monotheist. The woods are horrible; they teem with countless small and separate mysteries—unaccountable sights in the half-darkness, inexplicable sounds across the silence. Nobody with ears and eyes could fail, in a jungle, to be a believer in spirits, ghosts and devils. The Malays may call themselves Moslems; but they are still, at heart and by nature, animists.

Nor is it to the spirits alone that they pay their devotions. There is no God but God and Mohammed is his prophet. No doubt. But a cannon is cylindrical and, long before they became Moslems, the Javanese were worshippers of the reproductive principle in nature. An immemorial phallism has crystallized round the old gun, transforming it from a mere brass tube into a potent deity, to be propitiated with flowers and little lanterns, to be asked favours of with smoking incense. Men come and, standing before the sacred symbol, silently implore assistance. Women desirous of offspring sit on the prostrate God, rub themselves against his verdigrised sides and pray to him for increase. Even white ladies, it is said, may be seen at evening alighting inconspicuously from their motor-cars at the Penang Gate. They hurry across the grass to where the God is lying. They drop a few gardenias and a supplication, they touch the God's unresponsive muzzle; then hurry back again through the twilight, fearful of being recognized, of being caught in the flagrant act of worshipping at the shrine of a God who was being adored a thousand generations before Adam was ever thought of and beside whom the Gods of Zoroaster and the Vedas, of Moses and Christ and Mohammed are the merest upstarts and parvenus.

BATAVIA

At Weltevreden there is a plot of ground dedicated to the pleasures of the natives and called the Gambier Park. At the entrance gate you pay according to your nationality —Javanese five cents, foreign Orientals (Chinese or Arab) fifteen, and Europeans, half a gulden. We admitted the equitableness of the tariff—for in every tropical land the poorest people are always the inhabitants—shouldered the white man's burden to the tune of fifty cents apiece, and walked in. The thick, almost palpable darkness of a night overcast by tropical clouds was tempered by a few sparse arc-lamps and by the dim lanterns of mineral-water vendors.

Their light was reflected from puddles; it had been raining. The night felt and smelt like a hothouse. It seemed strange to be walking in the open. Surely there was a glass roof just overhead, there were glass walls all round us. And where were the hot-water pipes?

The sound of drums and bamboo xylophones, that tinkled out the endless and incoherent music of a dripping tap, drew us across the grass. Under a bright light twenty or thirty Javanese young men and girls were gravely dancing. Nobody spoke. They went through their evolutions without a word. I was reminded of the noiseless coming and going of an aquarium, of the mute ecstasies of embracing octopuses, of submarine battles, ferocious but inaudible. It is a strangely silent people, the Javanese. Some merman, perhaps, from the soundless depths among the corals was the first colonist of the island. We stood for some time watching the dumb Tritons in their batik skirts or trousers, the voiceless but, I am afraid, far from respectable nereids. Then, since one easily tires of goldfish, we strolled away in search of livelier entertainment.

But mum was still the word. Fifty yards away we found an open-air picture show. A crowd, as fishily dumb as the young dancers, stood or squatted in front of an illuminated screen, across which there came and went, in an epileptic silence, the human fishes of a cinema drama. And what a drama! We arrived in time to see a man in what the lady novelists call 'faultless evening dress,' smashing a door with an axe, shooting several other men, and then embracing against her will a distressed female, also in evening dress. Meanwhile another man was hurrying from somewhere to somewhere else, in motor-cars that tumbled over precipices, in trains that villains contrived to send full tilt into rivers—in vain, however, for the hurrying young man always jumped off the doomed vehicles in the nick of time and immediately found another and still more rapid means of locomotion. We did not stay to witness the foregone conclusion; but it was sufficiently obvious that the man in the hurry would find an aeroplane which would duly crash on the roof of the house where the distressed female was being embraced against her will. He would rush in and be just in time to prevent the consummation of a long protracted rape. (I may add parenthetically that rape, on the cinema, is always providentially leisurely; the villain takes things so easily that heroes invariably have the time to drive in Straight-Eights from Salt Lake City to New York before the virtuous resistance of the heroine can be overcome.) The villain would then be shot and the young man and distressed female would embrace, lengthily and with gusto, over his carcase.

The violent imbecilities of the story flickered in silence against the background of the equatorial night. In silence the Javanese looked on. What were they thinking? What were their private comments on this exhibition of Western civilization? I wondered. In North Africa, in India, I have also wondered. There are many races, skins of many shades; there are the colonies of many white nations, there are protectorates and mandated territories; there are nominally free countries that give 'concessions'—a great variety of political institutions and subject peoples. But there is only one Hollywood. Arabs and Melanesians, negroes and Indians, Malays and Chinamen—all see the same films. The crook drama at Tunis is the same as the crook drama at Madras. On the same evening, it may be, in Korea, in Sumatra, in the Sudan, they are looking at the same seven soulful reels of mother-love and adultery. The same fraudulent millionaires are swindling for the diversion of a Burmese audience in Mandalay, a Maori audience in New Zealand. Over the entire globe the producers of Hollywood are the missionaries and propagandists of white civilization. It is from the films alone that the untaught and untravelled member of a subject race can learn about the superior civilization which has conquered and is ruling him.

And what does he learn from the films? What is this famous civilization of the white men which Hollywood reveals? These are questions which one is almost ashamed to answer. The world into which the cinema introduces the subject peoples is a world of silliness and criminality. When its inhabitants are not stealing, murdering, swindling or attempting to commit rape (too slowly, as we have seen, to be often completely successful), they are being maudlin about babies or dear old homes, they are being fantastically and idiotically honourable in a manner calculated to bring the greatest possible discomfort to the greatest possible number of people, they are disporting themselves in marble halls, they are aimlessly dashing about the earth's surface in fast-moving vehicles. When they make money they do it only in the most discreditable, unproductive and socially mischievous way—by speculation. Their politics are matters exclusively of personal (generally amorous) intrigue. Their science is an affair of secret recipes for making money—recipes which are always getting stolen by villains no less anxious for cash than the scientific hero himself. Their religion is all cracker mottoes, white-haired clergymen, large-hearted mothers, hard, Bible-reading, puritanical fathers, and young girls who have taken the wrong turning and been betrayed (the rapes, thank goodness, are occasionally successful) kneeling with their illegitimate babies in front of crucifixes. As for their art—it consists in young men in overalls and large ties painting, in cock-lofts, feminine portraits worthy to figure on the covers of magazines. And their literature is the flatulent verbiage of the captions.

Such is the white man's world as revealed by the films,

a world of crooks and half-wits, morons and sharpers. A crude, immature, childish world. A world without subtlety, without the smallest intellectual interests, innocent of art, letters, philosophy, science. A world where there are plenty of motors, telephones and automatic pistols, but in which there is no trace of such a thing as a modern idea. A world where men and women have instincts, desires and emotions, but no thoughts. A world, in brief, from which all that gives the modern West its power, its political and, I like patriotically to think, its spiritual superiority to the East, all that makes it a hemisphere which one is proud to have been born in and happy to return to, has been left out. To the subject races of the East and South, Hollywood proclaims us as a people of criminals and mentally defectives. It was better, surely, in the old days before the cinema was invented, when the white men's subjects were totally ignorant of the world in which their masters lived. It was possible for them, then, to believe that the white men's civilization was something great and marvellous—something even greater, perhaps, and more extraordinary than it really was. Hollywood has changed all that. It has scattered broadcast over the brown and black and yellow world a grotesquely garbled account of our civilization. It has published a journal of our activities, but heavily censored. The political and scientific articles, the reviews of books, the essays, the reports of learned societies have been cut out; there are blanks where the reproductions of the works of art should be. Nothing has been left but the police court news, the feuilleton, the reports of the divorce cases. White men complain that the attitude of the members of the coloured races is not so respectful as it was. Can one be astonished?

What astonishes me is that the attitude remains as respectful as it does. Standing in the midst of that silent crowd of Javanese picture fans, I was astonished, when the performance attained its culminating imbecility, that they did not all with one accord turn on us with hoots of derision, with mocking and murderous violence. I was astonished that they did not all rush in a body through the town crying 'Why should we be ruled any longer by imbeciles?' and murdering every white man they met. The drivelling nonsense that flickered there in the darkness, under the tropical clouds, was enough to justify any outburst. But fortunately for us, the Oriental is patient and long-suffering. He is also cautious; for he knows, in the words of Hilaire Belloc, that

> Whatever happens, we have got
> The Maxim gun, and they have not——

'we' being the whites.

Maxim guns can check actions, but they cannot control thoughts. The coloured peoples think a great deal less of us than they did, even though they may be too cautious to act on their opinions. For this state of affairs the movies are not, of course, alone responsible. The spread of native education, the unedifying spectacle of the World War, the talk about self-determination and the sacredness of nationality, with promises of liberation made and never carried into effect—these have done much, perhaps most. But the share of Hollywood in lowering the white man's prestige is by no means inconsiderable. A people whose own propagandists proclaim it to be mentally and morally deficient, cannot expect to be looked up to. If films were really true to life, the whole of Europe and America would deserve to be handed over as mandated territories to the Basutos, the Papuans and the Andaman pygmies. Fortunately, they are not true. We who were born in the West and live there, know it. But the untutored mind of the poor Indian does not know it. He sees the films, he thinks they represent Western reality, he cannot see why he should be ruled by criminal imbeciles. As we turned disgusted from the idiotic spectacle and threaded our way out of the crowd, that strange aquarium silence of the Javanese was broken by a languid snigger of derision. Nothing more. Just a little laugh. A word or two of mocking comment in Malay, and then, once more, the silence as of fish. A few more years of Hollywood's propaganda, and perhaps we shall not get out of an Oriental crowd quite so easily.

BUITENZORG

THERE is a certain type of ingenious mind to which the function of decorative and applied art is simply and solely to make one object look like another and fundamentally different object. Wordsworth's Needlecase in the form of a Harp is classical. The same perverse ingenuity has begotten and is still begetting monsters as silly.

Personally, I have a weakness for these absurdities. I love the stucco that mimics marble, the washstands in the form of harpsichords, the biscuit boxes that look like Shakespeare's Complete Works tied together with an embroidered ribbon. My affection for these things prepared me to feel a special admiration for the flora of the equator. For the special and peculiar charm of tropical botany is that you can never be quite sure that it isn't zoology, or arts and crafts, or primitive religion. There are lilies in Malaya whose petals have become attenuated to writhing tentacles, so that they dangle on their stalks like perfumed spiders. There are palms whose fruits are vegetable porcupines. Dessert in Java is an affair of scarlet sea-urchins and baked potatoes: open the first—it contains the semblance of a plover's egg, hard boiled and peeled of its shell; and the potato proves to be full of a purplish custard flavoured with sherry, turpentine and chocolate. There are orchids in Singapore that might be pigeons, and others from which one recoils instinctively as though from the head of a snake. The gardens of the equator are full of shrubs that bloom with votive offerings to the Great Mother, and are fruited with coloured Easter eggs, lingams and swastikas. There are trees whose stems are fantastically buttressed to look like specimens of a late and decadent Gothic architecture; banyans pillared like the nave of a basilica; *Fici Elastiae* that trail the ropes and halters of a torture-chamber. There are red varnished leaves and leaves of shiny purple that look as though they were made of American cloth or patent leather. There are leaves cut out of pink blotting-paper; leaves mottled like the cover of a school notebook; leaves whose green is piped with lines of white or rose in a manner so sketchily elegant, so daring, so characteristically 'modern,' that they are manifestly samples of the very latest furniture fabrics from Paris.

MIRI, SARAWAK

It was on the point of raining when we anchored off Miri. The grey sky hung only a few feet above our masts; the sea below us was like grey oil, and between the ceiling of shifting vapours and the slowly heaving floor the air was unbreathable, like the steam of a hot bath. Half a mile away across the swell lay the land. The dark green forest came down to the water; and in little clearings, conquered from the trees, we could see a few dozens of European bungalows, a score or two of miniature Eiffel Towers marking the site of the oil wells which have called Miri into existence, a few cylindrical oil tanks, like white martello towers dotted along the coast. Out at sea, opposite a cluster of these white drums, a steamer lay at anchor; she was loading a cargo of oil from the submarine pipe-line, through which the wealth of Miri is pumped into the tankers that take it to the outer—the real—world. Beyond the near dark promontory on the right we could see, far off and sun-illumined, a range of fantastically jagged mountains.

Grey sky, grey sea, the forest, the oil wells in the forest, the little houses among the ever-encroaching trees, and beyond them, far away through the dim hot air, the jagged mountains of Borneo—it was mournful and sinister, abysmally unreal, the landscape of a dream, of a bad dream at that. Then the rain began to fall, a few warm drops, then a shower; the mountains became the ghosts of themselves, faded, faded and were gone. The shower quickened to a downpour, and even the near coast, the oil wells and the dolls' bungalows, even the black-green forest disappeared. Walled in by falling water, we found ourselves at the centre of a little universe, whose extremest limits were not a furlong distant. It was a lively world; for in spite of the rain our steamer continued to unload its cargo into the attendant lighters. A good deal of the cargo consisted of pork—in a potential and still living form—for the consumption of the Chinese coolies working on the oil fields. Each pig was separately and closely packed in a rattan basket, significantly shaped like the sausages into which its tenant was to be so soon transformed. These wicker sausages, with their living sausage meat inside them and visible between the bars, were swung out, ten at a time, by the crane and dropped into the lighter. Three or four coolies were ready to untie the bale and arrange the separate baskets, layer by layer, in the wallowing barge. By the time it was fully loaded, there must have been six or seven successive strata of pig in the lighter. There was little squealing or struggling inside the baskets; for when unloading day arrives, the Chinese take the precaution of putting a dose of opium in the pigs' breakfast. It was only when the crane let them drop with a particularly violent bump that the drugged beasts wriggled or uttered a grunt. Mostly they lay quite still, dosing and perhaps deliciously dreaming through the entire operation of being swung through the air, let fall and dumped or rolled into place above, between, below their fellows.

The spectacle was curious and, though not precisely pleasing, certainly less deplorable than that which the man-handling of animals generally affords. The pigs might be tossed about; but plunged, like so many De Quinceys, in a trance of opium, they were not aware of it. They might be closely packed—much more closely, indeed, than they could have been packed if they had been free and struggling—but, stretched within their sausages of rattan, they were neither crushed nor suffocated. In a space where, unprisoned, no more than twenty pigs could have stood, and that to the greatest possible discomfort of each squealing victim, a hundred were now conveniently packed. By means of opium and baskets the Chinese have solved a problem in humanitarianism as well as economics.

LABUAN

There had been squabblings between the deck passengers and the crew. We Olympians of the saloon were aware of it only by a dim and remote hearsay. But the fact was so true that, when we put in at Labuan, the Captain thought it necessary to pay off the two worst offenders among his Malay sailors and turn them off the ship. They took their pay, and one of them quietly departed; the other refused to move.

We saw him at a later stage of the proceedings—a young

man with a face like a copper statue's, a body classically built and dressed in the height of Malay fashion. A superb specimen of humanity—but he simply wouldn't leave the ship.

The Captain sent for the dock police. Two of them, looking very smart in khaki uniform, came on board, took a good look at the young man, who sat crouched in a dark corner, sullenly ruminating his grievances, and having looked, retired. A little later four more policemen joined them, and, standing at a safe distance, the six representatives of law and order cajolingly implored the young man to come quietly. Nothing, they pointed out, was going to be done to him; he was only being asked to leave the ship; he had a right to a free passage back to Singapore. The young man said nothing, or only growled like a tiger. Discouraged, the policemen reported to the Captain that they would have to go and fetch the Resident in person: the affair was too serious for them to deal with unsupported. They trooped away. Still squatting in his corner, the young man continued to chew his bitter and maddening cud of grievance.

We, being strangers to Malaya, began to wonder, rather impatiently—for the obstinate young man was delaying our departure—why something decisive was not done about him. Nor could we understand the obvious apprehensiveness of the deck passengers and crew, the look of anxiety on the faces of the officers. In our countries men value life—their own, if not other people's. Even desperate criminals will generally come quietly when they are cornered. To shoot and, sooner or later, be shot, or hanged, would be easy. But the respect and desire for life are too strong in them; rather than violently resist, they acknowledge defeat and go off resignedly to take the unpleasant consequences of it. The Malay, on the contrary, can easily work himself up into a state of mind in which all life, including his own, seems to him valueless, when the keenest pleasure and the highest duty are to kill and be killed. Our young obstinate, crouching in his corner and ruminating his grievances, was busily preparing himself to run *amok* at the slightest provocation from his enemies. The six policemen, the deck passengers, the crew, the officers —all knew it. The officers, indeed, had reasons for knowing it particularly well. For it was only a short time before that, on a ship belonging to the same company as ours, a Malay seaman had run *amok*, for some trivially inadequate reason, and killed upwards of a dozen people, including the Captain of the vessel. The Captain, it seems, was a kindly old gentleman with a snowy beard and Christian principles. He was sent for when the trouble began, and found the Malay knife in hand, and bloody. Instead of his revolver, he used persuasion. He remonstrated, he begged the Malay to be reasonable and give up his knife. The Malay replied by sticking it into his body. The deck looked like the last act of an Elizabethan tragedy before he was finally shot down.

We had not heard this story at the time. Ignorance is bliss, and we regarded our obstinate Malay as a rather tiresome joke and wondered why every one else took him so preposterously seriously.

The Resident came at last; his forces amounted now to no less than nine policemen. It was the critical moment; the general anxiety was at its height. Would the young heathen be got off the boat without the shedding of blood? The pockets of the Captain's jacket were weighed down with fire-arms; the Resident's trousers bulged about the hip. To have produced the pistols prematurely would have been infallibly to provoke the Malay's insane fury. To pull them out too late would be no less fatal. And to fire them at all in a small and crowded ship would be a danger in itself. The situation, for those who understood it and were responsible for its developments, was disagreeably ticklish. Ignorant, we looked on in amusement. And luckily our attitude turned out to be the right and appropriate one; the drama ended as a comedy, not in blood.

When the nine policemen went below to apprehend him, the Malay slipped past them and came bounding up the companion-ladder on to the promenade deck. He probably had an idea that, if he did come to running *amok*, it would be better to kill first-class Christian passengers than third-class Moslems and devil-worshippers. But he had not yet quite succeeded in warming himself to *amok* heat. Arrived on the top deck, the forces of law and order at his heels, he glared about him, but did nothing. There was a brief colloquy with the Captain and the Resident. He stood there obstinate; he continued to shake his head. He was waiting, no doubt, for the divine afflatus that would send him ecstatically slashing and stabbing among the infidels. But the spirit of holy murder was slow to descend. The Resident saw his opportunity, nodded to his men; simultaneously the nine policemen jumped on him. The Malay made a grab for the dagger in his belt; but the spirit of murder had arrived too late. The nine had him fast. In another moment the handcuffs were round his wrists.

The strained expression dissolved from every face. Cigarettes were lighted, men began to smile, to laugh and talk. And even the handcuffed captive suddenly became good-humoured. The ferocious young savage, who had been on the verge of murder and self-destruction, was transformed, as soon as it ceased to be possible for him to run *amok*, into a merry boy. He spoke to the policemen, he laughed;

and they, in the profundity of their sense of relief, laughed back at him, patted him on the shoulder, loved him. He was led off, almost a hero, down the gangway. In the midst of his escort, and followed by all the children and idlers of the town, he marched away down the road, towards the police station—the most important man, that afternoon, in Labuan.

The incident, for us, was almost enjoyable. It would have seemed a good deal less amusing if we had heard before, instead of afterwards, the story of the kindly old Captain, stabbed, with a dozen others, on his own ship, within five miles of Singapore.

The citizen of a law-abiding country, whose forty millions commit each year fewer crimes of violence than are committed in the single city of Chicago, I realized suddenly and forcibly the precarious artificiality of all that seems most solid and fundamental in our civilisation, of all that we take for granted. An individual has only to refuse to play the game of existence according to the current rules to throw the rule-observing players into bewildered consternation. There is a rule against violence, against taking the law into our own hands; it is a rule which most of us observe—so many, indeed, that a great number of people go through life accepting orderliness and non-violence as part of the scheme of nature. When somebody comes into their orbit who plays the game according to 'the good old rule, the simple plan'—that is, according to no rule—they are appalled, they are at a loss what to do, they are helpless.

The War did something to alter men's attitude towards the rules, but much less than might have been expected. Men went into the fighting line not, as our generals love to say when they make speeches to public school boys, because 'Man is a Fighting Animal,' but because they were law-abiding citizens obediently doing what the State told them to do. It was the duty of the soldier to commit violence and murder upon his country's enemies; but he did these things under orders, and the doing of them hardly impaired his normal law-abidingness. Considering the fact that, for four years, half the grown men in Europe were engaged in trying to murder one another, one can only be astonished that the post-war increase in crimes of violence has not been vastly greater. That it has not is a proof of how deeply the habit of playing according to the rules has become ingrained in us. In America, the greatest part of which is removed by only a couple of generations from the mediaeval epoch of pioneering, the habit of playing according to the rules has not had time to become so deeply ingrained as in the countries whose Middle Ages of uncontrolled and lawless violence are five hundred years away. Lynching, the Ku Klux Klan, ferocious strike-breaking are American institutions, the product of American history. In England, where men abandoned the right to take the law into their own hands some two or three hundred years ago, they would be almost unthinkable. Even crime is less bloodthirsty on our side of the water; and the wholesale murderous banditry that has filled the streets of American cities with armoured cars and sharpshooters is all but unknown with us. We are fortunate in our history. How profoundly fortunate, this absurd, but potentially tragical, incident at Labuan caused me intimately to realize.

SANDAKAN

SANDAKAN, like Jesselton, Kudat and, I suppose, all the other sea-coast towns of North Borneo, is a Chinese colony governed by a few white men inhabiting the bungalows in the suburbs. It is a picturesque place, has a marvellous natural harbour with a great red rock, like a second

Gibraltar, to guard its entrance, and is the port and capital of a little hinterland of coconut groves, rubber and tobacco plantations. A club-house and a golf course proclaim it to be, if not a part of the British Empire, at least a protectorate. (Examined in detail and at close quarters, our far-flung Empire is seen to consist of several scores of thousands of clubs and golf courses, dotted at intervals, more or less wide, over two-fifths of the surface of the planet. Large blond men sit in the clubs, or swipe the white ball down clearings in the jungle; blackamoors of various shades bring the whiskey and carry round the niblicks. The map is painted red. And to the casual observer, on the spot, that is the British Empire.) But to return to Sandakan. Besides a club and a golf course, it possesses four steam-rollers and a superbly metalled road, eleven miles long. At the eleventh milestone, the road collides with what seems an impenetrable wall of forest and comes abruptly to an end. You get out of your car and, examining the wall of verdure, find it flawed by a narrow crevice; it is a path. You edge your way in and are at once swallowed up by the forest. The inside of Jonah's whale could scarcely have been hotter, darker or damper. True, the jungle monster sometimes opens its mouth to yawn; there is a space between the trees, you have a glimpse of the sky, a shaft of thick yellow sunlight comes down into the depths. But the yawns are only brief and occasional. For the greater part of our stroll in the belly of the vegetable monster, we walked in a hot twilight. It was silent too. Very occasionally a bird would utter a few notes—or it might have been a devil of the woods, meditatively whistling to himself, as he prepared some fiendishly subtle and ingenious booby trap to terrify the human trespassers on his domain.

Nature is all very well half-way to the pole. Kept on short rations, she behaves decorously. But feed her up, give her huge doses of the tonic tropical sunlight, make her drunk with tropical rain, and she gets above herself. If Wordsworth had been compelled to spend a few years in Borneo, would he have loved nature as much as he loved her on the banks of Rydal Water? If the *Excursion* had been through equatorial Africa, instead of through Westmorland, old William's mild pantheism would have been, I suspect, a little modified.

It was with a feeling of the profoundest relief that I emerged again from the green gullet of the jungle and climbed into the waiting car. The Chinese chauffeur started the machine and we drove away, very slowly (for in Sandakan you hire a car by the hour, not by the mile; the drivers are marvellously cautious), we drove positively majestically down the eleven-mile road. I thanked God for steam-rollers and Henry Ford.

MANILA

MANILA is the capital of an American colony. That is a fact of which I was not for long permitted to remain in doubt. Within three hours of my landing, I had been interviewed by nine reporters, representing the entire press, English and Spanish, of the city. I was asked what I thought of Manila, of the Filippino race, of the political problems of the islands—to which I could only reply by asking my interviewers what *they* thought about these subjects and assuring them, when they had told me, that I thought the same. My opinions were considered by all parties to be extraordinarily sound.

When this sort of thing happens—and fortunately it very seldom happens except on United States territory—I am always set thinking of that curious scale of values by which, in this preposterous world, men and things are appraised. Take, for example, the case of the literary man. (I am a literary man myself, and so the matter interests me.) The literary man is invested, it seems to me, with a quite disproportionate aura of importance and significance. Literary men fairly pullulate in *Who's Who*. They are more numerously represented in that remarkable book than any other class of notorieties, with the possible exception of peers and baronets. Almost nobody who has sold five thousand copies and had a good review in the *Times Literary Supplement*, is missing from its pages. A dispassionate observer from Mars would be led, by a study of *Who's Who*, to suppose that a certain gift of the gab was the most important quality an inhabitant of this planet could possess. But is it?

Art and the artist have become tremendously important in our modern world. Art is spoken of with respect, almost with reverence as though it were something sacred; and every adolescent aspires to be an artist, as regularly and inevitably as every child aspires to be an engine-driver. Art is one of the things that have flowed in to fill the vacuum created in the popular mind by the decay of established religion. The priest, whose confessional functions have passed to the lawyer and the doctor, has bequeathed his mystical prestige, his dignity as a guardian of the sacraments, to the artist. Hence the enormous number of literary names in *Who's Who*. Hence the interviewers who flock to ask the wandering novelist his opinion about things of which he must necessarily be incompetent to speak. The obscure scientist, whose mental equipment may be incomparably superior to that of the literary man, is left in peace. The public, being incapable of understanding what he is talking about, takes no interest in him. He must achieve something spectacular before hostesses ask him out and reporters come to meet him at the station. The practical man is hardly more esteemed (unless, of course, he happens to be immensely rich) than the man of science. To many people a man who writes poetry (even very bad poetry) and has an opinion about post-impressionism, is necessarily more intelligent than even a first-class engineer, or capable official, or the organizer of a great industry. Doctors and mill-owners, government servants and lawyers can cross the seas without running the slightest risk of being buttonholed at every port by a crowd of newspaper men. They may be more intelligent than the man of letters, they may be better men doing work infinitely more valuable than his. They may be qualified by special knowledge to speak with authority about the things which reporters love to discuss; but they will be permitted to land unmolested. Their work lacks the prestige which attaches to art; moreover it is private work, confined to one place and to the actual time of its achievement. The novelist's work is public; it exists simultaneously in many thousands of places: it can be looked at over a long space of time—as long indeed (if his vogue lasts) as wood pulp can hold together.

As a mere spectator of the world, not an actor in it—one who looks on and forms opinions of what other people are doing, but does nothing himself—I feel the profoundest admiration for those who act, who impress their will on stubborn things, not merely on yielding ideas, who wield power over men directly, and not impersonally as the writer does by wielding power over weak words. I admire and envy; but I do not aspire to be their rivals. Born a spectator, I should make the poorest performer. I have a certain talent for using the opera-glasses and making appropriate comments. I have none for acting. It is better to be content with doing what one can do, than to make a fool of oneself by trying to do what one can't.

If I were set down to do some of the serious practical work that has to be done in order that spectators can watch the comedy in safety and comfort, I should behave like that Burmese king of whom it is written in the *Glass Palace Chronicle*: 'For the sake of his concubines he composed the Paramatthabinda, that they might know of mind and the qualities of mind, matter, *nirvana*, forms of being and personality. He would not even lend an ear to the affairs of the villages or kingdom. Whenever there was an inquiry to be made, power exercised, or point of law determined, he caused his son, Uzana, the heir apparent, to dispose thereof.'

I admire Uzana; but oh! I understand, I sympathize with, I have a fellow-feeling for his poor father. How infinitely pleasanter, if one happens to be born with a speculative mind and a gift of the gab, to chat with one's concubines about *nirvana* and the qualities of mind than to bother oneself with the affairs of the villages! Uzana was undoubtedly the better man; but his father, the distinguished author of 'Metaphysics in the Harem' and 'Kant for Concubines,' must have been the one whom everybody wanted to meet, who received letters from distant female correspondents, who got asked out to dinner, interviewed on the wharf and snapshotted walking with a friend in the Park. All these things would happen to him; and he—for I take it that he had really and seriously thought about the qualities of mind and the forms of matter—he would be astonished every time and, thinking of Uzana, he would feel embarrassed and even rather ashamed, as though he were an impostor.

AT SEA

FAMILIARITY blunts astonishment. Fishes do not marvel at water; they are too busy swimming in it. It is the same with us. We take our Western civilization for granted and find nothing intrinsically odd or incongruous in it. Before we can realize the strangeness of our surroundings, we must deliberately stop and think.

But moments come when that strangeness is fairly forced upon our notice, moments when an anomaly, a contradiction, an immense incongruity is suddenly illumined by a light so glaring that we cannot fail to see it. Such a moment came to me as I was crossing the Pacific. It was the first morning out of Yokohama. Coming out of my cabin, I was handed the day's bulletin of wireless news. I unfolded the typewritten sheet and read: 'Mrs. X, of Los Angeles, girl wife of Dr. X, aged 79, has been arrested for driving her automobile along the railroad track, whistling like a locomotive.' This piece of information had been transmitted through the ethereal holes between the molecules of air. From a broadcasting station more than five thousand miles away it had come to our ship in rather less time than it would have taken the sound of my voice to travel from one end of the promenade deck to the other. The labours of half a dozen men of genius, of hundreds of patient and talented investigators, had gone to creating and perfecting the means for achieving this miracle. To what end? That the exploits of young Mrs. X, of Los Angeles, might be instantaneously known to every traveller on all the oceans of the globe. The ether reverberated with the name of Mrs. X. The wave that bore it broke against the moon and the planets, and rippled on towards the stars and the ultimate void. Faraday and Clerk Maxwell had not lived in vain.

The wise men of antiquity (so say the Indians) knew all that we have learned about nature, and a great deal more besides. But they kept their science to themselves, or revealed it only in enigmas which cannot be interpreted except in the light of a previous knowledge of the answers. They were afraid that—men being what they are—their discoveries might be put to bad or futile uses. The ordinary man, they argued, is not to be trusted with the power which comes of knowledge. They withheld their science.

Being prejudiced in favour of the West and of the present, I have no great belief in the scientific attainments of the ancient sages of the Orient. But their wisdom is undeniable. The fruits of knowledge are abused and wasted; it is, alas, only too obvious. Disinterested men have given their lives to the search for truth, and we have turned their discoveries to the service of murder, or employed them to create a silly entertainment. The modern civilization of the West, which is the creation of perhaps a hundred men of genius, assisted by a few thousand intelligent and industrious disciples, exists for the millions, whose minds are indistinguishable in quality from those of the average humans of the palaeolithic age. The ideas of a handful of super-men are exploited so as to serve the profit and pleasure of the innumerable subter-men, or men *tout court*. The contemporary cave man listens in on instruments which he owes to the inspired labours of superior and, by comparison, divine intelligences. Negroid music shoots across the void into his ears, and the wisdom of such sages as Dr. Frank Crane; racing results and bed-time stories and the true tale of a young Mrs. X, of Los Angeles. The fire of Prometheus is put to the strangest uses. Gods propose, men dispose. The world in which we live may not be the best of all possible worlds: it is certainly the most fantastic.

Not being a super-man myself, I took the liveliest interest in young Mrs. X. After being arrested for whistling like a locomotive—whether by means of an instrument or with the unaided vocal cords was never made clear—she was bailed out of prison by her husband, the aged doctor. The time came for the hearing of her case. Mrs. X told the doctor that she proposed to forfeit her (or rather his) recognisances and run away. The doctor protested. Mrs. X then began to smash the furniture. The aged doctor telephoned for the police; they came, and Mrs. X was re-arrested on charges of assault. We on the Pacific waited in a dreadful suspense. A few days later, as we were crossing the hundred and eightieth meridian, we learned to our profound relief that a reconciliation had taken place. Aged Dr. X had withdrawn his charge; the girl wife had gone home quietly. What happened about the whistling business we never learned. The anonymous powers which purvey wireless news are strangely capricious. The name of Mrs. X no longer rippled out towards Aldebaran and the spiral nebulae. In the next morning's bulletin there was a little paragraph announcing the declaration of the General Strike. And Bébé Daniels had fallen off her horse and received contusions.

LOS ANGELES. A RHAPSODY

First Movement

Daylight had come to the common folk of Hollywood, the bright Californian daylight. But within the movie studio there shone no sun, only the lamps, whose intense and greenish-yellow radiance gives to living men and women the appearance of jaundiced corpses. In a corner of one huge barn-like structure they were preparing to 'shoot.' The camera stood ready, the corpse-lights were in full glare. Two or three cowboys and a couple of clowns lounged about, smoking. A man in evening dress was trusting to his moustache to make him look like an English villain. A young lady, so elegant, so perfectly and flawlessly good-looking that you knew her at once for the Star, was sitting in a corner, reading a book. The Director—it seemed a waste that such a profile should be *au-dessus de la mêlée* instead of in the pictures—gave her a courteous hail. Miss X looked up from her literature. 'It's the scene where you see the murder being committed,' he explained. Miss X got up, put away the book and beckoned to her maid, who brought her a comb and a mirror. 'My nose all right?' she asked, dabbing on powder. 'Music!' shouted the Director. 'Make it emotional.' The band, whose duty it is in every studio to play the actors into an appropriate state of soul, struck up a waltz. The studio was filled with a sea of melodic treacle; our spirits rocked and wallowed on its sticky undulations. Miss X handed back her powder-puff to the maid and walked up to the camera. 'You hide behind that curtain and look out,' the Director explained. Miss X retired behind the curtain. 'Just the hand first of all,' the Director went on. 'Clutching. Then the face, gradually.' 'Yes, Mr. Z,' came the quiet voice of the Star from behind the hanging plush. 'Ready?' asked the Director. 'Then go ahead.' The camera began to purr, like a genteel variety of dentist's drill. The curtain slightly heaved. A white hand clutched at its edge. 'Terror, Miss X,' called the Director. The white hand tightened its clutch in a spasm of cinematographic fear. The Director nodded to the bandmaster. 'Put some pep into it,' he adjured. Pep was put in; the billows of treacle rose higher. 'Now the face, Miss X. Slowly. Just one eye. That's good. Hold it. A little more terror.' Miss X heartrendingly registered her alarm. 'That's good. That's very good. O.K.' The camera stopped purring. Miss X came out from behind the curtain and walked back to her chair. Reopening her book, she went on quietly reading about Theosophy.

We moved on and, after halting for a few moments on our way to watch some more terror being registered (by a man this time and under a different Director), penetrated into the secret places of the studio. We pronounced pass-words, quoted the Manager's permission, disclaimed con-nections with rival companies, and were finally admitted. In one room they were concocting miracles and natural cataclysms—typhoons in bathtubs and miniature earthquakes, the Deluge, the Dividing of the Red Sea, the Great War in terms of toy tanks and Chinese fire-crackers, ghosts and the Next World. In another they were modelling prehis-toric animals and the architecture of the remote future. In cellars below ground, mysteriously lighted by red lamps and smelling of chemicals, a series of machines was engaged in developing and printing the films. Their output was enormous. I forget how many thousands of feet of art and culture they could turn out each day. Quite a number of miles, in any case.

Second Movement

Emerging, I bought a newspaper. It was Saturday's; a whole page was filled with the announcements of rival religious sects, advertising the spiritual wares that they would give away or sell on the Sabbath. 'Dr. Leon Tucker with the Musical Messengers in a Great Bible Conference. 3 Meetings To-morrow. Organ Chimes, Giant Marimba-phone, Vibraphone, Violin, Piano, Accordeon, Banjo, Guitar and other Instruments. Wilshire Baptist Church.' The Giant Marimbaphone was certainly tempting. But in the First Methodist Church (Figueroa at Twentieth) they were going to distribute 'Mother's Day Flowers to all Worshippers.' (On Mother's Day you must wear a red carnation if your mother is alive, a white one if she is dead. The florists are everywhere the most ardent of matriolaters.) Moreover, they had booked the exclusive services of Dr. James H. Maclaren, Dramatic Orator, who was going to give his well-known stunt, 'Impersonations of Lincoln and Roosevelt.' 'Dr. Maclaren,' we were informed, 'comes with a unique, original, eloquent, instructive and inspiring Message concerning two of our Great Presidents. Uplifting and inspiring. It will do your soul good. The wonderful Messages of these two Great Presidents will be brought home with new emphasis and you will feel that you have spent the evening in the company of Great Spirits. Hear the great organ, Quartet of Artists and Vested Chorus.' At the Hollywood Congregational Church there were to be moving pictures of Jackie Coogan in his crusade to the Near East; the prospect was a draw. But then so was the photograph of Miss Leila Castberg of the Church of Divine Power (Advanced Thought); her performance might not be very interesting—she was scheduled to preach at the Morosco Theatre on Divine Motherhood—but the face which looked out from her advertisement was decidedly pleasing. Less attractive, to the devout male at any rate, were the photos of Messrs. Clarke and Van Bruch; but the phrasing of their ad. was enough to counteract in the mind of the reader the effect produced by their portraits. 'IT'S ON, FOLKS, IT'S ON,' so the announcement ran. 'The tide is rising at an OLD-FASHIONED REVIVAL. Every night except Monday, 7.30 P.M. Soul-stirring sermons and songs. Special to-night! Hear 10 Evangelists—10. Van Bruch-Clarke Evangelistic Party.'

Jazz it up, jazz it up. Keep moving. Step on the gas. Say it with dancing. The Charleston, the Baptists. Radios and Revivals. Uplift and Gilda Gray. The pipe organ, the nigger with the saxophone, the Giant Marimbaphone. Hymns and the movies and Irving Berlin. Petting Parties and the First Free United Episcopal Methodist Church. Jazz it up! 'N. C. Beskin, the CONVERTED JEW, back from a successful tour, will conduct a tabernacle campaign in Glendale. "WHY I BECAME A CHRISTIAN?" Dressed in Jewish garb. Will exhibit interesting paraphernalia.' Positively the last appearance. The celebrated Farmyard Imitations. 10 Evangelists—10. The finest troupe of Serio-Comic Cyclists ever. Onward Christian Soldiers. Abide with me. I'm gonna bring a water melon to my girl to-night.

Third Movement

Mother's Day. (Mr. Herring of Indiana, 'The Father of Mother's Day.') But why not Flapper's Day? It would be more representative, more democratic, so to speak. For in Joy City there are many more Flappers—married as well as unmarried—than Mothers.

> Nunc vitiat uterum quae vult formosa videri,
> Raraque in hoc aevo est quae velit esse parens.

Thousands and thousands of flappers, and almost all incredibly pretty. Plumply ravishing, they give, as T. S. Eliot has phrased it, a 'promise of pneumatic bliss.' Of pneumatic bliss, but of not much else, to judge by their faces. So curiously uniform, unindividual and blank. Hardly more expressive—to the foreign eye, at any rate—than any of the other parts of that well-contoured anatomy which they are at such pains to display.

On the beaches of the Pacific that display was indeed superb. Mack Sennett Bathing Beauties by the hundred. They gambolled all round us, as we walked up and down in the windy sunlight along the sands. Frisking temptations. But we were three St. Anthonies—Charlie Chaplin and Robert Nichols and I—three grave theologians of art, too deeply absorbed in discussing the way of cinematographic salvation to be able to bestow more than the most casual attention on the Sirens, however plumply deserving.

Fourth Movement

Cocktail time. (We've dealt with the same bootlegger for upwards of two years now. A most reliable man.) Ice rattles in the shaker—a dance of miniature skeletons —and the genuinely reliable liquor is poured out. *À boire, à boire!* Long live Pantagruel! This is dry America. We climbed into our host's car and drove, it seemed interminably, through the immense and sprawling city. Past movie palaces and theatres and dance halls. Past shining shops and apartments and enormous hotels. On every building the vertical lines of light went up like rockets into the dark sky. And the buildings themselves—they too had almost rocketed into existence. Thirty years ago Los Angeles was a one-horse—a half-horse—town. In 1940 or thereabouts it is scheduled to be as big as Paris. As big and as gay. The great Joy City of the West.

And what joy! The joy of rushing about, of always being busy, of having no time to think, of being too rich to doubt. The joy of shouting and bantering, of dancing and for ever dancing to the noise of a savage music, of lustily singing.

(Yes, sir, she's my Baby.
No, sir, don't say 'Maybe.'
Yes, sir, she's my Baby now.)

The joy of loudly laughing and talking at the top of the voice about nothing. (For thought is barred in this City of Dreadful Joy and conversation is unknown.) The joy of drinking prohibited whiskey from enormous silver flasks, the joy of cuddling provocatively bold and pretty flappers, the joy of painting the cheeks, of rolling the eye and showing off the desirable calves and figure. The joy of going to the movies and the theatre, of sitting with one's fellows in luxurious and unexclusive clubs, of trooping out on summer evenings with fifty thousand others to listen to concerts in the open air, of being always in a crowd, never alone. The joy of going on Sundays to hear a peppy sermon, of melting at the hymns, of repenting one's sins, of getting a kick out of uplift. The joy, in a word, of having what is technically known as a Good Time.

And oh, how strenuously, how whole-heartedly the people of Joy City devote themselves to having a Good Time! The Good Times of Rome and Babylon, of Byzantium and Alexandria were dull and dim and miserably restricted in comparison with the superlatively Good Time of modern California. The ancient world was relatively poor; and it had known catastrophe. The wealth of Joy City is unprecedentedly enormous. Its light-hearted people are unaware of war or pestilence or famine or revolution, have never in their safe and still half-empty Eldorado known anything but prosperous peace, contentment, universal acceptance. The truest patriots, it may be, are those who pray for a national calamity.

On and on we drove, through the swarming streets of Joy City. (One automobile, sir, to every three and a quarter inhabitants.) The tall buildings impended, the lights whizzed up like rockets. On and on. Across an open space there suddenly loomed up a large white building, magically shining against the intensified blackness of the sky behind. (Just finished, sir, the Temple of the Elks.) From its summit the beams of half a dozen searchlights waved to heaven. They seemed the antennae of some vast animal, feeling and probing in the void—for what? For Truth, perhaps? Truth is not wanted in the City of Dreadful Joy. For Happiness? It is possessed. For God? But God had already been found; he was inside the shining Temple; he *was* the Temple, the brand new, million-dollar Temple, in which at this moment the initiates of the venerable Order of Elks were congregated to worship, not the effetely aristocratic Lady Poverty, but plain American Mrs. Wealth. Five or six hundred motor-cars stood parked outside the doors. What *could* those luminous antennae be probing for? Why, for nothing, of course, for nothing! If they waved so insistently, that was just for fun. Waving for waving's sake. Movement is a joy, and this is the Great Joy City of the West.

Fifth Movement

The restaurant is immense. The waiters sprint about, carrying huge dishes of the richest food. What Gargantuan profusion! Great ten-pound chops, square feet of steak, fillets of whale, whole turkeys stewed in cream, mountains of butter. And the barbarous music throbs and caterwauls unceasingly. Between each juicy and satiating course, the flappers and the young men dance, clasped in an amorous wrestle. How Rabelais would have adored it! For a week, at any rate. After that, I am afraid, he would have begun to miss the conversation and the learning, which serve in his Abbey of Thelema as the accompaniment and justification of pleasure. This Western pleasure, meaty and raw, untempered by any mental sauce—would even Rabelais' unsqueamish stomach have been strong enough to digest it? I doubt it. In the City of Dreadful Joy Pantagruel would soon have died of fatigue and boredom. *Taedium laudamus*—so reads (at any rate for the inhabitants of

Rabelais' continent) the triumphant canticle of Californian joy.

The restaurant is suddenly plunged into darkness. A great beam of light, like the Eye of God in an old engraving, stares down from somewhere near the ceiling, right across the room, squinting this way and that, searching—and at last finding what it had been looking for: a radiant figure in white, the singer of the evening. A good, though not superlatively good singer in the style of Ethel Levey or Jenny Golder.

> You gotta feed a chicken corn,
> You gotta feed a seal fish,
> You gotta feed a man (significant pause and
> *œillade*) Love.

And so on. The enthusiasm which greets these rhymed lectures in elementary physiology is inordinate. Being enthusiastic is a joy. We are in Joy's metropolis.

There is a final burst of applause. The divine eyelid closes down over God's shining eye. The band strikes up again. The dancing re-begins. The Charleston, the fox-trot. 'There is only one first-class civilization in the world to-day. It is right here, in the United States and the Dominion of Canada.' Monkeyville, Bryan, the Ku Klux Klan. 'Europe's is hardly second class, and Asia's is fourth to sixth class.' Jazz it up; jazz it up! And what did late, great Ambassador Page have to say? 'The whole continent (of Europe) is rotten, or tyrannical, or yellow dog. I wouldn't give Long Island or Moore County for the whole continent of Europe.' And with Coney Island added to Long Island and Los Angeles in the scale along with Moore County, he might have thrown in all Asia and the British Empire. Three cheers for Page! Yes, sir, 'American idealism has made itself felt as a great contributory force to the advancement of mankind.' Three cheers for George F. Babbit and the Rotary Club! And three cheers for Professor Nixon Carver! 'Prosperity,' the Professor has said, 'is coming to us precisely because our ideas are not materialistic. All these things (*e.g.* the Elks' Temple, the jazz bands, the movie palaces, the muffins at breakfast) are added to us precisely because we are seeking the Kingdom of God and His righteousness.' Three cheers more—thrice three! The Prof. deserves them.

It is almost midnight. A few minutes and it will be the Sabbath. A few hours and the Giant Marimbaphone will be proclaiming the glory of the new billion-dollar God. At the Ambassador Hotel (alas, too expensive for me to stay at) Dr. Ernest Holmes will be preaching on 'The Science of Jesus.' It is time to go home. Farewell, farewell. Parting is such sweet sorrow. Did Tosti raise his bowler hat when he said 'Good-bye'?

MEDITATION ON EL GRECO

THE pleasures of ignorance are as great, in their way, as the pleasures of knowledge. For though the light is good, though it is satisfying to be able to place the things that surround one in the categories of an ordered and comprehensible system, it is also good to find oneself sometimes in the dark, it is pleasant now and then to have to speculate with vague bewilderment about a world, which ignorance has reduced to a quantity of mutually irrelevant happenings dotted, like so many unexplored and fantastic islands, on the face of a vast ocean of incomprehension. For me, one of the greatest charms of travel consists in the fact that it offers unique opportunities for indulging in the luxury of ignorance. I am not one of those conscientious travellers who, before they visit a new country, spend weeks mugging up its geology, its economics, its art history, its literature. I prefer, at any rate during my first few visits, to be a thoroughly unintelligent tourist. It is only later, when my ignorance has lost its virgin freshness, that I begin to read what the intelligent tourist would have known by heart before he bought his tickets. I read —and forthwith, in a series of apocalypses, my isolated and mysteriously odd impressions begin to assume significance, my jumbled memories fall harmoniously into patterns. The pleasures of ignorance have given place to the pleasures of knowledge.

I have only twice visited Spain—not often enough, that is to say, to have grown tired of ignorance. I still enjoy bewilderedly knowing as little as possible about all I see between the Pyrenees and Cape Trafalgar. Another two or three visits, and the time will be ripe for me to go to the London Library and look up 'Spain' in the subject index. In one of the numerous, the all too numerous, books there catalogued I shall find, no doubt, the explanation of a little mystery that has mildly and intermittently puzzled me for quite a number of years—ever since, at one of those admirable Loan Exhibitions in Burlington House, I saw for the first time a version of El Greco's *Dream of Philip II*.

This curious composition, familiar to every visitor to the Escorial, represents the king, dressed and gloved like an undertaker in inky black, kneeling on a well-stuffed cushion in the centre foreground; beyond him, on the left, a crowd of pious kneelers, some lay, some clerical, but all manifestly saintly, are looking upwards into a heaven full of waltzing angels, cardinal virtues and biblical personages, grouped in a circle round the Cross and the luminous monogram of the Saviour. On the right a very large whale gigantically yawns, and a vast concourse, presumably of the damned, is hurrying (in spite of all that we learned in childhood about the anatomy of whales) down its crimson throat. A curious picture, I repeat, and, as a work of art, not remarkably good; there are many much better Grecos belonging even to the same youthful period. Nevertheless, in spite of its mediocrity, it is a picture for which I have a special weakness. I like it for the now sadly unorthodox reason that the subject interests me. And the subject interests me because I do not know what the subject is. For this dream of King Philip—what was it? Was it a visionary anticipation of the Last Judgment? A mystical peep into Heaven? An encouraging glimpse of the Almighty's short way with heretics? I do not know—do not at present even desire to know. In the face of so extravagant a phantasy as this of Greco's, the pleasures of ignorance are peculiarly intense. Confronted by the mysterious whale, the undertaker king, the swarming aerial saints and scurrying sinners, I give my fancy licence and fairly wallow in the pleasure of bewilderedly not knowing.

The fancy I like best of all that have occurred to me is the one which affirms that this queer picture was painted as a prophetic and symbolic autobiography, that it was meant to summarize hieroglyphically the whole of Greco's future development. For that whale in the right foreground—that great-grandfather of Moby Dick, with his huge yawn, his crimson gullet and the crowd of the damned descending, like bank clerks at six o'clock into the Underground—that whale, I say, is the most significantly autobiographical object in all El Greco's early pictures. For whither are they bound, those hastening damned? 'Down the red lane,' as our nurses used to say when they were encouraging us to swallow the uneatable viands of childhood. Down the red lane into a dim inferno of tripes. Down, in a word, into that strange and rather frightful universe which Greco's spirit seems to have come more and more exclusively, as he grew older, to inhabit. For in the Cretan's later painting every personage is a Jonah. Yes, *every* personage. Which is where *The Dream of Philip II.* reveals itself as being imperfectly prophetic, a mutilated symbol. It is for the damned alone that the whale opens his mouth. If El Greco had wanted to tell the whole truth about his future development, he would have sent the blessed to join them, or at least have provided his saints and angels with another monster of their own, a supernal whale floating head downwards among the clouds, with a second red lane ascending, strait and narrow, towards a swallowed Heaven. Paradise and Purgatory, Hell, and even the common Earth—for El Greco in his artistic maturity, every department of the universe, was situated in the belly of a whale. His Annunciations and Assumptions, his Agonies and Transfigurations and Crucifixions, his Martyrdoms and Stigmatizations are all, without exception, visceral events. Heaven is no larger than the Black Hole of Calcutta, and God Himself is whale-engulfed.

Critics have tried to explain El Greco's pictorial agorophobia in terms of his early, Cretan education. There is no space in his pictures, they assure us, because the typical art of that Byzantium, which was El Greco's spiritual home, was the mosaic, and the mosaic is innocent of depth. A specious explanation, whose only defect is that it happens to be almost entirely beside the point. To begin with, the Byzantine mosaic was not invariably without depth. Those extraordinary eighth-century mosaics in the Omeyyid mosque at Damascus, for example, are as spacious and airy as impressionist landscapes. They are, it is true, somewhat exceptional specimens of the art. But even the commoner shut-in mosaics have really nothing to do with El Greco's painting, for the Byzantine saints and kings are enclosed, or, to be more accurate, are flatly inlaid in a kind of two-dimensional abstraction—in a pure Euclidean, plane-geometrical heaven of gold or blue. Their universe never bears the smallest resemblance to that whale's belly in which every one of El Greco's personages has his or her mysterious and appalling being. El Greco's world is no Flatland; there is depth in it—just a little depth. It is precisely this that makes it seem such a disquieting world. In their two-dimensional abstraction the personages of the Byzantine mosaists are perfectly at home; they are adapted to their environment. But, solid and three-dimensional, made to be the inhabitants of a spacious universe, El Greco's people are shut up in a world where there is perhaps just room enough to swing a cat, but no more. They are in prison and, which makes it worse, in a visceral prison.

For all that surrounds them is organic, animal. Clouds, rock, drapery have all been mysteriously transformed into mucus and skinned muscle and peritoneum. The Heaven into which Count Orgaz ascends is like some cosmic operation for appendicitis. The Madrid *Resurrection* is a resurrection in a digestive tube. And from the later pictures we receive the gruesome impression that all the personages, both human and divine, have begun to suffer a process of digestion, are being gradually assimilated to their visceral surroundings. Even in the Madrid *Resurrection* the forms and texture of the naked flesh have assumed a strangely tripe-like aspect. In the case of the nudes in *Laocoon* and *The Opening of the Seventh Seal* (both of them works of El Greco's last years) this process of assimilation has been carried a good deal further. After seeing their draperies and the surrounding landscape gradually peptonized and transformed, the unhappy Jonahs of Toledo discover, to their horror, that they themselves are being digested. Their bodies, their arms and legs, their faces, fingers, toes are ceasing to be humanly their own; they are becoming—the process is slow but inexorably sure—part of the universal Whale's internal workings. It is lucky for them that El Greco died when he did. Twenty years more, and the Trinity, the Communion of Saints and all the human race would have found themselves reduced to hardly distinguishable excrescences on the surface of a cosmic gut. The most favoured might perhaps have aspired to be taenias and trematodes.

For myself, I am very sorry that El Greco did not live to be as old as Titian. At eighty or ninety he would have been producing an almost abstract art—a cubism without cubes, organic, purely visceral. What pictures he would then have painted! Beautiful, thrilling, profoundly appalling. For appalling are even the pictures he painted in middle age, dreadful in spite of their extraordinary power and beauty. This swallowed universe into which he introduces us is one of the most disquieting creations of the human mind. One of the most puzzling too. For what were El Greco's reasons for driving mankind down the red lane? What induced him to take God out of His boundless Heaven and shut Him up in a fish's gut? One can only obscurely speculate. All that I am quite certain of is that there were profounder and more important reasons for the whale than the memory of the mosaics—the wholly unvisceral mosaics—which he may have seen in the course of a Cretan childhood, a Venetian and Roman youth. Nor will a disease of the eye account, as some have claimed, for his strange artistic development. Diseases must be very grave indeed before they become completely co-extensive with their victims. That men are affected by their illnesses is obvious; but it is no less obvious that, except when they are almost *in extremis*, they are something more than the sum of their morbid symptoms. Dostoevsky was not merely personified epilepsy, Keats was other things besides a simple lump of pulmonary tuberculosis. Men make use of their illnesses at least as much as they are made use of by them. It is likely enough that El Greco had something wrong with his eyes. But other people have had the same disease without for that reason painting pictures like the *Laocoon* and *The Opening of the Seventh Seal.* To say that El Greco was just a defective eyesight is absurd; he was a man who used a defective eyesight.

Used it for what purpose? to express what strange feeling about the world, what mysterious philosophy? It is hard indeed to answer. For El Greco belongs as a metaphysician (every significant artist is a metaphysician, a propounder of beauty-truths and form-theories) to no known school. The most one can say, by way of classification, is that, like most of the great artists of the Baroque, he believed in the validity of ecstasy, of the non-rational, 'numinous' experiences out of which, as a raw material, the reason fashions the gods or the various attributes of God. But the kind of ecstatic experience artistically rendered and meditated on by El Greco was quite different from the kind of experience which is described and symbolically 'rationalized' in the painting, sculpture and architecture of the great Baroque artists of the *seicento*. Those mass-producers of spirituality, the Jesuits, had perfected a simple technique for the fabrication of orthodox ecstasies. They had cheapened an experience, hitherto accessible only to the spiritually wealthy, and so placed it within the reach of all. What the Italian *seicento* artists so brilliantly and copiously rendered was this cheapened experience and the metaphysic in terms of which it could be rationalized. 'St. Teresa for All.' 'A John of the Cross in every Home.' Such were, or might have been, their slogans. Was it to be wondered at if their sublimities were a trifle theatrical, their tendernesses treacly, their spiritual intuitions rather commonplace and vulgar? Even the greatest of the Baroque artists were not remarkable for subtlety and spiritual refinement.

With these rather facile ecstasies and the orthodox Counter-Reformation theology in terms of which they could be interpreted, El Greco has nothing to do. The bright reassuring Heaven, the smiling or lachrymose, but always all too human divinities, the stage immensities and stage mysteries, all the stock-in-trade of the *seicentisti*, are absent from his pictures. There is ecstasy and flamy aspiration; but always ecstasy and aspiration, as we have seen, within the belly of a whale. El Greco seems to be talking all the time about the physiological root of ecstasy, not the spiritual flower; about the primary corporeal facts of numinous experience, not the mental derivatives from them. However vulgarly, the artists of the Baroque were concerned with the flower, not the root, with the derivatives and theological interpretations, not the brute facts of immediate physical experience. Not that they were ignorant of the physiological nature of these primary facts. Bernini's astonishing *St. Teresa* proclaims it in the most unequivocal fashion; and it is interesting to note that in this statue (as well as in the very similar and equally astonishing *Ludovica Albertoni* in San Francesco a Ripa) he gives to the draperies a kind of organic and, I might say, intestinal lusciousness of form. A little softened, smoothed and simplified, the robe of the great mystic would be indistinguishable from the rest of the swallowed landscape inside El Greco's whale. Bernini saves the situation (from the Counter-Reformer's point of view) by introducing into his composition the figure of the dart-brandishing angel. This aerial young creature is the inhabitant of an unswallowed Heaven. He carries with him the implication of infinite spaces. Charmingly and a little preposterously (the hand which holds the fiery dart has a delicately crook'd little finger, like the hand of some too refined young person in the act of raising her tea-cup), the angel symbolizes the spiritual flower of ecstasy, whose physiological root is the swooning Teresa in her peritoneal robe. Bernini is, spiritually speaking, a *plein-airiste.*

Not so El Greco. So far as he is concerned, there is nothing outside the whale. The primary physiological fact of religious experience is also, for him, the final fact. He remains consistently on the plane of that visceral consciousness which we so largely ignore, but with which our ancestors (as their language proves) did so much of their feeling and thinking. 'Where is thy zeal and thy strength, the sounding of the bowels and of thy mercies towards me?' 'My heart is turned within me, my repentings are kindled together.' 'I will bless the Lord who hath given me counsel; my reins also instruct me in the night season.' 'For God is my record, how greatly I long after you all in the bowels of Jesus Christ.' 'For Thou hast possessed my reins.' 'Is Ephraim my dear son? . . . Therefore my bowels are troubled for him.' The Bible abounds in such phrases—phrases which strike the modern reader as queer, a bit indelicate, even repellent. We are accustomed to thinking of ourselves as thinking entirely with our heads. Wrongly, as the physiologists have shown. For what we think and feel and are is to a great extent determined by the state of our ductless glands and our viscera. The Psalmist drawing instruction from his reins, the Apostle with his yearning bowels, are thoroughly in the modern physiological movement.

El Greco lived at a time when the reality of the primary visceral consciousness was still recognized—when the heart and the liver, the spleen and reins did all a man's feeling for him, and the four humours of blood, phlegm, choler and melancholy determined his character and imposed his passing moods. Even the loftiest experiences were admitted to be primarily physiological. Teresa knew God in terms of an exquisite pain in her heart, her side, her bowels. But while Teresa, and along with her the generality of human beings, found it natural to pass from the realm of physiology into that of the spirit—from the belly of the whale out into the wide open sky—El Greco obstinately insisted on remaining swallowed. His meditations were all of religious experience and ecstasy—but always of religious experience in its raw physiological state, always of primary, immediate, visceral ecstasy. He expressed these meditations in terms of Christian symbols—of symbols, that is to say, habitually employed to describe experiences quite

Printed in Great Britain by
Butler & Tanner Ltd.,
Frome and London

different from the primary physiological states on which he was accustomed to dwell. It is the contrast between these symbols, with their currently accepted significance, and the special private use to which El Greco puts them —it is this strange contrast which gives to El Greco's pictures their peculiarly disquieting quality. For the Christian symbols remind us of all the spiritual open spaces—the open spaces of altruistic feeling, the open spaces of abstract thought, the open spaces of free-floating spiritual ecstasy. El Greco imprisons them, claps them up in a fish's gut. The symbols of the spiritual open spaces are compelled by him to serve as a language in terms of which he talks about the close immediacies of visceral awareness, about the ecstasy that annihilates the personal soul, not by dissolving it out into universal infinity, but by drawing it down and drowning it in the warm, pulsating, tremulous darkness of the body.

Well, I have wandered far and fancifully from the undertaker king and his enigmatic nightmare of whales and Jonahs. But imaginative wandering is the privilege of the ignorant. When one doesn't know one is free to invent. I have seized the opportunity while it presented itself. One of these days I may discover what the picture is about, and when that has happened I shall no longer be at liberty to impose my own interpretations. Imaginative criticism is essentially an art of ignorance. It is only because we don't know what a writer or artist meant to say that we are free to concoct meanings of our own. If El Greco had somewhere specifically told us what he meant to convey by painting in terms of Black Holes and mucus, I should not now be in a position to speculate. But luckily he never told us; I am justified in letting my fancy loose to wander.

MUSIC AT NIGHT